KU-371-492

CHEMICAL THERMODYNAMICS

CHEMICAL THERMODYNAMICS

BY

J. A. V. BUTLER, D.Sc.

COURTAULD RESEARCH FELLOW

COURTAULD INSTITUTE OF BIOCHEMISTRY

MACMILLAN AND CO., LIMITED

ST. MARTIN'S STREET, LONDON

1949

First Edition (2 vols.) 1928.
Second Edition 1935.
Third Edition 1939.
Fourth Edition (1 vol.) 1946.
Reprinted 1949

PRINTED IN GREAT BRITAIN

EXTRACTS FROM PREFACES TO FIRST EDITIONS

THE importance of the thermodynamical method in chemistry is now widely recognised and scarcely needs emphasizing. While there are several excellent larger treatises on the subject, which are suitable for the advanced student and for reference, the need has been felt of an elementary introduction to the subject which shall stress the underlying principles and at the same time give due attention to their applications. I have therefore ventured to prepare the present work, which is the outcome of several years' experience in teaching the subject. I have tried to present the subject in a logically precise, yet simple form, having in mind not only the student who intends to specialise in Physical Chemistry, but also that class of chemistry students which has only a very moderate knowledge of mathematics and little sympathy with mathematical methods. I shall be content if the book may help to promote the introduction of the thermodynamical method into the chemical curriculum at an early stage, as an essential part of the training of a chemist.

The applications of the theory to chemical processes have been selected from as wide a field as possible, and some topics have been included, which although not strictly thermodynamical, are most conveniently studied in this connection. The data given are to be taken as specimens of the results available, and are not intended to be exhaustive. Since it is not possible for the student to obtain a thorough grasp of the subject without working through numerical examples, I have added a collection of exercises to each chapter. For those who require a somewhat more limited course, I have marked with asterisks a number of sections which may be omitted at first reading, without loss of continuity.

Part II is concerned with the thermodynamical functions, energy, free energy and entropy, and their partial derivatives. In my experience it is desirable that the student should have some familiarity with the calculation of maximum work and the simpler applications of the first and second laws of thermodynamics before he embarks on the study of these quantities. This I endeavoured to provide in Part I, and my readers will find that they have already met some of these quantities, and in these circumstances the transition to the new methods will present no great difficulty.

It has been inevitable on this plan that I should cover again, in greater detail and from a more advanced point of view, some of the ground traversed in Part I, but I do not think this will be found to be a disadvantage. The exact distribution of material between the two parts is a matter of expedience, and I can only claim that the arrangement I have adopted has worked well in practice, the material of Part I forming a first course, and that of Part II a second course, which are studied in consecutive years. But this could easily be modified to suit other circumstances.

FOREWORD

THE fact that both Part I and Part II need to be reprinted at this time gives me the opportunity of bringing them both within the covers of one volume. I sincerely hope that this will not be considered an infliction by my former readers and users of Part I, and that they will be encouraged to look a little further and sample at least the earlier chapters of Part II. To teachers it will give a greater latitude in their courses and the possibility of introducing the concept of entropy (Chap. XI) at a much earlier stage, if they so desire.

I have also taken the opportunity of giving Part II a thorough revision so that it now covers most of the advances of the last decade. The book remains essentially practical in its outlook : it deals at length with applications, even when they take it out of the strictly thermodynamical field. It treats of thermodynamics as something to be used in everyday chemistry, a necessary tool of the chemist in the laboratory and in industry.

To this edition, the late Dr. W. J. C. Orr contributed, shortly before his untimely death, an Appendix on the Statistical Derivation of Thermodynamical Functions, which gives a concise but lucid treatment of this valuable method. I believe it will be of assistance to those who require at least a nodding acquaintance with the subject and a vantage point from which they may embark on the study of the larger works. I have also to express my indebtedness for his valuable suggestions and data for Chapter XIII.

J. A. V. B.

COURTAULD INSTITUTE OF BIOCHEMISTRY,
THE MIDDLESEX HOSPITAL MEDICAL SCHOOL,
LONDON, W. 1.

THE thermodynamical problem of the equilibrium of heterogeneous substances was attacked by Kirchhoff in 1855, when the science was yet in its infancy, and his method has been lately followed by C. Neumann. But the methods introduced by Professor J. Willard Gibbs, of Yale College, Connecticut, seem to me to be more likely to enable us, without any lengthy calculations, to comprehend the relations between the different physical and chemical states of bodies.

J. CLERK-MAXWELL
(as reported *Amer. J. of Science,* 1877)

CONTENTS

INTRODUCTION

There are two points of view from which the study of a chemical or physical process may be approached. In the first place, it may be pictured in terms of atoms and molecules and their motions. Thus in this, the kinetic aspect of things, the pressure of a gas is looked upon as a consequence of the bombardment of the containing vessel by the gas molecules in rapid motion. The vapour pressure of a liquid is that at which equal numbers of molecules leave the liquid and enter it from the gaseous phase in a given time. The study of processes from this point of view gives as a rule a definite picture of the mechanism of the change, but it is limited by the complexity of the laws governing the motions of atoms and molecules and by our ignorance of them.

There is another viewpoint from which such processes can be studied, namely, from a consideration of the energy changes involved. In the early part of the nineteenth century two general laws of energy were formulated which are believed to be universally true. The first states that in any change no energy is lost. The second gives a means of distinguishing processes which can occur of their own accord in any given circumstances from those which cannot. This is precisely what the chemist needs, a means of predicting whether under any particular circumstances a reaction can take place or not. In addition, if the laws of energy and their detailed consequences are to hold good for any given change, we find various relations which must hold between the properties of the substances undergoing change. We are thus able to predict the effect of changes of conditions on the equilibrium state of a system.

Thermodynamics is a deductive science. It takes as true the broad generalizations on which it is based, and seeks to deduce their detailed consequences in particular cases. It applies, moreover, to the behaviour of matter in bulk; that is, to quantities so great that the behaviour of any individual molecule is not observed. While, in kinetic theory, the motion of the individual particle is taken as the basis, and the attempt is made to deduce from it the behaviour of matter in quantity, in thermodynamics we are concerned with the observed behaviour of quantities of substances which contain innumerable individual particles. The laws of thermodynamics are the laws of the behaviour of assemblages of vast numbers of molecules.

An analogy to the two possible ways of studying material processes might be found in the two possible ways of approaching the study of social phenomena. Corresponding to the kinetic method we might study the behaviour of individuals and on that basis seek to interpret the behaviour of large assemblages of individuals. If we adopted the "thermodynamical" method we should observe directly the behaviour of large assemblages of individuals. Just as any generalization which we might be able to deduce from our study of the behaviour of crowds would not help much in predicting the movements of isolated individuals, so the laws of thermodynamics do not tell us anything about the behaviour of individual molecules. The application of thermodynamics to molecular systems could, in fact, be made without any reference to the atomic or molecular constitution of substances, but it is usually convenient, however, to make use of the language of atomic and molecular theories.

We shall make frequent use of the relation between the pressure and the volume of a gas. According to Avogadro's principle, in the limiting case at low pressures, equal volumes of gases under the same conditions of temperature and pressure contain equal numbers of molecules. The amount of a gas which occupies the same volume as the molecular weight of hydrogen (2·016 grams), when these conditions are fulfilled, is termed the *mol*. Strictly, the mol as a unit of quantity applies only to the gaseous state. When we speak, for example, of a mol of a substance in the liquid state we mean the amount of substance which gives rise to a mol of gas when the liquid is vaporised. It has nothing to do with the actual molecular weight of the substance in the liquid.

The relation between the pressure and volume of one mol of any gas at sufficiently low pressures is given by the *perfect gas equation* :

$$pv = RT$$

where R is a universal constant, which will be evaluated later. While this equation is true in the limit at low pressures for any gas, at higher pressures actual gases may deviate from it to a greater or less extent.

PART I.—ELEMENTARY THEORY AND ELECTROCHEMISTRY

CHAPTER I

THE FIRST LAW OF THERMODYNAMICS

The Conservation of Energy. The mechanical theory of heat had its origin in the observations of Count Rumford, published in 1798, on the great quantity of heat produced in the boring of cannon. According to the prevailing theories, heat was an imponderable fluid called caloric,* contained in matter in various amounts. The production of heat would, on this view, be ascribed to the escape of caloric in the reduction of massive metal to fine turnings, so that the turnings should contain in a given weight, less caloric than the massive metal. Rumford thought that a change in the amount of caloric should show itself by a change in the heat capacity, and determined the specific heats of the metal in a massive state and in fine turnings. He found that they were the same, and thus came to the conclusion that there was no escape of caloric in the boring and that the heat produced had its origin in the mechanical work performed. After

* Bacon, in his *Novum Organum*, defines heat as "a motion, expansive, restrained and acting in its strife upon the smaller particles of bodies." (Book II., Aphorism XX.) He seems to have come very near to a mechanical theory of heat.

describing experiments on the production of heat by friction, he says :

"We have seen that a very considerable quantity of heat may be excited by the friction of two metallic surfaces, and given off in a constant stream . . . without any signs of diminution or exhaustion . . . . It is hardly necessary to add, that anything which any insulated body or system of bodies can continue to furnish without limitation cannot possibly be a material substance ; and it appears to me to be extremely difficult, if not quite impossible, to form any distinct idea of anything capable of being excited and communicated in these experiments, except it be MOTION."

Humphry Davy also experimented (1799) on the production of heat by friction and concluded that the observable motion of massive bodies was converted by friction into motions of the small particles of which they are composed. Joule made many careful experiments (1840-1878) to determine the amount of heat produced by the expenditure of a given amount of mechanical work. He found that the same amount of heat is always produced by the same amount of work whatever the substance used and the method of working. He determined with considerable accuracy the amount of work required to produce a unit quantity of heat, a quantity which is known as the *mechanical equivalent of heat*. Meyer also determined this quantity (1842) by finding the change in the temperature of a gas when it performed a known amount of work by expansion against the atmosphere.

The earlier development of mechanics had led to the concept of the *energy* of a body, expressing the amount of work done in bringing it into a given position and state of motion. In mechanics two kinds of energy are recognised, kinetic and potential. Kinetic energy is the energy of motion ; it is the amount of work expended in bringing a body from rest into a given state of motion. Potential energy is the energy of position ; when a body is moved from one position to another under the action of forces exerted on it by other bodies (*e.g.* the force of gravitation), its potential energy increases by the amount of work done in changing its position.

The discovery by Joule of the equivalence of heat and work led to the recognition of heat as a third form of energy, so that when mechanical work is expended in frictional processes, the mechanical energy lost is accounted for by the energy of the heat produced. Other kinds of energy were soon recognised. Thus by the expenditure of work in a dynamo it is possible to produce an electric current, the energy of which can be converted into heat. Energy may be defined in general as work or anything which can be produced from or converted into work.* Energy of different kinds is often measured in different units. Thus work may be measured in ergs or foot-pounds, heat in calories, electrical energy in joules. The relations between these units must be determined by experiment.

The equivalence of the different forms of energy, approximately verified in a few cases, led to the enunciation, in different forms by Helmholtz, Clausius and Kelvin, of a general law of nature, the principle of the *Conservation of Energy*. This may be stated most simply as follows :

When a quantity of energy of one kind disappears an equivalent amount of energy of other kinds makes its appearance.

* J. R. Partington, *Chemical Thermodynamics*, p. 12.

The justification of this principle as an exact and universal law of Nature rests on the consequence that if it were not true it would be possible by a suitable cyclic taking advantage of the lack of equivalence, to create energy out of nothing.

The law of the Conservation of Energy is alternatively contained in the statement that energy cannot be created out of nothing, or destroyed.* Clausius expressed this by saying "*The total amount of energy of an isolated system remains constant; it may change from one form to another.*" Here an isolated system is a system of bodies which can neither receive from nor give energy to anything outside. If energy cannot be created or lost, its energy must remain constant. It is not possible to give an *a priori* proof that energy cannot be created. No one has ever been able to construct, or has found any phenomenon which would make it theoretically possible to construct a "perpetual motion machine," *i.e.* a cycle of operations which would produce energy from nothing. No phenomenon has ever been observed which is contrary to the principle. It is a generalisation from experience, and it constitutes the First Law of Thermodynamics.

* The equivalence of different forms of energy may be shown to be a consequence of the impossibility of creating energy out of nothing as follows. Consider a number of methods of converting energy of a kind P into energy of a kind Q. Suppose that by one method A, q units of energy of kind Q are obtained from p units of P and that by another method B, q units of Q can be obtained from p' units of P;

---

* Matter and energy are now known to be interconvertible. The Conservation of Energy has, therefore, been replaced by a wider principle of the Conservation of Mass + Energy. We shall not, however, be concerned with any phenomena in which the mass may vary.

no other kinds of energy being involved. Then it would be possible to change p units of P into q units of Q by method A, and then by the reverse of B to change to q units of Q into p' of P. The net result of the two transformations would be the creation of $p' - p$ units of P. Thus a given amount of energy P must always give rise to the same amount of energy Q, no matter what method or substances are used to effect the change.

Units of Energy. In the C.G.S. system mechanical work is measured in *ergs*. An erg is the work done by a force of one dyne acting over a distance of one centimetre. A dyne is the force which acting on the mass of one gram produces an acceleration of one centimetre per second per second. The force of gravity (at 45° latitude and at sea level) produces an acceleration of 980·6 cm./sec². The force of gravity acting on a body under these conditions is therefore 980·6 dynes per gram. The standard pressure of the atmosphere is the pressure of 76·0 cm. of mercury (density 13·59). The pressure of the atmosphere is therefore

$$76{\cdot}0 \times 13{\cdot}59 \times 980{\cdot}6 = 1{,}013{,}300 \text{ dynes per sq. cm.}$$

Heat is usually measured in *calories*, the calorie being the quantity of heat required to raise 1 gram of water 1° C. at 15° C. The mechanical equivalent of heat, taking the mean of the best modern determinations, is

$$1 \text{ calorie} = 4{\cdot}182 \times 10^7 \text{ ergs.}$$

Electrical energy is measured in joules, the joule being the energy of an electric current of one ampere, flowing through a potential difference of one volt for one second. By the definition of electrical units

$$1 \text{ joule} = 10^7 \text{ ergs} = 1/4{\cdot}182 \text{ or } 0{\cdot}2391 \text{ calories.}$$

Application of the First Law to Material Systems. Our system may consist of any mass of material, homogeneous or heterogeneous, whose behaviour we wish to investigate. When the system is altered from a state A to a state B, it may receive energy from or give it up to its surroundings. Since energy is not created or lost we say that the energy of the system has increased or decreased by the amount received or given up. We can now state two fundamental consequences of the first law.

1. When a system is altered from a state A to a state B, the energy change is perfectly definite and independent of the intermediate states through which the system passes. For if the energy change in going from A to B by one path (I) were less than that in a second path (II) (Fig. 1), the effect of bringing the system from A to B by path (I) and back from B to A by (II) would be an increase in the energy of the surroundings. But the system has been brought back into precisely its original state, so that energy must have been created, which is contrary to the first law.

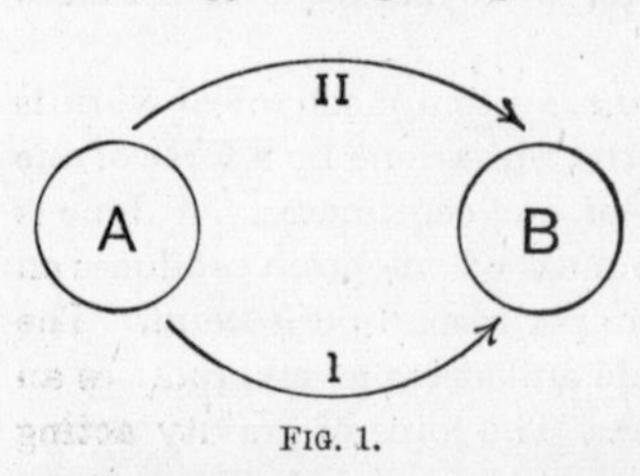

FIG. 1.

The energy change of the system in going from A to B may thus be expressed as the difference between its energy in state B and in state A, or

$$\underset{\text{Increase in energy. } A\to B}{\Delta E} = \underset{\text{Energy in } B}{E_B} - \underset{\text{Energy in } A}{E_A} \qquad (1)$$

2. The energy of the system may change through heat being given up to or taken from the surroundings or through work being done on or by the surroundings. Thus we have

$$\underset{\text{Increase in energy of system.}}{\Delta E} = \underset{\text{Heat absorbed by system.}}{q} - \underset{\text{Work done by system on surroundings.}}{w} \qquad (2)$$

The work done may be mechanical (as in an expansion

against the pressure of the atmosphere) or electrical (as in the production of a current, which may be used to drive an electric motor, in a galvanic cell). There are other ways in which work can be done (*e.g.* against magnetic forces), but these are the only ones with which we shall be concerned. For the present we shall consider mechanical work alone.

Work Done in Expansion against a Constant Pressure. The relation is obtained most easily by supposing that the system is contained in a cylinder fitted with a piston (itself weightless) of area a on which a pressure p can be applied.* When the volume of the system increases and the piston is forced back at distance d against pressure p, the work done is $p \times a \times d$. But $a \times d$ is the increase in volume Δv of the system; so that the work is $w = p\,\Delta v$.

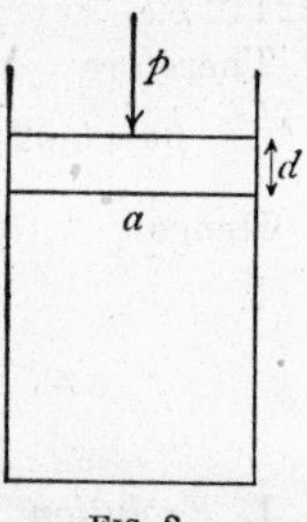

FIG. 2.

When the only work done by a system in a certain change is that due to an increase in volume against a constant pressure, we have therefore:

$$\Delta E = q - p\,\Delta v \quad \text{......................} (3)$$

We will calculate the value of the last term in some standard cases.

(1) *The work done when volume increases by* 1 *c.c. against a pressure of* 1 *atmosphere:*

The pressure of the atmosphere gives rise to a force of 1,013,300 dynes per sq. cm. The work done when the volume increases by 1 c.c. is evidently

1,013,300 ergs = 0·02423 calories.

This is known as the c.c. atmosphere.

Conversely, 1 calorie = 41·37 c.c. atmospheres.

* p is the force acting on the piston per unit area.

(2) *The work done when the volume increases by* 1 *litre against a pressure of* 1 *atmosphere* is

$$0{\cdot}02423 \times 1000 = 24{\cdot}23 \text{ calories.}$$

This is the litre atmosphere.

(3) *The work done when the increase in volume is the volume of* 1 *mol of a perfect gas :*

If v be the volume of the gas, the work done is pv.

But for a perfect gas, $pv = RT$, where R is the gas constant and T the absolute temperature. The volume of 1 mol of a perfect gas at standard atmospheric pressure and 0° C. is 22412 c.c.

Therefore

$$pv = 0{\cdot}02423 \times 22412 \text{ calories} = R \times 273 \text{ calories.}$$

Hence $$R = \frac{0{\cdot}02423 \times 22412}{273}$$

$$= 1{\cdot}988 \text{ calories.}$$

Examples.

1. *Evolution of a Gas in a Chemical Reaction.* The amount of heat evolved when 1 atomic weight (65·4 grams) of zinc is dissolved in a dilute solution of hydrochloric acid is 36200 calories at 18° C. One mol of hydrogen is produced in this reaction and the increase in the volume of the system may be taken as the volume of the hydrogen produced since the changes in volume of the other substances are so small in comparison that they may be neglected. The work done in the solution of this amount of zinc is thus $1{\cdot}99T$ calories or $1{\cdot}99 \times 291 = 582$ calories. We can find the total change in the energy of the system by (2), thus :

$$\Delta E = (-36200) \quad - \quad (582) \quad = -36782 \text{ calories.}$$

Heat absorbed. Work done.

2. *Work done in Vaporisation.* When 1 mol of water (18 grams) is vaporised at 100° C. the increase in volume may be taken as the volume of the vapour produced, since the change in volume of the liquid is small in comparison.

If we regard the vapour as a perfect gas, we find that, approximately :

$$\text{Work done} = p\Delta v = RT = 1{\cdot}99 \times 373 = 743 \text{ calories.}$$

The total amount of heat absorbed in the vaporisation of 18 grams of water at 100° C. is 9828 calories.

So that
$$\Delta E = q - p\Delta v = 9828 - 742$$
$$= 9086 \text{ calories.}$$

This is known as the " internal latent heat."

Heats of Reaction. According to (2) the heat absorbed in a reaction is the sum of the energy increase of the system and the work done :

$$q = \Delta E + w. \quad \text{......................(4)}$$

The heat absorbed therefore depends on the conditions under which the reaction is carried out. There are two common conditions, which we will consider.

1. *Reactions at Constant Volume.* No work is done in expansion, *i.e.* $w = 0$, so that the heat absorbed is equal to the increase in the energy of the system in the reaction

$$(q)_v = \Delta E = E_2 - E_1. \quad \text{....................(5)}$$

2. *Reactions at Constant Pressure.* In this case $w = p\Delta v = p(v_2 - v_1)$ where v_2 is the final volume and v_1 the original volume of the system. We have then

$$(q)_p = \Delta E + p\Delta v = E_2 - E_1 + p(v_2 - v_1)$$
$$= (E_2 + pv_2) - (E_1 + pv_1) \quad \text{..........(6)}$$

The heat absorbed in a reaction at constant pressure is thus equal to the increase in the value of the composite quantity $(E + pv)$ in going from the initial to the final state.

The quantity $(E + pv) = H$ has been called the *heat content* of the system, and we have for the heat absorbed in a reaction at constant pressure,

$$(q)_p = H_2 - H_1 = \Delta H. \quad \text{....................(7)}$$

It is evident that the heat content change in a reaction is related to the energy change by the relation :

$$\Delta H = \Delta E + p\Delta v, \quad \text{.....................(8)}$$

or if the increase in volume is due to the formation of n mols of a perfect gas,

$$\Delta H = \Delta E + nRT. \quad \text{.....................(9)}$$

Thermochemical Equations. It should be noted that ΔH and ΔE represent an increase in the heat content and energy of a system. They therefore correspond to an *absorption of heat.* It is useful to remember that the matter is considered from the standpoint of the system itself. An increase in the energy of the system is reckoned as positive, so that an *absorption* of heat appears as a positive quantity.

In works on thermochemistry and in tables of thermochemical data the opposite convention has often been employed and the evolution of heat represented by positive quantities.* To avoid confusion in using such data, it is best to rewrite them so that each figure represents ΔH or ΔE, the heat content increase or the energy increase of the system in the reaction.

In order to be perfectly explicit the equation expressing the reaction should be written down and the state of aggregation of the substances taking part, and the temperature at which the reaction is carried out should be indicated.

Thus the equation :

$$C(graphite) + O_2(g) = CO_2(g)\,;\ \Delta H_{288} = -94{,}000 \text{ calories}$$

indicates that when 12 grams of carbon in the form of

* By the " heat of reaction," the amount of heat evolved in the reaction is usually meant ; by the " heat of formation," the heat evolved in the formation of a compound from its elements.

graphite combine with 32 grams of oxygen gas to form gaseous carbon dioxide at 288° K. (15° C.), at constant pressure, the heat content decreases by 94,000 calories, *i.e.* 94,000 calories are evolved. If the carbon is in the form of diamond the heat evolved is greater by 180 calories. Thus

$$C(diamond) + O_2(g) = CO_2(g),\ \Delta H_{288} = -94{,}180 \text{ calories.}$$

In the same way the equation

$$2H_2(g) + O_2(g) = 2H_2O(l),\ \Delta H_{288} = -136{,}800 \text{ calories}$$

indicates that in the combination of the quantities of gaseous hydrogen and oxygen represented in the equation to form liquid water at 288° K., the heat content decreases by 136,800 calories.

Other heat effects are similarly represented. Thus when one mol of water is vaporised at 100° C. at constant pressure, 9828 calories are absorbed, so that we write

$$H_2O(l) = H_2O(g),\ \Delta H_{373} = 9828 \text{ calories.}$$

The heat of solution of a substance varies with the concentration of the solution, and it is necessary to specify precisely the conditions which obtain. Thus

$$KCl(s) = KCl(100H_2O),\ \Delta H_{288} = 4430 \text{ calories}$$

indicates that when the formula weight of KCl is dissolved in 100 mols of water, 4430 calories are absorbed. When a given weight of solute is dissolved in such a large quantity of the solvent that further dilution is not accompanied by any heat effect, we obtain the *heat of solution at infinite dilution.* An infinitely dilute solution is often indicated by the symbol (*aq*). Thus

$$HCl(g) = HCl(aq),\ \Delta H = -17{,}300 \text{ calories}$$

indicates that when a mol of HCl gas is dissolved in a very large quantity of water 17,300 calories are evolved.

Hess's Law of Constant Heat Summation. We have seen that the energy change (ΔE) of a system in going from one state A to another state B is independent of the path, *i.e.* of the intermediate states gone through. The same is true of the change in heat content ΔH, provided that the pressure remains constant throughout. For ΔH differs from ΔE by the sum of all the $p\Delta v$ terms for different stages of the change $A \rightarrow B$. If the pressure remains constant this sum is equal to $p(v_2 - v_1)$, where v_2 is the final and v_1 the initial volume and therefore depends only on the initial and final states. Since $\Delta E = (q)_v$ and $\Delta H = (q)_p$; the heat absorbed in a reaction or series of reactions depends only on the initial and final states and not on the intermediate stages, both when the volume and when the pressure remains constant throughout. This result was first enunciated by Hess in 1840, before the formulation of the general principle of the Conservation of Energy and it is known as Hess's Law of Constant Heat Summation. It is chiefly useful for obtaining heats of reaction which cannot be directly determined. The heat effect of a reaction can be determined in a calorimeter only if it takes place fairly quickly. As a rule the heats of formation of organic compounds from the elements cannot be determined directly, but if the heat of combustion of the compound and the heats of combustion of the elements are known, the heat of formation can be calculated.

Thus the heat of formation of methane can be calculated when we know its heat of combustion and the heats of combustion of its elements carbon and hydrogen. The heat of combustion of methane at constant pressure to carbon dioxide and liquid water at 15° C. is 212,600 calories, hence using the data of the previous section, we may write the scheme :

$$\begin{array}{lcl} & \Delta H = x & \\ C(\mathit{graphite}) + 2H_2(g) & \longrightarrow & CH_4(g) \\ \Delta H \quad \vert & +2O_2 \qquad\qquad +2O_2 & \vert \quad \Delta H \\ = -94{,}000 \quad \vert & CO_2(g) & \vert \quad = -212{,}600 \\ \;\; -136{,}000 \quad \llcorner & \longrightarrow \; + \; \longleftarrow & \lrcorner \\ & 2H_2O(l). & \end{array}$$

$$\text{Whence} \quad x = (-94{,}000 - 136{,}000) - (212{,}600)$$
$$= -17{,}400.$$

Thus

$$C(\mathit{graphite}) + 2H_2(g) = CH_4(g), \quad \Delta H_{288} = -17{,}400 \text{ calories.}$$

The result can also be obtained directly from the thermochemical equations :

$$\text{(I)} \quad C(\mathit{graphite}) + O_2(g) = CO_2(g), \quad \Delta H = -94{,}000 \text{ cals.}$$
$$\text{(II)} \quad 2H_2(g) \quad + O_2(g) = 2H_2O(l), \Delta H = -136{,}000 \text{ cals.}$$
$$\text{(III)} \quad CH_4(g) \quad + 2O_2(g) = CO_2(g) + 2H_2O(l),$$
$$\Delta H = -212{,}600 \text{ calories.}$$

Hence adding equations (I) and (II) and subtracting (III), we obtain

$$C(\mathit{graphite}) + 2H_2(g) - CH_4(g) = 0, \quad \Delta H = -17{,}400 \text{ cals.}$$

which may be rewritten in the form given above.

Heats of Formation. Since under ordinary conditions reactions occur more frequently at constant pressure than at constant volume, thermochemical data are usually tabulated as heat content changes. It is of course easy to calculate the corresponding energy changes.

The heat content change, ΔH, in the formation of a compound is the difference between the heat content of the compound and that of its elements (in a specified state and at the same temperature) and may be regarded as the heat content of the compound relative to its elements. In a chemical reaction the amounts of the elements on each side of the equation are necessarily equal, so that we may get the heat content changes in a reaction by taking the difference between the heat contents of the resultants and the reactants.

Thus for the reaction:

$$2H_2S(g) + SO_2(g) = 2H_2O(l) + 3S(rhombic).$$

Heat contents relative to elements	2×-5300	$-70,920$	$-136,740$	0

we have

$$\Delta H = -136,740 - (-10,600 - 70,920) = -55,220 \text{ calories.}$$

The heats of formation of some typical compounds are given below. The most extensive and reliable compilation of thermochemical data is F. R. Bichowský and F. D. Rossini's book *The Thermochemistry of Chemical Substances*. (Reinhold Pub. Corp., New York, 1936.)

TABLE I.

HEATS OF FORMATION OF COMPOUNDS AT 15° C.

			ΔH
$H_2(g)$	$+1/2O_2(g)$	$=H_2O(l)$	-68370 calories.
$C(graphite)$	$+O_2(g)$	$=CO_2(g)$	-94450
$C(graphite)$	$+1/2O_2(g)$	$=CO(g)$	-26840
$S(rhombic)$	$+O_2(g)$	$=SO_2(g)$	-70920
$1/2H_2(g)$	$+1/2Cl_2(g)$	$=HCl(g)$	-22060
$1/2H_2(g)$	$+1/2Br_2(l)$	$=HBr(g)$	-8650
$1/2H_2(g)$	$+1/2I_2(s)$	$=HI(g)$	5920
$S(rhombic)$	$+H_2(g)$	$=H_2S(g)$	-5300
$1/2N_2(g)$	$+3/2H_2(g)$	$=NH_3(g)$	-11000
$Na(s)$	$+1/2Cl_2(g)$	$=NaCl(s)$	-98300
$Na(s)$	$+1/2Br_2(g)$	$=NaBr(s)$	-86730
$Na(s)$	$+1/2I_2(s)$	$=NaI(s)$	-69280
$K(s)$	$+1/2Cl_2(g)$	$=KCl(s)$	-104360
$K(s)$	$+1/2Br_2(l)$	$=KBr(s)$	-94070
$K(s)$	$+1/2I_2(s)$	$=KI(s)$	-78870

Heat Capacities. The heat capacity of a system is the amount of heat required to raise its temperature 1°.* This depends on the conditions. If the volume is kept constant, all the heat added goes to increase the energy of the system, so that, if C_v is the heat capacity under this condition, when the temperature is raised from T_1 to T_2 the heat absorbed, $C_v(T_2-T_1)$ is equal to the increase in the energy of the system E_2-E_1, *i.e.*

$$C_v(T_2-T_1)=E_2-E_1,$$

or in the limit, for a small rise of temperature dT:

$$C_v=\frac{dE}{dT}. \qquad \text{(10)}$$

C_v is the heat capacity at constant volume.

When a system is heated at constant pressure it may expand and in doing so perform work against the applied pressure. The quantity of heat required to produce an increase of temperature of 1° is then greater than that at constant volume by the amount of work done in expanding. If v is the volume of the system, the increase in volume for 1° rise of temperature is dv/dT and the work done $p\,.\,dv/dT$. Hence the heat capacity at constant pressure is

$$C_p=C_v+p\,.\,\frac{dv}{dT}=\frac{dE}{dT}+p\frac{dv}{dT}.$$

But since

$$H=E+pv,$$

$$\frac{dH}{dT}=\frac{dE}{dT}+p\frac{dv}{dT}.$$

so that

$$C_p=\frac{dH}{dT}. \qquad \text{(11)}$$

* The heat capacity of a system must be distinguished from the specific heat of a substance. The latter is the heat required to raise the temperature of 1 gram of the substance 1°, the former is that required for the whole of a specified system, containing a known mass of a substance or substances.

***Kirchhoff's Equation.** The energy change in a reaction $A \rightarrow B$ is given by

$$\Delta E_{A\rightarrow B} = E_B - E_A,$$

hence
$$\frac{d(\Delta E_{A\rightarrow B})}{dT} = \frac{dE_B}{dT} - \frac{dE_A}{dT} = (C_v)_B - (C_v)_A. \text{......}(12)$$

Thus the rate at which $\Delta E_{A\rightarrow B}$ changes with the temperature is equal to the difference between the heat capacities at constant volume of the final system B (resultants) and the original system A (reactants).

In the same way

$$\Delta H_{A\rightarrow B} = H_B - H_A,$$

$$\frac{d(\Delta H_{A\rightarrow B})}{dT} = \frac{dH_B}{dT} - \frac{dH_A}{dT} = (C_p)_B - (C_p)_A. \text{......}(13)$$

The temperature coefficient of ΔH is therefore related in the same way to the heat capacities at constant pressure.*

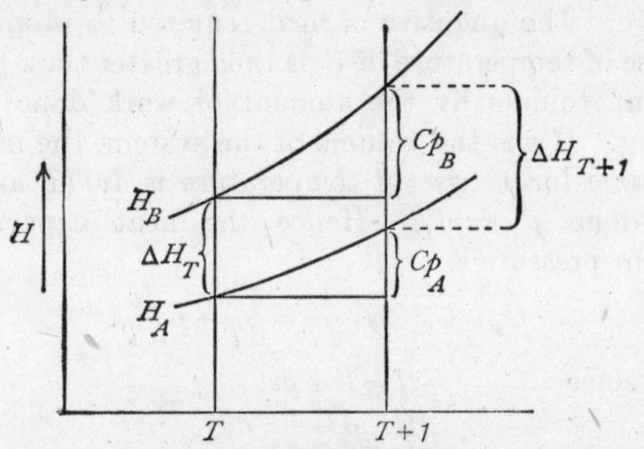

FIG. 3.—Kirchhoff's equation.

These are two forms of Kirchhoff's equation. The physical meaning is shown in Fig. 3.

The curves marked H_A, H_B represent the variation of the heat contents of the reactants (A) and of the resultants

* It must be emphasised that the heat capacities must refer to the amounts of substances given in the chemical equation defining ΔE or ΔH.

(B) with temperature. The distance between these curves at a given temperature T represents the heat content change in the reaction ($\Delta H = H_B - H_A$) at this temperature. If we erect verticals at temperatures T and $T+1$, the intercepts made by the two curves are equal to ΔH_T and ΔH_{T+1}. Since the increase in H_A for 1° rise of temperature is $(C_p)_A$ and the increase in H_B similarly $(C_p)_B$, we have

$$\Delta H_{T+1} = \Delta H_T + (C_p)_B - (C_p)_A.$$

Example. Knowing the heat capacities of water as liquid and as vapour, we find the variation of the heat of vaporisation with the temperature. Thus we have

$$H_2O(l) = H_2O(g), \quad \Delta H_{373} = 9650 \text{ calories.}$$
$$H_2O(l), \quad C_{p(373)} = 17{\cdot}82\ ;$$
$$H_2O(g), \quad C_{p(373)} = 8{\cdot}37.$$

Hence $\dfrac{d(\Delta H)}{dT} = 8{\cdot}37 - 17{\cdot}82 = -9{\cdot}45$ calories per deg.

Thus the heat of vaporisation decreases 9·45 calories for each degree rise of temperature. At 120° C., then,

$$\Delta H = 9650 - (9{\cdot}45 \times 20) = 9650 - 190 = 9460 \text{ calories.}$$

For an extended range of temperature it would be necessary to take into account the variation of the heat capacities with temperature. The formula obtained above may be used, however, quite rigidly over a range of temperature for which the mean heat capacities are known.

The relations between heat capacity and temperature are simpler for gases than for solids or liquids, and can in most cases be represented empirically over a considerable range of temperature by equations of the form

$$C_p = a + bT + cT^2 + dT^3 \ldots .$$

Table I. gives equations which represent the molar heat capacities of a number of gases over a very wide range of temperature from 0° C. to from 1000 to 2000° C., according to G. N. Lewis and M. Randall. (These equations are quite empirical; almost any function which varies to a first approximation linearly with T could be represented by a sufficient number of terms of this kind.)

We can obtain ΔC_p for a reaction by subtracting the equations for the reacting gases from those of the products of the reaction, taking note of the amount of each gas which enters into the reaction. Thus we obtain in general an equation of the form

$$\Delta C_p = \alpha + \beta T + \gamma T^2 + \delta T^3 \ldots .$$

Substituting this value in (13), we have

$$\frac{d(\Delta H)}{dT} = \alpha + \beta T + \gamma T^2 + \delta T^3 \ldots ,$$

and integrating, we find

$$\Delta H = \alpha T + \frac{\beta}{2} T^2 + \frac{\gamma}{3} T^3 + \frac{\delta}{4} T^4 \ldots + \Delta H_0, \quad \ldots\ldots (13a)$$

where ΔH_0 is the integration constant. ΔH_0 is evidently the value of ΔH when $T = 0$, but it cannot be identified with the value of the heat content change at absolute zero, for the heat capacity equations on which (13*a*) is based are never valid at low temperatures in the region of absolute zero. The values of ΔH_0 for some common reactions for use with the data in Table I*a* are given in Table I*b*.

TABLE I*a*.

EMPIRICAL EQUATIONS OF LEWIS AND RANDALL FOR THE HEAT CAPACITY OF GASES.

Monatomic gases; $C_p = 5{\cdot}0$.
H_2; $C_p = 6{\cdot}50 + 0{\cdot}0009T$.
O_2, N_2, NO, CO, HCl, HBr, HI; $C_p = 6{\cdot}50 + 0{\cdot}0010T$.
Cl_2, Br_2, I_2; $C_p = 7{\cdot}4 + 0{\cdot}001T$.
H_2O, H_2S; $C_p = 8{\cdot}81 - 0{\cdot}0019T + 0{\cdot}00000222T^2$.
CO_2, SO_2; $C_p = 7{\cdot}0 + 0{\cdot}0071T - 0{\cdot}00000186T^2$.
NH_3; $C_p = 8{\cdot}04 + 0{\cdot}0007T + 0{\cdot}0000051T^2$.
CH_4; $C_p = 7{\cdot}8 + 0{\cdot}005T$.

TABLE I*b*.

VALUES OF ΔH_0 FOR USE WITH TABLE I*a*.

			ΔH_0
$H_2(g)$	$+1/2O_2(g)$	$=H_2O(g)$	-57410 calories.
$1/2H_2(g)$	$+1/2Cl_2(g)$	$=HCl(g)$	-21870
$1/2H_2(g)$	$+1/2Br_2(g)$	$=HBr(g)$	-11970
$1/2H_2(g)$	$+1/2I_2(g)$	$=HI(g)$	-1270
$H_2(g)$	$+1/2S_2(g)$	$=H_2S(g)$	-19200
$SO_2(g)$	$+1/2O_2(g)$	$=SO_3(g)$	-22600
$1/2N_2(g)$	$+1/2O_2(g)$	$=NO(g)$	$+21600$
$NO(g)$	$+1/2O_2(g)$	$=NO_2(g)$	-14170
$1/2N_2(g)$	$+3/2H_2(g)$	$=NH_3(g)$	-9500
C (*graphite*)	$+1/2O_2(g)$	$=CO(g)$	-26600
C (*graphite*)	$+O_2(g)$	$=CO_2(g)$	-94100
C (*graphite*)	$+2H_2(g)$	$=CH_4(g)$	-14342

Example. For the reaction

$$H_2 + 1/2O_2 = H_2O(g),$$

we obtain from Table I the equations

(*a*) H_2O, $C_p = 8{\cdot}81 - 0{\cdot}0019T + 0{\cdot}00000222T^2$

(*b*) H_2, $C_p = 6{\cdot}5 + 0{\cdot}0009T$,

(*c*) $1/2O_2$, $C_p = 3{\cdot}25 + 0{\cdot}0005T$;

whence $\Delta C_p = (C_p)_{H_2O} - \{(C_p)_{H_2} + (C_p)_{1/2O_2}\}$

is obtained by subtracting equations (*b*) and (*c*), for the reactants from (*a*), that of the resulting system. Thus we find that

$$\Delta C_p = -0{\cdot}94 - 0{\cdot}0033T + 0{\cdot}00000222T^2$$
$$= \frac{d(\Delta H)}{dT}.$$

Integrating, we have

$$\Delta H = \Delta H_0 - 0{\cdot}94T - \frac{0{\cdot}0033T^2}{2} + \frac{0{\cdot}00000222T^3}{3}.$$

The value of ΔH_0 is obtained by substitution if we know ΔH at any one value of T. When $T = 273°$ (absolute), ΔH has been found to be -57780 calories. Substituting these values we find that $\Delta H_0 = -57410$ calories.

APPLICATIONS OF THE FIRST LAW TO GASES.

Heat Capacities. The heat capacity of a gas may be measured at constant pressure or at constant volume. The heat capacity at constant pressure is greater than that at constant volume by the amount of work done in expansion when the temperature is raised 1°.

For 1 mol of a gas, we have

$$C_p = C_v + p \, . \, dv,$$

but since for a perfect gas $pv = RT$, $p\,dv = R\,dT$; so that for 1° rise of temperature,

$$p\,dv = R$$

and

$$C_p = C_v + R. \qquad (14)$$

In words, the heat capacity of 1 mol of a perfect gas at constant pressure is greater than that at constant volume by $R (= 1{\cdot}99$ calories).

The thermal energy of a monatomic gas, according to the kinetic theory of gases, consists solely of the translational energy of motion of atoms in space, and is equal to $E = 3/2RT$. For such a gas

$$C_v = \frac{dE}{dT} = 3/2R,$$

$$C_p = 3/2R + R = 5/2R;$$

and the ratio of the heat capacities

$$C_p/C_v = 5/3 = 1{\cdot}67.$$

The energy of complex gases is greater than $3/2RT$ by the energies of vibration and rotation of the molecules. Hence the ratio

$$C_p/C_v = \frac{C_v + R}{C_v} = 1 + \frac{R}{C_v}$$

is smaller, the greater C_v is.

The following table gives some values.

TABLE II.

MOLAR HEAT CAPACITIES, ETC., OF GASES AT 0° C.

	(1) C_v	(2) C_p	(3) $\gamma = C_p/C_v$
Argon, A	2·98	4·97	1·67
Hydrogen, H_2	4·84	6·83	1·408
Nitrogen, N_2	4·90	6·89	1·408
Oxygen, O_2	4·90	6·89	1·39
Chlorine, Cl_2	5·85	7·84	1·34
Carbon dioxide, CO_2	6·80	8·79	1·31
Ammonia, NH_3	6·60	8·59	1·32
Ethyl ether, $(C_2H_5)_2O$	32	34	1·06

(1) Observed. (2) Calculated by (14).
(3) Determined independently.

Energy Relations in Volume Changes of a Gas. For a simultaneous change in the volume and temperature of a gas we may write our fundamental equation (4)

$$q = \Delta E + w,$$

in the form

$$q = \frac{\partial E}{\partial v} \cdot dv + \frac{\partial E}{\partial T} \cdot dT + w \quad \text{.........}(15)$$

$\partial E/\partial v$ is the rate at which the energy of the gas changes with its volume; $\partial E/\partial T = C_v$, the rate at which it changes with the temperature.

We must first ascertain the magnitude of $\partial E/\partial v$. Does the energy of a gas vary with its volume? Joule made an experiment to answer this question. Two cylinders I and II were connected by a stopcock (Fig. 4). I contained the

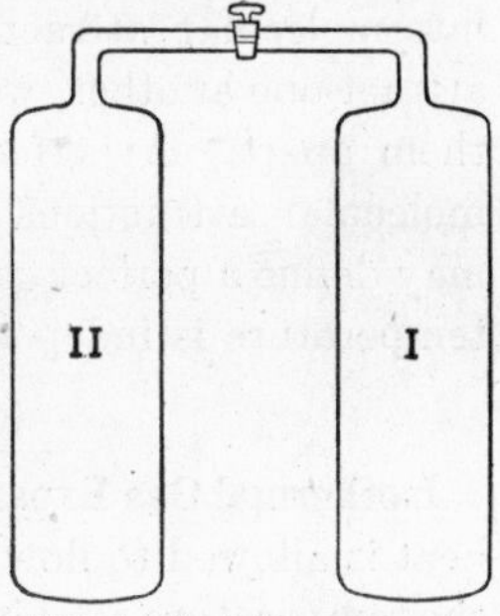

FIG. 4.—Joule's experiment.

compressed gas, II was evacuated. On opening the stopcock the gas expands into II until the pressure is the same in both cylinders. No work is done in this expansion, since the gas expands into a vacuum, so that w is zero. If the system is insulated so that no heat is received from the surrounding, q is also zero, so that

$$\frac{\partial E}{\partial v} \cdot dv = -C_v \cdot dT.$$

Therefore a variation of the energy of a gas with its volume will be shown by a change of temperature.

In an actual experiment the whole system, cylinders, gas, etc., is concerned in the temperature change so that C_v must be taken as the heat capacity of the whole system. Joule placed the cylinders in a bath of water and observed the temperature change by a thermometer in the water. He found that it was too small to be detected, and concluded that " no change of temperature occurs when air is allowed to expand without developing mechanical power."

This experiment is a crude one and it has been found by delicate experiments that with actual gases a small heat absorption does actually occur. This is due to intermolecular attractions. If the molecules of a gas attract one another, work is done in expansion in pulling them apart. A perfect gas is one in which the intermolecular attractions are infinitely small, so that we may define a perfect gas as one whose energy at constant temperature is independent of its volume or for which

$$(dE/dv)_T = 0. \quad \text{........................} (16)$$

Isothermal Gas Expansion. In an isothermal expansion heat is allowed to flow into or out of the system, so that the temperature remains constant. For a perfect gas the internal energy is independent of the volume, so that in (5), $\Delta U = 0$, and

$$\underset{\text{Heat absorbed.}}{q} = \underset{\text{Work done by gas.}}{w} \quad \text{.....................(17)}$$

The work done by a gas in expanding depends on the opposing pressure. Thus if the gas is allowed to expand into a vacuum no work at all is done. If the gas is confined in a cylinder fitted with a piston (itself weightless), it can be seen that the gas will only expand at all if the pressure exerted by the piston is less than p (Fig. 5). Thus a maximum amount of work is obtained when pressure acting on the gas is only infinitesimally less than p, say $p - dp$. The work done when the volume increases by a small amount dv, is thus $(p - dp)dv$, or $p \,.\, dv$, since we may neglect small quantities of the second order. As the volume increases the pressure falls according to the relation $pv = RT$, for 1 mol. The opposing pressure must be steadily reduced, so that it is at all stages a minute amount less than the gas pressure. The total work done by 1 mol of gas in a finite expansion from p_1 to p_2 is therefore obtained by summing the terms $p \,.\, dv$ for small stages, *i.e.* by the integral $\int_{p_1}^{p_2} p \,.\, dv$.

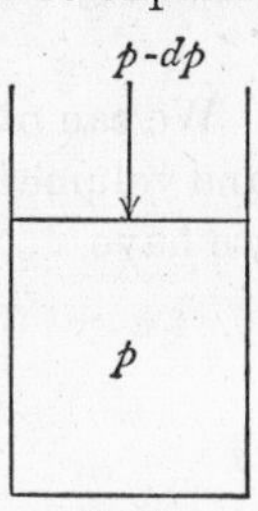

FIG. 5.

Since $p = RT/v$, we obtain

$$w = RT \,.\int_{v_1}^{v_2} \frac{dv}{v} = RT \,.\log(v_2/v_1) = RT \log(p_1/p_2). \quad \text{....(18)}$$

Adiabatic Gas Expansion. In an adiabatic change the system is thermally isolated, so that no heat can leave it or enter it from surrounding bodies. Therefore in the fundamental equation (5), $q = 0$, and thus

$$\Delta E + w = 0. \quad \text{.......................(19)}$$

In words the internal energy decreases by the amount of work done. In a small expansion we have for a perfect gas $\Delta E = C_v dT$, since the internal energy is not affected by change of volume, and $w = p \cdot dv$. Hence we obtain the characteristic equation for adiabatic changes in perfect gases :

$$C_v \cdot dT + p \cdot dv = 0. \qquad (20)$$

We can obtain from this the relation between pressure and volume in adiabatic changes. Substituting $p = RT/v$, we have

$$C_v dT + \frac{RT}{v} \cdot dv = 0,$$

or

$$\frac{Cv}{R} \cdot \frac{dT}{T} + \frac{dv}{v} = 0.$$

Whence by integration between limits $T_2(v_2)$ and $T_1(v_1)$,

$$\frac{C_v}{R} \log \left(\frac{T_2}{T_1}\right) + \log \left(\frac{v_2}{v_1}\right) = 0. \qquad (21)$$

Now substituting $R = C_p - C_v$, and putting

$$RT_2 = p_2 v_2 \quad \text{and} \quad RT_1 = p_1 v_1,$$

we find

$$\frac{C_v}{C_p - C_v} \log \left(\frac{p_2 v_2}{p_1 v_1}\right) + \log \frac{v_2}{v_1} = 0,$$

or

$$\log \left(\frac{p_2 v_2}{p_1 v_1}\right) + (\gamma - 1) \log \frac{v_2}{v_1} = 0,$$

where γ is the ratio of the heat capacities C_p/C_v;

$$\therefore \log \left(\frac{p_2 v_2^{\gamma}}{p_1 v_1^{\gamma}}\right) = 0,$$

and

$$p_2 v_2^{\gamma} = p_1 v_1^{\gamma} \qquad (22)$$

If we plot the pressure against the volume of a gas in an adiabatic expansion, we get a characteristic curve analogous to the $p - v$ curves representing variations of pressure with volume at constant temperature. Writing (22) in the form

$$(p_2/p_1) = (v_1/v_2)^\gamma,$$

we see that, since γ is greater than one, the fall of pressure in an adiabatic expansion from v_1 to v_2 is greater than in the corresponding isothermal expansion. (This is because in the adiabatic expansion the temperature also falls as the volume increases.) The adiabatic curves are therefore steeper than the isothermal curves. Fig. 6 illustrates this.

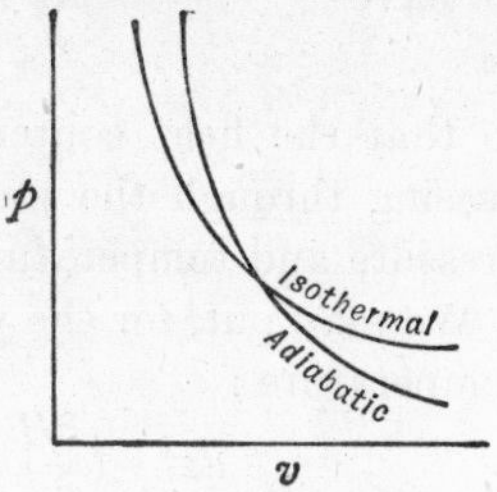

FIG. 6.—Isothermal and adiabatic expansion of a gas.

***The Joule-Thomson Effect.** Suppose that a gas is being forced through a plug of porous material and that the pressure is p_1 in front of the plug p_2 behind it (Fig. 7). Let the volumes occupied by 1 mol of gas at these pressures be v_1 and v_2. The work done on 1 mol of gas

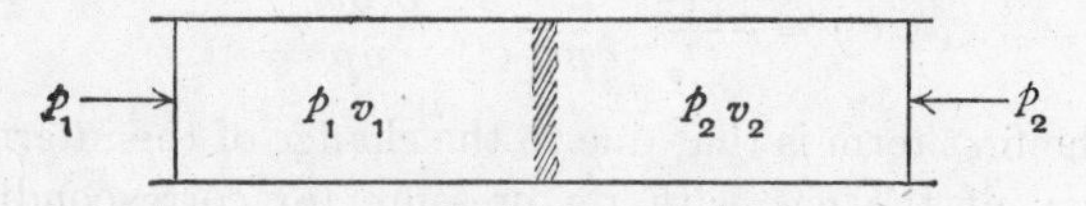

FIG. 7.—Porous plug experiment.

by piston I in forcing it through the plug is p_1v_1, the work done by the gas against piston II is p_2v_2, so that the total work done by the gas is $w = p_2v_2 - p_1v_1$. If the gas is a perfect one $p_1v_1 = p_2v_2$, and no work is done in expansion through the plug. In actual gases pv is not exactly constant and some work is done in the expansion. In addition the energy of the gas may vary with the pressure (Joule effect described previously). If no heat is received from or given to surroundings a temperature change must occur so as to compensate for these two effects.

Writing our fundamental equation (19), $\Delta E + w = 0$, in the form

$$E_2 - E_1 + p_2v_2 - p_1v_1 = 0,$$

we have

$$E_2 + p_2v_2 = E_1 + p_1v_1$$

or

$$H_2 = H_1,$$

so that the heat content of the gas does not alter in passing through the plug, *i.e.* the effect of changes of pressure and temperature on H compensate each other.

We may put, for the variation in H with pressure and temperature:

$$dH = \left(\frac{\partial H}{\partial T}\right) . dT + \left(\frac{\partial H}{\partial p}\right) . dp,$$

so that, in the case considered,

$$\left(\frac{\partial H}{\partial T}\right) . dT + \left(\frac{\partial H}{\partial p}\right) . dp = 0,$$

or

$$dT/dp = -\frac{(\partial H/\partial p)_T}{(\partial H/\partial T)_p} = -\frac{(\partial(E + pv)/\partial p)}{C_p}$$

$$= -\frac{1}{C_p} \cdot \frac{\partial E}{\partial p} - \frac{1}{C_p} \cdot \frac{\partial(pv)}{\partial p}.$$

The first term is that due to the change of the internal energy of the gas with its pressure (or corresponding change of volume). Since work is done against the attractive forces between the molecules when the volume is increased $\partial E/\partial p$ is always negative, and this factor gives rise to a cooling effect when the gas is expanded. The second term represents the work done in the expansion owing to the change in pv. For most gases pv first diminishes and then increases as the pressure is increased, at a given temperature (Fig. 8). Consequently at moderate pressures work is done by the gas when it expands through the plug and a cooling effect is obtained.

In the case of hydrogen and helium (except at very low temperatures) pv increases with increase of pressure, and the result of expansion is a heating effect which may be greater than the effect of the first term.

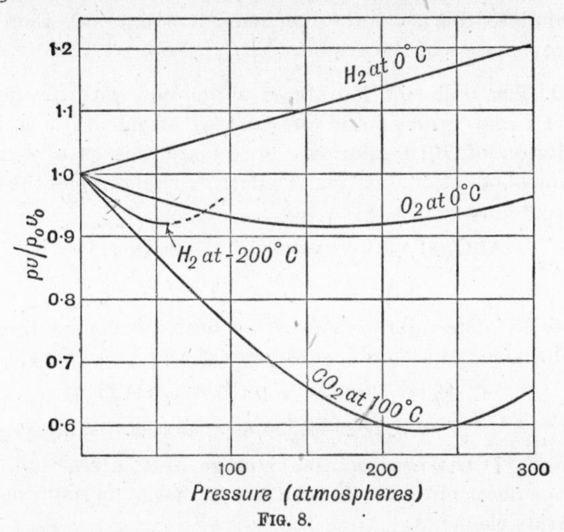

FIG. 8.

The Joule-Thomson effect is made use of in the liquefaction of gases. When most gases are allowed to expand through an orifice at moderate pressures their temperature falls and by the cumulative effect of a continuous circulation very low temperatures may be obtained. At ordinary temperatures hydrogen and helium rise in temperature, but below $-80 \cdot 5°$ C. in the case of hydrogen and at the temperature of liquid hydrogen in the case of helium a cooling effect is obtained.

Examples.

1. The latent heat of vaporisation of liquid helium is given as 22 calories per mol at its boiling point (4·29° K.).

How much of this is absorbed in doing work against the pressure of the atmosphere? (8·54 cals.)

2. The heat evolved in the solution of 1 gram atom of iron in dilute hydrochloric acid is 20,800 cals. at 18° C. Formulate this as a thermochemical equation. Find the energy change of the system (ΔE). ($\Delta E = -21{,}380$ cals.)

3. The union of 1 gram of aluminium with oxygen at 15° C. and atmospheric pressure is attended by a heat evolution of 7010 calories. Formulate this as a thermochemical equation. Using the data in Table I., find the heat content change in the reaction:

$$Al_2O_3(s) + 3C(\textit{graphite}) = 2Al + 3CO(g).$$

($\Delta H = +300{,}540$ cals.)

4. In determinations of the heat of combustion of naphthalene in a bomb calorimeter it was found that

$$C_{10}H_8(s) + 12O_2(g) = 10CO_2(g) + 4H_2O(l),$$
$$\Delta E_{288} = -1{,}234{,}600 \text{ calories.}$$

Find (1) the heat content change in this reaction, and (2) the heat content change in the formation of naphthalene from its elements.

((1) $\Delta H = -1{,}235{,}700$ cals., (2) $\Delta H = +22{,}100$ cals.)

5. Given the equations,

$$2C_6H_6(l) + 15O_2 = 12CO_2 + 6H_2O, \quad \Delta H_{288} = -1{,}598{,}700 \text{ cal.}$$
$$2C_2H_2(g) + 5O_2 = 4CO_2 + 2H_2O, \quad \Delta H_{288} = -620{,}100 \text{ ,,}$$

Find (*a*) ΔH and (*b*) ΔE, for the reaction $3C_2H_2(g) = C_6H_6(l)$.

($\Delta H = -130{,}800$ cals., $\Delta E = -129{,}700$ cals.)

6. Similarly find ΔH and ΔE at 15° C. for the reactions

$$CO_2(g) + H_2(g) = CO(g) + H_2O(l),$$
$$H_2S(g) + I_2(s) = 2HI(g) + S(\textit{rhombic}).$$

(1) $\Delta H = -760$ cals., $\Delta E = -170$ cals.
(2) $\Delta H = 17{,}120$ cals., $\Delta E = 16{,}500$ cals.

7. The heat content changes in the formation of the following compounds from their elements at 15° C. are

PbO, − 50,300 calories, SO_2, − 70,920 calories,
PbS, 19,300 calories.

Find (1) the heat content change, (2) the energy change of the system in the reaction $PbS + 2PbO = 3Pb + SO_2(g)$.

($\Delta H = 10{,}380$ cals., $\Delta E = 9800$ cals.)

*8. Using the data given in Table I. and the heats of solution given in the text, find the heat content change in the solution of sodium in very dilute hydrochloric acid. The heat of solution of NaCl in an infinite amount of water is $\Delta H = 1{,}020$ cals. ($\Delta H = -57{,}480$ cals.)

*9. The mean molar heat capacities of chloroform ($CHCl_3$) between 30° and 60° C. at constant pressure are, liquid, 28·2 ; vapour, 17·8. The latent heat of vaporisation per mol is 6980 calories at 60° C. Find its value at 30° C. (7290 cals.)

*10. In the reaction

$$CaCO_3 = CaO + CO_2(g), \quad \Delta H_{288} = 42{,}900 \text{ calories.}$$

The mean molar heat capacities between 20° C. and 600° C. at constant pressure are, CaO, 12·27 ; $CaCO_3$, 26·37 ; CO_2, 7·3. Find the heat content change at 600° C.

($\Delta H_{873} = 38{,}900$ cals.)

11. Find the maximum work obtainable in the expansion of a perfect gas from 1 atmosphere pressure to 0·1 atmosphere pressure, at 273° K., in (*a*) calories, (*b*) joules.

*12. Using the heat capacity data in Table I*a*, formulate equations for the variation with the temperature of the heat content changes in the reactions :

$$1/2N_2 + 3/2H_2 = NH_3 ;$$
$$CO_2 + H_2 = CO + H_2O(g) ;$$
$$1/2H_2 + 1/2Br_2 = HBr ;$$
$$CH_4 + 2O_2 = CO_2 + 2H_2O(g).$$

CHAPTER II

THE SECOND LAW OF THERMODYNAMICS

Spontaneous Changes. Some changes occur of their own accord in Nature, whenever the configuration of things is such as to make them possible. Thus water flows from a higher level to a lower level; heat from a hotter to a colder body; a solute diffuses from a stronger to a weaker solution; a substance dissolves (up to a certain limit) when it is put in contact with a solvent; hydrogen and oxygen combine to form water, though in this last case a suitable stimulus such as an electric spark may be required to start the reaction.

These are all spontaneous natural processes; they have one common characteristic that outside effort is required to cause the reverse change. Thus work must be done to take the water back to the higher level; to obtain hydrogen and oxygen from water. Conversely they can all be made to do work if properly conducted. The flow of water downhill can be made to do work if a suitable turbine is installed; the flow of heat from a hotter to a colder body can be made to do work in a suitable engine; the combination of hydrogen and oxygen can be made to yield work through the medium of a galvanic cell.

There is also a *maximum* amount of work which such a

process can perform. We have already calculated the maximum work of one simple process, the isothermal expansion of a gas. The maximum work is obtained, as in that case, when the opposing forces, against which work is done, are only infinitesimally less than the forces which tend to make the process go forward. If the forces opposing a change just balance the forces tending to make it go, a small decrease or increase in the opposing forces will cause the change to go forward or in the reverse direction. Under these conditions the change will only occur infinitely slowly, because the system only differs by an infinitesimal amount from a state of balance, but when it goes forward in these circumstances every bit of work that the system can do is obtained, and a quantity of work greater by an infinitesimal amount will be sufficient to bring about the reverse change.

This is the *reversible* way of carrying out a change. In contrast to it, natural spontaneous processes are essentially irreversible. In Nature the forces which cause changes to occur are never balanced. A change proceeds at a finite rate only if the forces causing it are much greater than the forces against it. The maximum work is never done. Thus in Nature, when water flows downhill under the force of gravity, or when heat flows from a hotter to a colder body in contact with it, no work is obtained.

The Second Law of Thermodynamics. The First Law is merely a statement of the equivalence of different forms of energy. It states that when energy of one kind disappears an equivalent amount of energy of other kinds makes its appearance. It does not give any guidance as to the conditions under which these changes may occur. Such guidance is given by the Second Law, which is a general statement of natural tendencies. It is a statement which distinguishes changes which occur of their own accord and those which do not, in given circumstances.

We may state the Second Law as follows: "*Spontaneous processes* (*i.e. the processes which may occur of their own accord*) *are those which when carried out under proper conditions, can be made to do work.*" We may add: "*If carried out reversibly they will yield a maximum amount of work; in the natural irreversible way the maximum work is never obtained.*" There are other ways of stating the principle. Thus the maximum work obtainable in a certain change is sometimes termed its *available energy*. In a natural spontaneous process the whole of the available energy is not obtained as work. Thus the result is that energy is made less available, it is *dissipated* or degraded. Thus we see that "*There is a general tendency in Nature for energy to pass from more to less available forms,*" and that "*Every irreversible process leads to the dissipation of energy.*" The last is Kelvin's statement of the Second Law, his "Law of the Dissipation of Energy."

It should be understood that in an irreversible process no *energy* is lost. When water flows downhill in the natural irreversible way, the available energy which might have been obtained as work appears as heat in the random motions of particles of the liquid.

Maximum Work and Chemical Affinity. The history of chemistry contains numerous attempts to discover and measure the driving force of chemical reactions, to get a concrete measure of chemical affinity, of the tendency of a reaction to go. One of the earliest of these was probably the idea that the heat evolved in a reaction would serve, since it was evident that most reactions which proceed with ease are exothermic. This idea was revived by Thomsen in 1854, and a little later Berthelot stated that "every chemical change which takes place without the aid of external energy tends to the production of the system which is accompanied by the development of the maximum amount of heat," a principle which he rather curiously called "The law of maximum work." But the existence of numerous endothermic reactions and of "balanced reactions," in which the reaction may proceed in either direction to a definite state of equilibrium, makes this principle untenable. It served to inspire the long-continued thermochemical researches of these two investigators.

In the preceding sections we have seen that a reaction may only proceed of its own accord if it can perform work in so doing. The *maximum work* of a reaction is thus the true measure of its tendency to go. For this reason the determination of the maximum work of chemical reactions is of great importance. In fact, the most important result of the application of thermodynamical methods to chemical problems is that it gives a true measure of "chemical affinity." Before proceeding we shall find the maximum work obtainable in some simple isothermal processes.

Three-Stage Isothermal Dilution Process. We can find the maximum work obtainable in the dilution of a given solution by the addition of a small quantity of the solvent, by conducting the dilution reversibly in the following way. We will first confine ourselves to the case in which the solute is involatile, *e.g.* sulphuric acid in water. The cylinders I and II (Fig. 9) contain, respectively, water and the given solution of sulphuric acid at temperature T. They are fitted with weightless pistons to which are applied pressures p_0 and p_1, which are just sufficient to balance the vapour pressures of water over the solvent and over the solution respectively.

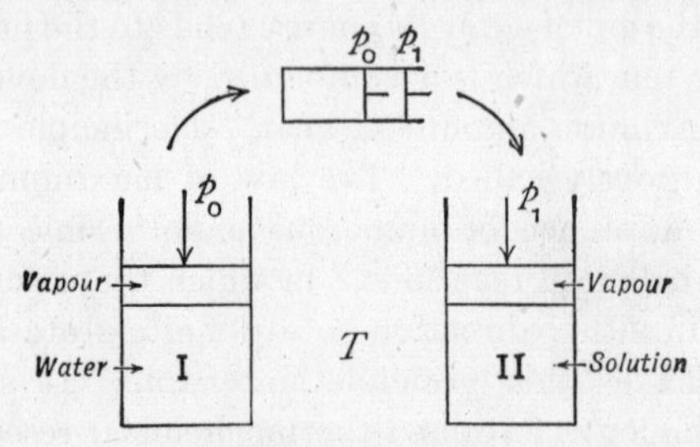

FIG. 9.—Three-stage distillation process.

We can transfer a small quantity of vapour from I to II reversibly by the following process.

I. Move the piston of I outwards, against applied pressure p_0, so as to cause the vaporisation of dx mols of water. The vapour pressure p_0 remains constant if the temperature is kept at T.

Work done against applied pressure $= p_0 \, dv_0$.

If we neglect the change in volume of the liquid dv_0 is the volume of dx mols of vapour at pressure p_0, and if the vapour behaves as a perfect gas,

$$p_0 \, dv_0 = dx \, . \, RT.$$

II. Isolate dx mols of vapour in I. This need not involve any work. Expand it in the usual way, reversibly and isothermally from p_0 to p_1.

Work done by vapour $= dx \, . \, RT \log p_0/p_1$.

III. Bring the expanded vapour into cylinder II at p_1. This need not involve any work. By moving piston inwards so as to decrease the volume of the vapour phase, cause dx mols of the vapour to be condensed.

Work done by applied pressure $= p_1\, dv_1$.

Neglecting change in volume of the solution,

$$p_1\, dv_1 = dx \,.\, RT.$$

Total work done by vapour against applied pressures

$$= dx \,.\, RT + dx\, RT \log p_0/p_1 - dx \,.\, RT$$
$$= dx \,.\, RT \log p_0/p_1.$$

The maximum work obtained in diluting the solution is thus

$$w = RT \log p_0/p_1 \qquad \text{......(22}a\text{)}$$

per mol of solvent added. This only applies if the amount of solvent added is so small that the concentration of the solution, and therefore its vapour pressure, is not appreciably altered.

Example. According to Regnault the vapour pressure of water over a solution of sulphuric acid and water containing 52·13 per cent. of sulphuric acid is 5·79 mm. mercury at 20° C. The vapour pressure of water at the same temperature is 17·54 mm. Hence the maximum work to be obtained when water is added reversibly to a relatively large quantity of this solution is

$$1{\cdot}99 \times 293 \times 2{\cdot}303 \log_{10} (17{\cdot}54/5{\cdot}79)$$
$$= 648 \text{ calories per mol.}$$

In just the same way we may transfer reversibly the solvent from one solution to another. If p_1 be the vapour pressure of the solvent over a solution (1) and p_2 its vapour pressure over a second (2), then the maximum work in the transfer of solvent from (1) to (2) is similarly

$$w = RT \log p_1/p_2 \text{ per mol.} \qquad \text{......(23)}$$

It is postulated that the amount of solvent transferred is so small relative to the amounts of the solutions that the concentrations of the latter are not appreciably altered.

This expression is, moreover, not limited to the case of a single volatile component. If there are two or more volatile substances in the solutions, the same process may be applied to any one of them, if it is supposed that the solutions are covered with semipermeable membranes permeable by this substance alone.

Semipermeable membranes are often used in thermodynamical arguments when it is desired to handle a single component of a mixture. Semipermeable membranes of various kinds are realisable, *e.g.* the membranes used in osmotic pressure experiments. But there is no need to ascertain whether a real membrane is available for each particular case since we are only concerned with the result of an ideal process, and provided the process is theoretically possible it does not matter how close an approximation to it could be reached in practice.

An ideal semipermeable membrane offers no resistance to the passage of a given substance, and is impermeable to all others. The vapour pressure of this substance outside the membrane will be equal to its partial vapour pressure inside. Thus the maximum work obtained in the transfer of any substance from a solution in which its partial vapour pressure is p_1 to a solution in which it is p_2, is also

$$w = RT \log p_1/p_2 \text{ per mol.} \quad \text{...............(23a)}$$

Three-Stage Process between Phases at the same Total Pressure. In the previous deduction the only pressure acting on each solution was its own vapour pressure. We shall have very frequently to deal with changes which take place under the pressure of the atmosphere. We will consider the maximum work of the three-stage process when both solutions are under the same total pressure P (*e.g.* the pressure of the atmosphere), also taking into account the changes in the volume of the solutions.

The three-stage process can be carried out as before by the use of a semipermeable membrane, permeable to the vapour. Through this the vapour can be withdrawn at its partial pressure p, whatever the external pressure acting on the solution,* and the transfer carried out as before. A suitable arrangement is shown in the diagram (Fig. 10).

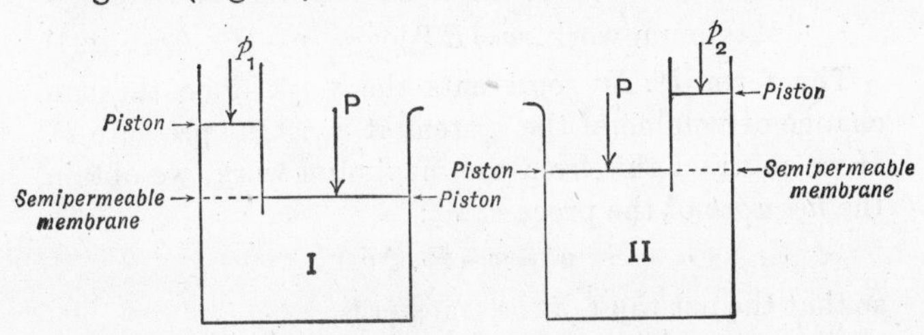

FIG. 10.—Three-stage distillation process under constant external pressure.

The terms of the process are as follows:

I. Withdraw 1 mol of the vapour at p_1 through the semipermeable membrane. If v_1 is its volume the work obtained is $p_1 v_1 = RT$.

If the volume of the solution I diminishes by δv_1, the work done *by* the external pressure P is $P \, . \, \delta v_1$.

II. Expand the vapour from p_1 to p_2.

Work obtained ; $RT \log p_1/p_2$.

* The vapour pressure of a liquid may be affected by increase of the external pressure. The effect is small, but p is the actual vapour pressure under the conditions.

III. Condense the vapour at p_2 into solution II through the semipermeable membrane. If v_2 is the volume of the vapour, work done by pressure p_2 in the condensation is $p_2 v_2 = RT$.

If the volume of solution II increases by δv, work done against the external pressure P is $P\delta v_2$.

Total work obtained in process

$$= RT \log p_1/p_2 + P(\delta v_2 - \delta v_1).$$

If we put $\delta v_2 - \delta v_1 = \Delta v$, the change in the volume of the whole system as a result of the transfer, we have

$$\text{Maximum work, } w = RT \log p_1/p_2 + P \,.\, \Delta v. \quad \text{...(24)}$$

The term $P \,.\, \Delta v$ represents the work done through change of volume of the system at constant pressure P. If we subtract this from the maximum work, we obtain the *net work* of the process, w':

$$w' = w - P \,.\, \Delta v,$$

so that the net work of the transfer is

$$w' = RT \log p_1/p_2.^{*} \quad \text{..................(25)}$$

Maximum Work of Changes of State. Ice and water are in equilibrium only at the melting point, but water can be supercooled and kept in the liquid form at lower temperatures. What is the maximum work of the change water → ice, when both are at the same temperature T and pressure P? The maximum work can be obtained by considering a three-stage distillation process similar to that used in the last section. Water vapour is withdrawn from the water at its vapour pressure p_1

* In the first deduction the volume changes of the solution were neglected. If they are taken into account (22*a*) becomes $w = RT \log (p_0/p_1) + (p_1 \,\delta v_1 - p_0 \,\delta v_0)$, which reduces to (25) for constant external pressure.

at T, expanded to a pressure p_2, equal to the vapour pressure of ice at the same temperature and condensed into the ice. The maximum work of the process (for the transfer of 1 mol of water vapour) is

$$RT \log p_1/p_2 + P . \Delta v,$$

where Δv is the resulting change of volume.

The net work of the process is $RT \log p_1/p_2$, the term $P . \Delta v$ being the work done through a change in volume of the system under the external pressure P. It is easy to see that at the melting point, when ice and water are in equilibrium $p_1 = p_2$, *i.e.* the vapour pressure of water is equal to the vapour pressure of ice. If this were not so, *e.g.* if p_1 were greater than p_2, when water and ice were put in contact under a given pressure at this temperature there would be a continuous distillation from the water to the ice phase, until the water had disappeared. This implies that when water and ice are in equilibrium the net work of the change, $RT \log p_1/p_2$, is zero.

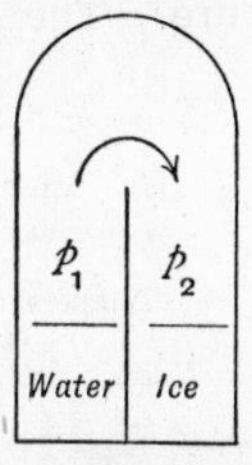

FIG. 11.

The same conclusion can be drawn on general grounds. We have seen that the maximum work of a given change is a measure of the tendency of that change to occur. For changes at constant pressure, we have divided the maximum work into a part, $P . \Delta v$ which is due entirely to the change in volume of the system and a part w', the net work of the process. The former measures the tendency of the system to increase its volume; it is balanced by the external pressure applied to the system. The net work therefore measures the tendency of the system to change when the applied pressure P is kept constant. Thus ice and water are in equilibrium with each other when the net work of the change is zero, *i.e.* when $p_1 = p_2$.

At temperatures below the melting point liquid water can change spontaneously into ice. The net work of the change water → ice must now be positive, otherwise there would be no tendency for the change to occur. Thus since $RT \log p_1/p_2$ is positive, $p_1 > p_2$, *i.e.* at temperatures below the melting point (supercooled) water has a greater vapour pressure than ice at the same temperature. The data given below confirm this.

TABLE III.

VAPOUR PRESSURES OF ICE AND WATER.

Temperature.	Vapour Pressures (mm. Hg.).		
	Ice.	Water.	
4		6·101	
3		5·685	
2		5·294	
1		4·926	
0	4·579	4·579	Super-cooled.
−1	4·216	4·256	
−2	3·879	3·952	
−3	3·566	3·669	
−4	3·276	3·404	
−5	3·008	3·158	

In the same way if it were possible to have ice at temperatures above melting point, its vapour pressure would be greater than that of water at the same temperature. The vapour pressure curves of ice and water thus intersect at the melting point, as is shown in Fig. 12.

These considerations are quite general. Two different forms of a substance have the same vapour pressure at the temperature at which they are in equilibrium with each other. At other temperatures the *stable form is that which has the lower vapour pressure.*

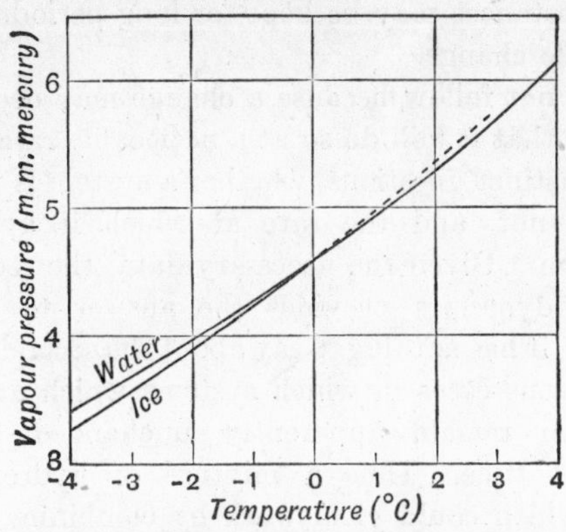

FIG. 12.—Vapour pressure of water and ice.

In the case of two allotropic modifications of the same substance, such as monoclinic and rhombic sulphur, the temperature at which the two forms are in equilibrium is known as the *transition point.* At this temperature the vapour pressures of the two forms are the same, *i.e.* the two vapour pressure curves intersect. At other temperatures the stable form is that which has the lower vapour pressure. Fig. 13 shows the vapour pressure curves of the two forms of sulphur; the transition point is at 95·5° C. and the rhombic form is stable at lower temperatures.

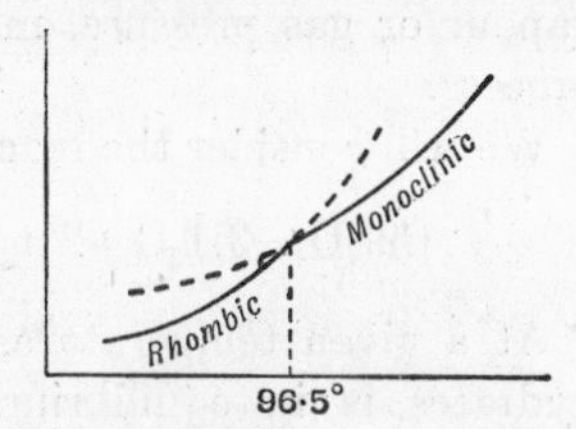

FIG. 13.—Vapour pressures of rhombic and monoclinic sulphur.

The form of a substance with the higher vapour pressure at a given temperature is *metastable.* It may change spontaneously into the stable form, but it often happens that the rate of change is very small and metastable substances may be kept for long periods without appreciable change.

It does not follow because a change may occur spontaneously that it *will* do so at a noticeable rate. There are two distinct questions, whether a system is in equilibrium or not, and the rate at which it approaches equilibrium. Given the necessary data, the second law of thermodynamics provides the answer to the first question ; it has nothing to say about the second. There are numerous cases in which systems which are not in equilibrium remain apparently unchanged for long periods of time. Thus a mixture of hydrogen and oxygen, which could yield work by combining to form water, is not in equilibrium, yet may be kept for an indefinite period without change. But if a suitable stimulus is applied the reaction starts and proceeds until the equilibrium state is reached.

Formation of Salt Hydrates. The maximum work of any process involving the transfer of a vapour or gas between two phases, both of which have a definite vapour or gas pressure, may be obtained by a similar process.

We will consider the reaction

$$CuSO_4 . 3H_2O + 2H_2O(l) = CuSO_4 . 5H_2O.$$

At a given temperature, a mixture of the two solid hydrates is in equilibrium with water vapour at a definite pressure, known as the dissociation pressure of the pentahydrate. If the vapour pressure is reduced below this value the pentahydrate will dissociate according to $CuSO_4 . 5H_2O = CuSO_4 . 3H_2O + 2H_2O$, until either the vapour pressure is restored or the supply of pentahydrate is exhausted. If the vapour pressure is increased the reverse process occurs, and the pentahydrate is formed from the trihydrate until either the equilibrium pressure is restored or the trihydrate completely changed to pentahydrate. At the dissociation pressure the reaction is therefore reversible. A minute increase or decrease of the vapour pressure will cause the reaction to proceed in either direction.

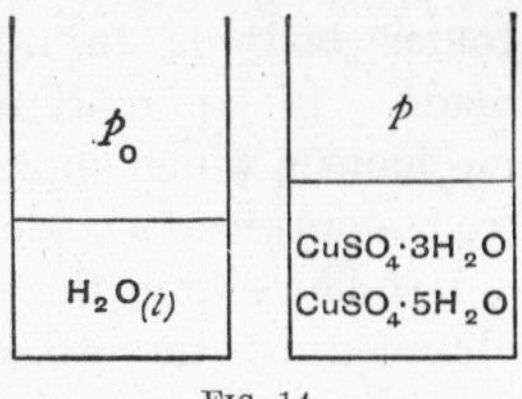

FIG. 14.

Let the dissociation pressure be p and the vapour pressure of liquid water be p_0, at the same temperature T and under a constant external pressure P. The maximum work of formation of pentahydrate from trihydrate and liquid water is obtained by withdrawing from the water 2 mols of water vapour at its pressure p_0, expanding this to the pressure p and finally condensing it into the mixture of salt hydrates at the equilibrium pressure p. The total work obtained is

$$w = 2RT \log p_0/p + P \,.\, \Delta v,$$

where Δv is the change in volume of the system as the result of the reaction. The net work of the reaction is thus

$$w' = 2RT \log p_0/p.$$

Example. At 20·5° the dissociation pressure for the above reaction is 5·06 mm. of mercury and the vapour pressure of water is 18·03 mm. The net work of the reaction is therefore

$$2 \times 1{\cdot}99 \times 293{\cdot}5 \times 2{\cdot}303 \log_{10} \frac{18{\cdot}03}{5{\cdot}06} = 1485 \text{ calories.}$$

THE CONVERSION OF HEAT INTO WORK.

Heat Engines. The flow of heat from a hotter to a colder body is an irreversible process, and can be made, with appropriate arrangements, to do work. A mechanism which obtains work from the passage of heat from a hotter to a colder body is known as a heat engine.

It follows from the second law that no work can be obtained by the passage of heat from one body to another at the same temperature, or from a colder body to a hotter one, since in neither case does heat flow of its own accord in that direction.

Work can only be obtained from heat through the agency of some working substance, which may perform mechanical work by expansion, etc. We wish to find the maximum amount of work obtainable from the passage of a definite quantity of heat from a body at a temperature T_2 to a body at a (lower) temperature T_1. In order to exclude work done by a change in the working substance it is necessary to bring the latter at the end of the operations into its original condition, *i.e.* it is necessary to consider a *cyclic process*.

We can obtain at once a general relation applicable of cyclic processes. If a substance is put through a series of operations, such that it is finally left in a state identical with its original state, we have

$$\Delta E = 0,$$

and by (2), $$\Sigma q = \Sigma w \qquad (26)$$

i.e. the sum of the amounts of heat absorbed in the cycle of operations is equal to the algebraic sum of the amounts of work done.

Carnot's Cycle. In order to obtain the *maximum* work obtainable in a cycle of operations, it is necessary that every stage should be carried out reversibly. Carnot's cycle is a typical reversible cycle of operations. We shall first consider the case in which the working substance is 1 mol of a perfect gas. We may suppose that the gas is confined in a cylinder fitted with a piston. The stages of expansion and compression are conducted reversibly, *i.e.* during an expansion the pressure on the piston is always less by an infinitesimal amount than that exerted by the gas; during a compression it is infinitesimally greater (*cf.* p. 29). Thus the maximum work is obtained in every stage.

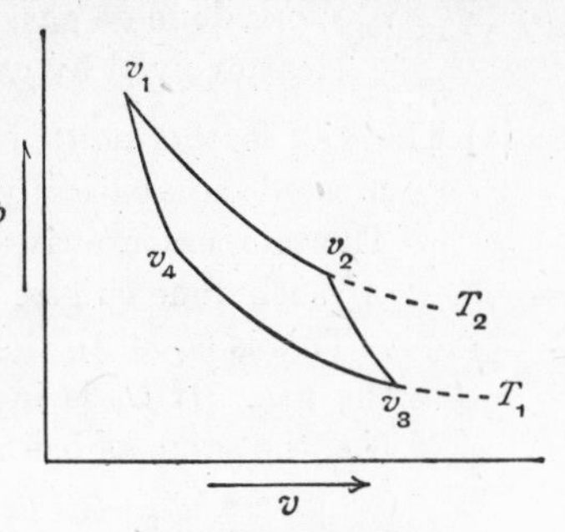

FIG. 15.—Carnot's cycle.

The operations are as follows (Fig. 15):

(1) The gas is expanded isothermally and reversibly at temperature T_2 from volume v_1 to volume v_2.

Work done by gas, $w_2 = RT_2 \log v_2/v_1$.

Heat absorbed by gas, $q_2 = w_2$.

(2) The gas is thermally isolated so that it cannot receive heat from or give heat to its surroundings, and is expanded further (adiabatically) from v_2 to v_3; the temperature drops to T_1.

Work done by gas, w'_2.

This must be equal to the decrease in the energy of the gas. If C_v is the heat capacity of the gas, this is equal to $C_v(T_2 - T_1)$, so that

$$w_2' = C_v(T_2 - T_1).$$

(3) The gas is compressed isothermally from v_3 to v_4 (which is on the adiabatic curve going through v_1).

Work done *on* gas, $w_1 = RT_1 \log v_3/v_4$.

Heat evolved by gas $(-q_1) = w_1$.

(4) The gas is thermally isolated and further compressed adiabatically to original volume v_1. The temperature rises to T_2.

Work done *on* gas, w'_1.

This is equal to the increase in the energy of the gas. If C_v is independent of the volume (*i.e.* the same as before):

$$w'_1 = C_v(T_2 - T_1).$$

For the whole cycle of operations, by (26),

$$\underset{\text{Total heat absorbed.}}{q_2 - (-q_1)} = \underset{\text{Total work done by gas in cycle.}}{w_2 + w_2' - w_1 - w_1' = W}.$$

Summing the work terms, we find

$$W = RT_2 \log v_2/v_1 - RT_1 \log v_3/v_4.$$

But, by (21), we have for the two adiabatic stages

$$\frac{C_v}{R} \log \frac{T_2}{T_1} = \log v_3/v_2$$

and

$$\frac{C_v}{R} \log \frac{T_2}{T_1} = \log v_4/v_1;$$

hence $\quad v_3/v_2 = v_4/v_1 \quad$ and $\quad v_2/v_1 = v_3/v_4$.

Therefore $\quad W = R(T_2 - T_1) \log v_2/v_1$ ....(27)

and

$$\frac{W}{q_2} = \frac{R(T_2 - T_1) \log v_2/v_1}{RT_2 \log v_2/v_1} = \frac{T_2 - T_1}{T_2}. \quad \text{........(28)}$$

The ratio W/q_2, *i.e.* the ratio of the work obtained in the cycle to the heat absorbed at the higher temperature is known as the *efficiency* of the process.

When the temperature difference between the two isothermal stages of a Carnot cycle is a small amount dT, we may write (28) in the form

$$\frac{dW}{q} = \frac{dT}{T},$$

or

$$dW = q\frac{dT}{T}, \quad \text{......................(29)}$$

dW is the work obtained in a cyclic process with temperature difference dT, in which the heat q is absorbed at temperature T.

Carnot's Theorem. This result, deduced for a perfect gas, holds good whatever the nature of the working substance, be it solid, liquid or gaseous. For according to an important theorem, first given by Carnot:

"*Every perfect engine working reversibly between the same temperature limits has the same efficiency, whatever the working substance.*"

A perfect engine is one which, working without frictional losses, obtains from its cycle of operations the maximum work obtainable. That is to say, every stage of the process is carried on reversibly, with the system only infinitesimally displaced from a state of balance and therefore infinitely slowly.

The theorem is proved by showing that if a working substance could be found for which the efficiency was greater than that of any other, it would be possible without the application of outside effort to transfer heat from a lower to a higher temperature, which contravenes the second law of thermodynamics.

* Suppose that we have two perfect engines I and II working between the same temperature limits T_2 and T_1. Let their efficiencies be x and x' and suppose that x' is greater than x. In the working of II, for the absorption

of q units of heat at higher temperature, a quantity of work $W = x'q$ is obtained, and $q - x'q$ units of heat are given out at the lower temperature. The work W may be used to run I backwards, so that it absorbs heat at the lower temperature T_1, and gives it out at the higher temperature T_2. Since the efficiency of this engine is x, the amount of heat given out at T_2 in its reversed action for work W is W/x or $x'q/x$. The quantity of heat taken in at T, is thus $W/x - W = x'q/x - x'q$.

Tabulating these results :

	I.	II.
T_2,	qx'/x evolved,	q absorbed,
	$W = x'q$ expended,	$W = x'q$ obtained,
T_1,	$qx'/x - x'q$ absorbed,	$q - x'q$ evolved,

we find that the net result of the working of both engines process is the absorption of $(x'/x)q - q$ units of heat at the lower temperature and the evolution of the same amount at the higher temperature. Thus if $x' > x$ it would be possible to transfer heat from a lower to a higher temperature without the expenditure of work. We therefore conclude that if the Second Law is true, all perfect engines have the same efficiency, and equation (28), which has been deduced for the case in which the working substance is a perfect gas, is universally valid.

Consequences of Carnot's Theorem. According to (28), the efficiency of a perfect engine $W/q_2 = \frac{T_2 - T_1}{T_2}$ is determined solely by the difference between the temperatures of the hotter and colder isothermal stages and the absolute temperature at which heat is absorbed. In chemical thermodynamics we are not so much concerned with the practical application of this result to the working of actual heat engines, as with the relations between the properties of substances which must hold if the theorem is to be universally true. The exploration of these relations, and the study of various cases of chemical equilibria in connection with them, will in fact occupy most of the remainder of this book. We shall first state some general results.

(*a*) *Isothermal Cycles.* When all the stages of a reversible cyclic process occur at the same temperature, since $T_2 - T_1 = 0$, the work obtained is zero. Therefore the maximum work obtained in going from a state *I* of a system to state *II* at the same temperature is the same whatever the path or intermediate stages, so long as the temperature remains constant throughout the change. If this were not so it would be possible to go from *I* to *II* by one path and return by another and so obtain work by an isothermal cycle. The maximum work of an isothermal change is therefore definite and depends only on the initial and final stages of the system.

Thus we may write

$$w = A_I - A_{II},$$

where A_I and A_{II} are quantities determined by the initial and final states of the system only. Just as the heat evolved in a change is equal to the decrease in the energy content, or heat content (according as the volume or pressure is constant), so, provided the temperature remains constant, the maximum work done in a change is equal to the decrease in the quantity A. A is known as the "maximum work function" of the system *; it can be regarded as the maximum work "content" of the system. When the system performs work its maximum work content decreases; thus, for a given change

$$\underset{\text{Maximum work.}}{w} = \underset{\text{Decrease in } A.}{-\Delta A}. \qquad (30)$$

* A = *Arbeit*, work.

The net work of a change, $w' = w - p\,\Delta v$, differs from the maximum work by the term $p\,\Delta v$ or $p(v_2 - v_1)$.

This term is the same whatever the path or intermediate stages, *provided that the pressure remains constant throughout.*

The net work of a change is thus the same for all possible paths provided that both the temperature and pressure remain constant, and under these conditions depends solely on the initial and final states of the system.

Thus $$w' = F_1 - F_{11},$$

where F_1 and F_{11} are quantities determined only by the initial and final states. Analogous to the maximum work function, F is the "net work function." It is usually known as the *free energy* of the system. Thus the net work done in a given change (at constant T and p) is equal to the decrease in the free energy of the system :

$$\underset{\text{Net work.}}{w'} = \underset{\text{Free energy decrease.}}{-\Delta F} \quad \text{.....................(31)}$$

*(*b*) *Conditions of Equilibrium.* Changes which occur spontaneously are characterised by their ability to perform work. We have seen that for changes which occur at constant temperature the maximum work yielded is definite and equal to the decrease in the maximum work function of the system. Thus if the system undergoes a spontaneous change at constant temperature, its maximum work function must decrease. A system is in equilibrium if there is no change which can spontaneously occur under the given conditions, so that the condition of equilibrium for changes at constant temperature is that there is no possible change whereby

the maximum work function can decrease, *i.e.* so long as the temperature remains constant the function A is a minimum.

This may be expressed by the condition

$$(\delta A)_T \geqq 0 \quad \text{.......................(32)}$$

for all possible changes.

Similarly for changes occurring at constant temperature and pressure the net work is definite and equal to the free energy decrease of the system. In any change which the system undergoes spontaneously under these conditions the free energy decreases, so that it is in equilibrium if there is no possible change, under the conditions, whereby its free energy can decrease, *i.e.* the free energy has a minimum value for the given temperature and pressure. This condition is expressed by

$$(\delta F)_{TP} \geqq 0 \quad \text{.......................(33)}$$

for all possible changes.

These conditions of equilibrium, although applicable to the conditions which are most often met with, do not include every possible variation. A more general condition is, however, obtained from Carnot's result, by the use of another function, *entropy*. This is discussed in Part II.

Examples.

1. The vapour pressure of a solution containing 50 grams of NaOH to 100 grams of water is 6·3 mm. of mercury at 20° C. That of pure water at the same temperature being 17·54 mm., find the maximum work obtainable in the addition of 1 mol of water to the solution. (597 cals.)

2. Find the net work of the change water → ice at $-3°$ C., using the data in Table III. (15·5 cals. per mol.)

3. The densities of water and ice at 0° C. and 1 atmos. are 0·9999 and 0·9168 grams per c.c. Find the maximum work of the change water → ice at this temperature.

(0·0906 c.c. – atmos. per gm.)

4. The dissociation pressure of the reaction

$$ZnSO_4 . 7H_2O = ZnSO_4 . 6H_2O + H_2O$$

is 8·41 mm. at 18° C. (Water at 18° C., 15·48 mm.).

Find the net work obtainable in the formation of

$$ZnSO_4 . 7H_2O \text{ from } ZnSO_4 . 6H_2O$$

and liquid water at this temperature. (353·4 cals.)

5. The dissociation pressure of thallous hydroxide, in the reaction

$$2TlOH = Tl_2O + H_2O$$

is 125 mm. at 100° C. Find the net work of the formation of 2TlOH from thallous oxide and liquid water at this temperature. (1,340 cals.)

6. The dissociation prəssure of the reaction

$$Na_2SO_4 . 10H_2O = Na_2SO_4 + 10H_2O$$

is 2·77 mm. at 0° C. Find (1) the net work of the formation of $Na_2SO_4 . 10H_2O$ from the anhydrous salt and liquid water at this temperature; (2) the work done on account of the volume change in the same reaction. The molecular volumes at 0° C. are $Na_2HO_4 . 10H_20$, 219 c.c.; Na_2SO_4, 53 c.c.; H_2O, 18 c.c.

((1) 2,732 cals.; (2) – 14 c.c. – atmos. = – 0·34 cals.)

CHAPTER III

THE APPLICATION OF THERMODYNAMICS TO CHANGES OF STATE

The Clausius Equation. It is well known that the melting point of a substance depends on the applied pressure. For a given pressure P the solid and liquid are in equilibrium with each other only at a definite temperature T, the melting point. At this temperature, since the two forms are in equilibrium, the net work of the change solid-liquid is zero, so that the maximum work obtainable is the work done through the change in volume. For a given weight of substance this is equal to $P(v_l - v_s)$, if v_l is the volume of the liquid and v_s that of the solid. We can introduce this change of state into a cyclic process in the following way (Fig. 16).

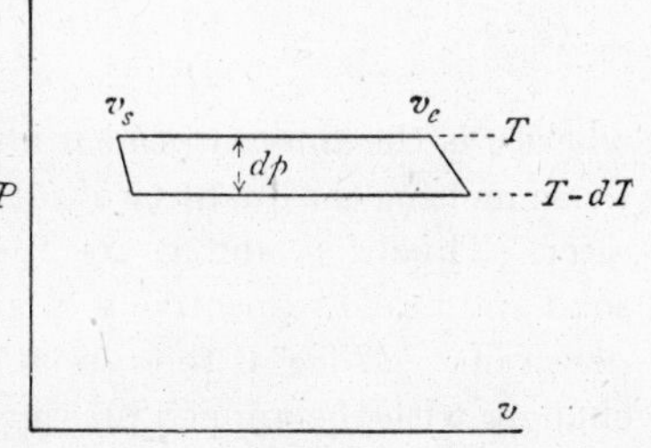

FIG. 16.—Clausius' equation.

(1) Melt a given weight of the solid at the melting point T corresponding to applied pressure P.

(2) Reduce the pressure on the liquid from P to

$P-dP$ and reduce the temperature to $T-dT$, which is the melting point at the new pressure.

(3) Cause the liquid to solidify at temperature $T-dT$ and pressure $P-dP$.

(4) Bring the solid back to temperature T and pressure P.

The work obtained in the whole cycle is equal to its area on the $P-v$ diagram, which to the first order of small quantities is

$$dW = dP \, . \, (v_l - v_s).$$

But by (29), $$dW = q\frac{dT}{T},$$

so that $$dP \, . \, (v_l - v_s) = q\frac{dT}{T},$$

or $$\frac{dT}{dP} = \frac{T(v_l - v_s)}{q}, \quad \text{.....................(34)}$$

where q is the amount of heat absorbed in the first stage, *i.e.* in melting the quantity of substance to which v_s and v_l refer. Thus if v_s and v_l are the volumes of 1 gram of solid and liquid respectively, q is the latent heat of fusion per gram. dT/dP is the rate at which the melting point changes with the applied pressure.

A similar relation holds in all cases of change of state. In general, if v_I is the volume of a given amount of substance in the initial state, v_{II} its volume in the final state and q the heat absorbed in the change I → II (for the same amount), the relation between the temperature and the equilibrium pressure at which the two forms are in equilibrium with each other is given by

$$\frac{dT}{dP} = \frac{T(v_{II} - v_I)}{q}. \quad \text{.....................(35)}$$

This is Clausius' equation.

Example. In the case of ice and water, the volume of the solid is greater than that of the same weight of liquid, hence $v_l - v_s$ is negative and since q is a positive quantity, dT/dp is negative, *i.e.* the melting point is lowered by increase of pressure.

We may calculate the lowering produced by an increased pressure of 1 atmosphere.

At 0° C., $v_l = 1{\cdot}000$ c.c. per gram ;

$T = 273,$

$v_s = 1{\cdot}091$ c.c. per gram ;

$\therefore\ v_l - v_s = -0{\cdot}091$ c.c. ; also $q = 80{\cdot}0$ calories per gram.

The volume change is expressed in c.c. and we are going to reckon pressure in atmospheres, so that the work done appears in the equation in c.c.-atmospheres. The heat absorbed is measured in calories. In order to obtain our result this must be converted into the same units. Since 1 calorie $= 41{\cdot}37$ c.c.-atmospheres, we have

$$dT/dp = \frac{-0{\cdot}091 \times 273}{80{\cdot}0 \times 41{\cdot}4}$$

$$= -0{\cdot}0075° \text{ per atmosphere.}$$

(Note that the numerator is a volume in c.c. multiplied by a temperature, the denominator is a quantity of energy expressed as volume in c.c. multiplied by a pressure in atmospheres. The quotient is therefore a temperature divided by pressure in atmospheres.)

Kelvin determined the effect of pressure in the melting point of ice in 1850 and found $dT/dp = -0{\cdot}0072$, in very fair agreement with the calculated value.

The Le Chatelier Principle.* Since q, the latent heat of fusion, is always positive, we see that if $v_l > v_s$, dT/dp is positive, *i.e.* the melting point is raised by increase of pressure. If $v_l < v_s$, dT/dp is negative and the melting point is lowered by increase of pressure. This is in

* Also associated with the name of Braun.

accordance with the Le Chatelier principle, which predicts qualitatively the effect of a change of conditions on the equilibrium state of a system. This principle states that if a constraint is applied to a system in equilibrium, the change which occurs is such that it tends to annul the constraint.

In the cases under consideration the constraint is an increase in the pressure applied to a system of liquid and solid in equilibrium with each other. According to the principle the change which occurs will tend to annul the increase in pressure, *i.e.* the volume will decrease. Thus if the solid has a smaller volume than the liquid, an increase in pressure will tend to cause solidification. In other words it will raise the melting point. If the liquid has the smaller volume an increase in pressure will favour fusion, *i.e.* lower the melting point.

The equation (35) predicts the same behaviour as the Le Chatelier principle. It goes further than the latter, however, for it gives quantitatively the change produced by a change of pressure. The Clausius equation can thus be regarded as a quantitative expression of the Le Chatelier principle as applied to changes of state.

We shall find at a later stage that the Second Law leads to equations for the effect of changes of conditions on various cases of chemical equilibria which are quantitative expressions of the behaviour to be expected according to the Le Chatelier principle. The latter is in fact an alternative, though possibly less comprehensive statement of the natural tendencies which are summed up in the Second Law.

Transition Points. The same considerations apply to the effect of pressure on the change of a substance from one modification to another. At every pressure the two modifications are in equilibrium with each other at a definite temperature, the transition point. Thus rhombic and monoclinic sulphur are in equilibrium at 95·5° C.

At lower temperatures the rhombic is the stable form, at higher temperatures the monoclinic. We may calculate the effect of change of pressure on the transition temperature by (35),

$$dT/dP = \frac{T(v_m - v_r)}{q},$$

where v_m and v_r are the volumes of a given weight of the two forms and q is the heat absorbed in the change $S_r \rightarrow S_m$, for the same amounts.*

Example. In this case

$$v_m - v_r = 0{\cdot}0126 \text{ c.c. per gram,}$$
$$q = 2{\cdot}52 \text{ calories per gram,}$$
$$T(\text{atmos.}) = 95{\cdot}5° \text{ C.}$$

Hence we find

$$dT/dP = \frac{(273 + 95{\cdot}5) \times 0{\cdot}0126}{2{\cdot}52 \times 41{\cdot}4} = +0{\cdot}045° \text{ per atmos.}$$

The observed figure is 0·05° C.

The Effect of Temperature on Vapour Pressure. We are now concerned with the reverse problem, *i.e.* the effect of temperature on the equilibrium pressure of two phases, liquid and vapour (or solid and vapour). The

* Heat is always absorbed in the change from the substance stable below the transition point to that stable above it, since by the Le Chatelier principle if we add heat to a system, *i.e.* attempt to raise the temperature, that change will occur which absorbs heat. Hence q is positive for the change from the form stable below the transition point to that stable above it, and the same rules for the effect of pressure apply as for the melting point.

pressure at which the vapour is in equilibrium with the liquid (or solid) is the vapour pressure of the latter (p. 54). Clausius' equation, therefore, gives the effect of change of temperature on the vapour pressure.

Inverting equation (35), we obtain

$$\frac{dp}{dT}=\frac{q}{T(v_g-v_l)}. \quad \text{.....................(36)}$$

In this case it will be convenient to take as the amount of substance to which the terms apply, 1 mol of vapour. Then q is the latent heat of evaporation of the substance per mol and v_g and v_l the volumes of the same amount as vapour and as liquid (or solid). Since v_g is much greater than v_l, we may neglect the latter, and if we assume that the vapour obeys the perfect gas law, we may put $$v_g=RT/p.$$

Thus (36) becomes

$$1/p\cdot\frac{dp}{dT}=\frac{q}{RT^2}. \quad \text{..................(37)}$$

Example. The latent heat of evaporation of water at 100° C. is 536 calories per gram or 9660 calories per mol. The vapour pressure of water at 100° C. is 760 mm. Hg. What is the rate of variation of the vapour pressure with temperature at this temperature ?

Inserting these values in (37), we have

$$dp/dT=760\times\frac{9660}{1{\cdot}99\times 373^2}$$

$$=26{\cdot}5 \text{ mm. per degree C.}$$

Thus at 101° C., $p=786{\cdot}5$ mm.

Equation (37) may be written

$$\frac{d\log p}{dT}=\frac{q}{RT^2}, \quad \text{.....................(38)}$$

and in this form it may be integrated to give the

variation of p with T over a range of temperature. If the range of temperature is comparatively small, so that q can be taken as constant, we find

$$\log p = \int \frac{q}{RT^2} dT = -\frac{q}{RT} + K, \quad \text{.............(39)}$$

where K is an integration constant. Thus the relation between $\log p$ and $1/T$ is a linear one, and if values of $\log p$ be plotted against corresponding values of $1/T$, a straight line is obtained (so long as q is constant). Fig. 17 shows the data for oxygen and nitrogen plotted in this way. The graphs of $\log p$ against $1/T$ are nearly straight lines over a considerable range of temperature. It is evident from (39) that the slope of this line is equal to $(-q/R)$, so that q may be determined by measuring the graph.

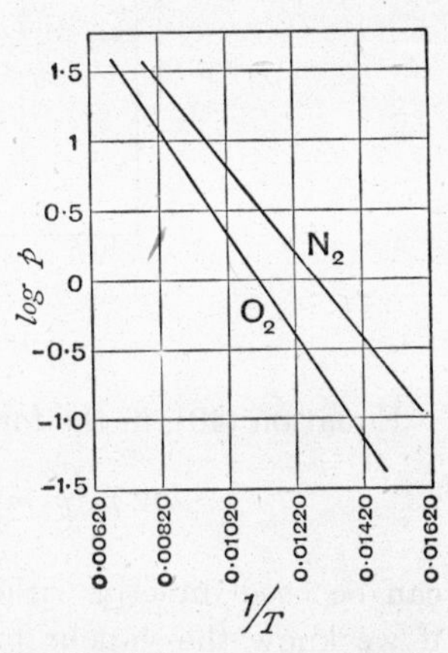

Fig. 17.—Vapour pressures of oxygen and nitrogen. (Dodge and Davies.)

This method of evaluating q is, perhaps, made clearer by Fig. 18, where $\log p_1$ and $\log p_2$ are two points corresponding to $1/T_1$ and $1/T_2$. Using (39):

$$\log p_1 = -\frac{q}{R} \cdot \frac{1}{T_1} + K,$$

$$\log p_2 = -\frac{q}{R} \cdot \frac{1}{T_2} + K;$$

$$\therefore \log p_1 - \log p_2 = -\frac{q}{R}\left(\frac{1}{T_1} - \frac{1}{T_2}\right), \quad \text{.........(40)}$$

so that
$$\frac{\log p_1 - \log p_2}{\left(\frac{1}{T_2} - \frac{1}{T_1}\right)} = \frac{q}{R}$$

and the left-hand side is obtained directly from the graph.

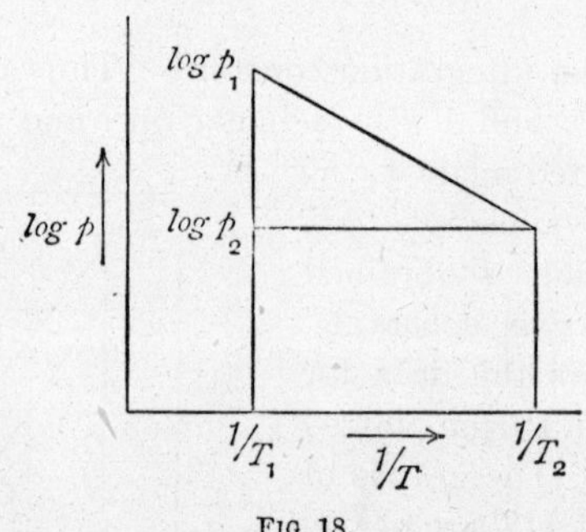

FIG. 18.

Equation (40), in the form

$$\log p_1/p_2 = -\frac{q}{R}\left(\frac{1}{T_1} - \frac{1}{T_2}\right), \quad \ldots\ldots\ldots\ldots(41)$$

can be used directly without plotting the data. Thus if we know the vapour pressures at two temperatures T_1 and T_2 we may find q, and conversely if we know q and p at one temperature we can calculate the vapour pressure at another temperature, within a range over which q can be taken as constant.

Change of Dissociation Pressure with Temperature. This case may be treated in the same way as vaporisation. For example, in the reaction

$$CaCO_3 = CaO + CO_2(g)$$

the increase of the volume can be taken, without appreciable error, as the volume of gas produced; the pressure at which the gas is in equilibrium with the solid phases is the dissociation pressure, and by (35), we have

$$\frac{dp}{dT}=\frac{q}{Tv_g}. \qquad (36a)$$

If we apply the equation to the production of 1 mol of CO_2, we may put $v_g = RT/p$, so that

$$1/p\,\frac{dp}{dT}=\frac{q}{RT^2}, \qquad (37a)$$

or

$$\frac{d\log p}{dT}=\frac{q}{RT^2}, \qquad (38a)$$

where q is the heat of dissociation per mol of gas produced.

Integrating this we find that

$$\log p = -\frac{q}{R}\cdot\frac{1}{T}+K, \qquad (39a)$$

so that as long as q can be taken as constant there is a linear relation between $\log p$ and $1/T$. Similarly integrating between limits p_1 and p_2 corresponding to temperatures T_1 and T_2, we obtain

$$\log p_1/p_2 = -\frac{q}{R}\left(\frac{1}{T_1}-\frac{1}{T_2}\right)=\frac{q}{R}\left(\frac{T_1-T_2}{T_1T_2}\right). \qquad (40a)$$

Example. The dissociation pressure of calcium carbonate is 34·2 cm. of mercury at 840° C., 42·0 cm. at 860° C.

Hence the heat of dissociation

$$q = R(\log p_1/p_2)\frac{T_1T_2}{T_1-T_2}$$

$$= 1{\cdot}99 \times 2{\cdot}303\left(\log_{10}\frac{42{\cdot}0}{34{\cdot}2}\right)\cdot\frac{1113\times 1133}{20}$$

$$= 31{,}530 \text{ calories.}$$

The dissociation of salt hydrates is exactly similar.

Fig. 19 shows the dissociation pressure plotted against the temperature and the logarithm of the dissociation

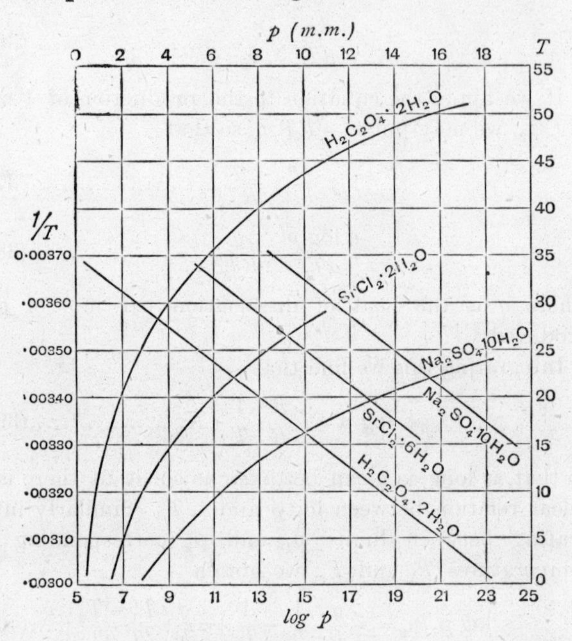

FIG. 19.—Dissociation pressures of salt hydrates. (Baxter and Lansing, in *J. Amer. Chem. Soc.*).

pressure plotted against the reciprocal of the absolute temperature in a number of cases.

Examples.

1. Naphthalene melts at 80·1° C., its latent heat of fusion is 35·62 calories per gram, and the increase in volume on fusion $(v_l - v_s)$ is 0·146 c.c. per gram. Find the change of melting point with pressure. (+0·0350° per atmos.)

2. The transition point of mercuric iodide, red → yellow, is at 127° C. The heat absorbed in the change is 3000 calories per mol, and the volume change approximately −5·4 c.c. per mol. Find the effect of change of pressure on the transition point. (−0·0174° per atmos.)

3. In the change aragonite → calcite the volume change is +2·75 c.c. per mol. The heat absorbed is approximately 30 calories per mol. If the transition point is −43° C., find the pressure at which aragonite becomes the stable form at 0° C. (*ca.* 84 atmos.)

4. Calculate the change in the vapour pressure of (*a*) ice, (*b*) water, at 0° C. for 1° change of temperature. (See Table III.)

The latent heats of vaporisation are: ice, 12,190 calories; water, 10,750 calories per mol.

(Water, 0·0332 cms.; Ice, 0·0376 cms. mercury.)

5. The following table gives the vapour pressures of mercury over a range of temperature. Plot *log p* against $1/T$ and determine the latent heat of vaporisation from the graph.

T° C.	*p* (mm.)	*T*° C.	*p* (mm.)	*T*° C.	*p* (mm.)
100	0·270	250	74·95	400	1495·6
130	1·137	280	158·38	430	2298·8
160	4·013	310	304·9	450	2996·1
190	12·137	340	548·6		
220	31·957	370	930·3		

6. The vapour pressure of boron trichloride is 562·9 mm. at 10° C. and 807·5 mm. at 20° C. Find its heat of vaporisation. (5,970 cals. per mol.)

7. The following figures give the dissociation pressures of $CuSO_4 . 3H_2O$ ($CuSO_4 . 3H_2O = CuSO_4 . H_2O + 2H_2O$).

Plot *log p* against $1/T$ and find the heat of dissociation at 50° C.

T° C.	p (mm.)	T° C.	p (mm.)
25·0	5·6	50·2	30·9
35·1	11·8	65·1	77·7
45·2	22·1	80·1	183·1

8. Similarly find the heat of dissociation of calcium carbonate at 750° C.

T° C.	p (mm.)	T° C.	p (mm.)
500	0·11	750	68
550	0·57	800	168
600	2·35	850	373
650	8·2	900	773
700	25·3	950	1490

9. The dissociation pressure of BaO_2 ($2BaO_2 = 2BaO + O_2$) at 735° C. is 260 mm.; at 775° C., 510 mm. Find the heat of dissociation. (35,400 cals.)

10. The melting point of bismuth is 271·0° C. at 1 atmos., and the volume change on melting is −0·00345 c.c. per gram. The latent heat of fusion of bismuth is 10·2 cals. per gram. Find the melting point at 5000 atmospheres pressure. (*ca.* 249°).

CHAPTER IV

DILUTE SOLUTIONS

Expression of Concentration. The composition of a solution can be expressed in a number of different ways. The commonest way of stating the concentration of a dilute solution is as the weight of solute in a given volume of solution. This method suffers from the defect that it is necessary to know the density of the solution before the relative weights of solute and solvent can be ascertained. Thus, if the solution contains w grams of solute per litre of solution, the density of which is d, the weight of the solution is $1000d$ grams and the amount of solvent contained in it $1000d - w$ grams. It is thus better, even in the case of dilute solutions, to express the concentration of solute as the weight dissolved in a given weight, say 1000 grams of solvent.

If the weight of solute in either case is divided by the molecular weight M, we obtain the corresponding molecular concentrations. These are sometimes distinguished by calling the number of mols of solute in one litre of solution the *molar concentration* (c), and the number of mols of solute in 1000 grams of solvent the *molal concentration* (m).

If we also divide the weight of the solvent by its molecular weight we can express the concentration of a solution as the relative number of mols of solute and solvent. Thus, if a given mass of solution contains w_1 grams of A and w_2 grams of B, the number of mols of A is w_1/M_1 and the number of mols of B, w_2/M_2. The behaviour of solutions can be most simply stated by expressing the amount of each component as its *molar fraction*, *i.e.* the ratio of the number of mols of this component to the total number of mols present in the solution. Thus if a solution contains n_1 mols of A and n_2 mols of B, we have :

$$\left.\begin{aligned}\text{Molar fraction of } A,\ N_1 &= \frac{n_1}{n_1+n_2}\\ \text{Molar fraction of } B,\ N_2 &= \frac{n_2}{n_1+n_2}\end{aligned}\right\} \quad \ldots\ldots\ldots(42)$$

The molal concentration of a binary solution is easily converted into the molar fraction. Thus, if the molecular weight of the solvent is M_0, the number of mols in 1000 grams is $1000/M_0$ and the molar fraction of solute is

$$N = \frac{m}{m + 1000/M_0}.$$

When water is the solvent $M_0 = 18{\cdot}01$, so that 1000 grams contain $1000/18{\cdot}01 = 55{\cdot}51$ mols. The molar fraction of a solute whose molal concentration is m is thus

$$N = \frac{m}{m + 55{\cdot}51}.$$

The Laws of Dilute Solutions. It is not possible to deduce from the laws of thermodynamics stated above how such properties of solutions as the vapour pressure, freezing point, boiling point and osmotic pressure vary with the concentration. But when the variation of one of these is known, that of the others can be calculated by thermodynamical methods. The behaviour of concentrated solutions often varies with the nature of the substances, but certain generalisations can be made, which are believed to be universally true, in extremely dilute solutions. These generalisations can be stated in a number of ways. They are expressed most simply in terms of the partial vapour pressures of the solvent and (when it is volatile) the solute. The generalisations are as follows:

(1) **Raoult's Law.** When an involatile solute is added to a solvent, the vapour pressure of the latter is depressed. Wüllner found (1858-1860) that the depression was proportional to the concentration of the solute. If p_1° is the vapour pressure of the pure solvent, and p_1 that of the solution at the same temperature, $(p_1^\circ - p_1)/p_1^\circ$ is the fractional lowering of the vapour pressure caused by the solute. Babo had found (1847) that, for a given solution, this quantity is independent of the temperature, and Raoult found (1886) that it is equal to the relative numbers of molecules of the solute and the solvent.

In a very dilute solution n_2/n_1 and n_2/n_1+n_2 are practically the same. Hence Raoult's law may be expressed as

$$\frac{p_1^\circ - p_1}{p_1^\circ} = \frac{n_2}{n_1+n_2}, \quad \text{..................(43)}$$

or,

$$p_1/p_1^\circ = 1 - \frac{n_2}{n_1+n_2} = \frac{n_1}{n_1+n_2},$$

or,

$$p_1 = p_1^\circ N_1; \quad \text{......................(44)}$$

i.e. the vapour pressure of the solvent is proportional to its molar fraction. The same holds true, of course, for solutions of volatile solutes; but in that case p_1 is the *partial* vapour pressure of the solvent.

Raoult's law is believed to be universally valid, at any rate at extremely small concentrations of the solute, provided that the proper molecular weights are employed in evaluating N_1. These are: for the solvent, the molecular weight is that which it has in the vapour; for the solute, the molecular weight in the solution itself. The reason for the former choice, which may at present be regarded as an experimental fact, is discussed in Part II.* The latter depends on the fact that it has been shown experimentally that the expression is valid in dilute solutions of many substances, using the molecular weight as given by the simplest chemical formula. The weight of this evidence is so strong that, when apparent deviations occur, we may conclude that the molecular weight used for the solute is incorrect, owing to its association or dissociation in the solution, rather than that Raoult's law is at fault. Hence the use of Raoult's law for determining molecular weights of solutes in dilute solutions.

In some cases, particularly with solutions of strong electrolytes, deviations from Raoult's law appear at quite small concentrations of the solute. In solutions of non-electrolytes in water, and in each other, it is frequently valid over a moderate range of dilute solutions. In the case of solutions which are miscible with each other in all proportions, it is occasionally valid over the whole range of concentration between $N_1=1$ and $N_1=0$. In that case, it can be shown that it also holds for the other component; *i.e.* $p_2=p_2^\circ N_2$ when N_2 varies from $N_2=1$ to $N_2=0$. Such solutions, which usually only occur when the components are closely related compounds, have been called *perfect solutions*.

* If the molecules of the solvent are partly *associated* in the vapour, the assignment of a molecular weight becomes difficult. In such cases an alternative statement of this law, such as is given in Part II, is to be preferred. For the present we shall suppose that the solvent is present in the vapour over the solution in the form of simple molecules, to which a definite molecular weight may be attached.

For the present we shall be concerned only with moderately dilute solutions, for which it may be supposed that the error made in assuming (44) to be true is small.

(2) **Henry's Law.** We turn now to the behaviour of solutes in dilute solutions. In 1803 Henry studied the solubility of gases in liquids and found that the concentration in the liquid was proportional to the pressure of the gas. Numerous more exact investigations have been made, and it has been found that Henry's law is strictly true in very dilute solutions, if the solute is in the same molecular state in the solution as in the vapour. Apparent exceptions occur, for example, when the solute exists as single molecules in the vapour and is associated in the solution.

In such a case Henry's law is more exactly defined by the statement that the ratio of the concentrations of a given molecular species in the gas and in the solution is a constant at a given temperature; and this is more exactly true the smaller the concentrations. The concentration of a molecular species in the solution may be expressed by m_2 (mols per 1000 gms. solvent) or N_2 (the molar fraction), while the concentration in the vapour is proportional to its partial pressure p_2.

Henry's law can thus be expressed by

$$\frac{p_2}{N_2}=K' ; \quad \text{or} \quad \frac{p_2}{m_2}=K'' ; \quad \ldots\ldots\ldots\ldots\ldots(45)$$

(for N_2 and m_2 are proportional to each other in sufficiently dilute solutions). Provided that p_2 and N_2 (or m_2) apply to the partial pressure and the concentration of the same molecular species, Henry's law is believed to be strictly and universally true in extremely dilute solutions.

To sum up, we have two experimental relations on which the theory of dilute solutions may be based. (1) Raoult's law states that the partial pressure of the solvent is proportional to its molar fraction in the solution; (2) Henry's law states that the concentration of each molecular species dissolved in the solution is proportional to its concentration (or partial pressure) in the

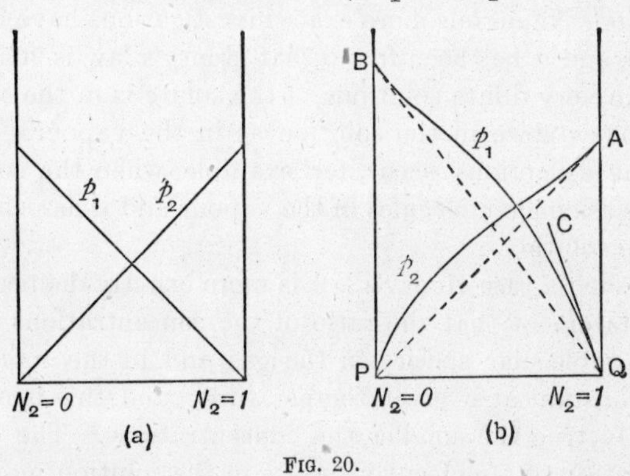

FIG. 20.

vapour. These laws are believed to be universally and strictly true, at any rate in the limit when the concentration of the solute is very small. The case in which Raoult's law holds also for the *solute*, *i.e.* $p_2 = p_2^\circ N_2$ when N_2 is small, is a special case of Henry's law, which is true only in particular cases. In these cases the constant K' of Henry's law has the particular value p_2°.

These relations are illustrated in Fig. 20, which shows the partial pressures of solutions of two liquids which are miscible in all proportions, plotted against their molar fractions. Case (*a*) is that in which the liquids form perfect solutions, *i.e.* Raoult's law holds for both components over the whole range of composition.

In case (*b*), Raoult's law does not hold over the whole range of composition, but it applies to the solvent when the concentration of the solute is small, *i.e.* the vapour pressure curve of the solvent at first follows the Raoult law relation $p_1 = p_1^\circ N_1$, which is represented by the dotted line PA.

Similarly the partial pressure of the solute is at first proportional to its concentration, *i.e.* the curve of p_1 at first lies on a straight line QC. The slope of this line is the constant of Henry's law, $p_2/N_2 = K'$, which does not necessarily coincide with the relation required by Raoult's law, which is represented by the dotted line QB.

Deductions from Henry's Law. Two phases are in equilibrium with each other when the partial pressure of every component which is common to both is the same in each phase. If it were not the same it would be possible to obtain work by the transfer of this substance from the one phase to the other, which is in conflict with the second law of Thermodynamics. Some important consequences can be deduced from this.

(1) *Distribution of a Solute between two Solvents.* Consider solutions of a solute in two solvents. If N_2', N_2'' are the molar fractions of the solute in the two solvents and p_2'; p_2'' the corresponding partial vapours, we shall have, if the solutions are so dilute that Henry's law applies,

$$p_2' = K'N_2' \; ; \quad p_2'' = K''N_2'',$$

where K', K'' are the appropriate constants of Henry's law in the two cases. Now suppose that the two solvents are practically immiscible. When the solutions are put in contact it is necessary for equilibrium that $p_2' = p_2''$, *i.e.* that

$$\frac{N_2''}{N_2'} = \frac{K'}{K''}.$$

Thus the ratio of the concentrations of the solute in the two solvents is constant, and this *distribution ratio* is equal to the (inverse) ratio of the two Henry's law constants.

It has been assumed here that the solute is in the same molecular state in the two solvents. The above applies strictly to the distribution of a single molecular species between the solvents. If, for example, the solute is present as single molecules (A) in one solvent and is largely associated into double molecules (A_2) in the other, the simple distribution law will not hold. The distribution ratio of *single molecules* between the two solvents will be a constant, *i.e.*

$$N_A''/N_A' = \text{const.},$$

but the concentration of single molecules is not simply proportional to the total concentration of the solute in this solvent.

According to the law of mass action, there will be an equilibrium between the single and double molecules in the second solvent, according to which

$$(N_A'')^2 = kN_{A_2}''.$$

The result will thus be a relation of the form

$$\sqrt{N_{A_2}''}/N_A' = \text{const.}$$

In the following table are given the distribution ratios of (1) trimethylaniline, (2) acetic acid, between water and chloroform at 25°. In the former case the distribution ratio is practically constant in the more dilute solutions, indicating that the solute is in the same molecular state in both solvents. In the latter case the simple distribution ratio is far from constant, but $\sqrt{c}$ (benzene)/c (water) is much more nearly constant, showing that acetic acid is largely associated into double molecules in benzene. The concentrations are given here in gram equivalents per litre.

TABLE IV.

DISTRIBUTION RATIOS BETWEEN WATER AND BENZENE.

Trimethylaniline.			Acetic Acid.			
c_B.	c_W.	c_B/c_W.	c_B.	c_W.	c_B/c_W.	$\sqrt{c_B}/c_W$.
0·0295	0·0584	0·505	0·0159	0·5793	0·0274	0·218
0·1237	0·2474	0·500	0·0554	1·3821	0·0401	0·170
0·2328	0·4663	0·499	0·2555	3·2984	0·0776	0·153
0·5861	1·1135	0·526	0·9053	6·9974	0·1294	0·134

(2) *Solubility of Solids.* The necessary condition of the equilibrium of a solid with its saturated solution is that the vapour pressure of the solid shall be equal to the partial vapour pressure of the same substance in the solution. Suppose that the vapour pressure of the solid is p_s. Let N_s', N_s'' be its molar fractions in saturated solutions in two solvents. If these solutions are sufficiently dilute, so that Henry's law may be applied, we thus have

$$p_s = K'N_s'\ ; \quad p_s = K''N_s''\ ;$$

i.e.

$$\frac{N_s''}{N_s'} = \frac{K'}{K''}.$$

The solubilities are thus inversely proportional to the constants of Henry's law. If the two solvents are immiscible, it follows (as can easily be shown) that the ratio of the solubilities is the same as the distribution ratio. If the two solvents are appreciably soluble in each other, the actual distribution ratio may be appreciably different, because we are then measuring not the distribution ratio between the pure solvents, but that of their saturated solutions. Thus water and ether dissolve each other to an appreciable extent and the distribution ratio obtained by shaking a solute with water and ether in contact with each other is really the distribution ratio for the mutually saturated solutions of water and ether.

Elevation of the Boiling Point by an Involatile Solute. The boiling point of a liquid is the temperature at which its vapour pressure is equal to the atmospheric pressure. Since the vapour pressure of a solution of an involatile solute is lower than that of the solvent at the same temperature, the temperature at which it reaches atmospheric pressure is higher, *i.e.* the boiling point is raised. Combining equation (43) for the depression of the vapour pressure caused by the solute with (38), which gives the change of vapour pressure with temperature, we can find the corresponding elevation of the boiling point.

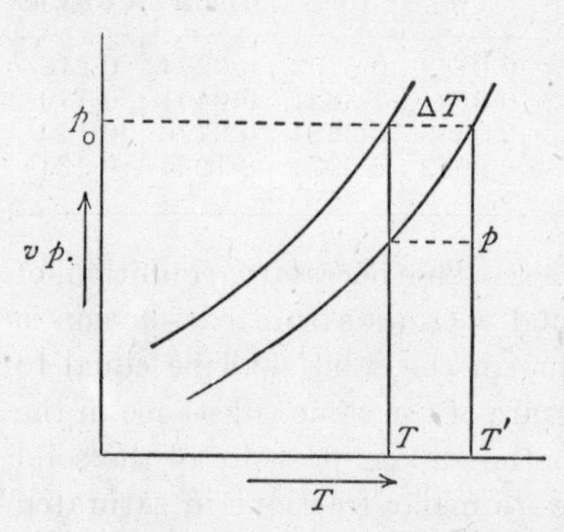

FIG. 21.—Elevation of the boiling point.

Let p° be the vapour pressure of the solvent at its boiling point T, and p that of the solution at the same temperature (Fig. 21).

Then by (43) $$\frac{p^\circ - p}{p^\circ} = \frac{n_2}{n_1 + n_2}.$$

We wish to find the temperature T' at which the vapour pressure of the solution is equal to p°. The variation of p with T is given by (38), viz. $d(\log p)/dT = \lambda/RT^2$, where λ is now the latent heat of evaporation of the solvent (from the solution) per mol. Integrating this between p (temperature T) and p° (temperature T'), we find

$$\log p^\circ/p = \frac{\lambda}{R}\left(\frac{1}{T} - \frac{1}{T'}\right) = \frac{\lambda}{R}\left(\frac{T' - T}{TT'}\right)$$

$$= \frac{\lambda}{R} \cdot \frac{\Delta T}{T^2}, \quad \text{.............................(46)}$$

where $\Delta T = T' - T$, is the elevation of the boiling point produced by the solute.

Now p°/p is a little greater than one, and since $\log(1 + x)$ is nearly equal to x when x is small, we may put

$$\log p^\circ/p = \log\left(1 + \frac{p^\circ - p}{p}\right) \approx \frac{p^\circ - p}{p}$$

and by (44), since $p/p_0 = n_1/(n_1 + n_2)$,

$$\frac{p^\circ - p}{p} = \frac{n_2}{n_1},$$

so that we can write down the result,

$$\Delta T = \frac{RT^2}{\lambda} \cdot n_2/n_1. \quad \text{...............(46a)}$$

This may be written as

$$\Delta T = \frac{RT^2}{\lambda} \cdot \frac{n_2}{n_1} = \frac{RT^2}{\lambda/M_1} \cdot \frac{n_2}{n_1 M_1} = \frac{RT^2}{L} \cdot C, \quad \text{.....(47)}$$

where, since n_2/n_1 is the number of mols of solute per mol of solvent, $n_2/n_1 M_1 = C$ is the number of mols of solute per gram of solvent and $\lambda/M_1 = L$ is the latent heat of evaporation of the solvent per gram.

The value of ΔT when $C = 1$, *i.e.* RT^2/L, is known as the molecular elevation of the boiling point (elevation produced by 1 mol in 1 gm. solvent). It is more usual to quote the molecular elevation for 1000 grams of solvent. Then $C = 0{\cdot}001$ and

$$\Delta T_{1000\,\text{gms.}} = 0{\cdot}001\,\frac{RT^2}{L} = \frac{0{\cdot}002T^2}{L}. \quad \ldots\ldots(48)$$

The following table gives data for the calculation of the molecular elevations of a number of solvents.

TABLE V.

Solvent.	Latent Heat of Evaporation (per gram.).	Boiling Point °C.	Boiling Point °K.	$\Delta T = \frac{0{\cdot}002T^2}{L}$.	Obs. Molecular Elevation (per 1000 gms.).
H_2O	536 cal.	100	373	0·515	0·52
CS_2	83·8	46·2	319	2·41	2·37
C_2H_5OH	205	78·8	352	1·198	1·15
CH_3OH	262	67	340	0·875	0·88
CH_3CO_2H	97	118	391	3·13	3·07
C_6H_6	92·9	80·3	353	2·67	2·67
NH_3	335	−33·5	240	0·333	0·34

The molecular elevation is also quoted for 1 mol in 1000 c.c. solvent since it is often convenient to determine the volume rather than the weight of the solution. Then in this case

$$\Delta T = \frac{0{\cdot}002T^2}{L\rho},$$

where ρ is the density at the boiling point.

Depression of the Freezing Point by a Solute. We can obtain the depression of the freezing point of a solvent by a known amount of a solute by making use of the consideration that for equilibrium (*i.e.* at the freezing point), the partial vapour pressure of the solvent over the solution must be equal to the vapour pressure of the solid solvent at the same temperature.

We will take the case of ice and water in order to fix our ideas (Fig. 22). The vapour pressure curves of ice and water intersect at the freezing point of water T_0, at which solid and liquid have a vapour pressure p°. The solution has at all temperatures a lower vapour

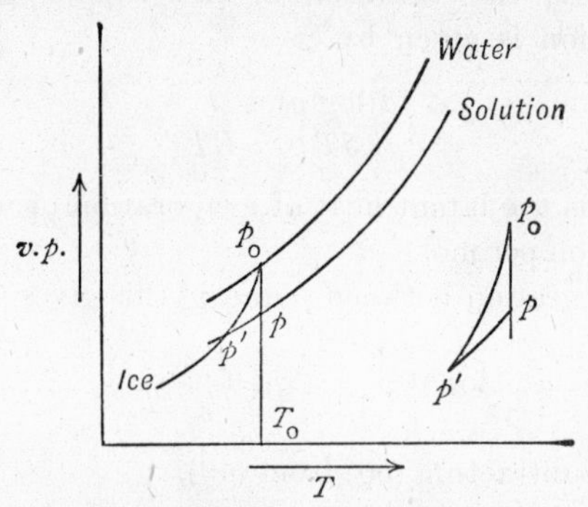

FIG. 22.—Depression of the freezing point.

pressure than the solvent. We wish to find the temperature at which the solution curve intersects the ice curve.

Let p be the vapour pressure of water vapour over the solution at T_0, and let the solution curve intersect the ice curve at a pressure p' and at a temperature T ($T_0 - T = \Delta T_0$, being the lowering of the freezing point). We are concerned with the small area enclosed by p°, p and p' (Fig. 23).

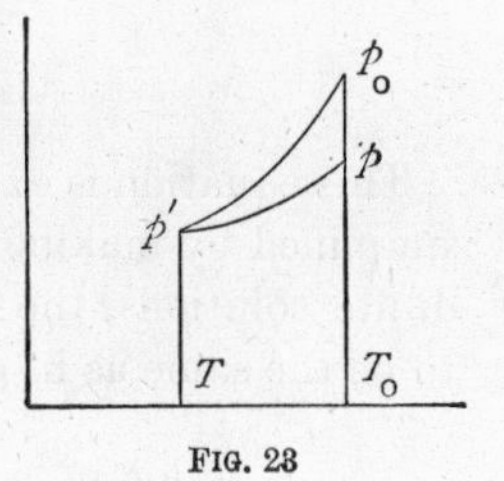

FIG. 23

The variation of the vapour pressure of ice with temperature is given by the equation

$$\frac{d(\log p)}{dT} = \frac{\lambda_s}{RT^2},$$

where λ_s is the latent heat of evaporation of ice per mol. Integrating this between p° and p' we obtain

$$\log p^\circ/p' = -\frac{\lambda_s}{R}\left(\frac{1}{T_0} - \frac{1}{T}\right). \quad \text{.............(49)}$$

Similarly, the variation of the vapour pressure of the solution is given by

$$\frac{d(\log p)}{dT} = \frac{\lambda_l}{RT^2},$$

where λ_l is the latent heat of evaporation of water from the solution per mol.

On integration between p and p' this gives

$$\log p/p' = -\frac{\lambda_l}{R}\left(\frac{1}{T_0} - \frac{1}{T}\right). \quad \text{...............(50)}$$

Thus, subtracting (50) from (49),

$$\log p^\circ/p = -\left(\frac{\lambda_s - \lambda_l}{R}\right)\left(\frac{1}{T_0} - \frac{1}{T}\right). \quad \text{.........(51)}$$

Now $\lambda_s - \lambda_l$, the difference between the latent heats of evaporation from ice and from the solution, is equal to λ_f, the latent heat of fusion of ice into the solution.

Hence

$$\log p^\circ/p = -\frac{\lambda_f}{R}\left(\frac{1}{T_0} - \frac{1}{T}\right) = -\frac{\lambda_f}{R}\left(\frac{T - T_0}{TT_0}\right)$$

$$= \frac{\lambda_f}{RT^2} \cdot \Delta T. \quad \text{.........(52)}$$

This equation is exact. For dilute solutions it may be simplified by making some approximations. Firstly, for dilute solutions, the latent heat of fusion can be taken to be the same as in pure water. Secondly, we can put

$$\log p^\circ/p \approx \frac{p^\circ - p}{p} = \frac{n_2}{n_1}.$$

Therefore the depression of the freezing point is

$$\Delta T = \frac{RT^2}{\lambda_f} \cdot \frac{n_2}{n_1} = \frac{RT^2}{\lambda_f/M_1} \cdot \frac{n_2}{n_1 M_1} = \frac{RT^2}{L_f} \cdot C. \quad ....(53)$$

This equation, of course, applies to any solvent: n_2/n_1 is the number of mols of solute per mol of solvent, $n_2/n_1M_1 = C$ is the number of mols of solute per gram of solvent and $\lambda_f/M = L_f$ is the latent heat of fusion of the solvent per gram.

The depression caused by one mol of solute per gram of solvent is thus RT^2/L_f. The molecular depression is usually quoted as the depression per mol of solute to 1000 grams of solvent, which is

$$\Delta T = 0{\cdot}001 RT^2/L_f = 0{\cdot}002 T^2/L_f.$$

As in the case of the molecular elevation of the boiling point, it is sometimes convenient to have it as the depression caused per mol of solute in a known volume of solvent. For 1000 c.c. this is $0{\cdot}002T^2/L_f\rho$, where ρ is the density of the solvent.

The following table gives data for the calculation of the molecular depressions of the freezing point and also observed depressions for non-electrolyte solutes.

TABLE VI.

Solvent.	Latent Heat of Fusion (per gram).	Freezing Point °C.	Freezing Point °K.	$\Delta T = \frac{0{\cdot}002T^2}{L}$.	Obs. Molecular Depression (per 1000 gms.).
H_2O	79·67	0°	273	1·858	1·85
C_6H_6	29·9	5·5	279	5·19	5·12
$H.CO_2H$	57·38	8	281	2·74	2·77
$CH_3.CO_2H$	43·7	17	290	3·82	3·9
C_6H_5OH	29·1	41·5	315	6·81	7·3
$C_6H_5NO_2$	22·6	3·9	277	6·80	6·9

Van't Hoff gave thermodynamical derivations of the equations for the elevation of the boiling point and depression of the freezing point in 1887. (As early as 1788, Blagden had shown that the freezing point depression was proportional to the concentration.) Raoult and Beckmann developed the methods of determining accurately the boiling points and freezing points of solutions.

Solubility and the Melting Point. In the last section we found the temperature at which the solid form of the substance we regarded as the solvent was in equilibrium with a solution of known composition. If we reverse the calculation, we may obtain the composition of the solution which is in equilibrium with the solid at a given temperature.

Thus the equations of the last section could be used to find the temperature at which solid benzene is in equilibrium with a solution of nitrobenzene in benzene, *i.e.* the freezing point of the solution. Conversely, we could find the composition of the solution which is in equilibrium with solid benzene at a given temperature, and this is equivalent to a calculation of the *solubility* of solid benzene in nitrobenzene at the same temperature. At its melting point solid benzene is in equilibrium with its pure liquid (*i.e.* a liquid in which the molar fraction of benzene is one), at lower temperatures solid benzene is in equilibrium with solutions in which its molar fraction is less than one. The curve giving the relation between the equilibrium temperature and the composition of the solution can be regarded either as the freezing point curve of solutions of nitrobenzene in benzene or as the solubility curve of solid benzene in nitrobenzene solutions.

In (52), if Raoult's law is obeyed, $p = p^\circ N$, and the equation takes the form

$$\log N = \frac{\lambda_f}{R}\left(\frac{1}{T_0} - \frac{1}{T}\right). \quad \text{................(54)}$$

This equation gives the temperature T at which the solid form of a substance is in equilibrium with a liquid in which its molar fraction is N, in terms of T_0, the melting point of the solid, and λ_f, its latent heat of fusion. It is only strictly applicable so long as λ_f remains constant.

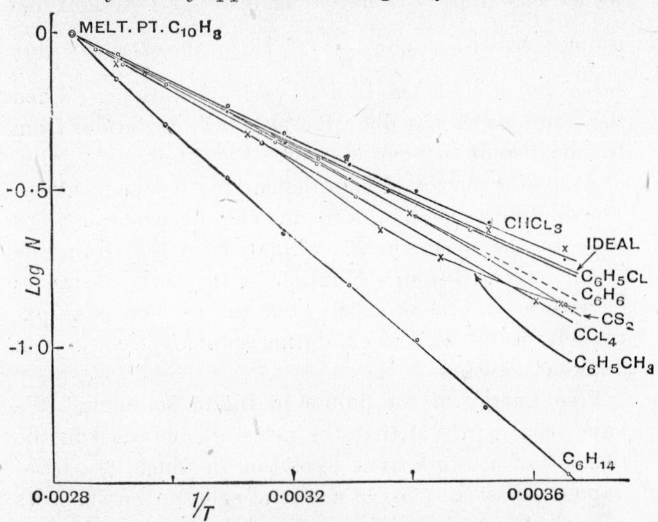

FIG. 24.—Solubility curves of naphthalene (J. H. Hildebrand and C. A. Jenks, *J. Amer. Chem. Soc.*).

Example. Naphthalene melts at 80° C. and the latent heat of fusion is 4440 calories per mol. We can calculate the molar fraction of naphthalene in a chloroform solution in equilibrium with solid naphthalene at 50° C. by (54).

Thus :

$$\log N = \frac{4440}{1\cdot99}\left(\frac{1}{353} - \frac{1}{323}\right),$$

$$N = 0\cdot556. \quad \text{(Observed } 0\cdot557.)$$

According to equation (54), the solubility of a substance (expressed as its molar fraction) should be the same, at the same temperature, in all solutions which obey

Raoult's law, *i.e.* in all perfect solutions. Writing the equation in the form

$$\log N = -\frac{\lambda_f}{R}\left(\frac{1}{T}\right) + \text{constant}, \quad \text{...........(55)}$$

we see that if $\log N$ is plotted against $\left(\frac{1}{T}\right)$ a straight line is obtained with slope $\left(\frac{-\lambda_f}{R}\right)$. This is the *ideal solubility curve*, which holds good for all perfect solutions. When the solutions do not obey Raoult's law, deviations from the ideal solubility curve occur. Fig. 24 shows a group of solubility curves of naphthalene plotted in this way. The solubilities in chloroform and chlorobenzene are very close to the ideal curve, calculated by (55) from the latent heat of fusion. Solutions with other substances deviate more or less widely, but the method is an extremely useful way of exhibiting solubility relations in different solvents.

Free Energy of the Solute in Dilute Solutions. We have seen (eqn. 25) that the net work obtained in the transfer of a solute from a solution in which its partial vapour pressure is p_2' to a second solution in which its partial vapour pressure is p_2'' is

$$w' = RT \log p_2'/p_2'' \text{ per mol.}$$

If the solutions are sufficiently dilute, so that Henry's law holds, we may write

$$\frac{p_2'}{p_2''} = \frac{N_2'}{N_2''}, \quad \text{or} \quad \frac{p_2'}{p_2''} = \frac{m_2'}{m_2''},$$

according to the method we use for expressing the concentrations. Therefore, for dilute solutions,

$$w' = RT \log N_2'/N_2'' \text{ (or } = RT \log m_2'/m_2''\text{).} \quad \text{...(56)}$$

Since the net work obtained is equal to the decrease of

free energy in the transfer, *i.e.* $w' = -\Delta F$, we have

$$\Delta F = -w' = RT \log N_2''/N_2' \text{ (or} = RT \log m_2''/m_2') \ldots\ldots(57)$$

This equation is more nearly exact the smaller the concentration, and is strictly true in the limit at extremely small concentrations.

There is no reason to suppose that involatile solutes (*i.e.* solutes whose partial pressures are too small to be measured) differ fundamentally from volatile solutes. In dilute solutions Raoult's law applies to the solvent irrespective of whether the solute is volatile or not. Now it can be shown (see Part II) that if Raoult's law applies in dilute solutions to the solvent, a relation like Henry's law must hold for the solutes. Consequently, (57) may be applied to find the net work of transfer even of involatile solutes from one concentration to another.

*** Osmotic Pressure and Vapour Pressures of Solutions.** A solvent tends to diffuse spontaneously into one of its solutions. If the solvent and solution are separated by a membrane which allows the solvent to pass without hindrance, but prevents the passage of the dissolved substance, the solvent will tend to flow through the membrane into the solution. The hydrostatic pressure which must be applied to the solution to stop the flow of solvent through the membrane is the osmotic pressure of the solution. It is the pressure which balances the tendency of the solvent to flow into the solution.

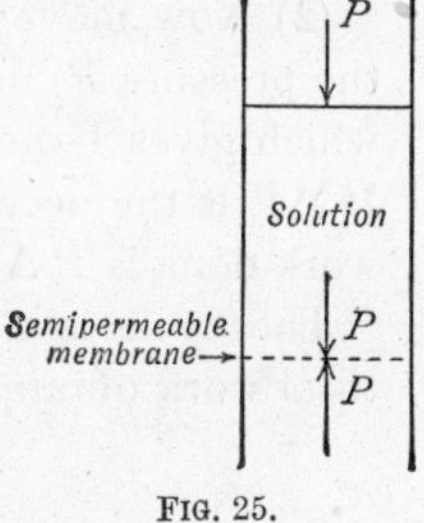

FIG. 25.

Now suppose that the semipermeable membrane is in the form of a movable piston between the solvent and the solution, and that the solution is under a hydrostatic pressure P which is equal to the osmotic pressure (Fig. 25). In order to prevent the movement of the piston a pressure P equal to the hydrostatic pressure of the solution must be applied to it. If this pressure be increased by an infinitesimal amount, the piston will begin to move inwards and the volume of the solution will decrease, solvent passing outwards through the membrane. In order to diminish the volume of the solution in this way by an amount dV, an amount of work PdV is done against the applied pressure.

We may now carry out the following cyclic process :

(1) Vaporise 1 mol of the solvent at its vapour pressure p_0, expand it reversibly to a pressure p equal to the partial pressure of the solvent over the solution (we shall assume that the partial pressure over the solution is not affected by the hydrostatic pressure P applied to the latter). Condense the vapour into the solution.

If the vapour obeys the simple gas law, the work obtained is

$$RT \log p_0/p.$$

(2) Now move the semipermeable piston up (against the pressure P) until a quantity of solvent equal to that which gives 1 mol of the vapour has passed through it. If ΔV is the decrease in the volume of the solution, the work done is $P\,\Delta V$.

The cycle is now complete and we may equate the total work obtained to zero, thus :

$$RT \log p_0/p = P\,.\,\Delta V. \quad \text{.................}(a)$$

So long as the conditions stated hold, this equation is thermodynamically exact. The following table gives some values of P for cane sugar solutions at 0° C., as directly measured and as calculated by the equation from the vapour pressure lowering.

TABLE VII.

Mols of Sugar per 1000 gms. Water.	P obs. (atmos.).	P calc. (atmos.).
0·1352	2·91 *	—
0·1375	—	2·99
0·2000	4·72 †	—
0·3000	7·09 †	—
0·3156	—	6·90
0·4992	—	11·7
0·5000	11·9 †	—
1·000	24·83 †	—
1·0089	—	24·4

If for dilute solutions we put as an approximation

$$\log p_0/p \approx \frac{p_0 - p}{p} \approx \frac{n_2}{n_1},$$

where n_2 is the number of mols of solute and n_1 that of the solvent in the solution, we obtain

$$P \,.\, \Delta V \,.\, n_1/n_2 = RT.$$

But n_1/n_2 is the number of mols of the solvent to 1 mol of solute, and ΔV is approximately equal to the volume of a quantity of solution containing 1 mol of solvent, so that $\Delta V \,.\, n_1/n_2$ is the volume of the solution containing 1 mol of solute. If we write this V, we have

$$PV = RT, \quad \text{........................}(b)$$

an equation analogous to the simple gas law.

Van't Hoff first gave the thermodynamical derivation of the relation between the osmotic pressure and the

* Earl of Berkeley and E. G. J. Hartley. † H. N. Morse.

vapour pressures of solutions in 1885, having previously shown from the experimental data of Pfeffer that the relation $PV = RT$ holds for the osmotic pressures of sugar solutions. He made the relation the basis of his deduction of the elevation of the boiling point and depression of the freezing point. It must be remembered that while (*a*) is thermodynamically exact (if the vapour obeys the simple gas law and if the effect of the applied pressure P on the vapour pressure of the solution is negligible), (*b*) depends on the approximations, and, even if the solution obeys Raoult's law, is not valid in concentrated solutions.

Examples.

1. The vapour pressure of a solution containing 11·94 gms. of glycocoll in 100 gms. water is 740·9 mm. at 100° C.

Find its boiling point, assuming that glycocoll is involatile and that the latent heat of the solution is equal to that of pure water. (100·74°.)

Calculate the molecular elevation of the boiling point of water from this result. (Δ(100 gms.) = 4·7.)

2. Calculate the molecular elevation of the boiling point of cyclohexane, C_6H_{12} (b. pt. 81·5° C., latent heat of vaporisation 87·3 calories per gram). (Δ(1000 gms.) = 2·88.)

3. A solution of 4·298 gms. of mannite in 100 gms. water showed a boiling point elevation of 0·121°. Assuming that mannite is a normal solute, find its molecular weight. (184·7.)

4. A solution containing 2·237 gms. of NaCl in 100 gms. water had a vapour pressure lower than that of pure water by 0·0553 mm. at 0° C. (water at 0°, 4·579 mm.). Find the temperature at which ice is in equilibrium with this solution

(1) approximately, by means of the result of Examples III. 4

(2) exactly, by (52). (– 1·26° C.)

5. p-Xylol freezes at 16° C. and its latent heat of fusion is 39·3 calories per gram. Find the molecular depression of the freezing point.

Calculate the freezing point of a solution of 10 gms. benzene in 1000 gms. p-xylol. ($\Delta T = 0{\cdot}545°$.)

6. A solution of 2·042 gms. of glycerol in 100 gms. of water had the freezing point −0·4140°.

Assuming that the solution obeys Raoult's law, find the latent heat of fusion of ice. (79·9 cals.)

7. Calculate the solubility of naphthalene in chlorobenzene at 60° C. (See Example, p. 75.) ($N = 0{\cdot}68$.)

*8. The vapour pressure of a solution containing 5 gms. of K_2SO_4 to 100 gms. water is 4·538 mm. at 0° C. Using (52), find the freezing point of this solution. (−0·933°.)

*9. The vapour pressure of a sucrose solution containing 1 mol to 1000 grams of water at 0° C. is 4·489 mm.

Find the osmotic pressure of this solution. (22·6 atmos.)

CHAPTER V

GAS REACTIONS

The Maximum Work of a Gas Reaction. The maximum work obtainable in a reaction between gases is determined by the use of a theoretical device known as the van't Hoff equilibrium box. It is a box which is kept at a constant temperature, containing a mixture of the reacting gases and the products of the reaction in equilibrium with each other. It is fitted with a number of semipermeable membranes through which each constituent of the equilibrium mixture can be separately introduced or withdrawn. It is supposed to contain an active catalyst of the reaction, so that equilibrium is always maintained within the box when substances are being introduced or withdrawn.

We will take as an example the reaction

$$2H_2 + O_2 = 2H_2O(g)$$

at some temperature T. Suppose that we have 2 mols of H_2 at some pressure p_{H_2} and 1 mol of oxygen at a pressure p_{O_2}, both at temperature T. We wish to find the maximum work obtainable when these two reactants are converted into water vapour, which is finally obtained at a pressure p_{H_2O}, at the same temperature.

Let us have an equilibrium box containing the substances at the partial pressures p_{eH_2}, p_{eO_2} and p_{eH_2O} at which they are in equilibrium with each other at T.

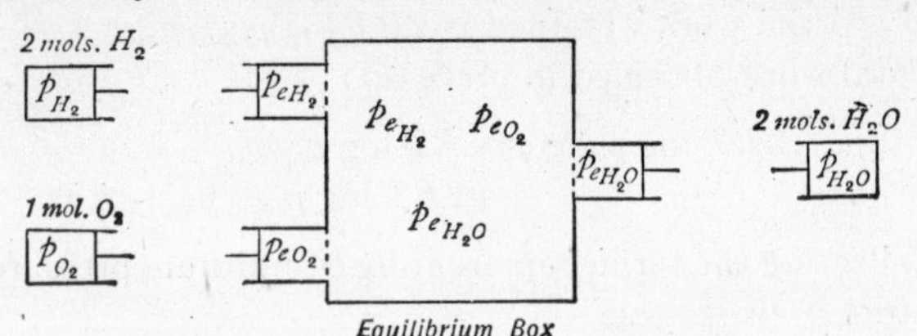

FIG. 26.—Maximum work of a gaseous reaction.

The process is as follows (Fig. 26):

(1) Expand the 2 mols of H_2 reversibly and isothermally from p_{H_2} to p_{eH_2}. Work obtained, $2RT \log p_{H_2}/p_{eH_2}$.

(2) Expand the 1 mol of O_2 reversibly and isothermally from p_{O_2} to p_{eO_2}. Work obtained, $RT \log p_{O_2}/p_{eO_2}$.

(3) The hydrogen and oxygen are now at the same pressures as their equilibrium pressures inside the box, and may be introduced through the appropriate semipermeable membranes at these pressures. While this is going on water vapour is withdrawn through its semipermeable membrane at p_{eH_2O}, so that the total amount of material in the box remains unchanged.

Work done in introducing 2 mols of $H_2 = 2RT$.
Work done in introducing 1 mol of $O_2 = RT$.
Work obtained in withdrawing 2 mols of $H_2O = 2RT$.
Total work obtained in stage (3),

$$2RT - RT - 2RT.$$

(4) We have now only to expand the 2 mols of water vapour from p_{eH_2O} to the final pressure p_{H_2O}. For a reversible, isothermal expansion, the work obtained is $2RT \log p_{eH_2O}/p_{H_2O}$.

Total work obtained in process,

$$w = 2RT \log p_{H_2}/p_{eH_2} + RT \log p_{O_2}/p_{eO_2} + 2RT \log p_{eH_2O}/p_{H_2O} - RT.$$

Collecting the terms representing equilibrium pressures separately, we obtain

$$w = RT \log \frac{p_e{}^2{}_{H_2O}}{p_e{}^2{}_{H_2} \cdot p_{eO_2}} - RT \log \frac{p^2{}_{H_2O}}{p^2{}_{H_2} p_{O_2}} - RT. \quad ...(58)$$

Now, if we start with all reactants at unit pressure and finish with resultants at unit pressure,

$$p^2{}_{H_2O}/p^2{}_{H_2} \cdot p_{O_2} = 1,$$

and the second term is zero. Then

$$w = RT \log \frac{p_e{}^2{}_{H_2O}}{p_e{}^2{}_{H_2} \cdot p_{eO_2}} - RT. \quad ....(59)$$

It has been shown (p. 49) that the maximum work of an *isothermal* process is definite and depends only on the initial and final states. w must therefore be independent of the pressures inside the box, provided they are *equilibrium* pressures and the quantity

$$\frac{p_e{}^2{}_{H_2O}}{p_e{}^2{}_{H_2} \cdot p_{eO_2}} = K_p \quad ....(60)$$

is therefore constant at a given temperature. It is called the equilibrium constant of the reaction, and the proof of its constancy amounts to a thermodynamic proof of the *law of mass action*. (59) may thus be written as

$$w = RT \log K_p - RT.$$

In this particular reaction we start with altogether 3 mols of gases and obtain finally 2 mols of gas, and the term $-RT$ appears because of the difference (-1) between the number of mols of gas on the right and on the left side of the equation.

In the general case

$$w = RT \log K_p + n\, RT, \quad \text{..............(61}$$

where n is as before the total number of mols of resultants minus the total number of mols of reactants.

Since the pressure is now the same at the end as at the beginning of the reaction we may also identify nRT with the work done by the system through its increase in volume. The volume increases by the volume of n mols of gas at the given pressure and temperature and the work done on this account is nRT. The net work obtainable from the reaction is therefore

$$w' = w - nRT = RT \log K_p. \quad \text{............(62)}$$

Since the net work obtained in a reaction is equal to the free energy decrease of the system we have further:

$$\Delta F = -w' = -RT \log K_p. \quad \text{............(63)}$$

This is the van't Hoff isotherm.

Example. At 1000° K. water vapour at 1 atmosphere pressure has been found to be dissociated into hydrogen and oxygen to the extent of 3×10^{-5} per cent.

The partial pressures in the equilibrium mixture are thus

$$p_{eH_2O} = 1,$$

$$p_{eH_2} = 3 \times 10^{-7},$$

$$p_{eO_2} = 3/2 \times 10^{-7},$$

since a molecule of water yields one molecule of hydrogen and half a molecule of oxygen.

Therefore for the reaction

$$2H_2 + O_2 = 2H_2O_{(g)} \text{ at } 1000^\circ \text{ K.}$$

$$K_p = \frac{p_e{}^2{}_{H_2O}}{p_e{}^2{}_{H_2} \cdot p_{eO_2}} = \frac{1}{9 \times 10^{-14} \times 3/2 \times 10^{-7}} = \frac{1}{1{\cdot}35 \times 10^{-20}}.$$

Thus the net work of this reaction is

$$w' = RT \log K_p = 1{\cdot}98 \times 1000 \times 2{\cdot}3 \log_{10} \frac{1}{1{\cdot}35 \times 10^{-20}}$$

$$= 1{\cdot}98 \times 1000 \times 2{\cdot}3 \times \log_{10} 10^{20} \div 1{\cdot}35$$

$$= +90{,}600 \text{ calories.}$$

The free energy decrease of the system in this reaction is thus 90,600 calories ($\Delta F = -90{,}600$ calories).

The Equilibrium Constants of a Gaseous Reaction. In general, for a gaseous reaction, at a given temperature, expressed by the equation

$$aA + bB \ldots \text{etc.} = qQ + rR \ldots \text{etc.}$$

(which means that a mols of the gas A, b mols of the gas B, etc.—the reactants—react and give rise to q mols of Q and r mols of R, etc.—the resultants), it can be shown, by a process similar to that given above, that, provided every gas obeys the perfect gas law, the following relation holds between their partial pressures at equilibrium:

$$\frac{(p_Q)^q (p_R)^r \ldots \text{etc.}}{(p_A)^a (p_B)^b \ldots \text{etc.}} = K_p, \qquad \ldots\ldots\ldots\ldots\ldots(64)$$

where K_p is the equilibrium constant, in terms of the partial pressures at that temperature.

The equilibrium constant is always written with the resultants in the numerator and the reactants in the denominator. It refers to the reaction represented in the chemical equation given. If the reaction be written differently (*e.g.* for half quantities) the equilibrium constant is not the same. Thus the equilibrium constant for the reaction

$$N_2 + 3H_2 = 2NH_3,$$

is
$$K_p = \frac{(p_{NH_3})^2}{(p_{N_2})(p_{H_2})^3};$$

while for the reaction written as

$$1/2N_2 + 3/2H_2 = NH_3$$

it is
$$K_p = \frac{p_{NH_3}}{(p_{N_2})^{\frac{1}{2}}(p_{H_2})^{\frac{3}{2}}}.$$

The equilibrium constant may be stated rather more concisely in terms of the logarithms of the partial pressures. Thus taking logarithms of both sides of (64), we obtain

$$\log K_p = q \log p_Q + r \log p_R \dots \text{etc.}$$
$$- a \log p_A - b \log p_B \dots \text{etc.},$$

which may be written

$$\log K_p = \Sigma a \log p_A, \quad \text{.....................(65)}$$

where the summation includes both reactants and resultants, it being understood that the terms for the reactants are given a negative sign.

The equilibrium constant of a gaseous reaction may also be expressed in terms of the concentrations of the various gases taking part. Thus if we put c_A, c_B ... etc. instead of the corresponding pressures in (64), we obtain

$$\frac{(c_Q)^q (c_R)^r \dots}{(c_A)^a (c_B)^b} = K_c, \quad \text{.....................(66)}$$

K_c is the equilibrium constant of the reaction in terms of the equilibrium concentrations of the gases.

The relation between K_c and K_p is easily obtained. Since $pv = RT$ for 1 mol of each gas, if we put $c = 1/v$ (*i.e.* reckon the concentration as the number of mols of gas in unit volume), we get $p = RT \,.\, c$. Replacing each partial pressure in equation (64) by $RT \,.\, c$, we get

$$\frac{(c_Q)^q (c_R)^r \ldots \times (RT)^{q+r \cdots}}{(c_A)^a (c_B)^b \ldots \times (RT)^{a+b \cdots}} = K_p.$$

Thus $$K_c \times \frac{(RT)^{q+r \cdots}}{(RT)^{a+b \cdots}} = K_p,$$

or $$K_c \,.\, (RT)^{q+r \cdots -a-b} = K_p,$$

which may be more concisely written

$$K_p = K_c (RT)^n, \qquad \ldots\ldots\ldots\ldots\ldots\ldots\ldots (67)$$

where $$n = q + r \ldots - a - b \ldots,$$

i.e. the total number of mols of resultants minus the total number of mols of reactants.

Taking logarithms of both sides of (67), we have

$$\log K_p = \log K_c + n \log (RT).$$

Thus for the reaction, $2H_2 + O_2 = 2H_2O(g)$,

$$n = 2 - 3 = -1,$$

so that $$K_p = K_c \,.\, (RT)^{-1}.$$

For the reaction,

$$2CO_2 = 2CO + O_2, \quad n = 3 - 2 = 1$$

so that $$K_p = K_c \,.\, (RT).$$

For the reaction, $H_2 + Cl_2 = 2HCl$, $n = 0$, and $K_p = K_c$. Thus when $n = 0$, *i.e.* when the number of mols of resultants is equal to the number of mols of reactants,

$$K_p = K_c.$$

In this case there is no change in volume when the reaction occurs at constant pressure.

Effect of Change of Pressure on a Gaseous Reaction. If we have a mixture of gases in equilibrium with each other at a certain temperature and increase the total pressure (by decreasing the volume of the system) the equilibrium constant, of course, remains unchanged. But the relative proportions of reactants and resultants may be altered. Thus if we increase the total pressure from P to xP, the partial pressures of all the constituents are momentarily increased in the same proportion. The partial pressure term on the left of (58) becomes

$$\frac{(xp_Q)^q(xp_R)^r \text{ etc.}}{(xp_A)^a(xp_B)^b \text{ etc.}} = K_p \cdot x^{q+r \cdots -a-b}.$$

It is obvious that if $(q+r \ldots -a-b \ldots)=0$, *i.e.* if the total number of mols of resultants is equal to the total number of mols of reactants, this is still equal to K_p, and the mixture is still in equilibrium. But if

$$(q+r \ldots -a-b-\text{etc.}) > 0,$$

the term on the left is greater than the equilibrium constant, and to restore equilibrium the partial pressures of the resultants must decrease and those of the reactants increase. Conversely, if $(q+r \ldots -a-b \ldots) < 0$, the term on the left is smaller than K_p and to restore equilibrium the reverse change must occur.

Thus we see that if the reaction occurs without change of volume, an increase of pressure has no effect on the relative amounts of reactants and resultants. If the reaction occurs with an increase of volume, at constant pressure, an increase of pressure causes the formation of the reactants at the expense of the resultants and *vice versa*. In general, *an increase of pressure favours the state with the smallest volume.* This is in accordance with the Le Chatelier principle, which states that when a constraint is applied to a system, a change will occur, if possible, which will tend to annul the constraint.

The Gibbs-Helmholtz Equation. In Chapter II (p. 47) we obtained the expression

$$q = T \frac{dW}{dT}$$

for a reversible cycle of operations, in which an amount of heat q is absorbed at temperature T, and dW is the work obtained in the cycle of operations when the difference of temperature between the two isothermal stages is dT. We have evaluated dW/dT for a number of cases in which the work terms of the various stages resulted from changes of volume of the system in certain changes of state. We will now consider the case in which the pressure remains constant throughout the cycle.

Thus we may have a cycle of operations in which (1) a reaction (not necessarily a gas reaction) occurs at constant pressure p at a temperature T, (2) the resultants are cooled at pressure p to temperature $T - dT$, (3) the reaction occurs in the reverse direction at the same pressure at $T - dT$, and (4) the reactants are heated to T again at pressure p.

Since the pressure remains constant throughout the cycle and the system at the end is in the same state as at the beginning, the sum of the terms $p\,\Delta v$ due to changes of volume must be zero. The total work obtained in the cycle is therefore the difference between the *net work* w' obtained in the first stage and the *net work* done when the reaction is reversed in the third stage at the lower temperature $T - dT$. If the net work of the reaction (in the forward direction) at $T - dT$ be $w' - dw'$, the total work obtained in the cycle is

$$w' - (w' - dw') = dw'.$$

Thus $$\frac{dW}{dT}=\frac{dw'}{dT}.$$

Therefore for a constant pressure cycle,

$$q=T\frac{dw'}{dT},$$

but the heat absorbed in the reaction is

$$q=\Delta E+w,$$

also $w=w'+p\,\Delta v$ and $\Delta E+p\,\Delta v=\Delta H$,

so that we may write

$$\Delta H+w'=T\left(\frac{dw'}{dT}\right)_p, \qquad \text{.................(68)}$$

for the reactions at constant pressure. The suffix p indicates that dw'/dT is the variation of the net work of the reaction with the temperature under the proviso that the pressure remains constant. This is usually known as the Gibbs-Helmholtz equation.

Since the net work of a change is equal to the free energy decrease of the system, *i.e.* $w'=-\Delta F$, we may write (68) in the form

$$\Delta H-\Delta F=-T\left(\frac{d(\Delta F)}{dT}\right)_p. \qquad \text{............(69)}$$

The van't Hoff Isochore. For a homogeneous gas reaction in which reactants and resultants are at unit pressure, we have found (66) that

$$w'=RT\log K_p;$$

$$\therefore \frac{dw'}{dT}=R\log K_p+RT\frac{d(\log K_p)}{dT}.$$

Multiplying throughout by T, we find

$$T\frac{dw'}{dT}=RT\log K_p+RT^2\frac{d\log K_p}{dT}$$

$$=w'+RT^2\frac{d(\log K_p)}{dT}. \qquad \text{.................}(a)$$

But, according to the Gibbs-Helmholtz equation,

$$T\left(\frac{dw'}{dT}\right)_p = w' + \Delta H, \quad \text{.................(b)}$$

where ΔH is the heat absorbed in the reaction at constant pressure.

Hence, comparing (*a*) and (*b*), we find :

$$\frac{d \log K_p}{dT} = \frac{\Delta H}{RT^2}. \quad \text{....................(70)}$$

This equation is known as the van't Hoff Isochore.

Integration of the Isochore. If ΔH remains constant over a range of temperature we may integrate (70) as follows :

$$\log K_p = \int \frac{\Delta H}{RT^2} . dT = \frac{-\Delta H}{RT} + \text{const.} \quad \text{........(71)}$$

Thus so long as ΔH remains constant the relation between $\log K_p$ and $1/T$ is a linear one. Below are given the equilibrium constants of the reaction

$$SO_2 + 1/2 O_2 = SO_3(g),$$

as determined by Bodenstein and Pohl over a range of temperature.

TABLE VIII.

EQUILIBRIUM CONSTANTS, $K_p = p_{SO_3}/p_{SO_2} . p^{\frac{1}{2}}_{O_2}$.

$T°$ K.	K_p.	$\log_{10} K_p$.
801	31·3	1·496
852	13·8	1·141
900	5·54	0·816
953	3·24	0·510
1000	1·86	0·268
1062	0·96	– 0·020
1105	0·68	– 0·202
1170	0·36	– 0·446

In Fig. 27 the values of $\log_{10} K_p$ are plotted against $1/T$. A nearly linear curve is obtained. The slope of this curve at a given point is equal to $-\Delta H/2{\cdot}303R$ and ΔH may be found by measuring it. (See p. 60 for the same operation with vapour pressure curves.)

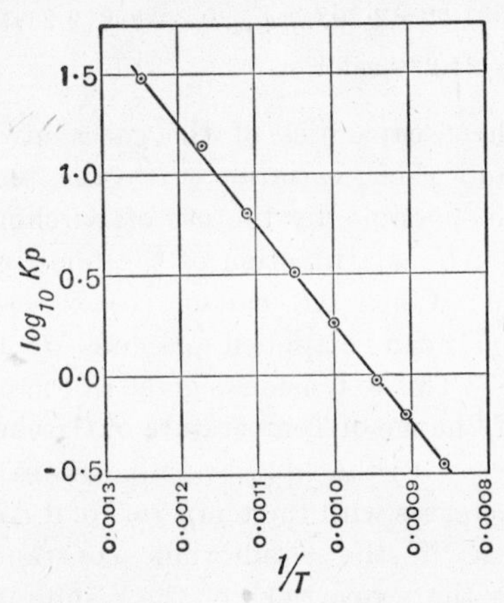

FIG. 27.—Effect of temperature on the equilibrium, $SO_2 + \frac{1}{2}O_2 = SO_3$.

If we integrate (71) between two temperatures T_1 and T_2, at which the equilibrium constants are K_p' and K_p'' respectively, we obtain

$$\log K_p' - \log K_p'' = -\frac{\Delta H}{R}\left(\frac{1}{T_1} - \frac{1}{T_2}\right), \quad \ldots\ldots(72)$$

so that, knowing the equilibrium constants at two temperatures, we may find the heat content change in the reaction.

Example. In the reaction between hydrogen and sulphur vapour to form hydrogen sulphide, viz.:

$$H_2 + 1/2S_2(g) = H_2S$$

the equilibrium constant, K_p, is 20·2 at 945° C. and 9·21 at 1065° C. Applying (72), we have

$$\log 20{\cdot}2 - \log 9{\cdot}21 = -\frac{\Delta H}{1{\cdot}99}\left(\frac{1}{1218} - \frac{1}{1338}\right).$$

Thus

$$\Delta H = -1{\cdot}99 \times 2{\cdot}303\,(\log_{10}20{\cdot}2 - \log_{10}9{\cdot}21)\left(\frac{1218 \times 1338}{120}\right)$$
$$= -21{,}230 \text{ calories.}$$

If the heat capacities of the gases involved in the reaction and their variation with the temperature is known, it is possible, by the use of Kirchoff's equation, to express ΔH as a function of the temperature over a wide range. When ΔH can be so expressed the integration in (71) can be applied to a much greater temperature range. This extension is given in Chapter XII.

Effect of Change of Temperature of Gaseous Equilibria. According to (70) the equilibrium constant of a gaseous reaction increases with the temperature if ΔH is positive. An increase in the equilibrium constant means an increase in the proportions of the resultants, so that if heat is absorbed in the reaction an increase in temperature favours the formation of the resultants. Conversely, if heat is evolved in the reaction an increase of temperature displaces the equilibrium in the direction of the reactants. This behaviour is again in accordance with the Le Chatelier principle, of which the van't Hoff isochore can be regarded as a particular quantitative expression.

Technically Important Gas Reactions. In order to illustrate the effect of changes of pressure and temperature on gaseous equilibria we shall discuss further some reactions of technical importance. In a technical process the aim is to produce the greatest possible yield of the desired product in a given time at the lowest cost. The thermodynamical equations which have been obtained make it possible to predict the effect of changes of pressure and temperature on the equilibrium state and the system, so that conditions can be chosen in which the equilibrium concentration of the desired product is most favourable. But in practice another factor has to be taken into account, *i.e.* the rate at which the reaction proceeds towards equilibrium. In general the rate of a reaction increases rapidly as the temperature rises. It may also be increased by the use of a suitable catalyst, and the most economical conditions are those in which the greatest amount of the product is obtained in a given time for the amount of catalyst available. Thus it may be more economical to choose conditions in which the equilibrium concentration of the product is less, if the loss is more than counterbalanced by an increase in the rate of the reaction.

(1) *The sulphuric acid contact process.* This depends on the reaction

$$SO_2 + 1/2O_2 = SO_3.$$

In this reaction there is a decrease in volume, so that an increase of pressure increases the equilibrium proportion of SO_3. The equilibrium constants are given on p. 100. Since K_p decreases with increasing temperature the proportion of SO_3 in the equilibrium mixture is greater the lower the temperature. At low temperatures even with a suitable catalyst the reaction becomes slow and the optimum temperature, at which the best yield is obtained in a given time, is about 450° C. This is shown by Knietsch's curves of the percentage proportions of sulphur trioxide formed at various temperatures (Fig. 28). At high temperatures (700-900° C.) the equilibrium proportion is very rapidly attained, but is low. At low temperatures (300-400°) the percentage of SO_3 in the equilibrium mixture is high, but equilibrium is only slowly reached. About 450° we get the highest conversion in the shortest time.

An increase of pressure would assist the reaction, but this is not conveniently carried out under the conditions. Since K_p decreases with rise of temperature, heat is evolved in the reaction and this is utilised in warming

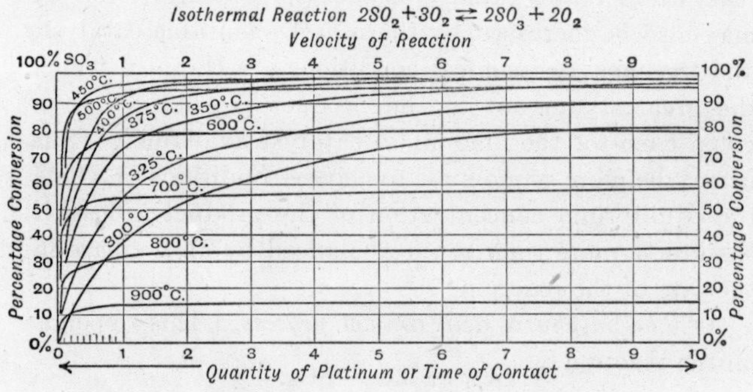

FIG. 28.—Effect of temperature on sulphur trioxide formation. (By permission of Messrs. Longmans, Green & Co.)

the reacting gas before it enters the catalyst chamber. The catalyst is usually a finely divided form of platinum on asbestos or some other basis.

(2) *The synthetic ammonia process.* The reaction

$$N_2 + 3H_2 = 2NH_3$$

is also accompanied by a decrease in volume so that an increase in pressure increases the proportion of ammonia in the equilibrium mixture. Heat is evolved in the reaction, so that the equilibrium constant (and the proportion of ammonia) diminishes as the temperature rises. At 1000° C. the proportion of ammonia formed is very small. The following table obtained by Haber gives the equilibrium percentages of ammonia at different temperatures and pressures.

TABLE IX.

Pressure (atmos.).	Equilibrium Percentage of Ammonia (by vol.).			
	550.	650.	750.	850° C.
1	0·077	0·032	0·016	0·009
100	6·7	3·02	1·54	0·874
200	11·9	5·71	2·99	1·68

Fig. 29 shows the values given by A. T. Larson (1924) of log K_p plotted against $1/T$ at a pressure of 300 atmo-

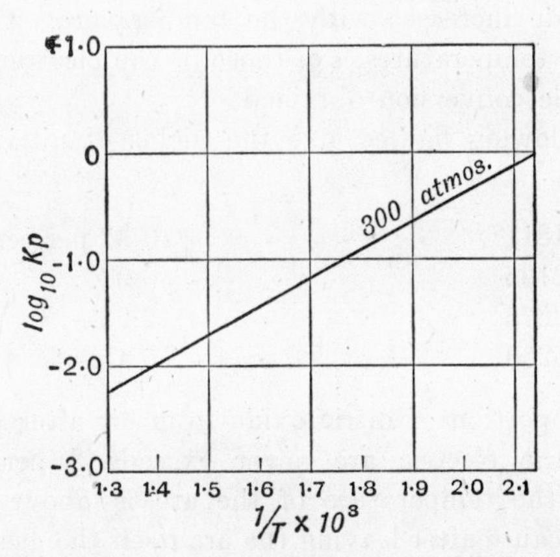

FIG. 29.—Effect of temperature on the ammonia equilibrium. (Larson.)

spheres. The variation of log K_p with $1/T$ is linear, as the isochore expression requires.

It is evident that the highest proportion of ammonia is obtained at a high pressure and at the lowest temperature consistent with a reasonable rate of reaction. In the Haber process a mixture of hydrogen and nitrogen is passed through a series of steel bombs containing the catalyst at 600° C. and 200 atmosphere pressure. After passing through each bomb the ammonia formed is removed by cooling the gas. In the Claude process still higher pressures of 900-1000 atmospheres are employed and a 20 per cent. conversion is obtained in a single operation.

(3) *Oxidation of atmosphere nitrogen:*

$$N_2 + O_2 = 2NO.$$

Heat is absorbed in this reaction, so that the yield of nitric oxide increases with the temperature. Only at very high temperatures, *e.g.* those of the electric arc, is appreciable conversion obtained.

The following figures give the yields of nitric oxide from air:

1811°	0·37 per cent.
2195	0·97.
2675	2·23.
3200	5 about.

The proportion of nitric oxide from air after passing through the electric arc never exceeds 2 per cent., although the temperature of the arc is above 3000°. This is because after leaving the arc itself the gases pass through regions of lower temperature, in which, however, the rate of attainment of equilibrium is still rapid, and the proportion of nitric oxide adjusts itself to the lower temperatures. The following figures show the times required for the half decomposition of pure nitric oxide at different temperatures:

627 - - - -	123 hours.
1027 - -	44 minutes.
1627 - - - -	1 second.
2027 - - - -	0·005 seconds.

At a temperature of 2000° the rate of decomposition of nitric oxide is still high. The aim of the process must therefore be to produce as high a temperature as possible (at least 3000°) and to cool the products with all possible speed below 1500° C. This is achieved in various nitrogen furnaces by blowing the gas rapidly through the arc. It is probable that the action of the arc is not simply a thermal one, but the reaction is influenced by the electric discharge.

(4) *Ammonia oxidation.* It can easily be shown that ammonia burns in oxygen, the products being nitric oxide and water:

$$4NH_3 + 5O_2 = 4NO + 6H_2O.$$

The equilibrium concentration of ammonia is vanishingly small at all temperatures between 500 and 1000° C. Ammonia should therefore be completely oxidised. The reaction is complicated in practice by the fact that if the mixture remains too long in the presence of the catalyst secondary reactions take place which reduce the yield of nitric oxide. The nitric oxide formed may react with the ammonia,

$$6NO + 4NH_3 = 5N_2 + 6H_2O,$$

and also at high temperatures the nitric oxide may split up into nitrogen and oxygen. As we have seen, the equilibrium concentration of NO in nitrogen and oxygen is only 2 per cent. at 2000° C. and 0·001 per cent. at 800° C. Consequently nitric oxide is really unstable at these temperatures and the rate of its decomposition may be great enough to cause appreciable loss. In practice, therefore, the mixture of gases is passed rapidly through platinum gauze stretched across the reaction vessels. The ammonia is oxidised almost instantaneously and the gases pass on quickly and are cooled to a lower temperature, so that the nitric oxide formed undergoes very little decomposition. Heat is evolved in this reaction, and while in one process (Frank and Caro) this gauze is electrically heated, in another (Kaiser) this is dispensed with; the gases are preheated to 300-400° and the heat evolved in the reaction is sufficient to keep the catalyst at the proper temperature.

(5) *Deacon chlorine process.* Hydrogen chloride is oxidised to chlorine by air when the mixture is passed over a suitable catalyst:

$$HCl + 1/4O_2 = 1/2H_2O + 1/2Cl_2.$$

Heat is evolved in this reaction and the equilibrium constant

$$K_p = \frac{p^{\frac{1}{2}}_{H_2O} \cdot p^{\frac{1}{2}}_{Cl_2}}{p^{\frac{1}{4}}_{O_2} \cdot p_{HCl}}$$

decreases as the temperature rises. The following are some figures:

TABLE X.

T (°C.).	*Kp*.	*T* (°C.).	*Kp*.
352	4·06	450	2·25
386	2·99	480	2·16
419	2·40	600	1·00

The greatest yield of chlorine is therefore obtained at the lowest temperature at which the catalyst is sufficiently efficient. The catalyst in this case is made by soaking bricks in cupric chloride and drying. The cupric chloride sublimes at about 500° C., which puts an upper limit to the permissible temperature.

(6) *The water gas reaction.* The reaction

$$CO + H_2O = CO_2 + H_2$$

is used industrially in the manufacture of hydrogen. Heat is evolved in this reaction and the equilibrium constant

$$K_p = \frac{p_{CO_2} \cdot p_{H_2}}{p_{CO} \cdot p_{H_2O}}$$

decreases as the temperature rises. The following table gives some values of $1/K_p$.

TABLE XI.

T (°C.).	$1/K_p$.*	T (°C.).	$1/K_p$.†
686	0·534	1255	2·68
786	0·840	1324	2·93
886	1·197	1495	3·83
1005	1·620	—	—

The proportion of hydrogen in the equilibrium mixture is the greater the lower the temperature. In order to reduce the amount of carbon monoxide in the gases after the reaction an excess of steam is used. The reaction is exothermic and with efficient heat regeneration little heat has to be supplied.

Further information on these technical processes may be found in *Thorpe's Dictionary of Applied Chemistry*, particularly in the articles "Sulphuric Acid" and "Nitrogen, Atmospheric, Utilization of."

* Hahn. † Haber and Richardt.

Heterogeneous Gas-solid Equilibria. Similar methods may be applied to the equilibrium of reactions involving both solids and gases. In order to use the van't Hoff equilibrium box with such reactions, it is supposed that the box contains the solids, together with the gases at their equilibrium pressures. Thus, for the reaction

$$CO_2 + C(s) = 2CO,$$

the equilibrium box will contain carbon and the two gases at pressures at which they are in equilibrium with it. It can easily be shown, by methods similar to those used above, that for equilibrium at a given temperature p_{CO}^2/p_{CO_2} is a constant. This ratio may therefore be taken as the equilibrium constant, *i.e.*

$$K_p = p_{CO}^2/p_{CO_2}.$$

The net work obtainable when carbon dioxide at unit pressure reacts at a temperature T with carbon to form carbon monoxide, also at unit pressure, can be shown to be

$$w' = -\Delta F = RT \log K_p ;$$

and the application of the Gibbs-Helmholtz equation gives

$$d \log K_p/dT = \Delta H/RT^2.$$

TABLE XII.

EQUILIBRIUM RATIOS AND CONSTANTS OF THE REACTION $C(\text{graphite}) + CO_2 = 2CO$.

$T°$ C.	%CO.	%CO_2.	K_p.
850	93·77	6·23	14·11
900	97·78	2·22	43·07
950	98·68	1·32	73·77
1000	99·41	0·59	167·5
1050	99·63	0·37	268·3
1100	99·85	0·15	664·7
1200	99·94	0·06	1665

Table XII. gives the equilibrium ratios of the concentrations of the two gases in contact with solid carbon (graphite) at various temperatures and at a total pressure of 1 atmosphere, as determined by Rhead and Wheeler.

This reaction is the basis of the manufacture of producer gas. When carbon dioxide is passed over hot coke or anthracite, it can be seen that a large yield of carbon monoxide is obtainable, if the time of contact is sufficient for equilibrium to be approached. The reaction results in an increase in volume and the yield of carbon monoxide is increased by decreasing the pressure. This is of no great practical importance, except in so far as it means that dilution of the gas mixture with an inert gas, such as nitrogen, does not decrease the proportion of CO obtained. The reaction is endothermic and the equilibrium constant is increased by raising the temperature. Heat has to be supplied in order to maintain the temperature. This is usually effected by carrying out the process intermittently. The temperature is raised by burning the coke in a stream of air until a sufficiently high temperature is reached, and a carbon dioxide rich gas is then passed until the temperature has become too low, when the temperature is raised again by passing more air.

There are many similar reactions of great industrial importance. The reduction of iron oxides in the blast-furnace is effected mainly by carbon monoxide. The important reactions are

$$(1)\ Fe_3O_4 + CO = 3FeO + CO_2, \quad K_1 = p_{CO_2}/p_{CO}.$$

$$(2)\ FeO + CO = Fe + CO_2, \quad K_2 = p_{CO_2}/p_{CO}.$$

The equilibrium proportions of the gases in these reactions have been determined and are shown in Fig. 30.

K_1 increases as the temperature rises and K_2 decreases. At about 500° the equilibrium proportions of CO and CO_2 are the same for reactions (1) and (2). At this point Fe_3O_4, FeO and Fe can exist in equilibrium with the same gas. At lower temperatures the Fe_3O_4 is reduced directly to Fe, for the proportion of carbon monoxide

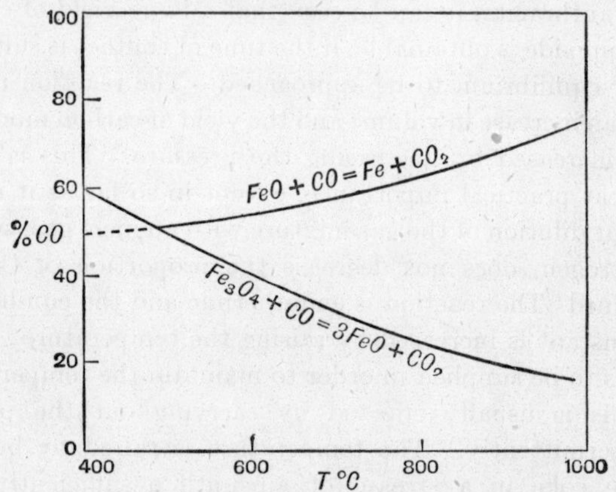

FIG. 30.—Reduction of iron oxides by carbon monoxide.

which is sufficient for the reaction (1) is more than is required for equilibrium in reaction (2).

The FeO will thus be reduced by the equilibrium gas of reaction. In the blast-furnace the matter is complicated by other reactions, such as $C + CO_2 = 2CO$, and by the solution of carbon in the iron.

Examples.

1. At 102° C. and a total pressure of 1 atmosphere, sulphuryl chloride is dissociated according to the equation

$$SO_2Cl_2 = Cl_2 + SO_2,$$

to the extent of 91·2%. Find (1) K_p, (2) the net work of the reaction at this temperature. ((1) 4·95 ; (2) 1190 cals.)

2. Using the data in Table VIII., find (1) the net work, (2) the maximum work of the reaction $SO_2 + \frac{1}{2}O_2 = SO_3$, at 1000° K. ((1) 1230 cals.; (2) 230 cals.)

3. A quantity of hydriodic acid was sealed up in a bulb and heated to 360° C. until equilibrium was attained. The fraction decomposed was found to be 0·197. Find the net work of the reaction $2HI(g) = H_2(g) + I_2(g)$ at this temperature. ($w' = -5300$ cals.)

4. The following are equilibrium constants, K_p, of the reaction $2H_2S = 2H_2 + S_2(g)$.

T° C.	K_p	T° C.	K_p
750	$0{\cdot}89 \times 10^{-4}$	1065	118×10^{-4}
830	$3{\cdot}8 \times 10^{-4}$	1132	260×10^{-4}
945	$24{\cdot}5 \times 10^{-4}$		

Plot log K_p against $1/T$ and find from the graph the heat content change of the reaction at 1000° C.

5. The degree of dissociation of hydrogen, $H_2 = 2H$, as determined by Langmuir, is $7{\cdot}5 \times 10^{-5}$ at 1500° C., $3{\cdot}3 \times 10^{-3}$ at 2000° C. Find the approximate heat of dissociation.

(120,000 cals.)

6. The following figures are given by Bodenstein for the reaction $2NO_2 = 2NO + O_2$.

T° K.	$\log_{10} K_p$	T° K.	$\log_{10} K_p$	T° K.	$\log_{10} K_p$
503·4	−4·078	627·5	−1·752	786·8	+0·214
519·5	−3·734	668·3	−1·164	796·3	+0·298
564·0	−2·844	685·0	−0·927	825·3	+0·570
593·1	−2·268	731·1	−0·379		

Plot log K_p against $1/T$ and find the heat content change in the reaction at 600° K.

7. The equilibrium constants of the reaction, $Br_2(g) = 2Br(g)$ are 0·00328 at 1223° K. and 0·0182 at 1323°K. Find the approximate heat of dissociation of Br_2.

(57,000 cals.)

CHAPTER VI

THE GALVANIC CELL

Galvanic Cells. A galvanic cell is an arrangement in which a chemical reaction gives rise to an electric current. If a piece of copper and a piece of zinc are placed in an acid solution of copper sulphate, it is found, by connecting the two metals to a suitable electrometer, that the copper is at a higher electrical potential (*i.e.* more positive) than the zinc. Consequently if the copper and zinc are connected by a wire positive electricity flows from the former to the latter. At the same time a chemical reaction goes on. The zinc goes into solution, forming the zinc salt, while copper is deposited from the solution on to the copper. This arrangement has the essential features of the Daniell cell.

Faraday's " law of electrochemical equivalents " holds for galvanic action as well as for electrolytic decomposition produced by an external battery. Thus, in a galvanic cell, provided that secondary actions are excluded, or accounted for, (1) the amount of chemical action is proportional to the quantity of electricity produced, (2) the amounts of different substances liberated or dissolved by the same amount of electricity are proportional to their chemical equivalents.

The quantity of electricity required to produce one

equivalent of chemical action (*i.e.* a quantity of chemical action equivalent to the liberation of 1 gram of hydrogen from an acid) has been very carefully determined. It is known to be 96,494 coulombs. This quantity of electricity, known as the Faraday (**F**), is thus produced in the Daniell cell by the passage into solution of one equivalent of zinc and the deposition of one equivalent of copper. The reaction represented by

$$Zn + CuSO_{4(aq)} = ZnSO_{4(aq)} + Cu$$

is therefore accompanied by the production of two faradays of electricity, since the atomic weights of zinc and copper both contain two equivalents.

Measurement of the Electromotive Force. The electromotive force of a cell is defined as the potential difference between the poles when no current is flowing through the cell. When a current is flowing through a cell and through an external circuit, there is a fall of potential inside the cell owing to its internal resistance, and the fall of potential in the outside circuit is less than the potential difference between the poles at open circuit.

In fact if R be the resistance of the outside circuit, r the internal resistance of the cell and E its electromotive force, the current through the circuit is

$$C = \frac{\mathrm{E}}{R + r}.$$

The potential difference between the poles is now only $\mathrm{E}' = CR$, so that $\mathrm{E}'/\mathrm{E} = R/R + r$.

The electromotive force of a cell is usually measured by the Poggendorff compensation method, *i.e.* by balancing it against a known fall of potential between two points of an auxiliary circuit. If AB (Fig. 31) is a uniform wire connected at its ends with a cell M, we may find a point X at which the fall of potential from A to X balances the electromotive force of the cell N. Then there is no current through the loop ANX, for the potential difference between the points A and X, tending to cause a flow of electricity in the direction ANX, is just balanced by the electromotive force of N which acts in the opposite direction. The point of balance is observed by a galvanometer G, which indicates when no current is passing through ANX. By means of such an arrangement we may compare the electromotive force **E** of the cell N, with a known electromotive force **E**′ of a standard cell N'; if X' be the point of balance of the latter, we have

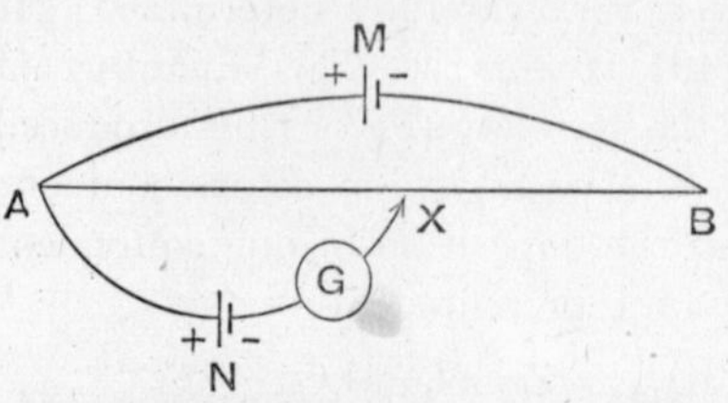

FIG. 31.—Poggendorff method of determining electromotive forces.

$$\frac{AX}{AX'} = \frac{\mathbf{E}}{\mathbf{E}'}.$$

The potentiometer is a slightly modified form of the Poggendorff principle. The slide wire is replaced by a number of coils of equal resistance and a slide wire whose resistance is equal to that of one of the coils. There is a further variable resistance, which is adjusted until the fall of potential down each coil has a definite value. In the commonest form of potentiometer, a lead accumulator (2 volts approx.) is used as the external electromotive force. The circuit consists of 17 or 18 coils of equal resistance, a slide wire calibrated so that 100 divisions are equal in resistance to a single coil (Fig. 32) and an adjustable resistance R which is varied until the fall of potential down each coil and down 100 divisions of the slide wire is 0·1 volt. Contacts are arranged so as to include in the circuit of the cell *N*, whose electromotive force is to be measured, any number of 0·1 volt coils and any fraction of the slide wire.

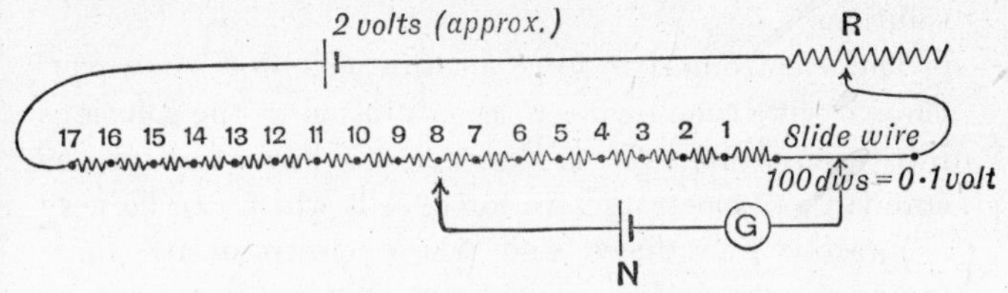

FIG. 32.—Diagram of potentiometer.

These contacts are adjusted until no current goes through the cell circuit, when the electromotive force of *N* may be read off directly in terms of the number of 0·1 volt coils and the fraction of the slide wire required to balance its electromotive force.

Standard Cells. The electromotive force of a galvanic cell is definite and reproducible only when each metal is in contact with a solution of one of its salts at a definite concentration. The electromotive force of the cell described in the first section of this chapter is indefinite because the zinc is not in contact with zinc salt at a definite concentration. If, however, we put the copper and the zinc in solutions of their salts of definite concentrations, and let the two solutions meet under conditions such that they do not diffuse into each other very rapidly, we get a cell of definite and, within narrow limits, reproducible electromotive force.

For practical purposes the two solutions are separated by a porous pot; for accurate measurements the two solutions (and electrodes) are contained in separate vessels, having side tubes by means of which the two liquids are put in contact in a suitable way. The cell may now be represented as :

$$Cu \mid CuSO_{4\,(aq.)} \;\vdots\; ZnSO_{4\,(aq.)} \mid Zn,$$

the dotted line representing the junction of the two solutions.

The electromotive force of this cell does, however, change with time owing to the diffusion of the solutions into each other. It is desirable to have for use, as standards of electromotive force, cells which can be very accurately reproduced and whose electromotive force remains constant for long periods. Several systems have been found which fulfil these conditions. We shall briefly describe two of them as examples of a type of cell having a very definite and reproducible electromotive force.

In the *Weston cell* the electrodes are pure mercury and a 12-13 per cent. amalgam of cadmium in mercury, respectively. Only one solution is used, a saturated solution of hydrated cadmium sulphate ($CdSO_4$, $8/3H_2O$). Saturation is ensured by the presence of crystals of this salt. The solution is also saturated with mercurous sulphate (Hg_2SO_4), crystals of which cover the mercury.

Thus the cell is

$$Hg \;\Big|\; \underset{(Saturated\ solution.)}{Hg_2SO_{4\,(s)},\ CdSO_4,\ 8/3H_2O_{(s)}} \;\Big|\; \text{Cd (12 per cent. in Hg).}$$

The mercury is the positive pole, the amalgam the negative pole. When the cell gives current, cadmium dissolves from the amalgam and mercury deposits on the mercury electrode according to the reaction

$$Cd_{(amalgam)} + Hg_2SO_4 = CdSO_4 + 2Hg.$$

However, since the solution is saturated with both Hg_2SO_4 and $CdSO_4$, $8/3H_2O$ and an excess of the solids is present, the result of removing some Hg_2SO_4 from the solution is that more of the solid salt dissolves and the concentration remains constant. Similarly when $CdSO_4$ is formed it crystallises out as $CdSO_4 . 8/3H_2O$. The reaction is therefore more accurately written

$$Cd_{(amal.)} + Hg_2SO_{4(s)} + 8/3H_2O = CdSO_4, 8/3H_2O_{(s)} + 2Hg_{(l)}.$$

The electromotive force **E** is 1·0183 volts at 20° C., and the temperature coefficient $d\mathrm{E}/dT = -0{\cdot}00004$ volts per degree.

A similar cell is the *Clark cell*, in which the cadmium amalgam is replaced by a 10 per cent. zinc amalgam, and the electrolyte is a saturated solution of $ZnSO_4 . 7H_2O$:

$$Hg \mid Hg_2SO_{4(s)}, ZnSO_4, 7H_2O_{(s)} \mid Zn \text{ (10 per cent. in Hg)}.$$
(*Saturated solution.*)

The electromotive force is 1·4324 volts at 15° C., with a temperature coefficient $d\mathrm{E}/dT = -0{\cdot}00119$ volts per degree. It is even more constant than the Weston cell, but it has a much higher temperature coefficient.

Electrical Energy. The electrical energy produced in a conducting circuit between two points *A* and *B* is the product of the quantity of electricity which passes through the conductor and the fall of electrical potential between *A* and *B*. The electrical energy produced in a galvanic cell is thus the product of the quantity of electricity and the electromotive force of the cell. If the quantity of electricity is measured in coulombs, and the electromotive force in volts, the energy is in volt-coulombs or joules (see p. 5). Thus for 1 equivalent of chemical action, 96494 coulombs are produced and the electrical energy obtained is

$$96494\mathrm{E} \text{ joules} = \frac{96494\mathrm{E}}{4{\cdot}182} \text{ calories}.$$

Example. The electromotive force of the Daniell cell is about 1·09 volts. For two equivalents of chemical action, *i.e.* for the solution of 65·4 grams of zinc and deposition of 63·6 grams of copper according to the equation

$$Zn + CuSO_{4(aq.)} = Cu + ZnSO_{4(aq.)};$$

the electrical energy obtained is

$$\frac{2 \times 96490 \times 1{\cdot}09}{4{\cdot}182} = 50{,}380 \text{ calories.}$$

Electrical Energy Obtained from a Reaction. It may now be asked, what is the relation between the electrical energy produced in a galvanic cell and the decrease in the energy content of the system as the result of the chemical reaction going on therein ? We shall only consider galvanic cells which work at constant (atmospheric) pressure. When a reaction occurs at constant pressure, without yielding any electrical energy, the heat evolved is equal to the decrease in the heat content of the system. In 1851 Kelvin made the first attempt to answer the question by assuming that in the galvanic cell the whole of the " heat of reaction " appeared as electrical energy, *i.e.* the electrical energy obtained is equal to the decrease in the heat content of the system. This was supported by measurements of the Daniell cell.

When the reaction

$$Zn + CuSO_{4(aq.)} = Cu + ZnSO_{4(aq.)}$$

is carried on in a calorimeter, an evolution of heat of 50,130 calories occurs, which agrees well with the value already obtained for the electrical energy yielded by the reaction.

This agreement, however, has proved to be a coincidence. In other reactions the electrical energy is sometimes less, sometimes greater than the decrease in heat content of the system. In the former case, the balance must appear as heat evolved in the working of the cell; in the latter case heat must be absorbed in the working of the cell to make up the difference. To maintain the Conservation of Energy, we must have:

$$\underset{\substack{\text{Electrical}\\\text{energy yielded}\\\text{by reaction.}}}{w'} = \underset{\substack{\text{Decrease in}\\\text{heat content}\\\text{of system.}}}{(-\Delta H)} + \underset{\substack{\text{Heat absorbed}\\\text{in the working}\\\text{of the cell.}}}{q.} \quad \text{.............(73)}$$

It is necessary, therefore, to determine q before the electrical energy yield can be found.

Application of the Gibbs-Helmholtz Equation. In the Poggendorff method of measuring electromotive force (Fig. 31) the electromotive force of the cell is balanced by an applied potential difference. If the applied potential difference is slightly decreased, the cell reaction will go forward and the cell will do electrical work against the applied potential difference. If it is slightly increased the reaction will occur in the reverse direction and work will be done by the external electromotive force on the cell. The reaction thus occurs *reversibly* in the cell when its electromotive force is balanced by an outside potential difference. Now when a reaction goes forward under these conditions, *i.e.* when the tendency of the reaction to go is just balanced by an external force, we know that the maximum work that the reaction can yield is obtained. In a reaction at constant pressure, work is necessarily done against the applied pressure if any volume change occurs and this work cannot be obtained as electrical energy. The electrical energy obtained under the conditions is therefore the *net work* of the reaction.

For z equivalents of chemical action, $z\mathbf{F}$ coulombs are produced. If $\mathbf{E}$ is the electromotive force of the cell, an applied potential difference **E** is required to balance it. The electrical work done when the reaction goes forward in a state of balance (or only infinitesimally removed from it) is thus $z\text{F} \,.\, \text{E}$, and this is equal to the net work of the reaction. Thus we have

$$w' = z\text{EF}. \qquad \text{.........................(74)}$$

It should be observed that w' is the electrical work done against the applied potential difference. If there is no opposing potential difference in the circuit, no work is done against an applied potential difference, the electrical energy $z\mathbf{EF}$ is dissipated in the circuit as heat.

Now according to the Gibbs-Helmholtz equation,

$$\Delta H + w' = T\left(\frac{dw'}{dT}\right)_p. \qquad \text{...........(68)}$$

Putting $w' = z\text{EF}$, and $dw'/dT = z\text{F} \cdot \dfrac{d\text{E}}{dT}$,

we get $$\Delta H + z\text{EF} = T \,.\, z\text{F} \,.\, \left(\frac{d\text{E}}{dT}\right)_p, \qquad \text{..........(74}\,a\text{)}$$

where $(d\text{E}/dT)_p$ is the temperature coefficient of the electromotive force (at constant pressure).

Comparing this equation with (73), we see that

$$T \,.\, z\text{F}\left(\frac{d\text{E}}{dT}\right)_p$$

corresponds with the heat absorbed in the working of the cell. Thus

$$\underset{\text{Heat absorbed in working of cell.}}{q} = \underset{\text{Electric work obtained.}}{w'} - \underset{\text{Decrease in heat content of system.}}{(-\Delta H)} = z\text{F} \,.\, T \,.\, \left(\frac{d\text{E}}{dT}\right)_p.$$

The sign of q thus depends on the sign of the temperature coefficient of the electromotive force.

(1) If $d\text{E}/dT$ is +ve, heat is absorbed in the working of the cell, *i.e.* the electrical energy obtained is

greater than the decrease in the heat content in the reaction.

$(w' - (-\Delta H)$ is positive.)

(2) If $d\text{E}/dT$ is $-$ve, heat is evolved in the working of the cell, *i.e.* the electrical energy obtained is less than the decrease in the heat content in the reaction.

$(w' - (-\Delta H)$ is negative.)

(3) If $d\text{E}/dT$ is zero, no heat is evolved in the working of the cell, *i.e.* the electrical energy obtained is equal to the decrease in the heat content in the reaction.

$(w' - (-\Delta H) = 0.)$

This is nearly the case with the Daniell cell.

Example. In the Clark cell the reaction

$$\text{Zn}(amalgam) + \text{Hg}_2\text{SO}_{4\,(s)} + 7\text{H}_2\text{O} = \text{ZnSO}_4 \,.\, 7\text{H}_2\text{O}_{(s)} + 2\text{Hg}_{(l)}$$

gives rise to two Faradays of electricity. The electrical energy obtained from the reaction is thus (data on p. 117):

$$z\text{EF} = \frac{2 \times 1{\cdot}4324 \times 96494}{4{\cdot}182} = 66100 \text{ calories.}$$

The heat absorbed in the working of the cell is

$$q = z\text{F}T\frac{d\text{E}}{dT} = -\frac{2 \times 96494 \times 288 \times 0{\cdot}00119}{4{\cdot}182}$$

$$= -15820 \text{ calories.}$$

Thus $\quad \Delta H = q - z\text{EF} = -81920$ calories.

Cohen calculated the heat of the reaction given from thermochemical data and obtained $\Delta H = -81127$ calories (at 18° C.) in good agreement with that calculated from the electrochemical data.

Origin of the Electromotive Force. We can now inquire how it comes about that certain reactions, when conducted in a galvanic cell, give rise to an electric current. In a typical cell, with two liquids, there are four junctions which may contribute to the electromotive force. Thus in the Daniell cell (Fig. 33) there are:

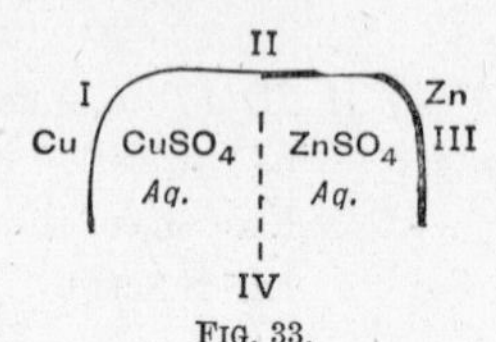

FIG. 33.

I. Junction of copper and copper sulphate solution.
II. Metal-metal junction between copper and zinc.
III. Junction of zinc and zinc sulphate solution.
IV. Junction of the two solutions.

Volta discovered in 1801 that if two insulated pieces of different metals are put in contact and then separated they acquire electric charges of opposite sign. Thus if the metals are zinc and copper, the zinc acquires a positive charge and the copper a negative charge. There is therefore a tendency for negative electricity to pass from the zinc to the copper. Volta believed that this tendency was mainly responsible for the production of the current in the galvanic cell. The solution served merely to separate the two metals and so eliminate the contact effect at the other end (Fig. 34).

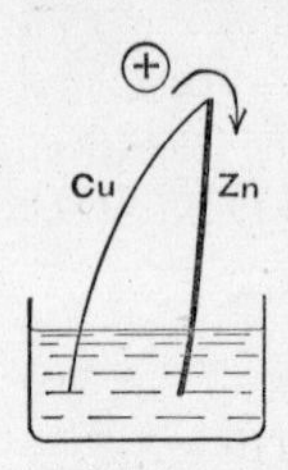

FIG. 34.

It soon became evident that the production of the current was intimately connected with the chemical actions occurring at the electrodes, and a "chemical theory" was formulated according to which the electrode processes were mainly responsible for the production of the current. Thus there arose a controversy which lasted, on and off, for a century.

On the one hand the chemical theory was strengthened,

(1) by Faraday's discovery of the equivalence of the current produced to the amount of chemical action in the cell, (2) by the relation between the electrical energy produced and the energy change in the chemical reaction, stated incompletely by Kelvin in 1851 and correctly by Helmholtz in 1882, and (3) by Nernst's theory of the metal electrode process which he put forward in 1889.

On the other hand, the "metal contact" theorists showed that potential differences of the same order of magnitude as the electromotive forces of the cells occur at the metal junctions. However, they fought a losing battle against steadily accumulating evidence on the "chemical" side. The advocates of the "chemical theory" ascribed these large contact potential differences to the chemical action of the gas atmosphere at the metal junction at the moment of separating the metals. They pointed out that no change occurred at the metal junction which could provide the electrical energy produced. Consequently for twenty years after 1890 little was heard of the metal junction as an important factor in the galvanic cell. Then (1912-1916) it was conclusively demonstrated by Richardson, Compton and Millikan, in their studies on photoelectric and thermionic phenomena, that considerable potential differences do occur at the junction of dissimilar metals. Butler, in 1924, appears to have been the first to show how the existence of a large metal junction potential difference can be completely reconciled with the "chemical" aspect.

Nernst's Theory of the Electrode Process. If we put a non-electrolyte like sugar into contact with water it goes into solution until equilibrium is reached, *i.e.* until the concentration of sugar in the solution is equal to its solubility. In the case of a metal dipping into a solution of one of its salts, the only equilibrium that is possible is that of *metal ions* between the two phases. For the solubility of the metal, as neutral metal atoms, is negligibly small. In the solution the salt is dissociated into positive ions of the metal and negative anions, *e.g.*

$$CuSO_4 = Cu^{++} + SO_4^{=},$$

and the electrical conductivity of metals shows that they are dissociated, at any rate to some extent, into metal ions and free electrons, thus :

$$Cu = Cu^{++} + 2\epsilon.$$

The positive metal ions are thus the only constituent of the system which is common to the two phases. The equilibrium of a metal and its salt solution therefore differs from an ordinary case of solubility in that only one constituent of the metal, the metal ions, can pass into solution.

Nernst, in 1889, supposed that the tendency of a substance to go into solution was measured by its *solution pressure* and its tendency to deposit from the solution by its osmotic pressure in the solution. Equilibrium was supposed to be reached when these opposing tendencies balanced each other, *i.e.* when the osmotic pressure in the solution was equal to the solution pressure.

In the case of a metal dipping into a solution containing its ions, the tendency of the metal ions to dissolve is thus determined by their solution pressure, which Nernst called the *electrolytic solution pressure*, P, of the metal. The tendency of the metal ions to deposit is measured by their osmotic pressure p.

Consider now what will happen when a metal is put in contact with a solution. We may distinguish the following cases :

(1) $P > p$. The electrolytic solution pressure of the metal is greater than the osmotic pressure of the ions, so that positive metal ions will pass into the solution. As a result the metal is left with a negative charge, while the solution becomes positively charged. There is thus set up across the interface an electric field which attracts positive ions towards the metal and tends to prevent any more passing into solution (Fig. 35a). The ions will continue to dissolve and therefore the electric field to increase in intensity until equilibrium is reached, *i.e.* until the inequality of P and p, which causes the solution to occur, is balanced by the electric field.

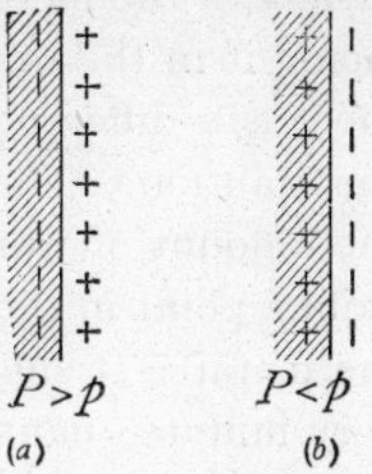

$P > p$ (a) $P < p$ (b)

FIG. 35.—Origin of the electrode potential difference.

(2) $P < p$. The osmotic pressure of the ions is now greater than the electrolytic solution pressure of the metal, so that the ions will be deposited on the surface of the latter. This gives the metal a positive charge, while the solution is left with a negative charge. The electric field so arising hinders the deposition of ions, and it will increase in intensity until it balances the inequality of P and p, which is the cause of the deposition (35b).

(3) $P = p$. The osmotic pressure of the ions is equal to the electrolytic solution pressure of the metal. The metal and the solution will be in equilibrium and no electric field arises at the interface.

When a metal and its solution are not initially in equilibrium, there is thus formed at the interface an *electrical double layer*, consisting of the charge on the surface of the metal and an equal charge of opposite sign facing it in the solution. By virtue of this double layer there is a difference of potential between the metal and the solution. The potential difference is measured by the amount of work done in taking unit positive charge from a point in the interior of the liquid to a point inside the metal. It should be observed that the passage of a very minute quantity of ions in the solution or *vice versa* is sufficient to give rise to the equilibrium potential difference.

Nernst calculated the potential difference required to bring about equilibrium between the metal and the solution in the following way. He determined the net work obtainable by the solution of metal ions by means of a three-stage expansion process in which the metal ions were withdrawn from the metal at the electrolytic solution pressure P, expanded isothermally to the osmotic pressure p and condensed at this pressure into the solution. The net work obtained in this process is

$$w' = RT \log P/p \text{ per mol.}$$

If V is the electrical potential of the metal with respect to the solution (V being positive when the metal is positive), the electrical work obtained when 1 mol of metal ions passes into solution is $zV\mathbf{F}$, where z is the number of unit charges carried by each ion. The total amount of work obtained in the passage of 1 mol of ions into solution is thus

$$RT \log P/p + zV\mathbf{F},$$

and for equilibrium this must be zero ; hence

$$V = -\frac{RT}{z\mathbf{F}} \log P/p.$$

Objection can be made to this calculation on the ground that the three-stage process which is employed does not correspond to anything which can really occur and is really analogous in form only to the common three-stage transfer. We will obtain a similar relation in a later section by a thermodynamical process to which this objection does not apply.

*** Kinetic Theories of the Electrode Process.** A more definite physical picture of the process at a metal electrode was given by Butler in 1924. According to current physical theories of the nature of metals, the valency electrons of a metal have considerable freedom of movement. The metal may be supposed to consist of a lattice structure of metal ions, together with free electrons either moving haphazard among them or arranged in an interpenetrating lattice. An ion in the surface layer of the metal is held in its position by the cohesive forces of the metal, and before it can escape from the surface it must perform work in overcoming these forces. Owing to their thermal agitation the surface ions are vibrating about their equilibrium positions, and occasionally an ion will receive sufficient energy to enable it to overcome the cohesive forces entirely and escape from the metal. On the other hand, the ions in the solution are held to the adjacent water molecules by the forces of hydration and in order that an ion may escape from its hydration sheath and become deposited on the metal, it must have sufficient energy to overcome the forces of hydration.

Fig. 36 is a diagrammatic representation of the potential energy of an ion at various distances from the surface of the metal. (This is not the *electrical* potential, but the potential energy of an ion due to the forces mentioned above.) The equilibrium position of an ion in the surface layer of the metal is represented by the position of minimum energy Q. As the ion is displaced towards the solution it does work against the cohesive forces of the metal and its potential energy rises while it loses kinetic energy. When it reaches the point S it comes within the range of the attractive forces of the solution. Thus all ions having sufficient kinetic energy to reach the point S will escape into the solution. If W_1 is the work done in reaching the point S, it is easily seen that only ions with kinetic energy W_1 can escape. The

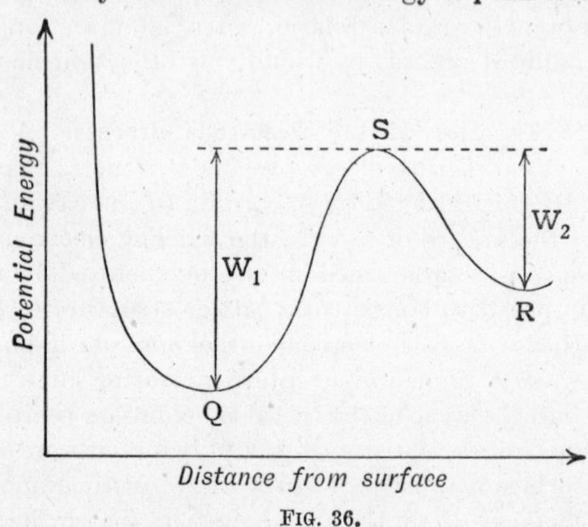

FIG. 36.

rate at which ions acquire this quantity of energy in the course of thermal agitation is given by classical kinetic theory as $\theta_1 = k'e^{-W_1/kT}$, and this represents the rate of solution of metal ions at an uncharged surface.

In the same way R represents the equilibrium position of a hydrated ion. Before it can escape from hydration sheath the ion must have sufficient kinetic energy to reach the point S, at which it comes into the region of the attractive forces of the metal.

If W_2 is the difference between the potential energy of an ion at R and at S, it follows that only those ions which have kinetic energy greater than W_2 can escape from their hydration sheaths. The rate of deposition will thus be proportional to their concentration (*i.e.* to the number near the metal) and to the rate at which these acquire sufficient kinetic energy. The rate of deposition can thus be expressed as $\theta_2 = k''ce^{-W_2/kT}$.

θ_1 and θ_2 are not necessarily equal. If they are unequal, a deposition or solution of ions will take place and an electrical potential difference between the metal and the solution will be set up, as in Nernst's theory. The quantities of work done by an ion in passing from Q to S or R to S are now increased by the work done on account of the electrical forces. If V' is the electrical potential difference between Q and S, and V'' that between S and R, so that the total electrical potential difference between Q and R is $V = V' + V''$, the total work done by an ion in passing from Q to S is $W_1 - zeV'$ and the total work done by an ion in passing from R to S is $W_2 + zeV''$, where z is the valency of the ion and e the unit electronic charge.* The rates of solution and deposition are thus

$$\theta_1 = k'e^{-(W_1 - zeV')/kT}; \quad \theta_2 = k''ce^{-(W_2 + zeV'')/kT}.$$

For equilibrium these must be equal, *i.e.*

$$k'e^{-(W_1 - zeV')/kT} = k''ce^{-(W_2 + zeV'')/kT},$$

or
$$V' + V'' = \frac{W_1 - W_2}{ze} + \frac{kT}{ze}\log c + \frac{kT}{ze}\log k''/k'.$$

If N_0 is the number of molecules in the gram-molecule, we may write

$$N_0(W_1 - W_2) = \Delta E, \quad N_0 e = \mathbf{F}, \quad N_0 k = R,$$

and we have then

$$V = \frac{\Delta E}{z\mathbf{F}} + \frac{RT}{z\mathbf{F}}\log c + \frac{RT}{z\mathbf{F}}\log k''/k'.$$

The final term contains some statistical constants which are not precisely evaluated, but it is evident that apart from this V depends mainly on ΔE, the difference of energy of the ions in the solution and in the metal.

Comparing with the Nernst expression we see that the solution pressure P is

$$\log P = \frac{\Delta E}{RT} + \log k''/k'.$$

* V' is the work done by *unit* charge in passing from S to Q; and V'' that done by unit charge in passing from R to S.

One of the difficulties of Nernst's theory, pointed out by Lehfeldt, was that the values of P required to account for the observed potential differences varied from enormously great to almost infinitely small values, to which it was difficult to ascribe any real physical meaning. This difficulty disappears when it is seen that P represents not merely a concentration difference, but includes a term representing the difference of energy of the ions in the two phases, which may be large.

Gurney and Fowler have investigated the electrode process using the methods of quantum mechanics. Their final equations are very similar to those given above.

The Metal-Metal Junction. We have seen that when two metals are put in contact there is a tendency for negative electricity, *i.e.* electrons, to pass from one to the other. We may say that metals have different *affinities* for electrons. Consequently at the point of junction electrons will tend to pass from the metal with the smaller to that with the greater affinity for electrons. Thus if the electron affinity of metal *II* is greater than that of metal *I* (Fig. 37), electrons will tend to pass from *I* to *II*. Thus metal *II* acquires an excess negative charge and metal *I* is left with a positive charge and a potential difference is set up at the interface which increases until it balances the tendency of electrons to pass from the one metal to the other. At this junction, as at the electrodes, the equilibrium potential difference is that which balances the tendency of the charged particle to move across the interface.

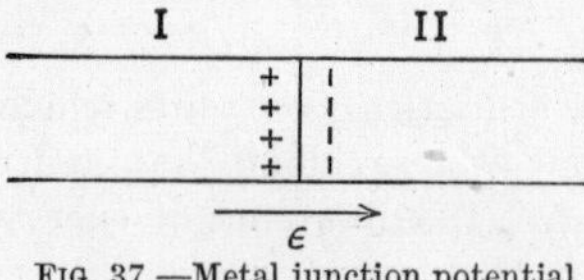

FIG. 37.—Metal junction potential difference.

By measurements of the photoelectric and thermionic effects, it has been found possible to measure the amount of energy required to remove electrons from a metal. This quantity is known as its *thermionic work function*, and is usually expressed in volts, as the potential difference through which the electrons would have to pass in order to acquire as much energy as is required to remove them from the metal. Thus if ϕ be the thermionic work function of a metal, the energy required to remove one electron from the metal is $e\phi$, where e is the electronic charge. The energy required to remove one equivalent of electrons (charge **F**) is thus $\phi\mathbf{F}$ or $\dfrac{96490\phi}{4{\cdot}182}$ calories. The thermionic work functions of a number of metals are given in the table below.

TABLE XIII

THE THERMIONIC WORK FUNCTIONS OF THE METALS.*

K	2·12 volts	Al	4·1 volts	Sn	4·38 volts
Na	2·29 ,,	Zn	3·57 ,,	Cu	4·16 ,,
Li	2·28 ,,	Pb	3·95 ,,	Ag	4·68 ,,
Ca	3·20 ,,	Cd	3·68 ,,	Pt	6·45 ,,
Mg	3·68 ,,	Fe	4·7 ,,		

The energy required to transfer an equivalent of electrons from one metal to another is evidently given by the difference between their thermionic work functions. Thus if ϕ_1 be the thermionic work function of metal *I*, ϕ_2 that of metal *II*, the energy required to transfer electrons from *I* to *II* per equivalent is (Fig. 38)

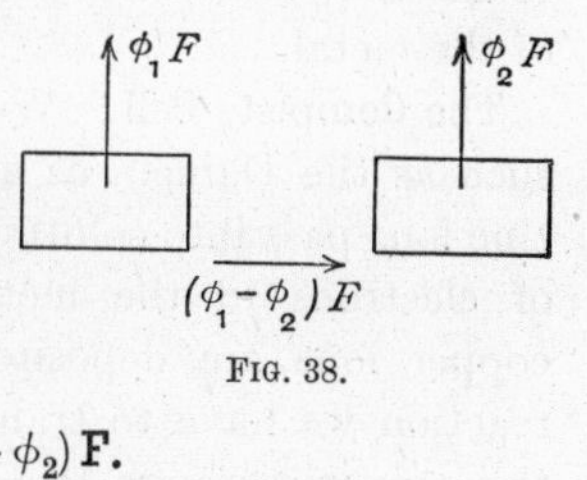

FIG. 38.

$$\Delta\mathbf{E} = (\phi_1 - \phi_2)\mathbf{F}.$$

* Collection of data by O. Klein and E. Lange, *Z. Electrochem.*, 43, 570, 1937.

The greater the thermionic work function of a metal, the greater is its affinity for electrons. Thus electrons tend to move from one metal to another in the direction in which energy is liberated. We have seen that this tendency is balanced by the setting up of a potential difference at the junction. When a current flows across a metal junction the energy required to carry the electrons over the potential difference is thus provided by the energy liberated in the transfer of electrons from the one metal to the other. The old difficulty that no apparent change occurred at the metal junction which could contribute to the electromotive force of a cell thus disappears.

It should be noted that the " thermionic work function " is really an energy change and not a reversible work quantity and is not therefore a precise measure of the affinity of a metal for electrons. When an electric current flows across a junction the difference between the energy liberated in the transfer of electrons and the electric work done in passing through the potential difference appears as heat liberated at the junction. This heat is a relatively small quantity, and the junction potential difference can be taken as approximately equal to the difference between the thermionic work functions of the metal.

The Complete Cell. We can now view a complete cell, such as the Daniell, as a whole. At the zinc electrode, zinc ions pass into solution leaving the equivalent charge of electrons in the metal. At the copper electrode, copper ions are deposited. In order to complete the reaction we have to transfer electrons from the zinc to the copper, through the external circuit. The external circuit is thus reduced to its simplest form if the zinc and copper are extended so as to meet at the metal junction.

Thus in the Daniell cell the reaction

$$Zn + Cu^{++}\ aq. = Zn^{++}\ aq. + Cu$$

occurs in parts, at the various junctions :

(1) Zinc electrode : $Zn = Zn^{++}_{(aq.)} + 2\epsilon_{(Zn)}$;
(2) Metal junction : $2\epsilon_{(Zn)} = 2\epsilon_{(Cu)}$;
(3) Copper electrode : $Cu^{++}_{(aq.)} + 2\epsilon_{(Cu)} = Cu$.

If the circuit is open, at each junction there arises a potential difference which just balances the tendency for that particular process to occur. When the circuit is closed there is an electromotive force in it equal to the sum of all the potential differences. Since each potential difference corresponds to the net work of one part of the reaction the whole electromotive force is equivalent to the net work or free energy decrease of the whole reaction.

Papers on the Mechanism of the Galvanic Cell. The earlier history is summarised in papers by Lodge, *B.A. Reports*, Montreal, 1884 ; *Phil. Mag.*, [5], 19, 1885 ; 49, 351, 1900.

Papers dealing with the measurement of the metal contact potential difference : Richardson and Compton, *Phil. Mag.*, 24, 592, 1912 : Millikan, *Phys. Rev.*, 7, 18, 1916 ; 18, 236, 1921 ; Hennings and Kadesch, *Phys. Rev.*, 8, 217, 1916.

On its rôle in the galvanic cell : Langmuir, *Trans. Amer. Electrochem. Soc.*, 29, 125, 1916 ; Butler, *Phil. Mag.*, 48, 927, 1924 ; Gurney and Fowler, *Proc. Roy. Soc.*, 136A, 378, 1932-

On the mechanism of the metal-solution potential difference : Nernst, *Z. physikal Chem.*, 4, 129, 1889 ; Butler, *Trans. Faraday Soc.*, 19, 729, 1924 ; Gurney and Fowler, *loc. cit.*

Examples.

1. Write down the reaction which occurs in the cell,

$$Cd \mid CdCl_2 \ (1{\cdot}006 \ M) \ ; \ AgCl(s) \mid Ag.$$

The electromotive force is 0·7123 volts at 20° C. (silver being the positive pole); find the net work of the reaction. (32,870 cals.)

2. The electromotive force of the cell,

$$Cu \mid CuSO_4 \ (0{\cdot}05 \ M), \ Hg_2SO_4(s) \mid Hg,$$

is 0·3928 volts at 25° C. (mercury positive). Write down the cell reaction and find the corresponding free energy change. (18,125 cals.)

3. The cell, Pb (0·72% amalgam) | $PbCl_2(s)$, $AgCl(s)$ | Ag,

has an electromotive force $E = 0{\cdot}4801$ volts at 16·7° C. The temperature coefficient is $dE/dT = -4{\cdot}0 \times 10^{-4}$ volts per degree. Find the heat content change in the cell reaction. ($\Delta H = -27{,}500$ cals.)

4. The cell, Cd (12·5% amalgam) | $CdI_2(1{\cdot}0 \ M)$, $Hg_2I_2(s)$ | Hg,

has the electromotive force $E = 0{\cdot}4309$ volts at 18° C. and $dE/dT = 4{\cdot}7 \times 10^{-4}$. Find (1) the free energy change in the reaction; (2) the heat absorbed in the reversible working of the cell; (3) the heat content change in the reaction.

($\Delta F = -19{,}880$ cals., $q = 6310$ cals., $\Delta H = -13{,}570$ cals.)

5. What cell would you employ to find the free energy change in the reaction,

$$Ag + HgCl(s) = Hg + AgCl(s) \ ?$$

If the electromotive force corresponding to this reaction is 0·0455 volts at 25° C., and the heat content change in the reaction is $\Delta H = 1275$ calories, find the amount of heat absorbed or evolved in the reversible working of the cell. Does this agree with the observation that the temperature coefficient of the cell is $dE/dT = 0{\cdot}000338$ volts per degree? ($q = 2325$ cals., from dE/dT, 2324 cals.)

CHAPTER VII

ELECTRODE POTENTIALS

Variation of the Potential Difference with Ion Concentration. Suppose that we have two pieces of a metal, for example, silver, dipping into solutions in which the metal ion concentrations are m_1 and m_2 respectively (Fig. 39).

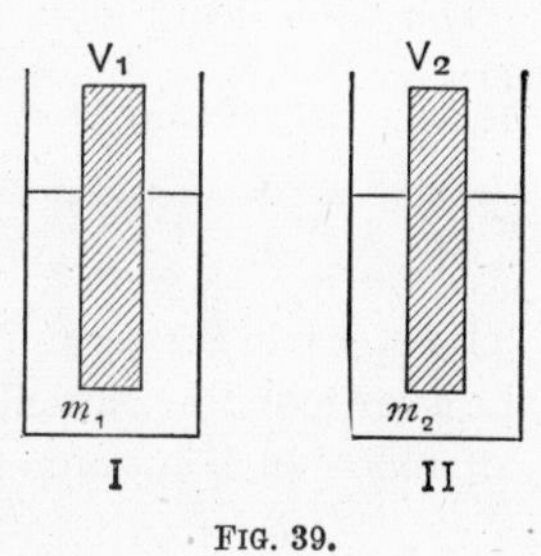

FIG. 39.

Let the equilibrium potential differences between the metal and the solutions be V_1 and V_2. We will suppose that the two solutions are at zero potential, so that the electrical potentials of the two pieces of metal are V_1 and V_2.

We may now carry out the following process:

(1) Cause 1 gram-atom of silver ions to pass into the solution from metal *I*. Since the equilibrium potential is established at the surface of the metal, the net work of this change is zero.

(2) Transfer the same amount (1 mol) of silver ions reversibly from solution *I* to solution *II*. The net work obtained is

$$w' = RT \log m_1/m_2,$$

provided that Henry's law is obeyed.

(3) Cause the gram-atom of silver ions to deposit on electrode *II*. Since the equilibrium potential is established, the net work of this change is zero.

(4) Finally, to complete the process transfer the equivalent quantity of electrons (charge, $-\mathbf{F}$) from electrode *I* to electrode *II*. The electrical work obtained in the transfer of charge $-\mathbf{F}$ from potential V_1 to potential V_2 is

$$-\mathbf{F}(V_1 - V_2).$$

The system is now in the same state as at the beginning (a certain amount of metallic silver has been moved from electrode *I* to electrode *II*, but a change of position is immaterial).

The total work obtained in the process is therefore zero, *i.e.*

$$-\mathbf{F}(V_1 - V_2) + RT \log m_1/m_2 = 0$$

or

$$V_1 - V_2 = \frac{RT}{\mathbf{F}} \log m_1/m_2. \quad \text{.............(75)}$$

If $m_2 = 1$ in the second solution and we put $V_2 = V_0$ for the corresponding potential difference (*i.e.* V_0 = potential difference in solution of unit concentration), we have

$$V_1 = V_0 + \frac{RT}{\mathbf{F}} \log m_1.$$

This holds for a metal giving univalent ions. In general for metal ions of valency z, each gram-atom of which is associated with $z\mathbf{F}$ units of electricity,

$$V_1 = V_0 + \frac{RT}{z\mathbf{F}} \log m_1. \quad \text{.............(75a)}$$

Converting to ordinary logarithms, we may write

$$\frac{RT}{z\mathbf{F}} \log m_1 = \frac{RT}{z\mathbf{F}} 2{\cdot}303 \log_{10} m_1.$$

The factor $2{\cdot}303\,\frac{RT}{\mathbf{F}}$ frequently occurs in electrochemical calculations and may be evaluated here.

$$\frac{2{\cdot}303RT}{\mathbf{F}}=\frac{2{\cdot}303\times1{\cdot}988\times298{\cdot}1\times4{\cdot}182}{96490}\text{ joules/coulombs}$$

$$=0{\cdot}0591\text{ volts at }25^\circ\text{ C.}$$

The factor may be taken as 0·058 at 18° C.

Concentration Cells with Liquid Junction. If the two solutions of Fig. 40 are put in contact we obtain a galvanic cell as :

$$\begin{array}{ccccccc} \text{Ag} & | & AgNO_3 & \vdots & AgNO_3 & | & \text{Ag} \\ & | & m_2 & \vdots & m_1 & | & \\ \longleftarrow & & & & & \longrightarrow & \\ V_2 & & & & & V_1 & \end{array}$$

If there is no potential difference at the liquid junction, the electromotive force of this cell is, by (78) :

$$\mathbf{E}=V_1-V_2=\frac{RT}{\mathbf{F}}\log m_1/m_2, \qquad \text{..........(76)}$$

if Henry's law holds good. If m_1 is greater than m_2, V_1 is greater than V_2, so that the electrode in the stronger solution forms the positive pole of the cell. Cells of this kind are called concentration cells with liquid junctions.

The liquid junction is a source of uncertainty. It is believed that the potential difference there is, at least partly, eliminated by interposing between the two solutions a concentrated solution of some salt which does react with them, *e.g.* potassium or ammonium nitrate. The following table, which gives some measurements made by Abegg and Cumming with this type of cell, shows that the observed electromotive forces are in fair agreement with the logarithmic equation at small concentrations.

SILVER CONCENTRATION CELLS.

$$\mathrm{Ag} \left| \begin{matrix} \mathrm{AgNO_3} \\ m_2 \end{matrix} \right. \vdots\ \mathrm{NH_4NO_3}\ \vdots \left. \begin{matrix} \mathrm{AgNO_3} \\ m_1 \end{matrix} \right| \mathrm{Ag.}$$

m_1	m_2	m_1/m_2*	$RT/\mathrm{F} \log m_1/m_2$	E obs.
0·1	0·01	10	0·058	0·0556
0·01	0·001	10	0·058	0·0579

Concentration cells have been employed to determine the solubilities of slightly soluble salts. Thus the solubility of silver chloride in a given chloride solution might be determined by making a concentration cell with two silver electrodes, one in a silver salt solution of known strength, the other in the solution saturated with silver chloride. Owing to the liquid junction and to deviations from Henry's law these measurements are only approximate.

Example. The electromotive force of the cell

$$\mathrm{Ag} \mid \mathrm{AgI}\,(s)\ \mathrm{KI},\ 0{\cdot}1\mathrm{N}\ \vdots\ \mathrm{AgNO_3}\ 0{\cdot}1\mathrm{N} \mid \mathrm{Ag}$$

is 0·814 volts at 20° C.

If the silver ion concentration on the left is x, we have approximately:

$$0{\cdot}814 = 0{\cdot}058 \log_{10} \frac{0{\cdot}1}{x}$$

or

$$\log_{10} \frac{0{\cdot}1}{x} = 14,$$

or

$$x = 0{\cdot}1 \times 10^{-14} = 10^{-15}.$$

Since the iodide ion concentration is 0·1, we have

$$(m)_{\mathrm{Ag}^+}(m)_{I^-} = 10^{-15} \,.\, 10^{-1} = 10^{-16}.$$

* No account is taken here of the possibly different degrees of dissociation of the silver nitrate solution. This question is dealt with later.

The Liquid Junction. In order to elucidate the influence of the liquid junction, we shall consider in more detail the nature of the process going on in the concentration cell.

We will consider the following cell :

$$\begin{array}{c|c:c|c} Ag & \begin{matrix} AgNO_3 \\ m_2 \\ II \end{matrix} & \begin{matrix} AgNO_3 \\ m_1 \\ I \end{matrix} & Ag \end{array}$$

$$\longrightarrow$$

If m_1 is greater than m_2, the electrode on the right is positive, and when the circuit is closed positive electricity passes through the cell in the direction shown by the arrow. The following changes occur in the cell, for the passage of one faraday of electricity :

(1) 1 equivalent of silver ions deposits on to the electrode from solution *I*, while 1 equivalent of silver ions dissolves from the electrode into solution *II*.

(2) The current is carried through the solution by the movement of the positive and negative ions. Let n_a be the transport number of the anion $n_k = 1 - n_a$, that of the cation. We will assume that the transport number is independent of the concentration. Then in the transport of the current through the solution a fraction n_a of the current is carried by the anions, $(1 - n_a)$ by the cations.

Thus in the electrolytic transport of the current, $(1 - n_a)$ equivalents of silver ions migrate from *II* to *I*, while n_a equivalents of nitrate ions migrate from *I* to *II*.

Thus, summing up the changes in the amounts of the ions in the two solutions, we have:

Solution *I*.	Solution *II*.
Ag^+ ions;	
-1 equivt. (deposited)	$+1$ equivt. dissolved
$+(1-n_a)$ equivts. (received from *II*)	$-(1-n_a)$ equivts. (migrate to *I*)
Total,	
$-n_a$ equivts.	$+n_a$ equivts.
NO^-_3 ions;	
$-n_a$ equivts. (migrate to *II*)	$+n_a$ equivts. (received from *I*)

The total effect of the working of the cell is thus the transfer of n_a equivalents of silver ions and n_a equivalents of nitrate ions from *I* to *II* and the only change in the working of the cell is thus the transfer of electrolyte from the stronger to the weaker solution. This is a process which occurs spontaneously; here in the concentration cell we have a mechanism through which the spontaneous change yields work.

If the ions obey Henry's law, the net work to be obtained in the transfer of n_a equivalents of silver ions and n_a equivalents of nitrate ions from concentration m_1 to concentration m_2 is

$$w' = 2n_a \,.\, RT \log m_1/m_2.$$

Equating this with the electrical work obtained in the same change in the cell, we have

$$\mathrm{EF} = 2n_a \,.\, RT \log m_1/m_2$$

or
$$\mathbf{E} = 2n_a \cdot \frac{RT}{\mathbf{F}} \log m_1/m_2.$$

In the previous section, taking the electrode processes only into account, we found

$$\mathbf{E} = \frac{RT}{\mathbf{F}} \log m_1/m_2;$$

thus the liquid junction potential difference, which is equal to the difference between these two expressions, is

$$\mathbf{E}_l = (2n_a - 1) \frac{RT}{\mathbf{F}} \log m_1/m_2. \quad \text{..........(77)}$$

Thus taking the transport number of the nitrate ion in dilute silver nitrate solution as 0·528, we have

$$\mathbf{E}_l = 0{\cdot}056 \times 0{\cdot}058 = 0{\cdot}0032 \text{ volts,}$$

when $m_1/m_2 = 10$. The potential difference is taken in the same direction as the electromotive force of the cell, *i.e.* the sign of $\mathbf{E}_l$ is that of solution *I*.

Objection can be made to this calculation on the grounds that the process at the liquid junction is not strictly reversible. The maximum (and net) work is only obtained when the process is strictly reversible at every stage. When we are considering the transfer of substance from one phase to another in contact with it, the condition of reversibility is fulfilled when the two phases are in equilibrium, *e.g.* when the tendency of ions to go into solution is balanced by the equilibrium potential difference. At the junction of two solutions of different concentrations equilibrium is not established and the irreversible process of diffusion from the stronger to the weaker solution goes on and is superimposed on the reversible changes which we have considered. The calculation of the liquid junction potential difference given above, though it probably leads to a result of the right order, is therefore not thermodynamically sound. Attempts have been made to amend it by taking account of the variation of transport numbers with concentration, but it should be accepted that the phenomenon is one to which thermodynamic methods are not strictly applicable and which is properly dealt with by kinetic methods.

From the kinetic point of view the origin of the potential difference can be described as follows. If the transport number of the anion is greater than 0·5, the mobility of the anions is greater than that of the cations. The anions therefore tend to diffuse more rapidly than the cations from the stronger to the weaker solution. Thus they tend to leave the cations behind, so that an electric separation occurs, the front of the diffusing layer, containing an excess of anions, becoming negatively charged and the rear with an excess of cations, positively charged.

The rate of diffusion of the cations is increased on account of the attractive force exerted by the negative charge in front of them, while the anions are retarded by the attraction of the positive charge behind. The electric separation and the potential difference it gives rise to will continue to increase until the rates of diffusion of the anions and cations are equalised by the electric forces. Then the electrolyte can diffuse without any further separation of the ions. It should be observed that if $n_a > n_k$ the negative side of the electrical double layer is that towards the more dilute solution and *vice versa.*

It has been found that while the potential difference at the junction of two solutions of the same electrolyte is easily reproduced, and remains constant with time if simple precautions are taken, that at the junction of two different solutions varies with time and depends on the method of making the junction. Reproducible and constant potential differences can, however, be obtained by continually renewing the junction. Lamb and Larson* have described a simple "flowing junction," by means of which very constant values are obtained. The

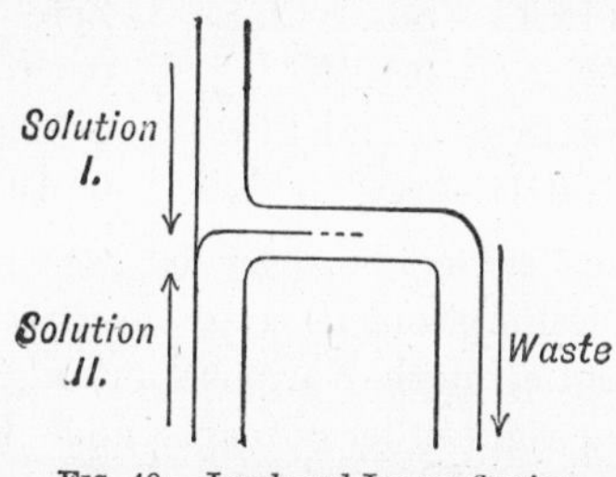

FIG. 40.—Lamb and Larson flowing junction.

two solutions from reservoirs connected with their respective electrodes meet at a T-junction (the heavier solution being below), and flow away through the third tube (Fig. 40). In this way the liquid junction is constantly renewed.

Roberts and Fenwick† have described a device in which the two solutions flow on to the two sides of a piece of mica, in which there is a small hole, where the constantly renewed contact of the two solutions occurs.

Expressions for the liquid junction potential differences of two unlike solutions have been given by Planck,

* *J. Amer. Chem. Soc.*, 42, 229, 1920.

† *Ibid.*, 49, 2787, 1927; cf. Lakhani, *J. Chem. Soc.*, p. 179, 1932.

Henderson, Lewis and Sargent and others,* but no entirely satisfactory formulation has been found. Some representative experimental values are given below (the solution given first is negative).

0·1*N*HCl	– 0·1*N*KCl	0·0270 volt.
0·1*N*HCl	– 1*N*KCl	0·0076
0·1*N*HCl	– *Sat.* KCl	Zero
*N*HCl	– 0·1*N*KCl	0·0592
*N*HCl	– *Sat.* KCl	Zero
0·1*N*NaCl	– 0·1*N*KCl	0·005
0·2*N*KBr	– 0·2*N*KCl	0·0004
0·2*N*NaOH	– 0·2*N*NaCl	0·019

These values cannot be regarded as certain as they are based on assumptions as to the precise values of the electrode potentials in the various solutions, but they are probably of the right order of magnitude. It can be seen that there is a large potential difference between equally concentrated solutions of HCl and KCl, which is due to the greater mobility of the hydrogen ion, but this disappears when the concentration of potassium chloride is increased. For this reason a saturated solution of KCl is often interposed between the two halves of a cell when it is desired to eliminate the liquid junction potential difference. There is some doubt as to whether it is always completely effective.

Standard Electrodes. The variation of the potential difference of an electrode with the nature of the solution in contact with it is usually observed by combining the electrode with another which is kept constant. It is

* Planck, *Annalen Physik,* 40, 561, 1891; Henderson, *Z. physikal Chem.*, 59, 118, 1907; 63, 325, 1908; Lewis and Sargent, *J. Amer. Chem. Soc.*, 31, 363, 1909.

convenient to use for this purpose standard electrodes, which can be easily reproduced and remain constant indefinitely. The potential differences of solid metals are much influenced by strains and it is no easy matter to prepare strainless electrodes which give exactly reproducible potential differences. For this reason mercury is usually employed for standard electrodes.

In order that the concentration of mercury ions in the electrolyte may remain constant, the mercury is covered with a slightly soluble salt. Thus the calomel electrode consists of mercury covered with solid mercurous chloride in a solution of potassium chloride of suitable strength. When normal (N), decinormal ($N/10$) and saturated potassium chloride solutions are used, we get respectively the "normal," "decinormal" and "saturated" calomel electrodes. Similar electrodes are obtained with mercurous sulphate in sulphuric acid solutions and mercurous oxide in alkaline hydroxide solutions.

Standard Potentials. If we combine a silver electrode in silver nitrate solution with a decinormal calomel electrode we get the cell:

$$\mathrm{Hg.} \;\Big|\; \mathrm{HgCl}_{(s)} \,,\; \underset{N/10}{\mathrm{KCl}} \;\vdots\; \underset{m_1}{\mathrm{AgNO_3}} \;\underset{V}{\Big|}\; \mathrm{Ag}$$

The electromotive force of this cell differs from the silver electrode potential difference by the sum of (1) the liquid junction potential difference, (2) the calomel electrode potential difference, and (3) the metal junction potential difference, Hg – Ag.

The first can be eliminated or its calculated value subtracted. We are left with an electromotive force **E** which differs from the electrode potential V by a constant amount. **E** can be regarded as the electrode potential of the silver electrode measured against the decinormal calomel electrode. Thus (75*a*) becomes

$$\mathbf{E} = \mathbf{E}^\circ + \frac{RT}{z\mathrm{F}} \log m, \quad\quad (78)$$

where $\mathbf{E}^\circ$ differs from V_0 by the same amount as **E** from V.

Equation (75) was obtained by making use of the equation

$$w' = RT \log m_1/m_2$$

for the net work of transfer of metal ions from concentration m_1 to concentration m_2. This is true only at small concentrations, when Henry's law is obeyed. We shall find at a later stage that solutions of electrolytes deviate considerably from this law in all but extremely dilute solutions. Consequently the variation of **E** with concentration given by equation (78) holds exactly only at very small concentrations. If we know the value of **E** at given values of m we may calculate by (78) the corresponding values of $\mathbf{E}^\circ$. If (78) held good exactly the value of $\mathbf{E}^\circ$ so obtained would be the same at all concentrations. Owing to deviations only the very dilute solutions give a constant value for $\mathbf{E}^\circ$. The limiting value of $\mathbf{E}^\circ$ as the concentration approaches zero is known as the *standard electrode potential.*

Putting the matter in another way, $\mathbf{E}^\circ$ according to (78) is the electrode potential, measured against the normal calomel electrode, in a solution of unit concentration ($m = 1$). However, since a solution of that strength deviates considerably from the limiting law, we prefer to calculate $\mathbf{E}^\circ$ from the values of **E** in very dilute solutions. We shall describe later a method of dealing with the deviations in the stronger solutions.

The Hydrogen Electrode. If a platinum electrode * is immersed in an aqueous solution and a stream of hydrogen is bubbled over it, it acquires a definite potential difference which depends on the pressure of the hydrogen and the concentration of hydrogen ions in the solution. It behaves, in fact, as a hydrogen electrode.

The process by which the potential difference is set up may be pictured as follows. A molecule of hydrogen may give up to the platinum two electrons, thus forming two hydrogen ions which go into solution :

$$H_2 \rightarrow 2H^+ + 2\epsilon_{(Pt)}.$$

A potential difference is thus set up which increases until the tendency of hydrogen to yield hydrogen ions in the solution is balanced.

The dependence of the potential difference on the pressure of the hydrogen and the concentration of hydrogen ions may be found by a process similar to that employed with metal electrodes.

Suppose that we have two hydrogen electrodes in which the pressure of the hydrogen gas is the same, dipping into solutions in which the concentrations of hydrogen ions are m_1 and m_2. It can easily be shown by the method used on p. 135 that if Henry's law is obeyed, *i.e.* if the net work of transfer of hydrogen ions from the one solution to the other is given by

$$w' = RT \log m_1/m_2,$$

the difference between V_1 and V_2 (the equilibrium potential differences at the two electrodes) is

$$V_1 - V_2 = \frac{RT}{\mathbf{F}} \log m_1/m_2. \quad \text{..........(79)}$$

* The platinum is usually platinised or coated with finely divided platinum, at which the equilibrium potential difference is more readily established.

In this case the pressure of the hydrogen gas may also vary, and it can be shown by similar methods that if the two electrodes are in contact with solutions of the same hydrogen ion concentration, but the hydrogen gas pressures are p_1 and p_2, the difference between V_1 and V_2 is

$$V_1 - V_2 = \frac{RT}{2\mathrm{F}} \log p_2/p_1.$$

(The factor 2 appears because 2 faradays are required to ionise 1 mol of H_2.) Thus if V_2 has the value V_0 when $m_2 = 1$ and $p_2 = 1$, we have

$$V_1 = V_0 + \frac{RT}{\mathrm{F}} \log m_1 - \frac{RT}{2\mathrm{F}} \log p_1 \quad \text{.............} (80)$$

If the pressure of the hydrogen gas is kept constant at the standard pressure of 760 mm. mercury, which is taken as the unit pressure, the variation of V with the hydrogen ion concentration is thus represented by

$$V_1 = V_0 + \frac{RT}{\mathrm{F}} \log m_1 \quad \text{...................} (81)$$

Measurements of the potential difference at the hydrogen electrode may be made, as before, by combining it with a standard electrode. Thus using the decinormal calomel electrode we might set up the cell :

$$\mathrm{Hg} \mid \mathrm{HgCl}_{(s)}, \mathrm{KCl}\ \mathrm{N}/10 \ \vdots\ \mathrm{HCl}(m) \mid \mathrm{H}_2.$$

If we subtract the liquid junction potential difference from the electromotive force of this cell, we are left with a value **E** which may be regarded as the hydrogen potential relative to the decinormal calomel electrode. Thus (81) becomes

$$\mathbf{E} = \mathbf{E}^\circ + \frac{RT}{\mathrm{F}} \log m.$$

Owing to the fact that considerable deviations from Raoult's law occur at moderate concentrations, **E**° is calculated from the corresponding values of **E** and m

in very dilute solutions. The limiting value of $E°$ so obtained, as the concentration approaches zero, is taken as the standard hydrogen electrode potential relative to the decinormal calomel electrode. The value obtained is $E° = -0{\cdot}3341$ volts at 25°.

A hydrogen electrode which has this potential relative to the decinormal calomel electrode is known as the *standard hydrogen electrode.* Owing to the deviations from Henry's law the solution does not necessarily contain unit concentration (molal) of hydrogen ions. Actually a hydrogen electrode in a solution of hydrochloric acid of approximately $m = 1{\cdot}35$ molal exhibits the standard electrode potential.

Standard Hydrogen Scale of Electrode Potentials. So far we have obtained standard electrode potentials relative to the decinormal calomel electrode. While it is convenient to take an electrode of this type as a standard in experimental work, it is necessary to have an ultimate standard to which all results can be referred. The standard which has been chosen for this purpose is the standard hydrogen electrode, as defined above.

Since the standard hydrogen electrode potential is $-0{\cdot}3341$ volts relative to the decinormal calomel electrode, conversely the potential of the latter is $+0{\cdot}3341$ relative to the standard hydrogen electrode and this is its value on the standard hydrogen scale. Therefore if we add 0·3341 volts to the electrode potentials which have been measured against the decinormal calomel electrode, we obtain the corresponding values on the standard hydrogen scale.

The following table gives the electrode potentials of some common standard electrodes on the standard hydrogen scale.

TABLE XIV.

Potentials of Standard Electrodes on Standard Hydrogen Scale.*

	$E_h(18°)$	$E_h(25°)$	dE_h/dT
Hg | Hg_2Cl_2, KCl, N	+0·2833	+0·2816	-24×10^{-5}
Hg | Hg_2Cl_2, KCl, N | KCl, N/10		+0·2812†	
Hg | Hg_2Cl_2, KCl, N/10	+0·3346	+0·3341	-7×10^{-5}
Hg | Hg_2Cl_2, KCl (sat.)	+0·249	+0·244	-76×10^{-5}
Hg | Hg_2SO_4, H_2SO_4 $m=0·1$		+0·668	
Hg | HgO, NaOH $m=0·1$		+0·034	

When the electrode potential is represented by a positive number on the standard hydrogen scale, the electrode is more positive than the standard hydrogen electrode, *i.e.* when the electrode is combined with the standard hydrogen electrode it forms the positive pole of the cell; and *vice versa*. Thus the potential of a copper electrode in a 0·05M solution of copper sulphate on the standard hydrogen scale is +0·2865 volts. This means that a cell made up of a standard hydrogen electrode and the copper electrode, viz.:

Standard hydrogen electrode	$CuSO_4$ 0·05M	Cu,

has an electromotive force of 0·2865 volts, the copper being the positive pole.‡

* The standard hydrogen potential is taken as zero at all temperatures.

† This is the potential of the normal calomel electrode together with the liquid junction potential difference between normal and tenth normal KCl.

‡ The liquid junction potential difference, if any, being allowed for.

The opposite convention as to the sign of electrode potentials is in common use by American physical chemists. These have adopted the custom of expressing the potential difference at an electrode as that of the solution with respect to the metal. Thus if the solution is more negative than the metal, the potential difference is expressed by a negative number. Electrode potentials on the hydrogen scale on this system have their sign reversed. Although there are certain advantages in this usage (thus, metals like sodium, which exhibit a great tendency to yield positive ions in solution and are commonly called electropositive metals, have positive electrode potentials), it introduces complications in ordinary electrochemical practice. As Gibbs pointed out, all that we can measure is the difference of potential of two pieces of metal, and it seems better to make use of the system which states the potentials of the metals with respect to the solutions.

The standard electrode potentials of the metals, etc., on the standard hydrogen scale may be distinguished by the symbol $\mathbf{E}_h^\circ$. Those which are known with accuracy are given in the table below.

TABLE XV.

STANDARD ELECTRODE POTENTIALS OF THE METALS $\mathbf{E}_h^\circ$ (25°).

Electrode	E_h°	Electrode	E_h°
Li, Li^+	−2·959	Tl, Tl^+	−0·336
Rb, Rb^+	−2·926	Sn, Sn^{++}	−0·136
K, K^+	−2·924	Pb, Pb^{++}	−0·12
Na, Na^+	−2·715	Pt, H_2, H^+	0·000
Zn, Zn^{++}	−0·762	Cu, Cu^{++}	0·345
Fe, Fe^{++}	−0·44	Hg, Hg_2^{++}	0·799
Cd, Cd^{++}	−0·402	Ag, Ag^+	0·798

It should be observed that an electrode potential on the hydrogen scale is not to be interpreted as a *potential difference*. It is the sum of three potential differences, viz.: (1) the hydrogen electrode potential difference,

(2) the metal electrode potential difference, (3) the metal junction potential difference between the metal and the platinum (or other noble metal) of the hydrogen electrode.

Examples. The equation

$$\mathbf{E} = \mathbf{E}^\circ + \frac{RT}{z\mathbf{F}} \log m$$

only holds exactly for very small values of m. Nevertheless it may be used to calculate the approximate value of **E** for any given value of m, with sufficient precision for most electrochemical calculations.

(*a*) What is the potential of a zinc electrode in a zinc chloride solution of $m = 0{\cdot}1$, as measured against the decinormal calomel electrode? The potential of this electrode on the standard hydrogen scale is

$$\begin{aligned}\mathbf{E}_h &= -0{\cdot}762 + 0{\cdot}029 \log_{10}(0{\cdot}1) \\ &= -0{\cdot}791 \text{ volts (approx.).}\end{aligned}$$

Since the decinormal calomel electrode is 0·335 volts more positive than the standard hydrogen electrode,

$$\mathbf{E}_{\text{cal.}} = \mathbf{E}_h - 0{\cdot}335.$$

Therefore $\mathbf{E}_{\text{cal.}} = -0{\cdot}791 - 0{\cdot}335 = -1{\cdot}126$ volts.

(*b*) If a piece of copper is put in a solution of silver nitrate, silver is deposited according to the equation

$$Cu + 2AgNO_3 = Cu(NO_3)_2 + 2Ag.$$

When equilibrium is reached the concentrations of copper and silver ions in the solution must be such that the electrode potentials of the two metals are the same. Otherwise the silver and copper in contact will form a galvanic cell and copper will continue to go into solution and silver to deposit until the electromotive force of the combination is zero.

The standard electrode potentials (standard hydrogen scale) of silver and copper are $+0{\cdot}799$ and $+0{\cdot}345$, so that their electrode potentials (at 18° C.) are

$$\mathbf{E}_{(Ag)} = +0{\cdot}799 + 0{\cdot}058 \log_{10}(m)_{Ag^+},$$

$$\mathbf{E}_{(Cu)} = +0{\cdot}345 + \frac{0{\cdot}058}{2} \log_{10}(m)_{Cu^{++}}$$

For equilibrium, $\quad E_{(Ag)} = E_{(Cu)}$,

or $\quad +0{\cdot}799 + 0{\cdot}058 \log_{10}(m)_{Ag^+} = +0{\cdot}345 + \frac{0{\cdot}058}{2} \log_{10}(m)_{Cu^{++}}$

or $\quad \log_{10} \frac{(m)_{Ag^+}}{\sqrt{(m)_{Cu^{++}}}} = -\frac{0{\cdot}454}{0{\cdot}058} = -7{\cdot}8$ approx.

The concentration of copper ions is evidently much greater than that of silver ions in the final solution.

Thus if $(m)_{Ag^+} = 1$ in the original solution, the concentration of copper ions after the reaction is practically $(m)_{Cu^{++}} = \frac{1}{2}$ (since two silver ions give place to one copper ion). Thus

$$(m)_{Ag^+} = \sqrt{0{\cdot}5} \times 10^{-7{\cdot}8}.$$

Hydrogen Ion Concentrations. Hydrogen electrodes are much used for determining hydrogen ion concentrations in aqueous solutions. If we take the standard hydrogen potential as zero, the hydrogen electrode potential in a solution of hydrogen ions of concentration $(m)_{H^+}$ is $0{\cdot}058 \log(m)_{H^+}$ at 18°.* The potential of the hydrogen electrode is usually measured by combining it with a standard electrode such as the normal calomel. The potential of this electrode on the standard hydrogen scale is $+0{\cdot}283$ volts at 18° C. Thus, the electromotive force of the combination

$$\mathrm{Hg} \mid \mathrm{Hg_2Cl_2}\ \mathrm{KCl}\ N/1 \mid \mathrm{H^+},\ (m)_{H^+} \mid \mathrm{H_2}$$

$$\overleftarrow{\quad} \qquad\qquad\qquad \overrightarrow{\quad}$$

$$0{\cdot}283 \qquad\qquad\qquad 0{\cdot}058 \log(m)_{H^+}$$

is $\quad E = 0{\cdot}058 \log_{10}(m)_{H^+} - 0{\cdot}283$,

or $\quad E + 0{\cdot}283 = 0{\cdot}058 \log_{10}(m)_{H^+}$.

The quantity $-\log_{10}(m)_{H^+}$ is usually known as the p_H value of the solution. Thus we have

$$E + 0{\cdot}283 = -0{\cdot}058 p_H.$$

* The potential is strictly $0{\cdot}058 \log a_{H^+}$, where a_{H^+} is the activity of hydrogen ions and the p_H is $-\log_{10} a_{H^+}$.

When another standard electrode is used, the appropriate value of the standard electrode potential (Table XIV) is of course employed. The liquid junction potential between the two solutions has been neglected here and it is desirable that it should be made as small as possible, either by choosing as the standard electrode one which has a solution similar to that under investigation (*e.g.* with alkaline solutions it is desirable to use an alkaline standard) or by interposing a suitable solution between the two cell solutions. Thus a " bridge " of saturated potassium chloride is often placed between the two solutions for this purpose.

Example. The potential of a hydrogen electrode in a solution containing acetic acid and sodium acetate, as measured against the normal calomel electrode, is

$$\mathbf{E} = -0{\cdot}516 \text{ volts.}$$

The potential of the hydrogen electrode on the standard hydrogen scale is

$$\mathbf{E}_h = -0{\cdot}516 + 0{\cdot}283 = -0{\cdot}233,$$

and $$\mathbf{E}_h = -0{\cdot}058 p_H \ ; \quad \therefore \ p_H = 4{\cdot}0.$$

We shall see later that there are other types of electrodes which depend in a similar way on the hydrogen ion concentration of the solution, and can be used to determine hydrogen ion concentrations.

Hydrogen electrodes of the kind described above cannot be used in solutions containing powerful oxidising agents, such as chromates, as these tend to set up an " oxidation potential " which interferes with the hydrogen potential. In many solutions of this kind the *glass electrode* has been found suitable. It depends on the fact, first discovered by Haber and Klemensiewicz, that the potential difference between a glass surface and an aqueous solution varies regularly with the p_H of the solution. The experimental arrangement is a small glass bulb A (Fig. 41), in the side of which a cup B with extremely thin walls (*ca*. 10^{-3} mm.) is blown. The bulb A is filled with a buffer solution of known p_H or sometimes with a potassium chloride solution and the cup B contains the solution of unknown p_H. The potential difference between the two solutions is measured by the two

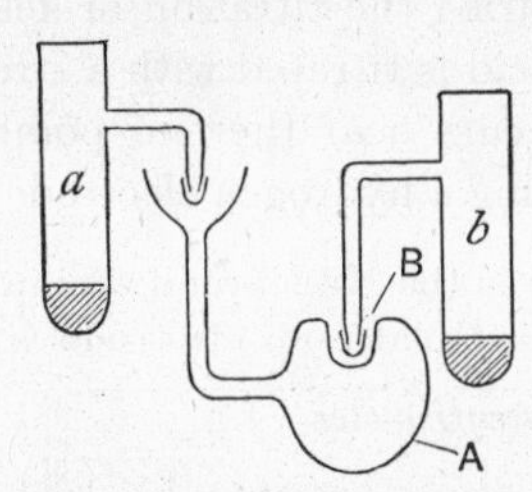

FIG. 41.—The glass electrode.

calomel electrodes a and b having tubes which dip into the two liquids. These tubes are fitted with caps which prevent the diffusion of the electrode solutions into the liquids. The resistance of the glass wall is very high and it is necessary to use an electrostatic instrument such as a Lindemann electrometer, or a valve electrometer, to measure the potential difference between a and b.

The potential difference between the two calomels is

$$V_{AB} = k + 0{\cdot}058\{(p_H)_A - (p_H)_B\}.$$

The quantity k, which is the potential difference across the glass when the solutions on the two sides are the same, remains approximately constant for each bulb, and can be determined from time to time by putting the same solution into A and B. The origin of the potential difference at the surface of the glass is not completely understood, but it probably depends on the adsorption of hydrogen ions by the glass, which gives rise to an "adsorption potential" which is proportional to the p_H of the solution. The glass electrode is very suitable for determining the p_H of biological solutions when only small quantities of liquid are available.

Potentiometric titrations. One of the most important applications of the hydrogen electrode is for following the changes of p_H during the titration of acids with alkalis. When a strong acid is titrated with a strong base a large change of p_H occurs near the end point, which can be observed by having a hydrogen electrode in the solution.

A suitable type is the Hildebrand dipping electrode (Fig. 42). The platinised platinum electrode is fixed in a tube,

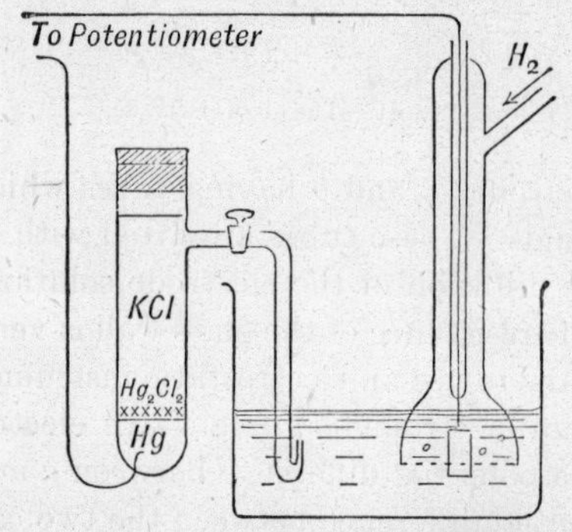

FIG. 42.—Arrangement for potentiometric titrations.

the open end of which dips into the solution, in such a position that it is partly in the solution and partly in the gas. The hydrogen enters at the upper part of the tube and escapes through small holes at the lower end. The potential is observed by coupling this with a suitable standard and the electromotive force of the whole combination is followed by a potentiometric arrangement.

Typical titration curves of dilute solutions (*ca*. $N/10$) of hydrochloric and acetic acids are shown in Fig. 43. In the case of the former the p_H remains close to unity until the neutralisation is nearly complete. Close to the

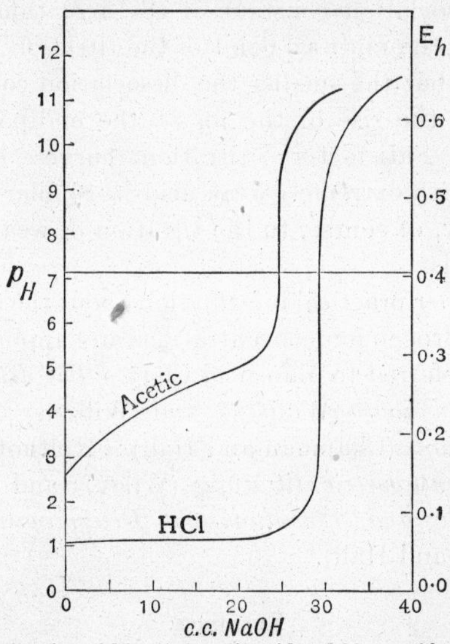

FIG. 43.—Titration of 25 c.c. of acetic acid and 30 c.c. of hydrochloric acid, with alkali of equivalent strength. (After Furman.)

neutralisation point it rises very suddenly and a very small excess of alkali takes it to about $p_H = 11$. The rise of the curve is so sharp that the end-point can be detected electrometrically with considerable precision. In the case of acetic acid, the p_H of the original solution is about 3 and the value rises as alkali is added, the curve being determined by the equilibrium $HA = A^- + H^+$, of which the equilibrium constant

$$K_a = [H^+][A^-]/[HA] \text{ is } 1{\cdot}75 \times 10^{-5}.$$

In the half-neutralised solution the concentrations of undissociated acid molecules and of ions are nearly equal, so that

$$[H^+] = K_a \quad \text{or} \quad p_H = -\log_{10} K_a.$$

The dissociation constant of the acid thus fixes the position of the midway point of the titration curve, and it follows that the smaller the dissociation constant K_a, the less is the rise of the p_H at the end-point of the titration. Satisfactory titration curves cannot be obtained with extremely weak acids. Similar considerations apply, of course, to the titration of weak bases by strong acids.

For further practical information about the determination of hydrogen ion concentrations and applications the reader is referred to Mansfield Clark's *The determination of hydrogen ions* (Williams and Wilkins); Britton's *Hydrogen ions* (Chapman and Hall); Kolthoff and Furman's *Potentiometric titrations* (Wiley); and Kolthoff's *Colorimetric and Potentiometric Determination of* p_H (Chapman and Hall).

Examples.

1. The cell, Hg | HgCl, KCl 0·1N || $AgNO_3$ 0·1 M | Ag, has (after correcting for the liquid junction potential difference) the electromotive force E = 0·3985 at 25° C. (silver positive). Find the potential of the silver electrode on the standard hydrogen scale. ($\mathbf{E}_h = 0{\cdot}7326$.)

2. The electromotive force of the cell,

$$\text{Ag} \mid \text{AgCNS}(s),\ \text{KCNS } 0{\cdot}1\text{ M} \mid \text{AgNO}_3\ 0{\cdot}1\text{ M} \mid \text{Ag},$$

is 0·586 volts at 18° C. Neglecting the liquid junction potential difference, find the approximate silver ion concentration in the thiocyanate solution, and hence the solubility product of AgCNS. (*s.p.* = *ca*. $1{\cdot}0 \times 10^{-12}$.)

3. The electromotive force of the cell,

$$Ag \mid AgIO_3(s),\ KIO_3\ 0{\cdot}1\ M \mid AgNO_3\ 0{\cdot}1\ M \mid Ag,$$

is 0·302 volts at 25° C. Find the approximate solubility product of $AgIO_3$ at this temperature. (*s.p.*=*ca* . 10^{-7}.)

4. The electromotive force of the cell,

Normal calomel electrode	KCl sat.	Potassium hydrogen phthalate M/20	H_2 1 atmos.,

is – 0·5158 volts at 18° C. If the liquid junction potential differences be taken as contributing 0·0004 volts, find the p_H of the potassium hydrogen phthalate solution.

(p_H=3·99.)

5. A hydrogen electrode in a solution made by mixing 20 c.c. of N/1 hydrochloric acid and 20 c.c. of N/1 sodium acetate and diluting the mixture to 100 c.c., had the potential – 0·4898 volts at 18° C. measured against the decinormal calomel electrode. Neglecting the liquid junction, find the p_H in this solution. (p=2·67.)

6. If an excess of metallic zinc is added to a solution of ferrous sulphate (m = 1), find the approximate concentration of the ferrous ions when equilibrium is reached. (Table XV.) **(10^{-11}.)**

CHAPTER VIII

OXIDATION POTENTIALS

Oxidation Potentials. Metals of variable valency yield two or more ions corresponding to different stages of oxidation. Thus an atom of iron may lose two electrons forming a ferrous ion or three electrons forming a ferric ion :

$$Fe = Fe^{++} + 2\epsilon,$$

$$Fe = Fe^{+++} + 3\epsilon.$$

A ferric salt acts as an oxidising agent by virtue of the ability of the ferric ion to take up one electron, thereby being converted into the ferrous ion

$$Fe^{+++} + \epsilon = Fe^{++}.$$

Similarly, a ferrous salt may function as a reducing agent because the ferrous ion may lose one electron in the reverse change and so be converted into the ferric ion. In general the ions of the metals may function as oxidising or reducing agents if they are able to take up or to lose electrons, so forming ions of lower or higher valency.

When an inert electrode* is put in a solution containing both ferrous and ferric ions, a definite potential difference is set up between it and the solution. The process which gives rise to this potential difference may be described as follows.

* That is, an electrode of a noble metal such as platinum.

Ferric ions, by virtue of their oxidising properties, tend to take electrons from the metal, thereby being converted into ferrous ions. On the other hand ferrous ions, owing to their reducing properties, tend to give electrons to the metal, thus becoming ferric ions. If the tendency of ferric ions to take electrons from the metal is greater than that of the ferrous ions to give up electrons, the metal will evidently lose electrons and become positively charged, while, because ferric ions with three positive charges are being replaced by ferrous ions with two, the solution will become negative. A potential difference is thus set up, which increases until it balances the tendency of ferric ions to take electrons from the metal. Conversely, if the tendency of ferrous ions to give up electrons is greater than that of the ferric ions to take them from the electrode, the latter will acquire a negative charge, and the potential difference so arising will increase until it brings the process to a stop.*

It is evident that an increase in the ferric ion concentration of the solution must make the electrode more positive, while an increase in the ferrous ion concentration makes it more negative. It can easily be shown, by arguments similar to those used before, that the relation between the potential difference and the ion concentration is in each case a logarithmic one. Thus, if E be the electrode potential measured against a suitable standard, it is found that

$$\mathbf{E} = \mathbf{E}^\circ + \frac{RT}{\mathbf{F}} \log (m)_{Fe^{+++}} - \frac{RT}{\mathbf{F}} \log (m)_{Fe^{++}}$$

or

$$\mathbf{E} = \mathbf{E}^\circ + \frac{RT}{\mathbf{F}} \log \frac{(m)_{Fe^{+++}}}{(m)_{Fe^{++}}}. \qquad \text{(82)}$$

* For a more detailed account of this mechanism, see Butler, *Trans. Faraday Soc.*, **19**, 734, 1924.

The following table gives the measurements of Peters with solutions containing different proportions of ferric and ferrous salts. The first two columns give the percentage proportions of ferric and ferrous salts, the third the observed electrode potentials measured against the normal calomel electrode, and the fourth the value of E° calculated from (82).

TABLE XVI.

OXIDATION POTENTIALS.

Normal calomel electrode ⋮ Fe^{+++}, Fe^{++} | Pt.

Fe^{+++}.	Fe^{++}.	E obs. (calomel).	E° (calomel).
0·5	99·5	0·296	0·428
1	99	0·312	0·427
2	98	0·331	0·428
10	90	0·375	0·430
50	50	0·427	0·427
90	10	0·483	0·428
99	1	0·534	0·419

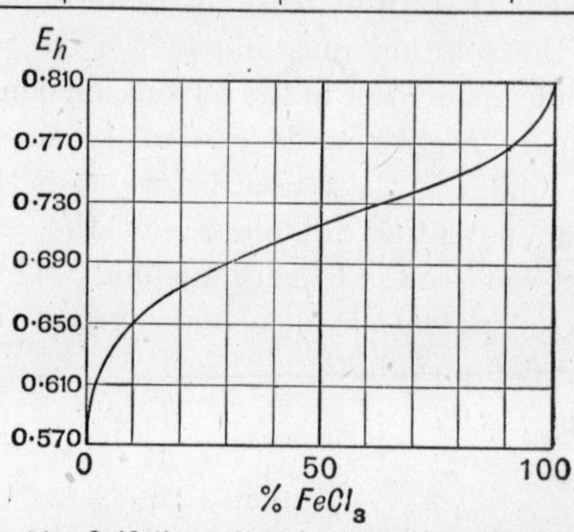

FIG. 44.—Oxidation potentials of ferrous-ferric mixtures.

If E is plotted against the percentage composition of the mixture, we get by (82) a bilogarithmic curve (Fig. 45).

E°, the standard electrode potential, is evidently equal to the value of E when $(m)_{Fe^{+++}} = (m)_{Fe^{++}}$, *i.e.* in the 50 per cent. mixture of ferric and ferrous ions.

If we add 0·282 to the value of E° measured against the normal calomel electrode, we obtain its value E°_h on the standard hydrogen scale. This corresponds to the electromotive force of the cell:

$$H_2(Pt) \mid H^+ \vdots \begin{matrix} Fe^{+++} \\ Fe^{++} \end{matrix} \mid Pt$$

under the standard conditions. The reaction

$$Fe^{+++} + \tfrac{1}{2}H_2 = H^+ + Fe^{++}$$

takes place when current is taken from this cell, and the electromotive force is a measure of its tendency to occur. The standard potential of the ferrous-ferric electrode can be regarded as a measure of the oxidising power of a solution containing ferric and ferrous ions in equal concentrations, taking the tendency of hydrogen to form hydrogen ions in the standard solution as zero.

If the charges of the two ions differ by z units, equation (85) becomes

$$E = E^\circ + \frac{RT}{zF} \log \frac{(m)_O}{(m)_R}, \quad \text{.................(83)}$$

where $(m)_O$ is the concentration of the ions in the higher and $(m)_R$ that of the ions in the lower state of oxidation. Thus in a solution of stannous and stannic ions the electrode reaction is

$$Sn^{++++} + 2\epsilon = Sn^{++},$$

and

$$E = E^\circ + \frac{RT}{2F} \log \frac{(m)_{Sn^{++++}}}{(m)_{Sn^{++}}}.$$

As in the previous cases the logarithmic formula only holds strictly for very small ion concentrations. Thus the standard electrode potential should be taken as the limiting value of $\mathbf{E}^\circ$ when the ion concentrations become very small. The standard electrode potentials of these oxidation reactions are not, however, known to a high degree of accuracy. The following table gives some values.

TABLE XVII.

STANDARD OXIDATION POTENTIALS (E_h°).

Cr^{++}	Cr^{+++}	$-0{\cdot}4$	Sn^{++}	Sn^{++++}	0·15
Ti^{+++}	Ti^{++++}	$-0{\cdot}37$	Tl^{+}	Tl^{+++}	1·21
$Fe(CN)_6^{\equiv\equiv}$	$Fe(CN)_6^{\equiv}$	$+0{\cdot}466$	Ce^{+++}	Ce^{++++}	1·44
Fe^{++}	Fe^{+++}	0·772	Co^{++}	Co^{+++}	1·82

Oxidation Potentials with Oxy-acid Ions. The elements of groups IV to VI of the periodic table frequently form oxy-acid ions which are easily reduced to lower states of oxidation and often give reversible oxidation potentials with their reduction products. Thus, the permanganate ion MnO_4^- is easily reduced to Mn^{++}, and if an inert electrode is put in a solution containing the two substances and reversible oxidation potential is set up.

The permanganate ion MnO_4^- can be regarded as a septivalent manganese ion, Mn^{+7}, which has taken up four oxygen ions :
$$Mn^{+7} + 4O^{=} = MnO_4^-.$$

In the reduction of permanganates to manganous ions the first step can be regarded as the dissociation of MnO_4^- into Mn^{+7} and $4O^{=}$. The oxygen ions combine with an equivalent quantity of hydrogen ions, forming water, while the Mn^{+7} ions may take up five electrons, being thereby reduced to Mn^{++} :

$$(1)\ MnO_4^- + 8H^+ = Mn^{+7} + 4H_2O,$$

$$(2)\ Mn^{+7} + 5\epsilon = Mn^{+2}\ ;$$

so that the whole reaction is :

$$(3)\ MnO_4^- + 8H^+ + 5\epsilon = Mn^{++} + 4H_2O.$$

The oxidation potential can be regarded as being due, primarily, to reaction (2). Thus we may put

$$\mathbf{E} = \mathbf{E}^{\circ\prime} + \frac{RT}{5\mathbf{F}} \log \frac{(m)_{Mn^{+7}}}{(m)_{Mn^{++}}}.$$

Applying the law of mass action to (1), we find that

$$\frac{(m)_{Mn^{+7}}}{(m)_{MnO_4^-}(m)^8_{H^+}} = K,$$

since the concentration of water may be taken as constant in dilute solutions,

whence $$\mathbf{E} = \mathbf{E}^{\circ} + \frac{RT}{5\mathbf{F}} \log \frac{(m)_{MnO'_4}(m)^8_{H^+}}{(m)_{Mn^{++}}},$$

where $$\mathbf{E}^{\circ} = \mathbf{E}^{\circ\prime} + \frac{RT}{5\mathbf{F}} \log K'$$

or $$\mathbf{E} = \mathbf{E}^{\circ} + \frac{RT}{5\mathbf{F}} \log \frac{(m)_{MnO_4^-}}{(m)_{Mn^{++}}} + \frac{RT}{\frac{5}{8}\mathbf{F}} \log (m)_{H^+}.$$

Other reactions of this type give rise to oxidation potentials which can be similarly formulated. Thus for the oxidation of a chromic salt to chromate :

$$Cr^{+++} + 4H_2O = CrO_4^{=} + 8H^+ + 3\epsilon,$$

we have $$\mathbf{E} = \mathbf{E}^{\circ} + \frac{RT}{3\mathbf{F}} \log \frac{(m)_{CrO_4^=}(m)^8_{H^+}}{(m)_{Cr^{+++}}}.$$

Solutions containing bromine and a bromate or iodine and an iodate also give reversible oxidation potentials. In the first case the reaction is :

$$\tfrac{1}{2}Br_2 + 3H_2O = BrO_3^- + 6H^+ + 5\epsilon,$$

and the corresponding equation for the electrode potential

$$\mathbf{E} = \mathbf{E}^{\circ} + \frac{RT}{5\mathbf{F}} \log \frac{(m)_{BrO_3^-}(m)^6_{H^+}}{(m)^{\frac{1}{2}}_{Br_2}}.$$

The standard electrode potentials of most processes of this kind are not known accurately. The following table gives some typical figures.

TABLE XVIII.

Electrode Reaction.	E_h°.
$V^{+++} + H_2O = VO^{++} + 2H^+ + \epsilon$	+0·4
$U^{++++} + 2H_2O = UO_2^{++} + 4H^+ + 2\epsilon$	0·41
$Mn^{++} + 4H_2O = MnO_4^- + 8H^+ + 5\epsilon$	1·5
$Cr^{+++} + 4H_2O = CrO_4^= + 8H^+ + 3\epsilon$	1·3
$\frac{1}{2}I_2 + 3H_2O = IO_3^- + 6H^+ + 5\epsilon$	1·20
$\frac{1}{2}Br_2 + 3H_2O = BrO_3^- + 6H^+ + 5\epsilon$	1·49

There are some oxidation-reduction processes which do not give rise to definite oxidation potentials. Thus, although the sulphite ion is readily oxidised to the sulphate ion :

$$SO_3^= + \tfrac{1}{2}O_2 = SO_4^=,$$

no definite electrode potential is obtained at an inert electrode in a solution containing sulphite and sulphate ions. In such a case the electrode potential is said to be inaccessible. It is evident that an oxidation-reduction process can only give rise to a reversible electrode potential when the oxidation and reduction take place primarily by the loss and gain of electrons. In these cases the essential process seems to be the gain and loss of oxygen atoms, and this cannot give rise to a potential difference at an electrode.

Electrodes with Elements Yielding Negative Ions. When chlorine gas is bubbled over an electrode of a noble metal in a chloride solution, a definite potential difference is set up, which is due to the tendency of chlorine molecules to take electrons from the metal forming chlorine ions, which pass into solutions :

$$Cl_2 + 2\epsilon = 2Cl^-_{(aq)}.$$

This process does not differ in any essential way from the oxidation potentials expressed above. It is easily shown that the variation of the electrode potential corresponding to this equation is

$$\mathbf{E} = \mathbf{E}^{\circ\prime} + \frac{RT}{2\mathbf{F}} \log(m)_{Cl_2} - \frac{RT}{\mathbf{F}} \log(m)_{Cl^-},$$

where $(m)_{Cl_2}$ is the concentration of chlorine and $(m)_{Cl^-}$ that of the chloride ion in the solution. For a constant value of $(m)_{Cl_2}$ the first two terms can be united, giving

$$\mathbf{E} = \mathbf{E}^{\circ} - \frac{RT}{\mathbf{F}} \log\,(m)_{Cl^-}.$$

It is more convenient to state the standard potential as that which corresponds to a chlorine gas pressure of 760 mm.

Similar electrode potentials are obtained with bromine and iodine, corresponding to the processes :

$$Br_2 + 2\epsilon = 2Br^-_{(aq)},$$
$$I_2 + 2\epsilon = 2I^-_{(aq)}.$$

In these cases the element is simply dissolved in the solution at a suitable concentration. The standard electrode potentials are stated for solutions saturated by the presence of liquid bromine and solid iodine. It should be observed that bromine and iodine form complex ions Br^-_3 and I^-_3 with bromine and iodide ions. Their electrode potentials depend on the concentrations of *free* bromide and iodide ions in the solution.

The standard electrode potentials on the standard hydrogen scale according to G. N. Lewis and his co-workers are :

(Pt) $Cl_{2(g)}$, Cl^-,	$\mathbf{E}_h{}^{\circ} = 1{\cdot}359$ volts.
(Pt) $Br_{2(l)}$, Br^-,	$\mathbf{E}_h{}^{\circ} = 1{\cdot}066$,,
(Pt) $I_{2(s)}$, I^-,	$\mathbf{E}_h{}^{\circ} = 0{\cdot}536$,,

Oxygen electrodes have also been employed. Oxygen may give rise to oxygen ions, $O^{=}$; but since in aqueous solution oxygen ions are converted almost completely into hydroxyl ions, according to the equation:

$$O^{=} + H_2O = 2OH^-,$$

the electrode reaction which may occur is:

$$\frac{1}{2}O_2 + H_2O + 2\epsilon = 2OH^-.$$

It has been found that the behaviour of oxygen electrodes is anomalous; it is difficult to get reproducible potentials, and the variation of the electrode potential with the oxygen pressure is not in accordance with this reaction. It is said that oxide formation occurring at the electrodes prevents the setting up of the equilibrium potential difference. The standard electrode potential of oxygen in hydroxide ion solutions can, however, be calculated from other data.

Potentiometric titrations of oxidation reductions. The end-points of many oxidation and reduction titrations can be easily determined by following the oxidation potential of the electrode. For example, if a ferrous sulphate solution is titrated with potassium permanganate in dilute sulphuric acid, the oxidation potential passes along the curve of Fig. 45 as the proportion of ferric salt to ferrous is increased. When the ferrous salt is completely oxidised a further addition of the reactant gives an excess of permanganate and the potential rises sharply to values characteristic of permanganate-manganous mixtures (Fig. 45). This sudden rise is easily detected and agrees very closely with the theoretical end-point of the reaction.

Numerous oxidation and reduction reactions can be followed in this way. Among the substances which have been used as oxidising agents are permanganates and dichromates, ceric sulphate, potassium iodate, bromate and ferricyanide and copper sulphate. As reducing agents the following have given good results : ferrous sulphate, iodides, arsenic trioxide, titanous and chromous salts, stannous chloride and ferrocyanides.

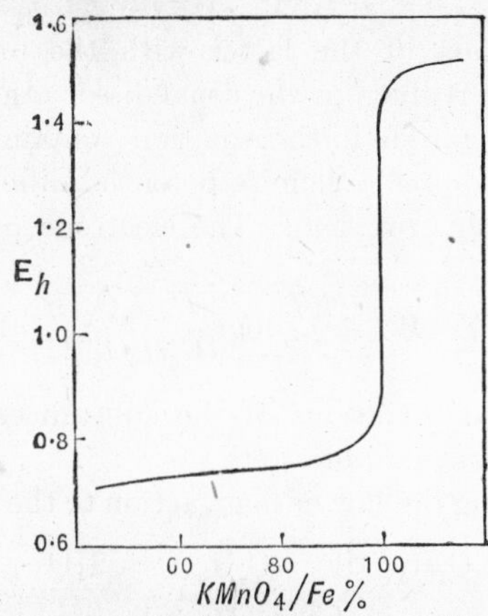

FIG 45.—Potentiometric titration of ferrous iron with permanganate.

For most purposes it is sufficient to place a bright platinum electrode in the solution and as the titration proceeds to follow its potential as measured against a suitable standard electrode by means of a potentiometric arrangement. Accurate measurements of the electromotive force of the combination are usually unnecessary ; it is sufficient to observe the point at which the sudden and frequently large charge of potential marking the end-point occurs. For practical details the reader is referred to Kolthoff and Furman's *Potentiometric Titrations* (Wiley and Chapman & Hall).

The Quinhydrone and Similar Electrodes. Hydroquinone is a weak acid which ionises in two stages as

$$C_6H_4(OH)_2 = C_6H_4O_2H^- + H^+ = C_6H_4O_2^= + 2H^+.$$

When quinone, $C_6H_4O_2$, is reduced to hydroquinone, we

may suppose that it first takes up two electrons forming the hydroquinone ion

$$C_6H_4O_2 + 2\epsilon = C_6H_4O_2^{=}.$$

The equilibrium of the latter with the undissociated hydroquinone is given by the usual dissociation equation.

An inert electrode in the solution containing the two substances acquires a definite potential difference corresponding to this reaction. The electrode potential, by (83), is thus

$$\mathbf{E} = \mathbf{E}_1{}^\circ + \frac{RT}{2\mathrm{F}} \log \frac{[C_6H_4O_2]}{[C_6H_4O_2^{=}]}, \quad \ldots\ldots\ldots\ldots(84)$$

where the concentrations of the substances are represented by the square brackets.

But applying the law of mass action to the equilibrium

$$C_6H_4(OH)_2 = C_6H_4O_2^{=} + 2H^+,$$

we have

$$\frac{[C_6H_4O_2^{=}][H^+]^2}{[C_6H_4(OH)_2]} = K,$$

or

$$[C_6H_4O_2^{=}] = K[C_6H_4(OH)_2]/[H^+]^2.$$

Substituting this in (87), we find that

$$\mathbf{E} = \mathbf{E}_1{}^\circ + \frac{RT}{2\mathrm{F}} \log K + \frac{RT}{2\mathrm{F}} \log \frac{[C_6H_4O_2][H^+]^2}{[C_6H_4(OH)_2]},$$

or

$$\mathbf{E} = \mathbf{E}^\circ + \frac{RT}{2\mathrm{F}} \log \frac{[C_6H_4O_2]}{[C_6H_4(OH)_2]} + \frac{RT}{\mathrm{F}} \log [H^+], \ldots(85)$$

where

$$\mathbf{E}^\circ = \mathbf{E}_1{}^\circ - RT/2\mathrm{F}(\log K).$$

In solutions which are not alkaline the degree of dissociation is small and the concentration $[C_6H_4(OH)_2]$ can be identified with the total concentration of hydroquinone present in the solution. It is evident that if the concentration of hydrogen ions is kept constant, the electrode potential is related to the percentage of quinone by a curve like Fig. 45, and if the proportions of quinone and hydroquinone are kept constant, the electrode potential varies with the hydrogen ion concentration in the same way as that of the hydrogen electrode and may be employed for determining hydrogen ion concentrations.

In the *quinhydrone* electrode a compound of quinone and hydroquinone ($C_6H_4O_2 . C_6H_4(OH)_2$, quinhydrone) is used for the purpose of keeping the proportions constant. The second term in (88) is now zero and the variation of the electrode potential with the hydrogen ion concentration is given by

$$\mathbf{E} = \mathbf{E}^\circ + \frac{RT}{\mathbf{F}} \log (m)_{H^+}.$$

The value of $\mathbf{E}^\circ$ is 0·7044 volts on the standard hydrogen scale. In alkaline solutions ($p_H > 8{\cdot}5$), the hydroquinone is appreciably dissociated and it is no longer possible to identify $[C_6H_4(OH)_2]$ with the total concentration of hydroquinone present. The quantity $\mathbf{E}^\circ$ then no longer remains constant and this expression cannot be used to determine the hydrogen ion concentrations without correction.

A considerable number of similar cases has been investigated by Biilmann, Conant, La Mer, Mansfield Clark and others. Equilibria of this kind are met with when one of the substances concerned in the reversible process is an acid or a base. Consider the following simple case. Let O be a neutral substance which gains one electron to form the ion R^- :

$$O + \epsilon = R^-.$$

The ion R^- is the anion of a weak acid RH, which has

the dissociation constant K_a. The fundamental equation for the electrode potential is

$$\mathbf{E} = \mathbf{E}_1{}^\circ + \frac{RT}{\mathbf{F}} \log \frac{[O]}{[R^-]}, \qquad \text{.............(86)}$$

but from the dissociation equilibrium, we have

$$[H^+][R^-] = [RH]K_a,$$

or
$$\frac{[RH]}{[R^-]} = \frac{[H^+]}{K_a},$$

i.e.
$$[R^-] = ([RH] + [R^-])\left(\frac{K_a}{[H^+] + K_a}\right),$$

where $[RH] + [R^-]$ is the total concentration of the reduced substance. Writing this as $[R_T]$ and substituting in (89), we have

$$\mathbf{E} = \mathbf{E}_1{}^\circ + \frac{RT}{\mathbf{F}} \log \frac{[O]}{[R_T]} + \frac{RT}{\mathbf{F}} \log \left(\frac{[H^+] + K_a}{K_a}\right). \qquad \text{...(87)}$$

Thus when K_a is small compared with $[H^+]$ this becomes

$$\mathbf{E} = \mathbf{E}^\circ + \frac{RT}{\mathbf{F}} \log \frac{[O]}{[R_T]} + \frac{RT}{\mathbf{F}} \log [H^+],$$

where
$$\mathbf{E}^\circ = \mathbf{E}_1{}^\circ - RT/\mathbf{F} \log K_a.$$

When K_a is large compared with $[H^+]$, the final term of (87) is zero and the electrode potential is no longer dependent on the hydrogen ion concentration.

A large variety of equations of this kind can be obtained, according to the nature of the dissociation of the substances taking part in the process. If, as in the case of quinone and hydroquinone, the reduced ion is the anion of a dibasic acid, the fundamental reduction process is

$$\mathrm{O} + 2\epsilon = \mathrm{R}^=,$$

where the ion $\mathrm{R}^=$ is the anion of the acid $\mathrm{RH_2}$. If the first and second stage dissociation constants of this acid are K_{a1} and K_{a2}, it can be shown by similar methods that the equation for the electrode potential is

$$\mathbf{E} = \mathbf{E}^\circ + \frac{RT}{2\mathbf{F}} \log \frac{[O]}{[R_T]} + \frac{RT}{2\mathbf{F}} \log (K_{a1}K_{a2} + K_{a1}[H^+] + [H^+]^2). \quad \ldots(88)$$

The first and second stage dissociation constants of hydroquinone are

$$K_{a1} = 1{\cdot}75 \times 10^{-10} \quad \text{and} \quad K_{a2} = 4 \times 10^{-12}.$$

If $[H^+] > 10^{-8}$ the first two quantities in the final term of this equation are negligible compared with $[H^+]^2$ and the equation reduces to (85). When $[H^+] > 10^{-8}$ the term $K_{a1}[H^+]$ begins to be appreciable.

In general the electrode potential may be represented by equations of the type

$$\mathbf{E}_h = \mathbf{E}_h{}^\circ + \frac{RT}{z\mathbf{F}} \log \frac{[O_T]}{[R_T]} + \frac{RT}{z\mathbf{F}} \log f([H^+]), \quad \ldots(89)$$

where $[O_T]$ and $[R_T]$ are the total concentrations of the oxidised and reduced forms of the substance and $f([H^+])$ is a function of the hydrogen ion concentration, which depends on the nature of the equilibria between the substances and hydrogen ions. When working with solutions of a constant p_H, it is convenient to write this as

$$\mathbf{E}_h = \mathbf{E}_h{}^{\circ\prime} + \frac{RT}{z\mathbf{F}} \log \frac{[O_T]}{[R_T]},$$

where $\mathbf{E}_h{}^{\circ\prime}$ is a function of the hydrogen ion concentration.

Oxidation-reduction Indicators. Reversible potentials of this type are established in solutions of many dyestuffs and their reduction products. Fig. 46 shows the variation of the electrode potential in a number of cases of this kind with the proportions of the substance in the reduced and oxidised forms at the constant $p_H = 7$. The middle

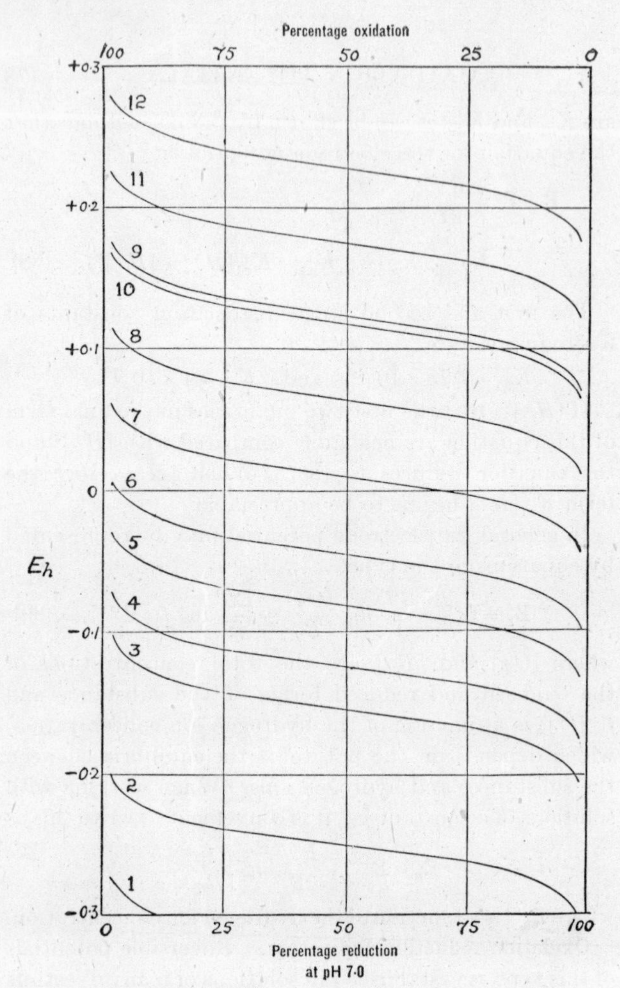

FIG. 46.—Variation of potential (E_h) with percentage reduction.*

1. Neutral red.
2. Phenosafranine.
3. Potassium indigo-monosulphonate.
4. Potassium indigo-disulphonate.
5. Potassium indigo-trisulphonate.
6. Potassium indigo-tetrasulphonate.
7. Methylene blue.
8. Lauth's violet.
9. Naphthol-2-sodium sulphonate-indo-2 : 6-dichlorophenol.
10. Naphthol-2-sodium sulphonate-indophenol.
11. Thymol-indophenol.
12. Phenol-indophenol.

* Reproduced by permission of British Drug Houses, Ltd., from their pamphlet on *The Colorimetric Determination of the Oxidation Balance.*

points of these curves (for which $[O_T]=[R_T]$) are the values of $E_h{}^{\circ\prime}$ for $p_H=7$. Fig. 47 shows how the values of $E_h{}^{\circ\prime}$ vary with the p_H. In all these cases $z=2$.

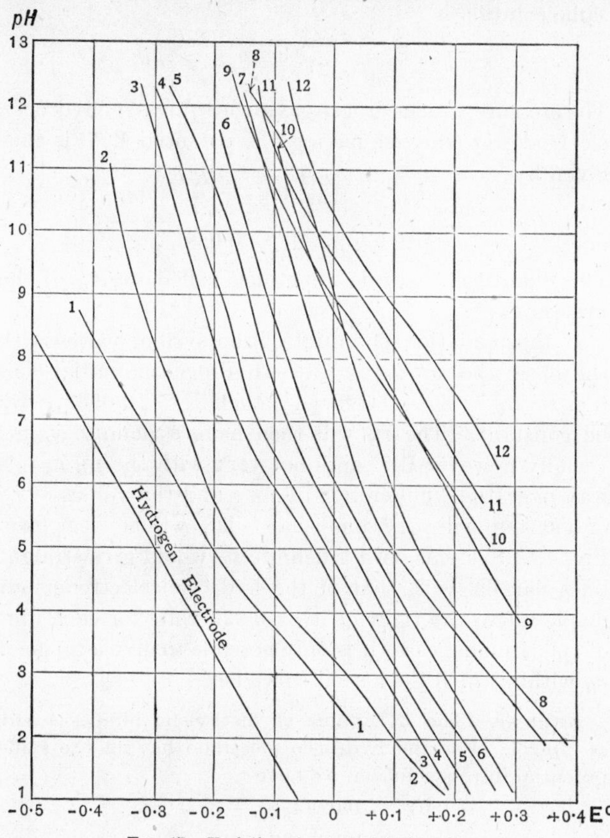

FIG. 47.—Variation of potential ($E_h{}^{\circ\prime}$) with p_H.*

The potentials of these systems are sometimes specified in terms of the equivalent hydrogen electrode. Let

$E_h^{\circ\prime}$ be the potential of the 50 per cent. mixture of the substance and its reduction product in a solution of given p_H. The potential of a hydrogen electrode in the same solution is

$$E_h = -\frac{RT}{2F}\log p - \frac{RT}{F}\,p_H.$$

The pressure, p, of hydrogen gas in the equivalent hydrogen electrode, *i.e.* the one having the potential $E_h^{\circ\prime}$, is thus given by

$$E_h^{\circ\prime} = -\frac{RT}{2F}\log p - \frac{RT}{F}\,.\,p_H,$$

or
$$-0{\cdot}029\log p = E_h^{\circ\prime} + 0{\cdot}058\,p_H.$$

The quantity $-\log p$ is sometimes called the r_H of the system.

If the oxidation potential of the system varies with the p_H in the same way as the hydrogen potential does (*i.e.* if $E_h^{\circ\prime} = E_h^{\circ} - 0{\cdot}058\,.\,p_H$), then $E_h^{\circ\prime} + 0{\cdot}058 p_H$ will be constant. The r_H will then have a definite value. Usually however $E_h^{\circ\prime}$ does not vary with the p_H in this way over the whole range of p_H's and the values of r_H of a system will vary somewhat. This will be clear from Fig. 48. Systems with a definite r_H would give straight lines parallel with that of the hydrogen electrode, but displaced to the right of it by 0·029 volts for each unit of r_H. In most cases it is only possible to give a range of r_H within which the actual curve lies.

Example. The $E_h^{\circ\prime}$ value of methylene blue is $+0{\cdot}01$ at $p_H = 7$. For the hydrogen electrode having the same potential in this solution, we have

$$0{\cdot}01 = -0{\cdot}029\log p - 7\times 0{\cdot}058,$$

or
$$-\log p = 0{\cdot}426/0{\cdot}029 = 14{\cdot}7.$$

This is the r_H value. If measured at other p_H's, somewhat different values are obtained.

The following table gives the values of $E_h^{\circ\prime}$ at $p_H = 7{\cdot}0$ and the approximate r_H range of some systems of this kind.

TABLE XIX.

OXIDATION-REDUCTION INDICATORS.

	$E_h^{\circ\prime}$ at $p_H = 7$.	r_H range.
Neutral red	−·325	2-4
Janus green	−·255	5-7
Phenosafranine	−·252	5-7
Indigo di-sulphonic acid	−·125	8-10
Indigo tri-sulphonic acid	−·081	9·5-11·5
Indigo tetra-sulphonic acid	−·046	11-13
Methylene blue	+·011	13·5-15·5
Lauth's violet	+·063	15-17
Tolylene blue	+·115	16-18
1-Naphthol–2-Na-sulphonate-indophenol	+·123	16·5-18·5
Thymol-indophenol	+·174	18-20
Phenol-indophenol	+·227	20-22
Bindschedler's green	+·224	20·5-22·5
Diphenylamine sulphonic acid	—	26-28

Uses of Oxidation-reduction Indicators. The substances described above are dyestuffs which are coloured in their oxidised forms, while their reduction products are colourless leuco-compounds. For this reason they may be used as indicators of the oxidation potentials of solutions into which they are introduced. If the oxidation potential of the solution is appreciably more positive than the appropriate $E_h^{\circ\prime}$ value of the indicator, the latter will remain fully oxidised and exhibit its full colour; but if the oxidation potential is appreciably more negative than the $E_h^{\circ\prime}$ value the indicator will be almost completely reduced to the colourless form. Near the $E_h^{\circ\prime}$ value it is possible to judge from the intensity of the colour the proportions of the coloured and colourless forms and so estimate the oxidation potential of the solution.

These substances can be used for indicating the end-points of oxidation and reduction reactions. For example, if a ferrous salt is titrated with a dichromate solution, the oxidation potential increases suddenly at the end-point, as in Fig. 45. An indicator having a $\mathbf{E}_h{}^{\circ\prime}$ value at the p_H of the solution which is greater than the potentials of the ferrous-ferric mixtures, but less than those of solutions containing dichromate, will be oxidised as soon as the oxidation of the iron is completed and the colour change will indicate the completion of the oxidation. Most of the substances listed in Table XIX have $\mathbf{E}_h{}^{\circ\prime}$ values which are too low for this purpose, but diphenylamine and its sulphonic acid have been found to be suitable.

Ferrous and ferric ions also form complex ions with certain organic bases (which are related like the ferrocyanide and ferricyanide ions) and can be reversibly oxidised or reduced. They are fairly stable and in certain cases have very high oxidation potentials, and since the oxidised and the reduced ions have characteristic colours, they can be used as indicators in permanganate and dichromate oxidations. Examples of these substances are $\alpha-\alpha'$ dipyridyl and *o*-phenanthroline, whose structures are given below.

o-phenanthroline. $\alpha-\alpha'$ dipyridyl.

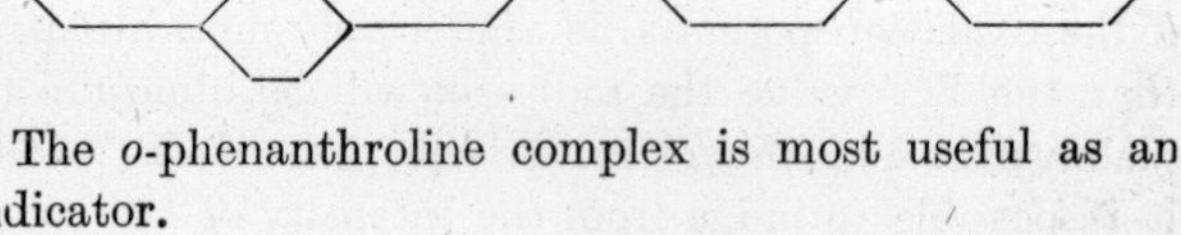

N N N N

The *o*-phenanthroline complex is most useful as an indicator.

The normal oxidation potential, corresponding to the reaction

$$(C_{12}H_8N_2)_3Fe^{++} \rightleftarrows (C_{12}H_8N_2)_3Fe^{+++} + \epsilon,$$

is $E_H = 1 \cdot 14$ volts in 1M sulphuric acid. It should be practically independent of the acidity. The colour of the reduced ions is red and that of the oxidised ions a deep blue.

Another example is the estimation of vanadium in steel. The vanadium is reduced to the vanadous condition by zinc amalgam. The solution is separated and reoxidised by copper sulphate or iodine, using phenosafranine or neutral red as the indicator. So long as any vanadous salt remains the dye is present in the colourless leuco-form, but as soon as the oxidation is complete, it is oxidised and gives its colour to the solution. Similar methods for the determination of chromium and tungsten are available.

In Miller's method for the determination of dissolved oxygen in water, the water is buffered with alkaline tartrate and titrated with ferrous sulphate solution, using phenosafranine as indicator. The fading of the colour of the latter indicates that the reduction of the dissolved oxygen is complete. Methylene blue can be used for indicating the end-point of the reduction of Fehling's alkaline copper sulphate solution by reducing sugars. The sugar is added to the Fehling's solution and the methylene blue retains its colour until the reduction of the copper is complete, when the addition of a slight excess of sugar reduces the methylene blue.

These substances have also been used for estimating the oxidation potentials in biological fluids such as milk, soils and sewage. Fresh milk has a higher oxidation potential than that which has undergone bacterial decomposition and it is possible by the use of suitable indicators to estimate its freshness. Attempts have also been made by the micro-injection of indicators into living cells to determine the oxidation potentials in their interior. Bacteria often bring about characteristic changes of oxidation potential in the media in which they are living, which can sometimes be used for distinguishing them.

Further information will be found in Kolthoff's *Die Massanalyse*, or Kolthoff and Furman's *Volumetric Analysis* (Wiley). *Studies on oxidation reduction*, U.S. Hygienic Laboratory Bulletin No. 151, by W. Mansfield Clark and others, contains a great mass of information and copious references. The biochemical aspects are reviewed in L. F. Hewitt's *Oxidation-reduction potentials in bacteriology and biochemistry* (London County Council).

* **Semiquinones.** Most organic oxidation and reduction processes involve the loss or gain of two electrons, and until recently there was little evidence of one-electron processes. It is well known that hydroquinone and quinone form a compound quinhydrone, which was regarded as a molecular compound of the two,

$$C_6H_4(OH)_2 . C_6H_4O_2,$$

which dissociates on solution. It is true that an acid solution of this substance has the properties of a mixture of quinone and hydroquinone, but in alkaline solution it exhibits strong colours which are not shown by either of the simple substances. The investigation of these solutions is hindered by irreversible secondary changes which take place in the presence of alkali, but other cases have been found in which the oxidation of hydroquinone-like compounds occurs in two distinct stages. Fig. 48 shows the titration curve of a substance which exhibits this type of behaviour.

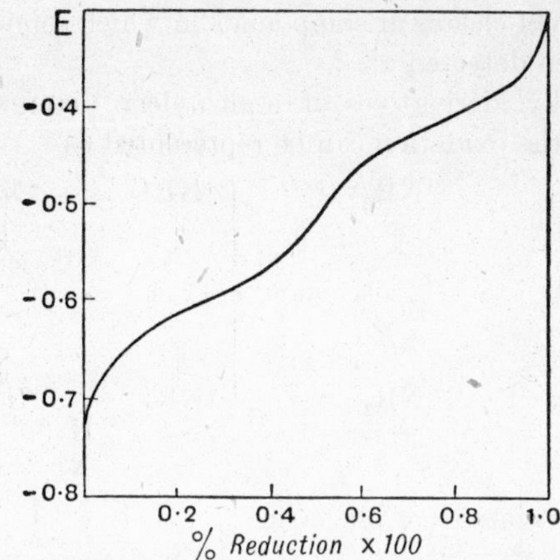

Fig. 48.—Oxidation of anthrahydroquinone in 50% pyridine at 50°. (Geake and Lemon). Oxidising agent, potassium ferricyanide.*

The two stages of the oxidation may be represented by the following scheme :

OH / OH (Hydroquinone.) or O^- / O^- (Hydroquinone Ion.) → O^- / O (Semiquinone Ion.) → O / O (Quinone.)

The intermediate substance, when it can be distinguished, is called a semiquinone. The single negative charge of the semiquinone ion can be regarded as shared by the two oxygens, or perhaps oscillating between them, giving a symmetrical structure, which can be represented as

O⟨ ⟩O
ε

The semiquinones are invariably highly coloured compounds and are frequently unstable.

* In Fig. 48, for % *reduction* read % *oxidation.*

The chief classes of compounds in which semiquinones have been detected are :

(1) Alkyl derivatives of *p*-phenylene diamine. The steps of the oxidation can be represented as

NR_2 … NR_2 → $^+NR_2$ … NR_2 or ϵ { $^+NR^2$ … $^+NR_2$ } → $^+NR_2$ … $^+NR_2$

(2) Derivatives of phenazine:

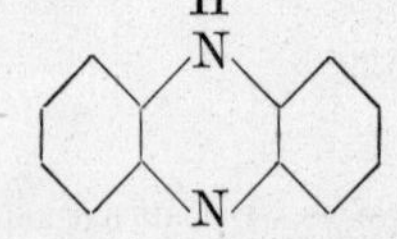

(3) Alkyl halide derivatives of $\gamma-\gamma'$ dipyridyl (viologens) :

N … N → [^+RN … NR^+] Cl_2

$\gamma-\gamma'$ dipyridyl. Alkyl dipyridyl chloride (Viologen).

The two stages of the reduction may be represented as

R, N^+, N^+, R → R, N^+, N^+, R (ϵ) → R, N, N, R

Viologen Ion. Semiquinone. Reduced form.

(4) Anthraquinone and derivatives.

(5) Various groups of dyes, such as indophenols, flavins, indigos.

For further information, see L. Michaelis, *Chem. Revs.*, **16**, 243, 1935; Michaelis and others, *J. Amer. Chem. Soc.*, **60**, 250, 1545, 1617, 1667 (1938); Geake and Lemon, *Trans. Faraday Soc.*, **34**, 1409, 1938.

Examples.

1. What galvanic cells would you construct in order to measure the free energy changes in the following reactions?

$$Hg + PbI_2(s) = Pb + HgI_2(s),$$
$$CuSO_4(aq.) + H_2 = H_2SO_4(aq.) + Cu,$$
$$HgCl(s) + FeCl_2(aq.) = Hg + FeCl_3(aq.),$$
$$I_2(s) + H_2 = 2HI(aq.),$$
$$Na + \tfrac{1}{2}Cl_2 = NaCl(aq.),$$
$$C_6H_4O_2(s) + H_2 = C_6H_4(OH)_2(s).$$

2. The potential of a quinhydrone electrode in a certain solution, as measured against the normal calomel electrode, is +0·188 volts at 18°. What is the p_H of the solution? ($p_H = 4$.)

3. At what hydrogen pressure would the hydrogen electrode have the same potential as the quinhydrone electrode ($\mathbf{E}_h{}^\circ = +0{\cdot}704$) in the same solution?

$$(p = 10^{-24\cdot2};\; r_H = 24{\cdot}2.)$$

* 4. Noyes and Braun found that when silver is placed in a solution of ferric nitrate equilibrium was reached in the reaction $Ag + Fe^{+++} = Ag^+ + Fe^{++}$, when the ratio

$$[Fe^{++}][Ag^+]/[Fe^{+++}]$$

was 0·128 at 25°, at very small ion concentrations. Find the electromotive force of the cell

$$Ag \mid Ag^+;\quad Fe^{++},\ Fe^{+++} \mid Pt$$

under standard conditions. ($\mathbf{E}^\circ = 0{\cdot}0527$ volts.)

* 5. Can you deduce a relation between the electrode potentials of Fe/Fe^{+++}, Fe/Fe^{++} and the oxidation potential of ferrous and ferric ions? (*Note.*—When an iron electrode is in equilibrium with both ferrous and ferric ions the three potentials must be the same.) Using the standard electrode potentials :

$$Fe, \quad Fe^{++}; \qquad \mathbf{E}_h^\circ = -0{\cdot}44;$$
$$Fe^{++}, \; Fe^{+++}; \qquad \mathbf{E}_h^\circ = +0{\cdot}75;$$

find the standard electrode potential of iron in a solution containing ferric ions. **($\mathbf{E}_h^\circ = 0{\cdot}542$ volts.)**

CHAPTER IX

ELECTROLYSIS

The Decomposition Voltage. If we have two copper electrodes in a solution of copper sulphate, as in the copper coulometer, and connect them to a battery, we find that any electromotive force however small will cause electrolysis to take place. But if instead of copper we use platinum electrodes we find that no appreciable amount of electrolysis occurs until the applied electromotive force has reached a certain value called the *decomposition voltage.* This may be investigated by means of the apparatus shown in Fig. 49. The variable electromotive force which is applied to the electrodes is supplied by the battery B, which produces a fall of potential down the resistance R. A voltmeter V registers the potential difference applied to the electrodes and an ammeter A, the current which passes through the solution. When the circuit is closed the current quickly settles down to a steady value, and if this be plotted

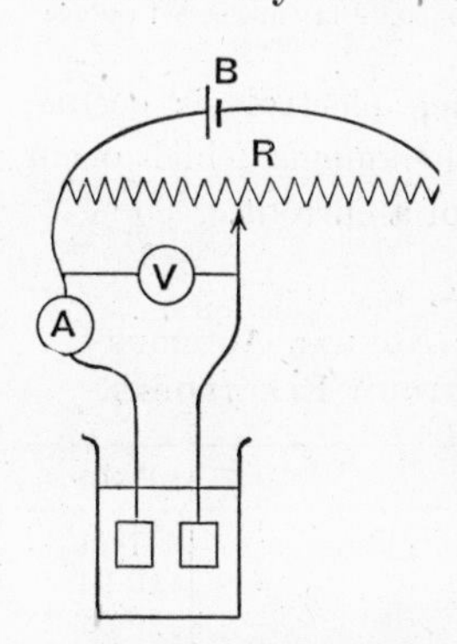

FIG. 49.—Apparatus for decomposition voltages.

against the applied potential difference, we get a curve like Fig. 50. The voltage at which the sharp rise of the curve begins is the decomposition voltage. The decomposition voltages of some aqueous solutions are given in Table XX. We shall see later that in many cases the decomposition voltage is not a definite quantity. It is, however, useful as indicating approximately the voltage necessary to produce electrolysis at a small but appreciable rate. In order to understand the conditions under which electrolysis occurs, it is necessary to examine the phenomena which occur at electrodes during the passage of a current.

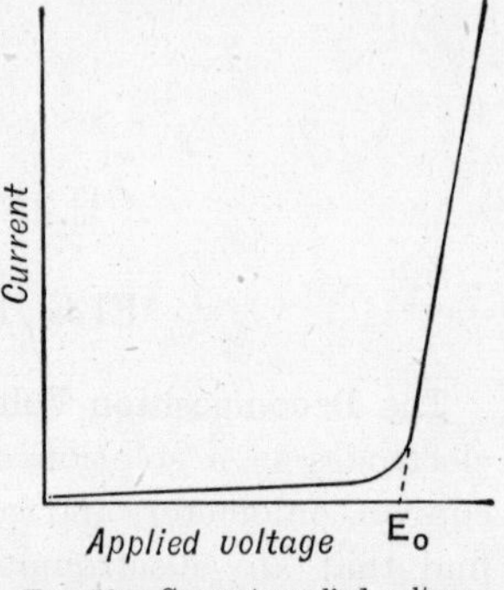

Fig. 50.—Current-applied voltage curve.

TABLE XX.

Decomposition Voltages of Normal Aqueous Solutions with Bright Platinum Electrodes.

	Volts.		Volts.
$ZnSO_4$	2·35	HCl	1·31
$ZnBr_2$	1·80	HBr	0·94
$NiSO_4$	2·09	HI	0·52
$NiCl_2$	1·85	H_2SO_4	1·67
$Pb(NO_3)_2$	1·52	HNO_3	1·69
$Cd(NO_3)_2$	1·98	H_3PO_4	1·70
$CdSO_4$	2·03	$CH_2Cl . CO_2H$	1·72
$CdCl_2$	1·88	$HClO_4$	1·65
$CoCl_2$	1·78	NaOH	1·69
$CoSO_4$	1·92	KOH	1·67
Ag_2SO_4	0·80	NH_4OH	1·74
$AgNO_3$	0·70	CH_3NH_3OH(0·25N)	1·75

Polarisation of Electrodes. When a moderate current is passed through a reversible electrode, such as the calomel electrode, the potential is only displaced by a slight amount from its reversible value ; such an electrode is said to be unpolarisable. When, however, the potential difference is displaced by the passage of a current from its value at open circuit, as happens in many cases, the electrode is said to be polarised. Sometimes the polarisation is due merely to a change in the concentration in the vicinity of the electrode of the substance which determines the electrode potential. Thus, if we electrolyse a solution of silver nitrate with two silver electrodes, silver is deposited at the cathode and dissolves at the anode. Since diffusion in the solution is comparatively slow, it may happen that in the vicinity of the cathode the solution becomes impoverished in silver ions, while in the vicinity of the anode the reverse happens. On this account there will be a difference of potential between the two electrodes. Polarisation of this kind can be reduced or eliminated by thorough stirring of the solution. Polarisation also occurs when concentration changes are eliminated, and is then due to the inability of the electrode process to take place until the potential has reached an appropriate value.

The potential of an electrode during the passage of a current may be observed by means of the apparatus shown in Fig. 49, if a reference electrode is put in liquid contact with the solution, for the difference of potential between it and one of the electrolysing electrodes can be observed during the progress of the electrolysis by means of a suitable potentiometric arrangement. It is difficult, however, under these conditions to keep the electrolysing current constant, and since it is often desirable to observe the potential of the electrode at a constant current, it is more convenient to make use of the arrangement shown in Fig. 51. The electrolysing current is provided by a high tension battery *B* (a dry battery of 100 volts is suitable for small currents) in series with a high resistance *R*. The current passing is then only slightly influenced by changes of the resistance of the electrolyte or of the potential difference between the electrodes. In order to avoid including in the measured potential difference any of the fall of potential in the electrolyte which is produced by the passage of the current through it, it is desirable to bring the orifice of the connecting tube of the reference electrode very close to the surface of the electrode which is under investigation.

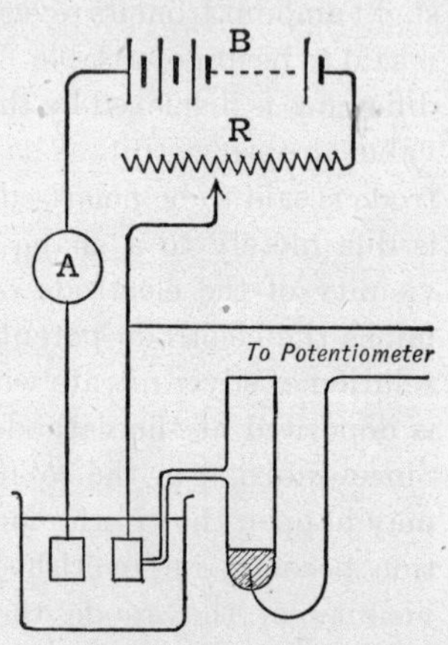

FIG. 51.—Apparatus for studying electrolysis with constant currents.

The total potential difference between the two electrodes of an electrolytic cell during the passage of a current is obtained by adding to the difference of the electrode potentials the fall of potential produced by the current in the electrolyte. Thus if V_1 and V_2 are the actual potentials of the electrodes (measured against a suitable standard in such a way as not to include any of the fall of potential through the electrolyte), the total difference of potential between the electrodes (as measured by a voltmeter connected to them) is

$$E = V_1 - V_2 + iR,$$

for if i is the current and R the effective resistance of the electrolyte, iR is the change of potential produced by the current in the electrolyte.

We will now consider in turn the conditions under which processes of various types occur at the electrodes.

Deposition of Metals at the Cathode. Le Blanc found that the deposition of a metal at the cathode occurs at the same potential as that which the deposited metal exhibits in the same solution. Thus the cathode potential at the point at which cadmium begins to be deposited from a cadmium sulphate solution is $-0{\cdot}72$ volts with respect to the normal calomel electrode, while metallic cadmium had the potential $\mathbf{E}_c = -0{\cdot}70$ in the same solution.

There is practically no deposition of metal until the decomposition potential is reached. Le Blanc endeavoured to find how much metal must be deposited on a platinum electrode before it gives the characteristic potential of the metal. He found that the amount was analytically inappreciable. Probably it corresponds to a layer only a few atoms thick.

Fig. 52 shows the cathode potential-current curves for the electrolysis of some metallic salt solutions. It must be remembered that the electrode potential of a metal is diminished by $0{\cdot}058/z$ volts for each 10-fold diminution of the ion concentration. This has an important bearing on the analytical separation of metals by electro-deposition.

Example. If we electrolyse a solution containing molar quantities of zinc and cadmium salts, cadmium begins to be deposited at the cathode when the potential is $\mathbf{E}_h = -0{\cdot}40$.

For each 10-fold diminution of the concentration of cadmium ions the cathode potential is reduced by approximately 0·029 volts. Zinc begins to be deposited at $E_h = -0{\cdot}76$ volts, so that the concentration of cadmium ions when the decomposition potential of the zinc salt is reached is reduced $\frac{0{\cdot}36}{0{\cdot}029} \times 10$ times. It is evident that an analytically complete separation may be obtained.

To ensure a good separation the decomposition potentials of two metals should be at least 0·2 volts apart. The addition of a substance which forms complex ions with the ions of a metal may greatly depress the electrode

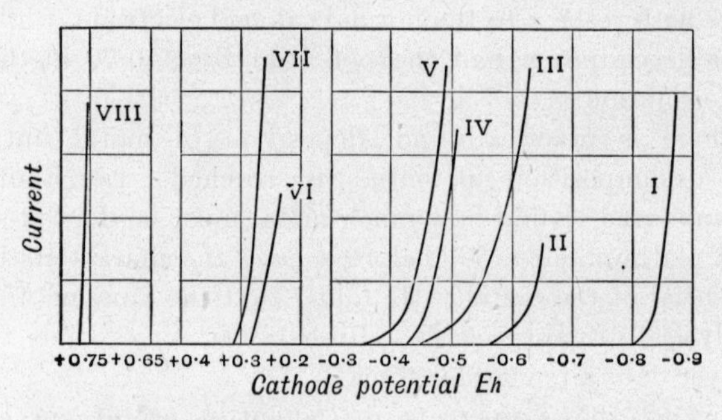

FIG. 52.—Cathodic deposition of metals from solutions. (Foerster.)

I. $Zn/n\ ZnSO_4$.
II. $Fe/n\ FeSO_4 + 0{\cdot}5\%\ H_3BO_3$.
III. $Ni/n\ NiCl_2 + 0{\cdot}5\%\ H_3BO_3$.
IV. $Cd/n\ CdSO_4$.
V. $Co/n\ CoSO_4 + 0{\cdot}5\%\ H_3BO_3$.
VI. $Cu/n/10\ CuSO_4$.
VII. $Cu/n\ CuSO_4$.
VIII. $Hg/0{\cdot}66n\ HgNO_3$, $0{\cdot}1n\ HNO_3$.

potential. Thus the potential of silver in normal silver nitrate is $E_h = +0{\cdot}80$, but when potassium cyanide is present $(m=1)$, $E_h = -0{\cdot}51$. By the use of suitable additions separations can be effected which would otherwise be impossible or incomplete.

Liberation of Hydrogen at the Cathode. At a platinised

platinum electrode hydrogen is liberated practically at the reversible hydrogen potential of the solution. With other electrodes a more negative potential is required to secure its liberation. The difference between the reversible hydrogen potential and the actual decomposition potential in the same solution is known as the *hydrogen overvoltage* of the metal.

Approximate determinations of the hydrogen overvoltage can be made by observing the potential of the cathode when the current-voltage curve shows that appreciable electrolysis is taking place, or by making the cathode very small and observing its potential when the first visible bubble of gas appears. The first method was used by Coehn and Dannenberg and the second by Caspari, and their values are given in Table XXI.

These cannot be regarded as very definite, but they give some idea of the order of the overvoltages of different metals.

TABLE XXI.

HYDROGEN OVERVOLTAGES.

Electrode.	Coehn and Dannenberg.	Caspari.
Platinised platinum	0·000	0·005
Smooth platinum	—	0·09
Iron	0·03	0·08
Silver	0·07	0·15
Nickel	0·14	0·21
Copper	0·19	0·23
Tin	—	0·53
Lead	0·36	0·64
Zinc	—	0·70
Mercury	0·44	0·78

In 1905 Tafel * made measurements with solutions which had been freed from oxygen, and found that the hydrogen overvoltage at mercury electrodes was a function of the current, which could be represented by

$$i = ke^{-aV}, \qquad (90)$$

where i is the current, k a constant characteristic of the electrode and V the potential of the cathode. He found

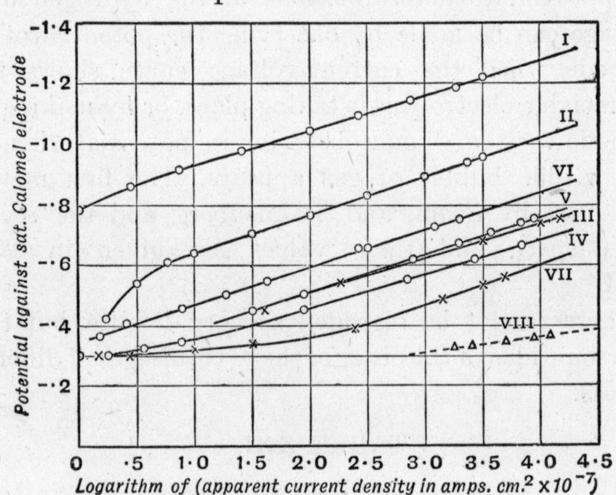

FIG. 53.—Variation of overvoltage with current density (Bowden and Rideal).

Curve		Curve	
I.	Mercury.	VI.	Polished silver.
II, III.	Platinised mercury.	VII.	Bright platinum.
IV, V.	Etched silver.	VIII.	Spongy platinum.

(In curve VIII. current density as expressed in amps. × 10^{-6}).

that the numerical value of the constant a was half the factor $\mathbf{F}/RT$, which appears so frequently in electrochemical calculations. This was confirmed by Lewis and Jackson,† by Harkins and Adams ‡ and by Bowden and

* *Z. physikal Chem.*, 50, 641, 1905.
† *Z. physikal Chem.*, 56, 207, 1906.
‡ *J. Physical Chem.*, 29, 205, 1925.

Rideal,* who also showed that the dependence of a on the temperature was in accordance with this expression.†

Taking logarithms of (90), we may write

$$\log_{10} i = \text{const.} - \frac{\mathbf{F}V}{2 \,.\, 2{\cdot}303RT},$$

or

$$-\frac{dV}{d \log_{10} i} = \frac{2 \,.\, 2{\cdot}303RT}{\mathbf{F}}. \qquad \text{(91)}$$

The theoretical value of the factor $2 \,.\, 2{\cdot}303RT/\mathbf{F}$ is 0·116 volts at 18°, *i.e.* according to this equation the cathode potential becomes 0·116 volts more negative for each 10-fold increase in the current. Some of Bowden's experimental curves are shown in Fig. 53. The observed slope at about 15° C. varies from about 0·110 to 0·120 for metals with a high overvoltage. Bowden's observations on the variation of the slope $dV/d \log i$ at mercury are given in the following table.

TABLE XXII.

Temperature.	$-dV/d \log_{10} i$.	$\mathbf{F}dV/2{\cdot}3RTd \log_{10} i$.
273	0·108	2·0
309	0·123	$2{\cdot}0_4$
345	0·141	2·0

The Oxygen Overvoltage. Similarly effects have been observed in the liberation of oxygen at the anode. The reversible oxygen potential has not been realised, but it can be calculated from free energy data (see Part II). It is found that the anode potential at most metals must be considerably more positive than this calculated value

* *Proc. Roy. Soc.*, 120 *A*, 59, 1928.

† *Ibid.*, 126, 107, 1929.

in order to cause the liberation of oxygen at any appreciable rate. Comparative figures, obtained by Coehn and Osaka, of the oxygen overvoltages for the free evolution of oxygen at anodes of different metals are given in Table XXIII.

TABLE XXIII.

OXYGEN OVERVOLTAGES.

Nickel (spongy)	0·05
Nickel	0·12
Cobalt	0·13
Iron	0·24
Lead	0·31
Silver	0·41
Platinum (platinised)	0·24
Platinum (polished)	0·44
Gold	0·53

It will be observed that metals which have a high hydrogen overvoltage usually have a low oxygen overvoltage, and *vice versa*.

Bowden* has observed that Tafel's relation between the overvoltage and the current also holds for the liberation of oxygen, and the slopes of the $dV/d \log i$ curves are the same for the hydrogen overvoltage; *i.e.*

$$\frac{dV}{d \log_{10} i} = \frac{2.2{\cdot}303RT}{\mathrm{F}} \quad (=0{\cdot}116 \text{ at } 18°).$$

The three halogens, chlorine, bromine and iodine are liberated from solutions of their salts at practically the equilibrium potential at platinised platinum, but at other electrodes a more positive potential is usually required.

* *Proc. Roy. Soc.*, 126A, 107, 1929.

Thus it has been stated that at bright platinum electrodes chlorine requires an overvoltage of 0·7 volts and bromine 0·3 volts, while iodine is still liberated at the equilibrium potential.

Decomposition Voltages of Acids and Bases. When aqueous solutions of many acids and bases are electrolysed, the products are hydrogen at the cathode and oxygen at the anode. Thus the ultimate process is the decomposition of water into hydrogen and oxygen. The minimum electromotive force required to effect this should be the electromotive force of the hydrogen-oxygen cell in the same solution, viz.:

$$H_2 \;\Big|\; \begin{matrix}\text{Aqueous}\\ \text{Solution}\end{matrix} \;\Big|\; O_2.$$

The reaction in this cell is the formation of water from hydrogen and oxygen:

$$H_2 + \tfrac{1}{2}O_2 = H_2O,$$

and the electromotive force should correspond to the free energy charge of this reaction, and therefore be independent of the nature of the solution except in so far as the free energy of water is affected by the dissolved substance. In dilute solutions this may be regarded as negligible.

We have already referred to the anomalous behaviour of the oxygen electrode (p. 166). The theoretical electromotive force of this cell, as computed from the free energy change in the reaction determined by other methods, is 1·22 volts. Actually values between 1·04 and 1·14 volts are obtained. The decomposition voltages of acids and bases which give hydrogen and oxygen as the products of electrolysis, with bright platinum electrodes, are in the neighbourhood of 1·70 volts (Table XX). This value may be regarded as the sum of the theoretical decomposition voltage and the two overvoltages :

Theoretical decomposition voltage - -	1·22
Anode overvoltage - - - -	0·44
Cathode overvoltage (about) - - -	0·04
	1·70

Theories of the Overvoltage. Numerous theories have been suggested to account for the overvoltage required for the liberation of hydrogen and other gases. The formation of hydrogen may be represented by

$$H^+ + \epsilon \rightarrow H \rightarrow \tfrac{1}{2}H_2,$$

i.e. the immediate product of the discharge of hydrogen ions must be atomic hydrogen, from which molecular hydrogen is subsequently formed. If the combination of hydrogen atoms into molecules is a comparatively slow process, hydrogen atoms will be formed at the electrode faster than they unite with each other to form the molecules, and there will thus be an accumulation of atomic hydrogen near the electrode. The potential of the electrode will then not be that of the hydrogen electrode under ordinary conditions, but that produced by the atomic hydrogen present. If the latter is more " electromotively active " or has a greater tendency to ionise than molecular hydrogen, the potential will be displaced in the negative direction during the passage of the current.

Other substances, such as metallic hydrides (Newbery), negative hydrogen ions (Heyrovsky), and also molecular hydrogen (Nernst) have also been suggested as possible products of the electrolysis which might produce a displacement of the potential in a similar way. Another view was that the hydrogen formed at the cathode gave rise to an obstructive film having a considerable "transfer resistance," in which the passage of the current gives rise to a potential fall which is included in the measured value (Newbery).

More recently it has been realised that the overvoltage may arise from the conditions necessary to bring about the first stage, viz. the discharge of hydrogen ions. In the classical electron theory the rate of escape of electrons from a metal having a thermionic work function ϕ is $i = ke^{-\phi/RT}$. If there is a potential difference V at the surface of the metal, the work done by electrons in escaping from the metal is increased to $\phi + \mathbf{F}V$ per equivalent, and the modified rate of escape is

$$i = ke^{-(\phi + \mathbf{F}V)/RT}.$$

The rate of escape of electrons may thus be greatly increased by giving V a negative value, and the overvoltage may be regarded as the value of V which enables electrons to escape from the metal at the required rate. Since ϕ is a constant for each metal, the relation between the current and the electrode potential may be written as $i = k' . e^{-\mathbf{F}V/RT}$. This is of the same form as Tafel's experimental equation, except that the exponent of the latter is half this value. Erdy-Grusz and Volmer * suggested that the rate-determining step was the transfer of hydrogen ions to adsorption positions on the surface of the electrode, which is similarly influenced by the potential difference, but it was supposed that a fraction α of the whole potential difference was effective in determining the rate of this transfer. The experimental relation is accounted for if $\alpha = \frac{1}{2}$. Gurney and

* *Z. physikal Chem.*, 150 A, 203, 1930; also 162 A, 53, 1932; cf. Frumkin, *ibid.*, 160 A, 116, 1932.

Fowler * have shown, however, that the factor $\frac{1}{2}$ may arise in another way.

* *Gurney's Theory of Overvoltage.* According to quantum mechanics a metal has a series of energy levels, each of which is capable of being occupied by two electrons. Each level is specified by the amount of energy required to remove an electron from it into free space. At absolute zero of temperature all the levels up to a value Φ° are completely filled with their quota of electrons,

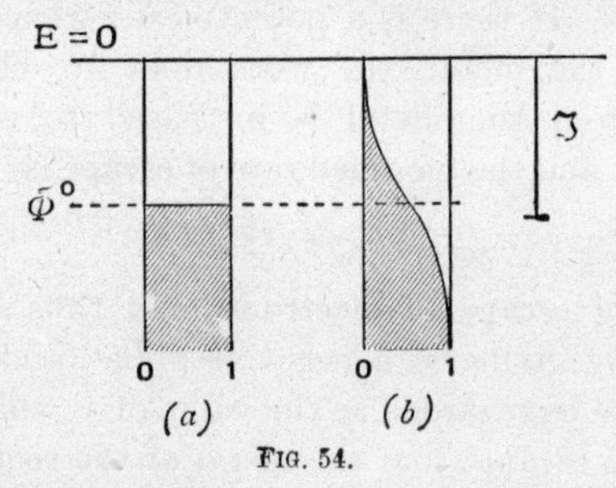

FIG. 54.

while the levels above Φ° (*i.e.* those for which the energy change is $<\Phi^\circ$) are empty. At temperatures above absolute zero some electrons are able to pass from the occupied levels below to levels above Φ°, so that there is then a range of levels which are partly filled with electrons. This is shown diagrammatically in Fig. 54. The energy of the various levels is plotted downwards (since the electrons in the metal have less energy than in free space), and the fraction of the levels at a given value of E which is occupied by electrons is indicated by the breadth of the shaded parts. Case (*a*) is at absolute zero, where all the levels up to Φ° are com-

* *Proc. Roy. Soc.*, 134 A, 137, 1931 ; *Trans. Faraday Soc.*, 28, 368, 1932.

pletely occupied ; and case (*b*) at a higher temperature where there is a gradual transition.

The isolated hydrogen atom also has a number of energy levels, in one of which the electron is present. The energy required to remove it from the lowest or "ground level" is the ionisation energy $\mathfrak{I}$. According to quantum mechanics electrons are not definitely localised, but are capable of passing at a finite rate through a "potential barrier" (*i.e.* a region which according to classical mechanics they have insufficient energy to penetrate) to neighbouring energy levels of equal energy. Thus if hydrogen ions are near the surface of a metal, electrons will be able to pass from occupied levels in the metal to the unoccupied levels of the ions which have equal energies.

The condition for the transfer of electrons from the metal to hydrogen ions is thus, in case (*a*),

$$\Phi^\circ < \mathfrak{I}.$$

(If $\mathfrak{I} < \Phi^\circ$, there are no electrons in the metal having energies which overlap the vacant energy levels $0 - \mathfrak{I}$ of the ions.) Similarly a transition of electrons from hydrogen atoms to a metal can only occur if $\Phi^\circ > \mathfrak{I}$. At temperatures above absolute zero, case (*b*), there are some electrons in levels higher than Φ°, but their number decreases very rapidly with decrease of Φ, so that these conditions remain approximately true.

We have now to consider what modification of this scheme is necessary in an aqueous solution, when the hydrogen ions are not isolated, but are present in the hydrated form H_3O^+. When this ion gains an electron the immediate product is the unstable neutral molecule H_3O, *i.e.*

$$H_3O^+ + \epsilon = H_3O.$$

The energy change in this process can be found from the following cycle :

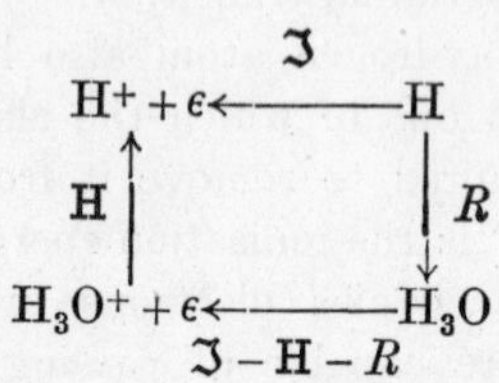

H is the hydration energy of the hydrogen ion (*i.e.* the energy required to remove it from the solution into free space), and R the energy required to form H_3O from a hydrogen atom and a water molecule. The arrows show the directions in which energy is absorbed. Gurney calls the quantity $E_n = \mathfrak{I} - \mathbf{H} - R$ the *neutralisation energy.* It has the same function for dissolved hydrogen ions as the ionisation energy $\mathfrak{I}$ has for the isolated hydrogen atom. Electrons will thus be able to pass from the metal to the solution if there are occupied levels in the metal having energies higher than E_n. This may be expressed as before, at an uncharged surface, by the condition $\Phi° < E_n$.*

If there is a potential difference V (metal positive) between the metal and the solution, the energy levels of the metal will be depressed by an amount $\mathbf{F}V$, since the work done by electrons in escaping from the metal is increased by this amount. The condition of neutralisation is then $\Phi° + \mathbf{F}V < E_n$. It is then evident that the overvoltage is the displacement of the electrode potential which enables this condition to be satisfied.

In order to obtain a relation between the electrode potential difference and the rate of neutralisation of

* All these energies refer to one equivalent of electrons or of hydrogen ions, etc.

hydrogen ions, it is necessary to take into account another factor. We have assumed that all the hydrogen ions in the solution have the same neutralisation energy. This is not necessarily the case, for if **H**° is the energy of hydration of an ion in its lowest quantum state there will be other ions in quantum states of greater energy, and having therefore lower values of **H**. For each value of **H** there will be a corresponding value of R (the repulsive energy), which decreases as the distance between the ion and the water molecule is increased. Thus if $E_n°$ is the neutralisation energy of a hydrated ion in the state

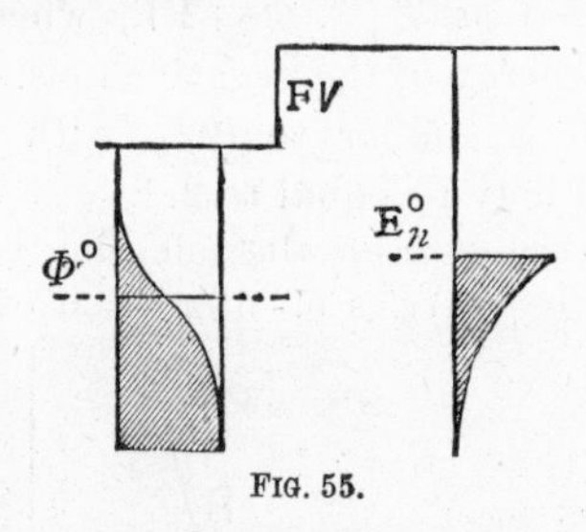

FIG. 55.

having the greatest hydration energy, other ions will have larger values of E_n. The state of affairs at an electrode is thus that shown in Fig. 55. The left of the diagram, as in Fig. 54, shows the distribution of electrons among the energy levels of the metal. These levels are displaced downwards a distance **F**V by the potential difference V at the surface of the metal. The width of the shaded part on the right shows the relative numbers of ions having the various neutralisation energies. The rate of transfer of electrons from the metal to the ions is obtained by integrating over the shaded areas their probabilities of transition from the metal to states of equal energy in the ions. The result of this calculation, as carried out by Gurney, is

$$i = ke^{(E_n{}^{\circ} - \Phi^{\circ} - \mathbf{F}V)/\gamma RT}, \quad \ldots\ldots\ldots\ldots\ldots\ldots(92)$$

where γ is an approximately constant quantity, which is greater than unity. If $\gamma = 2$, this is in agreement with Tafel's equation.

Gurney made a similar calculation for the rate of liberation of oxygen at the anode. In this case the transfer of electrons takes place from hydrated oxygen (or hydroxyl) ions in the solution to unoccupied levels in the metal. The condition for the transfer is approximately expressed as $E_n{}^{-} < \Phi^{\circ} + \mathbf{F}V$, where $E_n{}^{-}$ is the neutralisation energy of the negative ions. The result of the calculation is similar to (92), with an analogous factor γ, which may be equal to 2.

The factor γ arises from the following considerations.* Fig. 56 shows the energies of interaction of the hydrogen

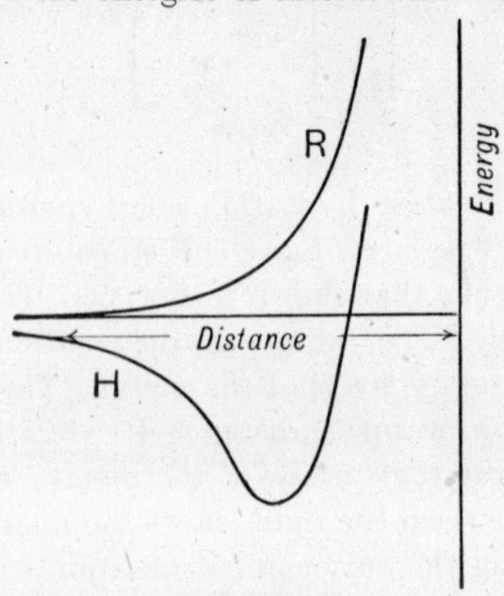

FIG. 56.—Energy of interaction of the hydrogen atom and ion, with a water molecule.

* This simplified argument was given by Butler, *Proc. Roy. Soc.*, **157**, 423, 1936.

ion and the hydrogen atom respectively as functions of the distance from the water molecule. The force between the hydrogen ion and the water molecule is attractive except at small distances, where it becomes repulsive. The curve of the energy of interaction (hydration energy) therefore has the form of the curve **H**. The force between a hydrogen atom and a water molecule is repulsive at all distances and gives rise to the energy curve R.

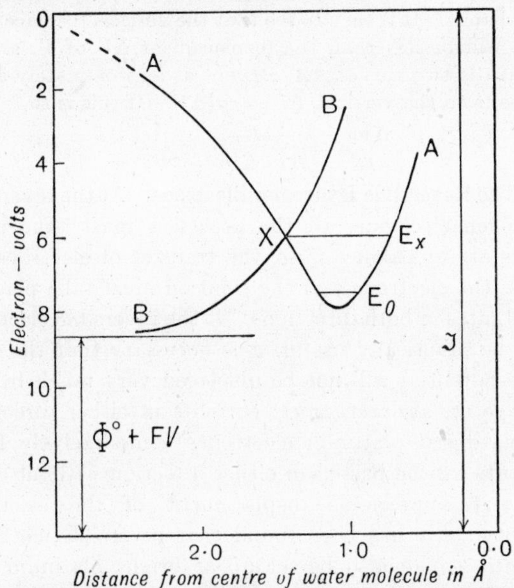

FIG. 57.—Condition of neutralisation of hydrated hydrogen ions.

The condition of neutralisation $\Phi^\circ + \mathbf{F}V < \mathfrak{I} - \mathbf{H} - R$ may be written as $\Phi^\circ + \mathbf{F}V + R < \mathfrak{I} - \mathbf{H}$. In Fig. 57, the curve AA represents $\mathfrak{I} - \mathbf{H}$, and the curve BB, $\Phi^\circ + \mathbf{F}V + R$. This condition is satisfied only by ions in states represented by points on the curve AA to the left of the intersection point X, *i.e.* with energies greater than E_x. The fraction of the ions having this energy is $e^{-(E_x-E_0)/RT}$, where E_0 is the energy of the ions in the state of lowest energy. The rate of neutralisation is therefore proportional to this quantity, and therefore

$$i = \text{const.} \times e^{-(E_x-E_0)/RT},$$

or

$$\log i = \text{const.} - (E_x - E_0)/RT.$$

When the potential difference V is changed, the position of the curve BB and therefore the intersection point X, will also change. It is easy to see that the vertical displacement of X will be less than the displacement ΔV of V, and in fact if the two curves AA, BB cut at approximately equal angles from the vertical, $\Delta E_x = ca\frac{1}{2}\Delta V$. If this is so,

$$\frac{\Delta \log i}{\Delta V} = \frac{-\Delta E_x}{RT \, . \, \Delta V} = -\frac{1}{2RT}.$$

*** The Reversible Hydrogen Electrode.** At the reversible hydrogen electrode, all the processes must take place in a state of balance ; *i.e.* the transfer of electrons between the electrode and the solution must take place at equal rates in both directions. If the reversible electrode is to be practically useful, it is necessary that the electrode potential will not be displaced very much by the passage of, at least, small currents in either direction. At platinised platinum electrodes comparatively large currents can be passed in either direction without causing any appreciable displacement of the electrode potential. It has been found that reversible electrode potentials may also be set up at bright platinum surfaces, if these are "activated" by alternately making them the anode and the cathode in the solution.* It is probable that, in this process of activation, surface contamination and particularly deposits of lead and arsenic are removed.†

* Butler and Armstrong, *J. Chem. Soc.*, 743, 1934.

† Volmer and Wick, *Z. physikal Chem.*, **172**, 429, 1935.

At such "active" electrodes the overvoltage is small, and with small currents it varies *linearly* with the current. This linear relation can easily be understood if the transfer of electrons from the electrode to the solution and in the reverse direction both obey Tafel's relation. If i_0 is the rate of transfer in both directions at the reversible potential V_0, the rates of the two processes at another potential V will be given by: *

$$i' = i_0 e^{-\mathrm{F}(V-V_0)/\gamma RT},$$
$$i'' = i_0 e^{+\mathrm{F}(V-V_0)/\gamma' RT};$$

and the actual current passing through the electrode will be the difference between the rates of transfer in the two directions, viz.

$$i = i' - i'' = i_0\{e^{-\mathrm{F}(V-V_0)/\gamma RT} - e^{+\mathrm{F}(V-V_0)/\gamma RT}\}.$$

For small values of $V - V_0$, this may be approximated to

$$i = i_0 . \mathrm{F} . \frac{V_0 - V}{RT}\left(\frac{1}{\gamma} + \frac{1}{\gamma'}\right).$$

The displacement of the potential caused by a current i therefore depends on the magnitude of i_0, and if ΔV is small i_0 must be large compared with i.† For a practically reversible electrode i_0 should be at least 10^{-4} amps.

The mechanism illustrated by Fig. 57 does not, however, account for the reversible electrode. This diagram shows the conditions of formation of isolated hydrogen atoms. These must subsequently combine to form molecular hydrogen H_2, which has a considerably lower energy than that of the isolated hydrogen atoms, and will therefore be represented in Fig. 57 by a line considerably below *BB*. It will there-

* The rate of transfer of electrons from the metal to the solution will be decreased and that of the reverse change increased by increasing V, *i.e.* making the electrode more positive. The Tafel factors γ, γ' for the two processes are not necessarily equal.

† See Erdey Grúsz and Volmer, *Z. physikal Chem.*, 150, 203, 1930; Butler, *Trans. Faraday Soc.*, 28, 379, 1932; Hammett, *ibid.*, 29, 770, 1933; Hoekstra, *Z. Phys. Chem.*, 166, 77, 1933; Butler, *Z. Electrochem.*, 44, 55, 1938.

fore be much more difficult for hydrogen molecules than for hydrogen atoms to lose electrons and become hydrogen ions. It is possible that a potential could be found at which the processes $H^+ + \epsilon \rightleftharpoons \frac{1}{2}H_2$ occur at equal rates, but the actual rate in either direction would be very small, and would not be sufficient for a practically reversible electrode.

There is, however, another possibility, *i.e.* that the hydrogen atoms are formed not in the free state, but adsorbed on the surface of the metal.* If A is the adsorption energy of atomic hydrogen (which may be regarded as a function of the distance of the hydrogen atom from the metal surface), the neutralisation energy will be

$$\mathfrak{J} - \mathbf{H} + A.$$

If the neutral atom at the instant of its formation in the region between the water molecules and the metal surface ($H_2O - H - Me$) is regarded as being under the influence of both the repulsive forces of the water molecule and the attractive (adsorptive) forces of the metal, the neutralisation energy will be $E_n = \mathfrak{J} - \mathbf{H} + A - R$, and the condition of neutralisation will become

$$\Phi + \mathbf{F}V > E_n,$$

or

$$\Phi + \mathbf{F}V + R - A > \mathfrak{J} - \mathbf{H}.$$

This is illustrated by Fig. 58, which shows the energy relations in the region between the metal surface and the nearest water molecules. CC is the curve showing how the adsorption energy A varies with distance from the surface. The known adsorption energy of hydrogen atoms on nickel has been used in constructing this curve. AA represents $\mathfrak{J} - \mathbf{H}$, and BB, $\Phi + \mathbf{F}V + R$, as in Fig. 57. Combining BB and CC, we get $C'C'$, representing

* Butler, *Proc. Roy. Soc.*, 157, 423, 1936; cf. Horiuti and Polanyi, *Acta Physicochimica*, 2, 505, 1935.

$\Phi + \mathbf{F}V + R - A$. The new intersection point X' (of $C'C'$ with AA) is much lower than the original intersection X (of AA with BB), *i.e.* it is easier to form adsorbed hydrogen than free hydrogen. It will evidently be possible by

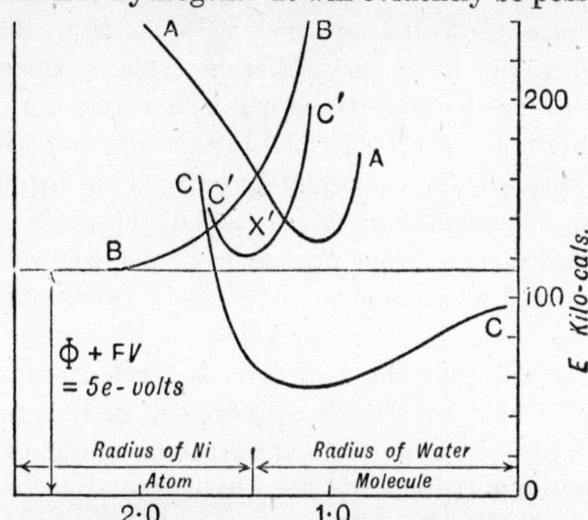

FIG. 58.—Mechanism of reversible hydrogen electrode.

varying the potential difference to realise a state in which this process, which we may represent as

$$H_3O^+ + Me + \epsilon \rightleftharpoons H_2O + H - Me,$$

occurs at equal rates in both directions, and since the critical energy X' is only a little higher than the minima of the curves AA and CC on each side, the rates of these processes under the equilibrium conditions may be quite large, *i.e.* this process can give rise to a practical reversible electrode.

The formation of adsorbed hydrogen in this way is only the first step in its liberation. It must next be desorbed. If we assume that it is desorbed by *two* nearby adsorbed atoms leaving the surface as a hydrogen molecule, it follows that the rate of desorption will be kx^2, where x is the fraction of the surface covered by adsorbed hydrogen. Hydrogen will therefore accumulate at the electrode until the rate of desorption is equal to its rate of formation, *i.e.* $kx^2 = i$. Now different electrodes may have very different rates of desorption, but for every electrode there will be a maximum rate at which hydrogen can be formed in this way, viz. the rate of desorption from a completely covered surface ($x = 1$). If a larger current than this is passed, the potential will change until some other process by which hydrogen can be formed can come into operation. Such a process might be something similar to Gurney's process, with the difference that the hydrogen is formed at a metal surface covered by adsorbed hydrogen, or it is possible that a hydrogen atom formed by the discharge of H_3O^+ may combine with an adsorbed hydrogen atom, viz.

$$H_3O^+ + H - Me + \epsilon \rightarrow H_2O + H_2 + Me.^*$$

† **Electrolytic Separation of Hydrogen Isotopes.** After the discovery by Urey of the heavy isotope of hydrogen of mass 2 (deuterium), it was found by Washburn and Urey and by G. N. Lewis that it could be concentrated in aqueous solutions by electrolysis.† The hydrogen liberated at the cathode contains a smaller proportion of deuterium than the water undergoing electrolysis, so that the residual solution in the electrolytic cell gets continually richer in deuterium. Suppose the amounts of hydrogen and deuterium in the electrolyte are repre-

* A theory that the rate determining step is the accumulation of atomic hydrogen at the electrode has been developed by Hickling and Salt (*Trans. Faraday Soc.*, 38, 474, 1942).

† Lewis and Macdonald, *J. Chem. Physics*, 7, 341, 1933.

sented by $[H]$ and $[D]$, and when a small amount of electrolysis is performed the amounts in the liberated gas are $d[H]$ and $d[D]$; then the ratio of the proportion of H and D in the liberated gas to those in the water is called the electrolytic separation coefficient, α, *i.e.*

$$\frac{d[H]}{d[D]}=\alpha\frac{[H]}{[D]},$$

or

$$\frac{d \log [H]}{d \log [D]}=\alpha.$$

The values of α obtained vary somewhat with the nature and state of the electrode metal and the conditions of the electrolysis. Thus Topley and Eyring* found values between 5 and 8 (*i.e.* the proportion of D in the liberated gas was $\frac{1}{5}$ to $\frac{1}{8}$ of that in the liquid) for electrodes of lead, bright platinum, iron, copper, nickel and silver, while platinum black and activated platinum gave lower separations of from 3 to 4. The factor seems to be about the same in acid and alkaline solutions.

Appleby and Ogden† suggested that factors between 30 and 100 could be obtained in water of low deuterium concentration, but Walton and Wolfenden‡ could not confirm this result.

Horiuti and Okomoto§ found that metal electrodes could be divided into two classes, comprising (1) Ag, Ni, Pt, Au, Cu, Pb (in alkali), having separation factors between 6 and 7 ; (2) Hg, Sn, Pb (in acid) having separa-

* *Ibid.*, 2, 217, 1934 ; cf. Bell and Wolfenden, *Nature*, 133, 25, 1934 ; *Proc. Roy. Soc.*, A 144, 22, 1934 ; *J. Chem. Soc.*, 286, 1936 ; Brown and Daggett, *J. Chem. Physics*, 3, 216, 1935 ; Tronstad and Brun, *Z. Electrochem.*, 40, 556, 1934.

† *J. Chem. Soc.*, 163, 1936. ‡ *Ibid.*, 1677, 1937.

§ *Sci. Papers Inst. Phys. Chem. Res., Tokyo*, 28, 231, 1936 ; 29, 223, 1936.

tion factors about 3. Walton and Wolfenden * confirmed this, and also found that in the first group the temperature coefficient of α was large and negative, and in the second zero or positive. The former suggest that in both cases the first step is the formation of adsorbed hydrogen by the process

$$H_3O^+ + Me + \epsilon \rightarrow H_2O + H - Me,$$

and molecular hydrogen is formed in the first group by direct desorption :

$$(1)\ 2H - Me \rightarrow H_2 + 2Me \quad (\alpha = 6 - 7) :$$

and in the second group by the electrochemical process :

$$(2)\ Me - H + H_3O^+ + \epsilon = Me + H_2 + H_2O \quad (\alpha = 3).$$

As shown above (p. 208), there is an upper limit to the rate of liberation of hydrogen by process (1), and even with active electrodes process (2) would come into operation when the current exceeded this rate. We should therefore expect the separation factor with metals of group (1) to diminish at large current densities. A certain decrease often occurs, but not as much as might be expected. On the other hand, Eucken and Bratzler † found that electrode poisons, which increase the overvoltage,‡ also diminish the separation factor. These substances presumably act by becoming adsorbed on the surface and thereby reducing its effective area, so that the real current density is increased.

Bowden and Kenyon § found that at a mercury electrode the overvoltage was 0·13 volts higher in 98 per cent. D_2O than at the same current density in ordinary water.

* *Trans. Faraday Soc.*, 34, 436, 1938.

† *Z. physik. Chem.*, 174, 273, 1935.

‡ Jenckel and Bräuker, *Z. anorg. Chem.*, 221, 249, 1935.

§ *Nature*, 135, 105, 1935.

The slope of the $V - \log i$ curve is the same, so that under these conditions the rate of discharge of H_3O^+ is 13·5 times as great as that of deuterium ions, D_3O^+, at the same electrode potential. This ratio is appreciably greater than the separation factors obtained with solutions containing small proportions of deuterium. Walton and Wolfenden suggest that this means that the rate-determining step involves two hydrogen atoms. In pure D_2O the rate will be that of the formation of D_2, while in small proportions of deuterium the separation factor will be determined by the rate of formation of HD, and the factor in the latter case should be the square root of the former.

It is also necessary to take into account the possibility that the exchange reaction

$$DH + H_2O = H_2 + DOH$$

may occur, so that the gas which leaves the electrode may differ in deuterium content from that initially formed. Farkas and Farkas * found the equilibrium constant of the reaction to be 3·8 at 15°, *i.e.* the ratio of the concentration of deuterium in water to that in the gas in equilibrium with it is 3·8 for small proportions of deuterium. The separation coefficient should have this value, irrespective of the discharge rates, when the liberated gas has the opportunity to exchange and come into equilibrium with the water. It was found that when electrolysis was carried out with platinised electrodes, the evolved gas had the equilibrium composition, but with mercury the amount of exchange is quite negligible. Hirota and Horiuti † give the order of the

* *Proc. Roy. Soc.*, **146 A**, 623, 1934.

† *Sci. Papers, Inst. Phys. Chem. Res.*, **30**, 151, 1936.

activity of the metals in promoting the exchange reaction as Pt>Ni>Fe>Cu>Au>Ag>Hg.

* **Establishment of the Overvoltage.** Bowden and Rideal * made experiments to determine the quantities of electricity required to establish the hydrogen overvoltage at metallic electrodes. They found that in order to obtain reproducible results it was necessary to saturate the solutions with pure hydrogen which had been carefully freed from traces of oxygen. The change of the potential with time in the first instants after making the electrode the cathode is observed by photographing the movements of the fibre of an Einthoven galvanometer, which is so arranged that its displacement is proportional to the potential difference between the electrode and a reference electrode. Fig. 59 shows the changes observed at a mercury cathode, using a current density of 4×10^{-5} amps./cm.^{2}. The electrode potential at first changes linearly with the time, but in the vicinity of the overvoltage the slope decreases and eventually a constant value is reached, at which the discharge of hydrogen ions takes place at a rate equal to the current.

At first, the potential being considerably more positive than the hydrogen overvoltage, the rate of transfer of electrons from the metal to ions in the solution is negligible compared with the current, and the whole of the flow of electricity in the circuit goes to increase the charge of the double layer, *i.e.* electrons accumulate on the metal side and positive ions on the solution side of the double layer, but there is no appreciable transport of electricity across the double layer. The initial slope of the curve of Fig. 59 thus measures the *capacity* of the electrode, *i.e.* the increase of the charge on the two sides

* *Proc. Roy. Soc.*, **120 A**, 59, 1928.

of the electrode required to increase the potential difference by 1 volt. If i is the current, the increase of the charge of the double layer in the time dt is $i\,dt$, and if dV is the change of potential difference under these conditions, the capacity is

$$B = \frac{i\,dt}{dV}. \qquad (93)$$

Bowden and Rideal found that at mercury cathodes, the

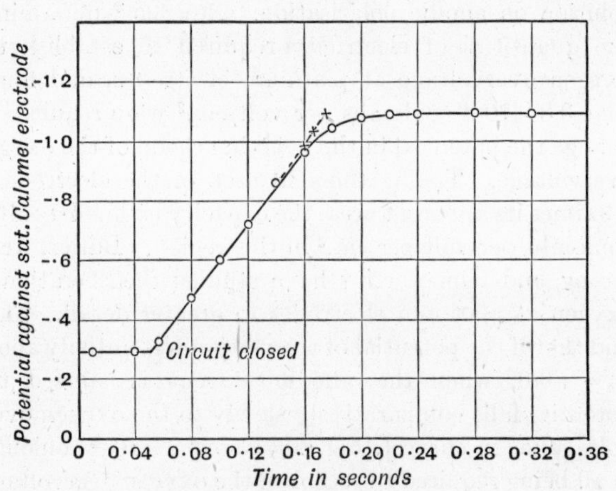

FIG. 59.—Change of potential of mercury electrode on starting cathodic current (Bowden and Rideal).

true area of which was assumed to be equal to the measured area, the value of B was 6×10^{-6} coulombs per volt per cm.^{2}. Assuming that other metal surfaces have the same area, they were able by measuring the capacity in this way to determine the real areas of electrodes of solid metals. Proskurnin and Frumkin * have, however, obtained considerably higher values for

* *Trans. Faraday Soc.*, 31, 110, 1935; see *ibid*, 36, 117, 1940

the capacity of mercury in sulphuric acid solutions ($18-20 \times 10^{-6}$ coulombs per volt per cm.^{2}), using an all-glass apparatus, and have suggested that the low values previously obtained were due to the partial covering of the electrode surface by adsorbed paraffins and similar materials derived from stopcocks, etc.

The establishment of the oxygen overvoltage can only be studied at inert electrodes which do not pass into solution on anodic polarisation. Bowden * determined the quantities of electricity required to establish the oxygen overvoltage at platinum electrodes, and found that $3 \cdot 8 \times 10^{-4}$ coulombs per volt/cm.^{2} were required to change the potential in the neighbourhood of the oxygen overvoltage. Taking the real area of the electrode as 3·3 times its apparent area, the capacity is thus $1 \cdot 1 \times 10^{-4}$ coulombs per volt per cm.^{2} in this region. Butler, Armstrong and Himsworth † have studied the liberation of oxygen at platinum electrodes in greater detail. They find that if the potential of the platinum is initially about $\mathbf{E}_h = +0 \cdot 6$, when the anodic current is started the potential falls comparatively slowly to the oxygen overvoltage (as in curve I, Fig. 60), about 9×10^{-4} coulombs in all being required to establish the oxygen overvoltage. If the current is now reversed, the potential rises at first linearly and much more rapidly (curve II), and if, when the potential has not become more negative than $\mathbf{E}_n = 0 \cdot 9$, the electrode is again made the anode, the potential falls again at the same rapid rate to the oxygen discharge point. The quantity of electricity required for the original process corresponds approximately with

* *Proc. Roy. Soc.*, 125 A, 446, 1929.

† *Proc. Roy. Soc.*, 137 A, 604, 1932; 143 A, 89, 1933; also Butler and Drever, *Trans. Faraday Soc.*, 32, 427, 1936.

that required to liberate an amount of oxygen sufficient to give a single layer of adsorbed oxygen atoms over the electrode surface. It is therefore suggested that a layer of adsorbed oxygen is formed before the oxygen overvoltage is reached. So long as this is not destroyed, the quantities of electricity required to change the potential (as in curves II and III) correspond to the double layer capacity of the electrode.* But if the electrode potential is taken by cathodic polarisation to $E_h = +0{\cdot}4$, the

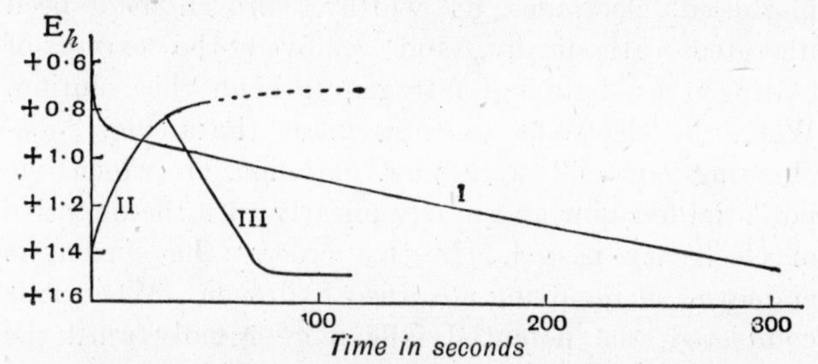

FIG. 60.—Changes of potential prior to establishment of oxygen overvoltage (Butler and Armstrong).

oxygen layer is destroyed and an anodic polarisation curve I is again obtained.

We may now enquire if any similar phenomenon occurs at cathodes before hydrogen is liberated. The behaviour of cathodes is more complicated, because hydrogen is often readily adsorbed on the electrode from solutions containing molecular hydrogen. Experiments in hydrogen containing solutions, as that in Fig. 59, are inconclusive, because the electrode may be covered by adsorbed hydrogen at the beginning. Alternatively, if a cathode at which hydrogen has been liberated is made

* The value of B as given by these curves was 1×10^{-4} coulombs per volt for an electrode having an estimated area of 3 $cm.^2$.

the anode, the removal of the adsorbed hydrogen by the process $[H] \rightarrow H^+ + \epsilon$ should be detected. However, if an active hydrogen electrode is made the anode, the hydrogen removed by this electrolytic process is replaced by adsorption from the solution, and the potential remains near the reversible hydrogen potential so long as any molecular hydrogen can reach the electrode by diffusion. This diffusion can, however, be avoided in various ways. Frumkin and collaborators * took platinised electrodes at which hydrogen had been liberated cathodically, and removed the excess of hydrogen by bubbling nitrogen through the solution. When the electrode was now made the anode, " discharging curves " were now obtained, in which the potential fell slow and nearly linearly with the quantity of electricity passed. In this process the current is employed in removing adsorbed hydrogen. When it is completed, the potential falls more rapidly until the point at which adsorbed oxygen can be formed is reached. If the potential is not made too positive, this process is reversible, for on reversing the current the curve of potential against coulombs is retraced.

Another method of avoiding the diffusion of hydrogen to the electrode was used by Pearson and Butler.† If very large anodic currents (1 to 4) amps./cm.²) are used, the discharging process takes place very quickly, and there is no time for any appreciable diffusion from the solution. A typical example of the " discharging curves " obtained in this way, with bright platinum electrodes, is shown in Fig. 61. The first stage (α) represents the

* *Acta Physicochimica, U.R.S.S.*, 3, 791, 1935; 4, 911, 1936; 5, 819, 1936; 6, 195, 1937; 7, 327, 1937.

† *Trans. Faraday Soc.*, 34, 1163, 1938.

removal of a monatomic layer of adsorbed hydrogen. When this is completed the potential falls more rapidly (stage β) and then a second slower stage (γ) occurs, which requires twice as many coulombs as α. This pro-

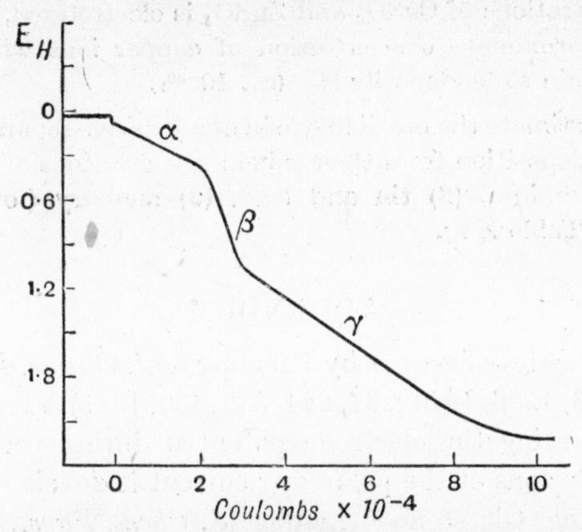

FIG. 61.—Anodic oscillogram of platinum electrode (0·5 cm.^{2}) in dilute sulphuric acid.

cess, which is identical with that which occurs in Fig. 60, curve I, is the deposition of a number of adsorbed oxygen atoms equal to the number of hydrogen atoms removed in stage α.

For further information on electrode processes the reader is referred to the author's *Electrocapillarity: The Physics and Chemistry of Charged Surfaces*, 1940 (Methuen).

Examples.

1. Estimate the decomposition voltages of normal solutions of the following salts with bright platinum electrodes : $HgNO_3$, $SnCl_2$, $FeSO_4$, Na_2SO_4, LiCl. (Use Tables XV, XXI, XXIII.)

2. What would be the decomposition voltage of sulphuric acid with a gold anode and nickel cathode? (*ca.* 1·9).

3. The standard electrode potentials of zinc and copper are − 0·76 and + 0·34. If a solution which contains molar concentrations of $CuSO_4$ and $ZnSO_4$ is electrolysed, what is the approximate concentration of copper ions when zinc ions begin to be deposited? (*ca.* 10^{-30}.)

4. Estimate the possibility of a quantitative separation by electrodeposition from their mixed salt solutions of (1) iron and cadmium, (2) tin and lead, (3) mercury (-ous) and silver (Table XV).

ADDENDUM

In a series of papers by Hickling *et al.* (*Trans. Faraday Soc.*, **36**, 1226, 1940 ; **37**, 224, 333, 450, 1941), a technique of observing the electrode potential during very short interruptions of the polarising current is developed.

Eyring, Glasstone & Laidler (*J. Chem. Phys.*, 7, 1053, 1939 ; see also *ibid.*, 9, 91, 1941) developed a theory of hydrogen overvoltage in which the rate of liberation of hydrogen is independent of the hydrogen ion concentration. This has been criticised by Butler (*ibid.*, **9**, 279, 1941).

The student should also consult the Faraday Society's discussion on *The Electrical Double Layer*, *Trans. Faraday Soc.*, **36**, 1–322, 1940.

CHAPTER X

ELECTROLYSIS (*Continued*).

Reversible Oxidation and Reduction Processes. If an electrode at which a reversible oxidation potential (such as that set up by ferrous and ferric ions, or quinone and hydroquinone) is established is made the cathode and a small current is passed, reduction occurs at a potential which is only slightly displaced from the reversible value. Similarly on anodic polarisation with small currents oxidation is effected at a potential only slightly displaced (in the positive direction) from the reversible value.

The reversible potential of an oxidation-reduction system is that at which electrons pass from the electrode to the oxidant and from the reductant to the electrode at equal rates, which are not inappreciable and may be comparatively large. When the potential is displaced in, say, a negative direction the rate of transfer of electrons from the electrode to the reductant is increased, while the rate of transfer in the reverse direction is diminished. The rate at which reduction occurs is the difference between these two rates, and it can easily be seen that a change of the potential of a few millivolts will be sufficient for electrolysis with a small current.* There is thus no necessity for a large overvoltage, to effect reduction or oxidation at a reversible electrode.

However, it has been found that with larger currents, while the potential at the beginning of the electrolysis is near the reversible potential, after a time (which depends on the current) it rises to a value near that at which hydrogen (or oxygen) are liberated. This phenomenon is due to *concentration polarisation.* It occurs whenever a substance is used up in an electrolytic process faster than it can diffuse to the electrode from the bulk of the solution. This is a very common occurrence in the electrolysis of aqueous solutions, and may conveniently be described here.

Concentration Polarisation. Some typical curves of the change of potential with time during the electrolytic reduction of methylene blue to methylene white at a platinum electrode in unstirred solutions are shown in Fig. 62.† At first the potential remains near the reversible oxidation potential of the solution (*ca.* $-0{\cdot}2$), but after an interval, which increases rapidly as the current

* If k is the rate of transfer of electrons to and from the electrode at the equilibrium potential V_0, by analogy with the hydrogen ion discharge process the rate of transfer from electrode to oxidant at the potential V is $i' = ke^{-a'(V-V_0)}$, while the rate of the reverse process (which is influenced in the opposite direction) is $i'' = ke^{+a''(V-V_0)}$. The net rate of reduction is thus

$$i = i' - i'' = -k(a' + a'')(V - V_0) \text{ (approx.)}.$$

a' and a'' are not necessarily equal to the a of the hydrogen ion discharge process, but for small values of $V - V_0$, i is proportional to the displacement of the potential, and if k is not very small, an appreciable current can be passed, when $V - V_0$ is only a few millivolts.

† Butler and Armstrong, *Proc. Roy. Soc.*, 139 A, 406, 1933.

is decreased, it rises rather quickly to potentials at which hydrogen is liberated. The time from the start of the electrolysis to the middle of the rapid rise is called the transition time (τ).

Sand * supposed that the transition occurred when the

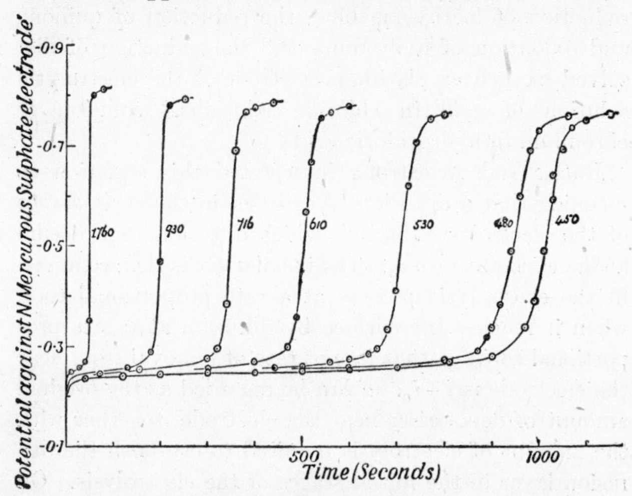

Fig. 62.—Cathodic polarisation of 0·04% methylene blue solution (currents, amps. × 10^{-7}).

concentration of the depolariser at the electrode surface was reduced to zero. Using Fick's diffusion equation and making certain assumptions about the concentration gradient near the surface, he calculated that the transition time should be related to the current and the concentration of the depolariser by

$$\tau = k(c/i)^2,$$

and experiments on the deposition of metals supported

* *Phil. Mag.*, 1, 45, 1901; *Z. physikal Chem.*, 35, 641, 1900; *Trans. Faraday Soc.*, 1, 1, 1905.

this. More recently, however, it has been found that the simpler relation

$$\tau(i - i_0) = \alpha,$$

where i_0 and α are constants for a given solution, holds for a wide range of currents in many cases, such as the reduction of methylene blue, the reduction of quinone and oxidation of hydroquinone,* the reduction of dissolved oxygen at platinum electrodes,† the electrolytic solution of gold in chloride solutions,‡ solution of chromium in hydrochloric acid.§

Butler and Armstrong interpreted this equation as meaning that a diffusion layer is set in the early stages of the electrolysis through which diffusion then occurs at the constant rate i_0. The depolariser is then removed in the electrolytic process at a rate proportional to i, when it reaches the surface by diffusion at a rate proportional to i_0, so that its net rate of removal from near the electrode is $i - i_0$. α can be regarded as the original amount of depolariser near the electrode, together with the amount of electrolysis required to establish the diffusion layer in the initial stages of the electrolysis. On this view both i_0 and α should be proportional to the concentration of the depolariser, and this has been found to be the case.

From the observed values of i_0 and the diffusion coefficients of substances it is possible to calculate the approximate thickness of the layer of non-uniform concentration through which diffusion takes place. Values

* Butler and Armstrong, *loc. cit.*

† *Proc. Roy. Soc.*, 143 A, 89, 1933.

‡ Shutt and Walton, *Trans. Faraday Soc.*, 30, 914, 1934; Butler and Armstrong, *ibid.*, 30, 1173, 1934; 34, 806, 1938.

§ Roberts and Shutt, *ibid.*, 34, 1455, 1938.

between 10^{-2} and 10^{-3} cm. have been obtained for unstirred solutions.* If the solution is stirred, the thickness of the layer becomes smaller and the rate of diffusion is increased and the limiting current i_0 is then greater. Thus in order to obtain the greatest possible amount of electrolysis before the transition occurs, it is desirable to use as large a concentration and as small a current as may be practicable, and to stir the solution as vigorously as possible.

In many investigations the complete potential-time curves (like Fig. 62) have not been determined, but the

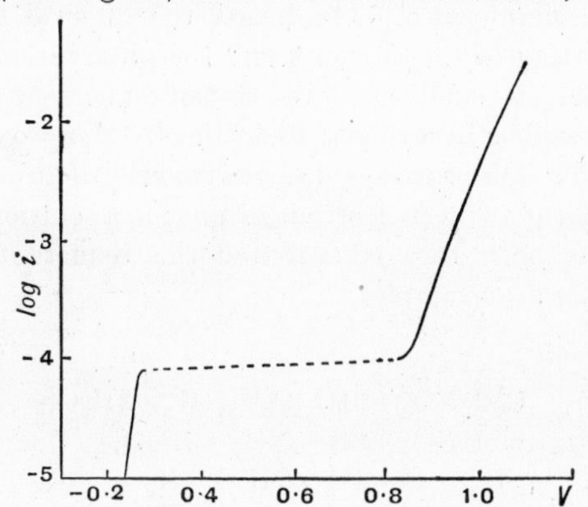

FIG. 63.—Current-potential curve of cathodic process, showing transition.

current-voltage curve has been constructed by noting the potential reached in a convenient time (say 5 mins.) after starting the current. In most cases an apparently constant potential is reached in this interval, and if the values are plotted against the currents they give rise to curves like Fig. 63, which shows a transition to a higher

* Cf. Wilson and Youtz, *Ind. Eng. Chem.*, 15, 603, 1923.

potential at a certain value of the current which is sometimes called the transition current. It is evident from Fig. 62 that when observations are made after an interval of, say, 300 secs., the potential will be found to be still on the first stage if the current is small, but if the current is large the transition will have taken place and the final value will have been reached. At some intermediate value of the current the potential will be on the transition stage at the time of observation. This will be the "transition current," but since it obviously depends on the time at which the observations are made, it has no definite significance. The longer the interval between the starting of the currents and the observation of the potential, the smaller will the transition current be.

Irreversible Electrolytic Reductions. Many oxidation and reduction processes do not give rise to any definite potential at an inert electrode dipping in a solution which contains both the oxidant and the reductant. The following are examples.

Reductions :

$$C_6H_5NO_2 + 6H = C_6H_5NH_2 + 2H_2O,$$
$$HNO_3 + 8H = NH_3 + 3H_2O,$$
$$HCO_2H + 4H = CH_4O + H_2O,$$
$$NaNO_3 + 2H = NaNO_2 + H_2O.$$

Oxidations :

$$NH_3 + 3O = HNO_2 + H_2O,$$
$$NaHSO_3 + O = NaHSO_4,$$
$$HIO_3 + O = HIO_4.$$

Nevertheless, these reactions can often be easily brought about by electrolysis, the reductions taking place under suitable conditions at the cathode and the oxidations at the anode. In many cases it is probable that the primary product of the electrolysis is hydrogen at the cathode and oxygen at the anode, which then react with the substances present in the solution. But although a vast amount of empirical information as to the best conditions for carrying out individual reactions has been accumulated, few generalisations can be made and the mechanisms of these processes need fuller investigation.

Haber and Russ * investigated the electrolytic reduction of nitrobenzene, and, on the assumption that the electrode behaved like a hydrogen electrode, they represented the electrode potentials measured during the reduction by

$$E = E^{\circ} + \frac{RT}{\mathrm{F}} \log \frac{[\mathrm{H}^{+}]}{[\mathrm{H}]}, \qquad \text{.............. (94)}$$

where [H] is the concentration of free hydrogen near the electrode. The latter is determined by the equality of its rate of formation i and its rate of reaction with the depolariser. If the reaction is represented as

$$\mathrm{X} + n\mathrm{H} \rightarrow \mathrm{XH}_{n},$$

the rate will be $k[\mathrm{X}]\,[\mathrm{H}]^{n}$, where [X] is the depolariser concentration, and therefore when the hydrogen reacts as fast as formed, $i = k[\mathrm{X}]\,[\mathrm{H}]^{n}$.

Introducing this into (108), we get

$$E = E^{\circ} + \frac{RT}{\mathrm{F}} \log\,[\mathrm{H}^{+}] + \frac{RT}{n\mathrm{F}} \log \frac{k[\mathrm{X}]}{i}.$$

It was found that this represented the dependence of E on the current and depolariser concentration in alkaline solutions of nitrobenzene at electrodes of platinum, gold and silver when n was taken as 1. But the derivation assumes that the electrode always acts as

* *Z. physikal Chem.*, 44, 641, 1903 ; 47, 257, 1904.

a reversible hydrogen electrode, its potential being determined by the concentration of "free" hydrogen near the electrode. We have seen that ordinary smooth electrodes of these metals do not behave in this way, and their potential during the liberation of hydrogen is not determined by the amount of hydrogen present near the electrode, so that Haber's theory is no longer tenable.

Leslie and Butler * suggested that electrolytic reduction might take place in three ways :

(1) by direct transfer of electrons from the electrode to the depolariser ;
(2) by reaction between the depolariser and "free" or loosely attached atomic hydrogen ; †
(3) by reaction between the depolariser and adsorbed hydrogen.

It is possible to distinguish these cases by studying the conditions under which reduction occurs. It is clear at the outset that (3) will be more likely to occur at reversible and low overvoltage electrodes from which hydrogen is easily desorbed ; while (2) will probably occur at high overvoltage electrodes at which the rate of desorption is small and "free" hydrogen is formed. If the reaction is a purely secondary reaction between "free" hydrogen and the reducible substance, in the absence of disturbing factors the potential will be that at which hydrogen is normally liberated when no depolariser is present. Leslie and Butler found this to be the case with acetone, sodium formate and pyridine at lead electrodes.

* *Trans. Faraday Soc.*, 32, 989, 1936.

† This would include hydrogen loosely attached to an adsorbed film of hydrogen covering the electrode, as MeH ... H.

Tafel * showed that the reduction of substances like pyridine and compounds containing the keto group, which are difficult to reduce, can be readily accomplished at cathodes of mercury and lead, while little or no reduction takes place at a platinum electrode. He concluded that a high overvoltage was necessary, and in order to secure this it is desirable that the cathode metal should be free from impurities, as even traces of foreign metals lower the overvoltage considerably. It is clear that in these cases the reduction is effected by the free or loosely attached atomic hydrogen which is formed at these electrodes.

On the other hand some substances, such as unsaturated acids, *e.g.* cinnamic acid, are more easily reduced at platinised platinum and similar electrodes than at electrodes having a high overvoltage. In such cases it is probable that the reduction is effected by adsorbed hydrogen, and it would appear that the process only differs from catalytic hydrogenation, which takes place easily at the same surfaces, in that the hydrogen is produced by electrolysis on the electrode surface.

In other cases the reduction occurs at potentials which are considerably less negative than those required for the liberation of hydrogen at the same electrode. For example, in dilute solutions of nitrobenzene reduction occurs at $E_h = 0{\cdot}0$ to $0{\cdot}2$ volts at a mercury cathode, while the potential required for the liberation of hydrogen at the same rate is $E_h = -0{\cdot}8$ to $-1{\cdot}2$ volts. It is obvious therefore that the reduction cannot be effected by reaction with hydrogen as ordinarily formed at this electrode. It is possible that the reduction is effected by the adsorbed hydrogen, which might be formed at the

* *Z. physikal Chem.*, 34, 187, 1900.

more positive potential, but it is unlikely that hydrogen adsorbed on mercury, being very firmly bound, would be very reactive. It is more probable that the reduction occurs by direct electron transfer from the electrode to nitrobenzene, giving rise to the ion $C_6H_5NO_2^=$, which reacts irreversibly with hydrogen ions to form the first reduction product, nitrosobenzene :

$$C_6H_5NO_2 \xrightarrow{2\epsilon} C_6H_5NO_2^=,$$

$$C_6H_5NO_2^= + 2H^+ \rightarrow C_6H_5NO + H_2O.$$

It might be asked why nitro- and nitroso-benzene in this case do not give rise to a reversible oxidation potential. The reason is, presumably, that the ion $C_6H_5NO_2^=$ is not in reversible equilibrium with the nitrosobenzene.

Nitrosobenzene is more easily reduced than the original nitrobenzene, so that it does not accumulate in the solution. Its formation was proved by Haber by adding hydroxylamine and α-naphthol, with which it forms and precipitates $C_6H_5N \cdot NC_{10}H_6OH$. The reduction to phenyl-hydroxylamine probably occurs by a process analogous to the first stage, viz. :

$$C_6H_5 \cdot NO \xrightarrow{2\epsilon} C_6H_5 \cdot NO^= \overset{2H^+}{\rightleftarrows} C_6H_5NH \cdot OH,$$

but in this case the second step is believed to be reversible. The reduction of the hydroxylamine to aniline occurs rapidly at electrodes of zinc, lead, tin, copper, mercury ; but not to any great extent at platinum, nickel and carbon. This last stage may therefore be effected by " free " atomic hydrogen.

Various side products may also be formed under

suitable conditions. In alkaline solution azoxybenzene may be formed by the following reaction :

$$C_6H_5NO + C_6H_5NH \cdot OH \rightarrow C_6H_5 \cdot N_2O \cdot C_6H_5 \; ;$$

and this substance may be further reduced at a high overvoltage electrode to hydrazobenzene,

$$C_6H_5 \cdot NH \cdot NH \cdot C_6H_5,$$

and the latter reacts also with nitrobenzene to give azobenzene, $C_6H_5 \cdot N_2 \cdot C_6H_5$. Either of these substances may be obtained by suitably varying the conditions. For example, at low overvoltage electrodes, phenylhydrazine is formed in neutral or slightly neutral solutions and azoxybenzene in alkaline solutions. The latter is only slightly soluble in cold water, and to obtain its reduction products it is necessary to increase its solubility by using a suitable solvent.

Electrolytic Oxidations. Electrolytic oxidations might be brought about by any of the following processes :

A. A primary electrochemical oxidation by the direct transfer of electrons from the substance to the electrode, *e.g.* $Cl^- \rightarrow \frac{1}{2}Cl_2 + \epsilon$.

B. A secondary oxidation brought about by a primary product of the electrolysis, such as :

(1) Atomic oxygen.

(2) Adsorbed oxygen.

(3) Any other primary product of the electrolysis, *e.g.* peroxides formed on the electrode surface.

It is sometimes possible to distinguish between these processes by observing the electrode potentials and other circumstances under which the oxidation takes place. We will take as an illustration the oxidation of sodium sulphite solutions, which has been extensively studied.

Foerster and Friesner found * that the main products were sulphate and dithionate, but since the yield of dithionate was influenced by the nature and previous treatment of the electrode, the latter rejected the simple electrochemical mechanism ($2SO_3^{=} \rightarrow S_2O_6^{=} + 2\epsilon$), and suggested that in both cases the oxidation was effected by oxygen :

$$SO_3^{=} + O \rightarrow SO_4^{=},$$

$$2SO_3^{=} + O \rightarrow S_2O_6^{=} + O^{=}.$$

Essin † suggested that no dithionate could be formed until a certain pressure of oxygen was reached, but Glasstone and Hickling ‡ found that this view is untenable, since the formation of dithionate is not diminished by making the electrode potential less positive. These authors suggest that hydrogen peroxide, formed by the discharge of hydroxyl ions, viz.

$$OH^- \rightarrow OH + \epsilon, \ 2OH = H_2O_2,$$

is the primary product which brings about the oxidation.§

On this view it is supposed that dithionate is formed by the action of hydrogen peroxide alone, while sulphate is formed both by hydrogen peroxide and its decomposition product oxygen. Hence any circumstance which favours the decomposition of hydrogen peroxide will decrease the yield of dithionate and increase that of sulphate. In agreement with this, the addition of such substances as Mn^{++}, Fe^{++}, Co^{++}, etc., which are known to be catalysts for the decomposition of hydrogen peroxide, decrease the yield of dithionate ; but their action can be alternatively explained since it is known that with solutions containing traces of

* *Ber.*, 35, 2515, 1902 ; *Z. physikal Chem.*, **47**, 659, 1904 ; *Z. Electrochem.*, 10, 265, 1904.

† *Ibid.*, 34, 78, 1928. ‡ *J. Chem. Soc.*, 135, 829, 1933.

§ For a full account of this view, see *Chem. Revs.*, 25, 407, 1939.

these ions oxide films are deposited on the anode, and the change in the nature of the electrode surface is quite capable of producing the variation of the oxidation products. The yield of dithionate is also a maximum at p_H's between 7 and 9, which is explained by the consideration that increase of p_H increases the proportion of sulphite ions, $SO_3^=$ (in acid solutions SO_2 or HSO_3^- ions are present) and decreases the stability of hydrogen peroxide. Very similar observations have been made in the electrochemical oxidation of thiosulphate to tetrathionate, $2S_2O_3^= \rightarrow S_4O_6^=$.*

Butler and Leslie † found that in solutions of $p_H 7$ the oxidation begins at potentials more negative than that at which adsorbed oxygen is formed and at which no electrochemical process occurs in the absence of the sulphite. In this case it is difficult to avoid the conclusion that the primary process is the discharge of sulphite ions, followed by either polymerisation or reaction with water:

$$\begin{array}{ccccc} SO_3^= & \rightarrow & SO_3^- & \rightarrow & SO_3 \\ & & \downarrow & & \downarrow H_2O \\ & & S_2O_6^= & & H_2SO_4 \end{array}$$

In more alkaline solutions the potential at which adsorbed oxygen is formed moves to more negative potentials, and coincides with the potential at which the oxidation of the sulphite takes place. In these solutions ($p_H \geqq 9$), oxidation of the sulphite ions by adsorbed oxygen, viz. $SO_3^= + O \rightarrow SO_4^=$, is also possible, and this explains the decrease in the yield of dithionate which is observed.

There are many other oxidation processes which involve the discharge or partial discharge of anions and their polymerisation. The more important types are:

* Glasstone and Hickling, *J. Chem. Soc.*, 2345, 2800, 1932.

† *Trans. Faraday Soc.*, 32, 435, 1936.

(1) *Formation of Peracids and their Salts.* Persulphates are formed at the anode by the electrolysis of sulphate solutions: $2SO_4^{=} \rightarrow S_2O_8^{=} + 2\epsilon$. The necessary conditions are (1) a high concentration of sulphuric acid or sulphate ions, (2) a high current density and preferably a low temperature, (3) smooth platinum is the best electrode; very little persulphate is formed at platinised anodes. Similar methods are used for the formation of perphosphates (*e.g.* $K_2P_2O_8$) and percarbonates (*e.g.* $(K_2C_2O_6)$.

(2) *The Kolbe Reaction.* The formation of hydrocarbons and other substances by the electrolysis of solutions of alkali salts of fatty acids. The typical reaction is

$$2CH_3COO^- \rightarrow C_2H_6 + 2CO_2 + 2\epsilon,$$

but under various circumstances side reactions may occur, giving rise to methane, olefines (more especially with the higher acids), alcohols and esters. The mechanism of these reactions is still being discussed, and, for a review of the arguments, readers should consult Glasstone and Hickling's *Electrolytic Oxidation and Reduction* (Chapman & Hall).

Many neutral organic molecules can also be oxidised at anodes. In many cases the oxidation is effected by adsorbed or free oxygen. But in some cases peroxides are involved. For example, the oxidation of iodic to periodic acid takes place with 100 per cent. efficiency at an electrode of lead peroxide and with only 1 per cent. efficiency at smooth platinum. In the former case, the oxidation is probably effected by lead peroxide, which is electrolytically re-formed on the anode.

Electrolytic oxidations are sometimes facilitated by

the addition of catalysts, called oxygen carriers, to the electrolyte. These are usually salts of metals which exist in more than one state of oxidation. Thus, ceric sulphate is a good catalyst in many oxidations. When a suspension of anthracene in sulphuric acid is electrolysed, only a small amount of oxidation occurs, but if ceric sulphate is added anthraquinone is formed with a current efficiency of 80 per cent. The oxidation is, presumably, effected by the ceric ions, and the reduction product is re-oxidised at the anode. Salts of chromium, vanadium and manganese can also be used in this way.

The Electrolysis of Brine Solutions. When an aqueous solution of sodium chloride is electrolysed, the discharge potential of hydrogen ions at the cathode is reached long before that of sodium ions ($Na \rightarrow Na^+$, $E_0 = -2{\cdot}71$ volts). Hydrogen is therefore liberated and an excess of hydroxyl ions remains in the solution. Chlorine is liberated at the anode. If the anode and cathode solutions are separated by means of a diaphragm, the products of electrolysis are thus hydrogen and sodium hydroxide at the cathode, chlorine at the anode. If the anode and cathode solutions are continually mixed we get a series of reactions, the conditions of which have been investigated by Foerster. The following are the more important.

Chlorine reacts with the alkaline solution, yielding sodium hypochlorite :

$$Cl_2 + 2NaOH = NaCl + NaClO + H_2O.$$

With efficient mixing practically all the chlorine reacts in this way. The passage of 2 faradays of electricity is evidently necessary for the production of one molecular weight of NaClO.

The sodium hypochlorite may react in several ways :

(1) At the cathode it may be reduced by the nascent hydrogen there formed. This reduction may be prevented by the addition of a little potassium chromate to the solution. Its action is attributed by Müller to the reduction of chromate ions $CrO_4^{=}$ to chromic ions Cr^{+++} and the formation of chromium chromate which forms a film on the cathode and keeps the bulk of the solution away from the nascent hydrogen.

(2) At the anode hypochlorite ions are discharged and the products react to form chlorate ions:

$$ClO^- = ClO + \epsilon$$

$$6ClO + 3H_2O = 2ClO_3^- + 6H^+ + 4Cl^- + \tfrac{3}{2}O_2.$$

The hydrogen ions formed are neutralised by the hydroxyl ions formed at the cathode. In this reaction one faraday is evidently required for the discharge of one molecular weight of hypochlorite ions, with the subsequent formation of an equivalent amount of chlorate and the evolution of an equivalent of oxygen.

As the electrolysis proceeds, the concentration of sodium hypochlorite will increase until it is decomposed in (2) as fast as it is formed. The concentration then remains steady. Since two faradays are required for the formation of one molecule of hypochlorite, and one for its discharge, two-thirds of the current passed in the steady state will be employed in the formation of hypochlorite, one-third in its discharge, which results in the production of an equivalent of oxygen. The ultimate result of the passage of 3 faradays of electricity through the solution is thus the formation of an amount of chlorate containing two equivalents of oxygen, and the liberation in the free state of one equivalent of oxygen

($\frac{1}{2}$O). The current efficiency in the steady state is therefore 67 per cent.

The course of the electrolysis at bright platinum electrodes is shown in Fig. 64. At the beginning hypochlorite is formed with nearly 100 per cent. efficiency. As its concentration increases chlorate begins to be

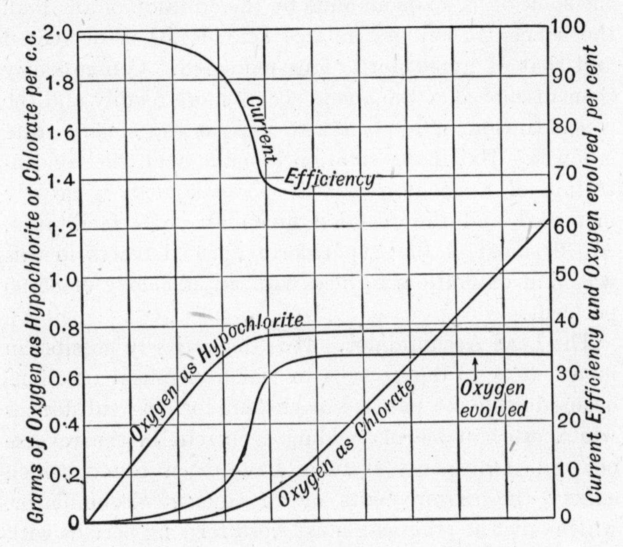

FIG. 64.—Electrolysis of brine solutions. (Foerster.)

formed with the consequent liberation of free oxygen and fall in current efficiency. When the concentration of hypochlorite has reached the steady state the current efficiency has fallen to 66·7 per cent. and the oxygen evolution is 33·3 per cent. of the total electrolytic action. The concentration of chlorate increases continuously as the electrolysis proceeds.

(3) Hypochlorous acid may also react directly with hypochlorite ions, thus:

$$2HClO + ClO^- = ClO_3^- + 2HCl.$$

In weak solutions and at low temperatures this reaction is slow and has little influence on the electrolysis. If the solution is made alkaline by the addition of an alkali the concentration of the free acid HClO is decreased and that of hypochlorite ions increased. Consequently their discharge at the anode occurs more readily and the concentration of hypochlorite ions in the steady state is lower. But if the solution is made acid, the concentration of hypochlorous acid (a weak acid) is greatly increased and the reaction given above is facilitated. At 70° most of the hypochlorite formed reacts in this way and chlorate is formed with an efficiency of 85-95 per cent.

The Lead Accumulator. It is theoretically possible in many ways to devise cells in which chemical reactions occur during the passage of current forming substances which are capable of yielding a current in the reverse change. Only two systems have been found which satisfy the requirements of an efficient accumulator, which must be practical, must work for long periods with little attention, must be capable of being charged and discharged almost indefinitely and have a high efficiency. These are the lead accumulator and Edison's iron-nickel cell.

The lead accumulator was originated by Planté, who found that two lead plates in dilute sulphuric acid served the purpose. When current is passed, lead dioxide PbO_2 is formed at the anode, but the amount obtained in a single charge is very small. Planté therefore formed his plates by alternately making each plate the anode and the cathode. The lead dioxide formed at the anode in the first charge is reduced to spongy lead when that plate is made the cathode. After many reversals a thick layer of the dioxide is obtained on one plate and a layer of spongy lead at the other. Plates made by this process were expensive and Faure introduced a method of forming the deposits rapidly. The lead plates were made in the form of grids for holding artificial deposits. These were first filled with a paste of PbO or Pb_3O_4 with sulphuric acid (*i.e.* $PbSO_4$), which for positive plates was oxidised electrolytically to lead dioxide and for negative plates reduced to lead in a finely divided form. These plates, although less expensive than those made by the Planté method, are much weaker and the active deposits have a tendency to fall out.

Thus in the charged accumulator the positive plates are covered with lead dioxide, the negative plates with spongy lead. Planté was of opinion that the process of charging simply consisted in the oxidation of lead to lead dioxide (by nascent oxygen) at the positive plate and the reduction of oxides of lead to metallic lead at the negative plate. But Gladstone and Tribe observed that changes in the concentration of the sulphuric acid occur during the charge and discharge which are proportional to the amount of current passed, and that a quantity of lead sulphate is formed during the discharge proportional to the amount of current taken from the cell. They therefore put forward the *sulphate theory*, according to which the reactions occurring during the process of discharge are :

Negative plate :

$$Pb + SO_4^{=} = PbSO_4 + 2\epsilon \quad \ldots\ldots\ldots\ldots\ldots (a)$$

Positive plate :

$$PbO_2 + 2H^+ + H_2SO_4(aq.) + 2\epsilon = PbSO_4 + 2H_2O, \quad ...(b)$$

or for the whole reaction in discharge :

$$PbO_2 + Pb + 2H_2SO_4(aq.) = 2PbSO_4 + 2H_2O. \quad ....(c)$$

Gladstone and Tribe were able to show that the amount of lead sulphate formed and the decrease in the amount of sulphuric acid during the discharge were in accordance with (*c*). The reactions during charge are the reverse of these equations.

That the cell reaction is correctly represented by (*c*) was confirmed by Dolezalek by the study of the energy relations of the cell. The electromotive force of the cell, at open circuit, with 21 per cent. sulphuric acid, is 2·01 volts at 15° C. and its temperature coefficient is $d\mathrm{E}/dT = 0{\cdot}00037$ volts per degree. Thus applying the Gibbs-Helmholtz equation in the form given by (74*a*), we find that the heat content change in the reaction is

$$\Delta H = -z\mathrm{E}F + zF \, . \, T \, . \, \frac{d\mathrm{E}}{dT}$$

$$= -\frac{2 \times 2{\cdot}01 \times 96540}{4{\cdot}18} + \frac{2 \times 96540 \times 288 \times 0{\cdot}00037}{4{\cdot}18}$$

$$= -92400 + 4900 = -87500 \text{ calories.}$$

This is in fairly good agreement with the value,

$$\Delta H = -89400 \text{ calories,}$$

obtained directly by calorimetric measurements.

Charge and Discharge Effects. The electromotive force mentioned above is that of the charged accumulator at open circuit. During the passage of current polarisation effects occur which cause variations of the voltage during charge and discharge. Fig. 62 shows typical charge and discharge curves. During the charge the electromotive force rises rapidly to a little over 2·1 volts and remains steady, increasing very slowly as the charging proceeds (Fig. 65). At 2·2 volts oxygen begins to be liberated at the positive plates and at 2·3 volts hydrogen at the negative plates. The charge is now completed and the further passage of current leads

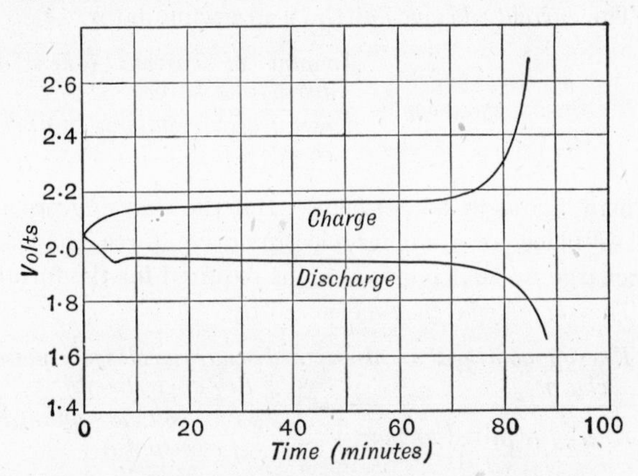

FIG. 65.—Charge and discharge curves of the lead accumulator.

to the free evolution of gases and a rapid rise in the electromotive force. If the charge is stopped at any point the electromotive force returns, in time, to the equilibrium value. During discharge it drops rapidly to just below 2 volts. (The preliminary " kink " is due to the formation of a layer of lead sulphate of high resistance while the cell is standing, which soon gets dispersed). The electromotive force falls steadily during the discharge, when it has reached 1·8 volts the cell should be recharged, for the further withdrawal of current causes the voltage to fall rapidly.

The difference between the charge and discharge curves is due to changes of concentration of the acid in contact with the active materials of the plates. These are full of small pores in which diffusion is very slow, so that the concentration of the acid is greater during the charge and less during the discharge than in the bulk of the solution. This difference results in a loss of efficiency.

The *current efficiency* of the lead accumulator, *i.e.*

$$\textit{Current efficiency} = \frac{\textit{Amount of current taken out during discharge}}{\textit{Amount of current put in during charge}}$$

is high, about 94-96 per cent. But the charging process takes place at a higher electromotive force than the discharge, so that more *energy* is required for the former. The *energy efficiency* measured by

$$\frac{\textit{Energy obtained in discharge}}{\textit{Energy required to charge}} = \frac{\Sigma(\textit{discharge voltage} \times \textit{quantity of electricity})}{\Sigma(\textit{charge voltage} \times \textit{quantity of electricity})}$$

is comparatively low, 75-85 per cent.

The Edison Iron-Nickel Accumulator. In the discharged state the negative plate of this cell is iron with hydrated ferrous oxide, and the positive plate nickel with a hydrated nickel oxide. When charged the ferrous oxide is reduced to iron, and the nickel oxide is oxidised to a hydrated peroxide. The cell reaction may thus be represented by

$$FeO + 2NiO \underset{\text{discharge}}{\overset{\text{charge}}{\rightleftharpoons}} Fe + Ni_2O_3.$$

The three oxides are all hydrated to various extents, but

their exact compositions are unknown. In order to obtain plates having a sufficiently large capacity, the oxides have to be prepared by methods which give particularly finely divided and active products. They are packed into nickel-plated steel containers, perforated by numerous small holes—an arrangement which gives exceptional mechanical strength. The electrolyte is usually a 21 per cent. solution of potash, but since hydroxyl ions do not enter into the cell reaction, the electromotive force (1·33 to 1·35 volts) is nearly independent of the concentration. Actually, there is a difference between the amount of water combined with the oxides in the charged and discharged plates. Water is taken up and the alkali becomes more concentrated during the discharge, while it is given out during the charge. The electromotive force therefore depends to a small extent on the free energy of water in the solution, which in turn is determined by the concentration of the dissolved potash. Actually 2·9 mols of water are liberated in the discharge reaction, as represented above, and the variation of the electromotive force between 1·0 N and 5·3 N potash is from 1·351 to 1·335 volts. The potential of the positive plate is +0·55 and that of the negative plate −0·8 on the hydrogen scale.

The current efficiency, viz. about 82 per cent., is considerably lower than that of the lead accumulator. The voltage during the charge is about 1·65 volts, rising at the end to 1·8, while during the discharge it falls gradually from 1·3 to 1·1 volts. Hence the energy efficiency is only about 60 per cent.

Literature. Further information about technical and other aspects of electrolysis may be found in the following books :

Allmand and Ellingham's *Applied Electrochemistry* (Arnold).

Foerster's *Electrochemie wassriger Lösungen* (J. A. Barth).

Glasstone's *Electrochemistry of Solutions* (Methuen).

Creighton's *Principles and Applications of Electrochemistry* (Wiley).

Brockman's *Electro-Organic Chemistry* (Wiley).

Glasstone and Hickling's *Electrolytic Oxidation and Reduction* (Chapman & Hall).

ADDENDUM

For a detailed consideration of concentration polarisation, especially at cathodes, see Agar and Bowden (*Ann. Reports Chem. Soc.*, 35, 90, 1938); and G. E. Coates (*J. Chem. Soc.*, 484, 1945).

PART II.—THERMODYNAMICAL FUNCTIONS AND THEIR APPLICATIONS

CHAPTER XI

ENTROPY AND FREE ENERGY

In the previous chapters we have been mainly concerned with the energy changes and the maximum work obtained in typical chemical changes. We considered each change by itself, determined by a suitable method the maximum work of which it was capable under any given conditions, and by the use of the laws of thermodynamics were then able to determine the characteristics of the state of equilibrium and to calculate the effect thereon of changes of temperature and pressure. We now wish to formulate these relations in a somewhat more analytical way, which will enable many problems to be solved with ease which would require the consideration of complicated and often clumsy cyclic processes by the methods we have hitherto used. This involves the use of *thermodynamical functions*; that is, quantities which have definite values in any state of a system irrespective of how it has been brought into that state.

The first two such functions, namely the *energy* E and

heat content H, were introduced in Chapter I. In Chapter II we mentioned two other quantities the *maximum work function* A and the *free energy* F. It was shown that the maximum work of a process could be represented as the change in these quantities at constant temperature, and at constant temperature and pressure respectively. In other words it was shown that at constant temperature the maximum work of a process is a constant quantity which depends only on the initial and final states of the system. Similarly it was shown that at constant temperature and pressure the net work of a process is also definite. But these statements are not true if the temperature varies during the change from the initial to the final state. Under these conditions we have seen that varying amounts of work can be obtained according to the path actually followed. Consequently we have only shown that the maximum work function and the free energy can be used as thermodynamic functions if the condition of constant temperature (or constant temperature and pressure) is maintained.

We now wish to remove this limitation and to show that there are quantities, which we call as before the maximum work function and the free energy, which, like the energy, have definite values in any state of the system.

The construction of such functions requires in the first place the consideration of another quantity, also a thermodynamic function, namely the *entropy*.

Entropy. Consider a simple Carnot cycle, in which a quantity of matter, which is supposed to be always in a state of internal equilibrium, is put through a reversible cycle of operations (Fig. 66), consisting of two isothermal stages (I and III) at temperatures T_1 and T_2 ($T_1 > T_2$) respectively and two connecting adiabatic stages (II and IV). Let the quantity of heat absorbed from surrounding bodies in the isothermal stage I be q_1 and that absorbed in the isothermal stage III be q_2 (normally heat is evolved in the isothermal stage at the lower temperature T_2; q_2 is then a negative quantity). Then W, the work obtained in the whole cycle, must be equal to the total amount of heat absorbed, *i.e.*

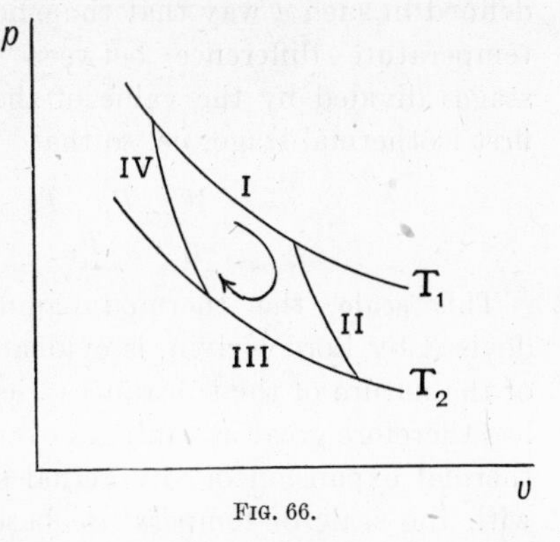

FIG. 66.

$$W = q_1 + q_2. \quad \text{.....................(95·1)}$$

The ratio of the work obtained to the heat absorbed at the higher temperature, or W/q_1, may be called the efficiency of the process.

Now Carnot's theorem states that all reversible cyclic processes working between the same two temperatures have the same efficiency. If this were not the case, as has been shown (see p. 47), it would be possible by the use of two such cyclic processes having different efficiencies and working one in the forward and one in the backward direction, to transfer heat from a colder to a hotter body (*i.e.* to reverse a spontaneous change) without the application of any outside effort. This is contrary to the Second Law of Thermodynamics.

The ratio W/q_1 is therefore the same for all reversible cycles working between the same two temperatures, and is independent of the nature of the system employed as working substance. A scale of temperature may be defined in such a way that the efficiency is equal to the temperature difference between the two isothermal stages divided by the value of the temperature of the first isothermal stage, *i.e.* so that

$$\frac{W}{q_1} = \frac{T_1 - T_2}{T_1}. \quad \text{......................(95·2)}$$

This scale, the thermodynamic temperature scale devised by Lord Kelvin, is evidently quite independent of the nature of the substances used to establish it, and has therefore great advantages over a scale based on the thermal expansion of any actual substance. It agrees with the scale of temperature based upon the thermal expansion of a perfect gas.

Substituting (95·1) in (95·2),we have

$$\frac{q_1 + q_2}{q_1} = \frac{T_1 - T_2}{T_1},$$

or

$$\frac{q_2}{q_1} = -\frac{T_2}{T_1},$$

i.e.

$$\frac{q_2}{T_2} + \frac{q_1}{T_1} = 0. \quad \text{..............................(96)}$$

Thus in a simple Carnot cycle the algebraic sum of the quantities of heat absorbed, each divided by the absolute temperatures at which the absorption takes place, is zero.

Now any reversible cycle whatever may be resolved into a number of elementary Carnot cycles. Consider a cyclic process tracing out the closed path AB on the p-v diagram (Fig. 67). We may resolve this cycle into a large number of simple Carnot cycles each having two isothermal and two adiabatic stages. On Fig. 67 are drawn some isothermal and adiabatic lines for the system which form a number of Carnot cycles, the outside boundaries of which approximate roughly with the closed cycle AB. Every section of the isothermals which is not on the outside boundary is shared by two adjacent Carnot cycles. Thus the element XY is shared by the cycles I and II, and the quantities of work obtained in passing along the isothermal XY in the two cycles are

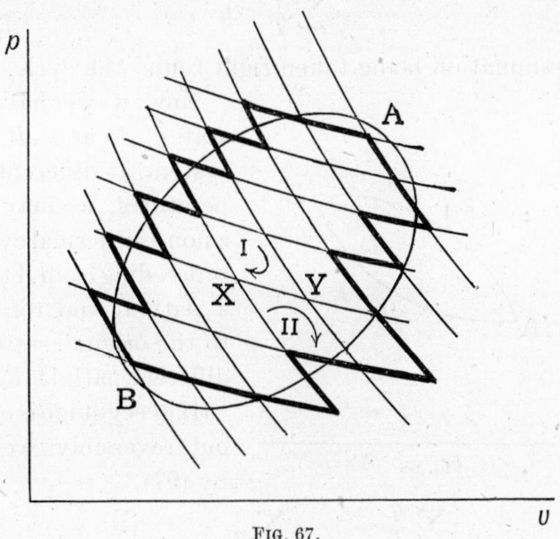

FIG. 67.

equal and opposite. The heat terms corresponding to the element XY also cancel out. It follows that all the heat and work terms corresponding to the shared sides balance out and we are left with only the terms for the outside boundary of the collection of Carnot's cycles. It is evident that by drawing the isothermals and adiabatics very close together we may make the outside boundaries of the Carnot cycles agree as closely as we wish with the actual boundary of our cycle AB.

For a single Carnot cycle we may write (96) as

$$\sum \frac{q}{T} = 0.$$

The same applies to a collection of Carnot cycles, and therefore to any reversible cyclic process, which as we have just seen can be resolved into a number of Carnot cycles. Therefore we may write for any reversible cyclic process

$$\sum \frac{q}{T} = 0, \quad \text{.........................(97)}$$

the summation being taken right round the cycle.

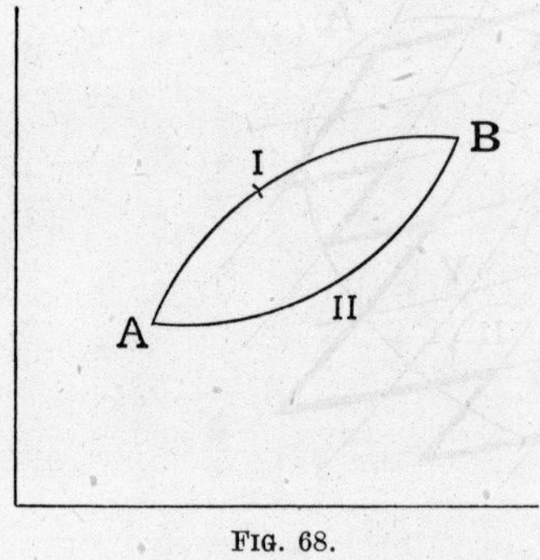

FIG. 68.

Now if we have two states A and B of a system, at different temperatures, we may make a non-isothermal cycle by proceeding from A to B by a path I, and returning to the original state by a different path II (Fig. 68).

If every stage is carried out reversibly, we have by (97),

$$\sum \frac{q}{T}_{(A\rightarrow B)_{\text{I}}} + \sum \frac{q}{T}_{(B\rightarrow A)_{\text{II}}} = 0,$$

where the first term represents the sum of the q/T terms for the passage from A to B by path I, and the second term the same quantity for the passage from B to A by path II. Reversing the direction of the second term, we have

$$\sum \frac{q}{T}_{(A\rightarrow B)_{\text{I}}} - \sum \frac{q}{T}_{(A\rightarrow B)_{\text{II}}} = 0,$$

or

$$\sum \frac{q}{T}_{(A\rightarrow B)_{\text{I}}} = \sum \frac{q}{T}_{(A\rightarrow B)_{\text{II}}}.$$

Thus, since we have placed no restriction on the path from A to B, except that it shall be reversible, the quantity $\frac{q}{T}_{(A \to B)}$ must be a constant for all reversible paths from A to B. This quantity thus depends only on the initial and final states A and B and not on the intermediate stages, and may be regarded as the difference between the values of a function of the state of the system in the two given states. This function is called the *entropy*. If S_A denotes the entropy of the system in the state A, and S_B that in the state B, the entropy change in going from A to B is

$$\Delta S = S_B - S_A = \sum \frac{q}{T}_{(A \to B)}, \quad \ldots\ldots\ldots\ldots\ldots (98)$$

the summation in the last term being taken over any reversible path between A and B.

It is important to notice that since the entropy change depends only on the initial and the final states of the system, it is the same however the change is conducted, whether reversibly or irreversibly. But it is only equal to $\sum \frac{q}{T}$ when the latter is evaluated for a reversible change.

As a consequence of this we can make a fundamental distinction between reversible and irreversible processes. Consider a change of a system from a state A to a state B. If carried out reversibly, the entropy change of the system is

$$\Delta S_{\text{system}} = \sum \frac{q}{T}.$$

Now all the heat absorbed by the system must come from some surrounding bodies, and it is a condition of reversibility that every element of heat absorbed must be taken from a body which has the same temperature as the system itself in this particular state. (The absorption of heat from bodies at other temperatures would necessarily introduce some irreversibility.) Therefore the entropy change of the surrounding bodies must be

$$\Delta S_{\text{surroundings}} = -\sum \frac{q}{T},$$

since the surroundings give up the quantities of heat which are absorbed by the system and at the same temperatures. Thus for a reversible process

$$\Delta S_{\text{system}} + \Delta S_{\text{surroundings}} = 0, \quad \ldots\ldots\ldots\ldots(99)$$

i.e. in a reversible change the total entropy change of the system and its surroundings is zero.

On the other hand, in an irreversible change, the entropy change of the system in passing from the initial state A to the final state B is the same;

$$\Delta S_{\text{system}} = S_B - S_A.$$

But this is no longer equal to $\Sigma q/T$ for the change. When a system undergoes an irreversible change, it performs less than the maximum amount of work, and since $q = \Delta E + w$, absorbs a smaller quantity of heat than in the corresponding reversible change. $\Sigma q/T$ is thus less in this case than in the reversible process. If the heat absorbed by the system at every stage comes from bodies at the same temperature, and the heat is transferred reversibly, the entropy decrease of the surroundings is $\Sigma q/T$.* Therefore the entropy decrease of the surround-

* The temperature of the bodies from which heat is absorbed by the system cannot be less than the temperature of the system, for heat will not pass from a body at a lower to a body at a higher temperature by itself. Hence the entropy decrease of the surroundings may be less than $\Sigma q/T$, but cannot be greater.

ings is less than the increase of entropy of the system, or

$$-\Delta S_{\text{surroundings}} < \Delta S_{\text{system}},$$

or

$$\Delta S_{\text{system}} + \Delta S_{\text{surroundings}} > 0. \quad \text{........(100)}$$

To sum up, let us consider the system which undergoes change and the outside bodies, with which heat is exchanged, as one " system," which we may suppose to be entirely isolated from the action of any other bodies. We may state the following rules :

(1) when a reversible change occurs in any part of an isolated system, the total entropy remains unchanged ;

(2) when an irreversible change occurs in any part of an isolated system, the total entropy increases.

The Calculation of Entropy Changes. (1) *Isothermal Changes.* In order to find the entropy change of an isothermal process we need only carry out the process reversibly and divide the heat absorbed by the absolute temperature. For example, at the melting point of a solid, the solid and liquid forms of the substance are in equilibrium with each other, and the absorption of heat at constant pressure causes a change of the solid into liquid under reversible conditions. The entropy change in the fusion of a given mass of the solid is therefore

$$\Delta S = \frac{\Delta H}{T}, \quad \text{....................(101)}$$

where ΔH is the heat absorbed, *i.e.* the latent heat of fusion of the given mass of the solid, and T the absolute temperature at which the fusion takes place. The entropy change in vaporisation in similarly obtained.

Examples.

1. The latent heat of fusion of water at its melting point under a pressure of 1 atmosphere (273° K.) is 1438 calories per gram molecule. The entropy change is therefore

$$\Delta S = \frac{1438}{273 \cdot 1} = 5 \cdot 27 \text{ calories/degrees.}$$

2. The latent heat of vaporisation of water at 373·1° K. (1 atmosphere pressure) is 9730 calories per gram molecule. The entropy change is therefore

$$\Delta S = \frac{9730}{373 \cdot 1} = 26 \cdot 5 \text{ calories/degrees.}$$

This is the difference between the entropy of a gram molecule (18 grams) of water vapour at 1 atmosphere pressure and 373·1° K. and that of liquid water at the same temperature.

In the isothermal expansion of a perfect gas, the energy change is zero and the heat absorbed is equal to the work performed by the gas. For a reversible expansion of a gram molecule of the gas from a pressure p_1 to a pressure p_2, the heat absorbed is thus

$$q = w = RT \log p_1/p_2.$$

The entropy change is thus

$$\Delta S = q/T = R \log p_1/p_2. \quad \ldots\ldots\ldots\ldots(102)$$

It should be observed that the entropy change of the gas has this value whether the expansion is conducted reversibly or not (but it can only be calculated from the heat absorbed in the reversible process). In an irreversible expansion the work done by the gas, and the heat absorbed from the surroundings is less than that given above. The entropy *decrease* of the surroundings is therefore less than the increase in the entropy of the gas.

Consequently when a gas expands irreversibly there is an increase in the total entropy of the gas and its surroundings.

(2) *Non-isothermal Changes.* To find the entropy change of a reversible non-isothermal process, we must sum the quantities of heat absorbed, each divided by the absolute temperature at which the absorption takes place. It is always possible to add heat reversibly to a body, thereby increasing its temperature, if the body is placed in contact with sources of heat which have a temperature only infinitesimally higher than that of the body itself. Under these circumstances the absorption of heat takes place very slowly and the body remains in a state of thermal equilibrium (uniform temperature) throughout. The heat absorbed in raising the temperature of a body from T to $T+dT$, at constant pressure, is $dH=C_p dT$, and the entropy change is therefore

$$dS=\frac{dH}{T}=\frac{C_p}{T}\,.\,dT. \qquad \text{..............(103)}$$

To find the entropy change in a finite change of temperature from T_1 to T_2, we must integrate this expression between the given temperature limits, *i.e.*

$$\Delta S_{T_1}^{T_2}=\int_{T_1}^{T_2}\frac{C_p}{T}\,.\,dT. \qquad \text{..............(104)}$$

Examples.

1. The molar heat capacity of helium (a monatomic gas) between $-200°$ C. and $0°$ C. is 5·0. The entropy change between these temperatures is therefore

$$\Delta S_{73}^{273}=\int_{73}^{273}\frac{5}{T}\,.\,dT=\int_{73}^{273}5\,.\,d\log T$$
$$=5\log_e\frac{273}{73}=6{\cdot}61 \text{ calories/degrees.}$$

2. The molar heat capacity of liquid mercury between $-40°$ C. and $+140°$ C. is given by the equation

$$C_p = 8{\cdot}42 - 0{\cdot}0098T + 0{\cdot}0000132T^2.$$

The entropy change between these temperatures is thus

$$\Delta S_{233}^{413} = \int_{233}^{413} \left(\frac{8{\cdot}42 - 0{\cdot}0098T + 0{\cdot}0000132T^2}{T} \right) dT$$

$$= 8{\cdot}42 \log_e \left(\frac{413}{233} \right) - 0{\cdot}0098(413 - 233) + \frac{0{\cdot}0000132}{2}(413^2 - 233^2)$$

$$= 4{\cdot}82 - 1{\cdot}76 + 1{\cdot}54 = 4{\cdot}60 \text{ calories/degrees.}$$

Criteria of Equilibrium. Irreversible changes can only occur in a system of bodies which is not in a state of equilibrium. When equilibrium is established no irreversible changes are possible and consequently, when the absorption of heat from outside bodies is excluded, there are no possible changes whereby the entropy can increase. Thus when an isolated system of bodies, the energy of which is constant, is in equilibrium, its entropy has a maximum value. Regarding the universe as an isolated system, Clausius therefore summed up the generalisation of natural tendencies which is contained in the Second Law of Thermodynamics by the statement—"The entropy of the universe tends to a maximum."

We have here also a very valuable criterion of chemical equilibrium. A system is in equilibrium if no variations in its state can occur spontaneously. If there is any variation in its state (which does not alter its energy) which causes an increase of entropy, the system cannot be in equilibrium, for this variation may occur spontaneously. (It does not follow that it *will* occur.) Gibbs therefore gave the following proposition as a general criterion of equilibrium :

GIBBS'S FIRST CRITERION.

For the equilibrium of any isolated system it is necessary and sufficient that in all possible variations in the state of the system which do not alter its energy, the variation of the entropy shall either vanish or be negative.

In using this criterion we need generally only consider infinitesimally small variations, for an infinitesimally small variation must necessarily precede a finite one, and if the former cannot occur neither can the latter. The criterion can therefore be written in the form :

$$(\delta S)_E \leqq 0, \quad \text{.........................(105)}$$

$(\delta S)_E$ denotes the variation of the entropy in an infinitesimal variation of the state of the system, for which the energy remains constant.

The criterion can be expressed in an alternative form which is more convenient for practical use. Consider some particular state of a system (not necessarily a state of equilibrium). If there is another state which has less energy but the same entropy, we can by adding heat, arrive at a state which has the same energy and more entropy than the original state, *i.e.* if there is a state with less energy and the same entropy, there is also a state with more entropy and the same energy. But if this is the case the original state cannot be a state of equilibrium. It is therefore a characteristic of a state of equilibrium that the energy is a minimum for constant entropy. This is stated in the following proposition of Gibbs :

GIBBS'S SECOND CRITERION.

For the equilibrium of any isolated system it is necessary and sufficient that in all possible variations in the state of the system which do not alter its entropy, the variation of its energy shall either vanish or be positive.

For the same reasons as those given in connection with the first criterion, we may express this condition as follows :

$$(\delta E)_S \geqq 0, \quad \text{.......................(106)}$$

$(\delta E)_S$ denotes the variation of the energy in an infinitesimal variation, for which the entropy remains constant.

The Functions A and F. In practice we meet very frequently with cases of equilibrium for which it is a condition that the temperature or the temperature and pressure remain constant. The treatment of such problems is facilitated by the use of two other functions which we shall now discuss.

These functions are defined by the equations

$$A = E - TS, \qquad (107)$$

$$F = E - TS + pv = H - TS. \qquad (108)$$

All these quantities have definite values in every state of a system, so that A and F are thermodynamic functions of the state of the system.

In order to show the significance of these quantities, consider first a change of state of a system from a state I to a state II which are both at the same temperature T. The change in A is

$$\begin{aligned} \Delta A &= A_{II} - A_I \\ &= (E_{II} - TS_{II}) - (E_I - TS_I) \\ &= E_{II} - E_I - T(S_{II} - S_I) \\ &= \Delta E - T\Delta S. \qquad (109) \end{aligned}$$

Now if the change be carried out reversibly $T\Delta S$ is equal to the heat absorbed q, and $\Delta E - q$ is by (2) equal to $-w$, *i.e.*

$$\Delta A = -w, \qquad (110)$$

where w is the maximum work of the change. The increase in A, in a change at constant temperature, is thus equal to the work performed on the system in carrying out the change reversibly. Similarly a decrease in A is equal to the maximum work performed by the system.

The maximum work of a change is, as we have seen, a definite quantity only so long as the temperature remains constant throughout. But in A we have a function which has a definite value for every state of a system without restriction, which is such that the change in its value reduces, for a constant temperature process, to the maximum work. A can thus be regarded as the *maximum work function.*

We have used the maximum work as a criterion of equilibrium for systems which are maintained at constant temperature. A system is in equilibrium at constant temperature if there is no process whereby it could perform work, *i.e.* no process whereby the function A might be decreased. We can thus write as the criterion of equilibrium at constant temperature :

$$(\delta A)_T \geqq 0, \quad \text{.....................(111)}$$

i.e. in all possible variations in the state of a system, while the temperature remains constant, the variation of the maximum work function A shall either vanish or be positive.

Secondly, consider a change of state of a system from a state I to a state II, which are both at the same temperature T and pressure p. The change in F is

$$\begin{aligned}\Delta F &= F_{\text{II}} - F_{\text{I}} \\ &= (E_{\text{II}} - TS_{\text{II}} + pv_{\text{II}}) - (E_{\text{I}} - TS_{\text{I}} + pv_{\text{I}}) \\ &= \Delta E - T\Delta S + p\Delta v. \quad \text{.......................(112)}\end{aligned}$$

As in the previous case, $T\Delta S$ is the heat absorbed when the change is carried out reversibly, so that

$$\Delta F = -(w - p\Delta v) = -w', \quad \text{...........(113)}$$

for $p\Delta v$ is the work done against the constant pressure p in the volume change Δv, and $w - p\Delta v$ is equal to the *net work* of the change w'. The increase in F for a change at constant temperature and pressure is thus equal to the net work performed on the system in carrying out the change reversibly. The decrease of F in such a change is similarly equal to the net work performed by the system. F can therefore be regarded as the *net work function.* It is known as the *free energy.* F itself has a definite value for every state of a system without restriction. But for changes at constant temperature and pressure, the change in F becomes equal to the net work performed on the system.

A system is in internal equilibrium at constant temperature and pressure if there is no change whereby net work could be obtained, *i.e.* if no process can occur in it whereby the value of F is decreased. We can therefore write as the criterion of equilibrium at constant temperature and pressure :

$$(\delta F)_{T,p} \geqq 0, \quad \text{.....................(114)}$$

i.e. in all possible variations in the state of a system, which do not alter its temperature and pressure, the variation of the free energy F shall either vanish or be positive.

The functions H, A and F were first employed by J. W. Gibbs in his monumental papers on the application of thermodynamics to material systems.*

The notation used in this volume is mainly that of Lewis and Randall,† but it will be of assistance to those who refer to the original papers of Gibbs to give his symbols.

Lewis and Randall.	Gibbs.	Name.
E	ϵ	Energy.
S	η	Entropy.

* *Scientific Papers*, vol. i. (Longmans Green).

† *Thermodynamics and the Free Energy of Chemical Substances* (1923).

Lewis and Randall.	Gibbs.	Name.
H	χ	Heat function for constant pressure (G.) or Heat content (L. and R.).
A	ψ	Available energy.
F	ζ	Free energy (L. and R.). Thermodynamic Potential or Gibbs's function.*

A certain amount of confusion has arisen in the literature because Helmholtz used the term free energy for A. Massieu, in 1869, was the first to use functions like A and F, and to demonstrate their usefulness. The functions he used, in our notation, were

$$\frac{-E+TS}{T} \text{ or } -\frac{A}{T} \text{ and } \frac{-E+TS-pv}{T} \text{ or } -\frac{F}{T}.$$

Planck has also made use of the latter function, which has the same properties in a system at constant temperature and pressure as the entropy at constant energy and volume.

Variation of the Functions A and F with Temperature and Pressure. First of all we must formulate how the energy of a system may vary. The energy may be varied in three ways, (1) by the absorption of heat, (2) by performing work on its surroundings, (3) by a change in its amount or composition. With changes of the last kind we shall frequently be concerned in the remaining chapters of this book. For the present consider a body having

* A joint committee of the Chemical, Faraday and Physical Societies recommended G for Free Energy, and this symbol is to be found in recent British papers. I have decided to adhere to the American practice of using F for free energy since a great majority of the papers containing data comes from the other side of the Atlantic.

a constant composition, a uniform temperature T and a pressure p. Suppose that this body absorbs a small quantity of heat dq and increases in volume by a small amount dv. The increase in its energy, by (2) is

$$dE = dq - p\,dv.$$

but since the increase in entropy is $dS = dq/T$ (since all very small changes of a system which is in a state of equilibrium are necessarily reversible) and therefore in any small change of our body we have

$$dE = T\,dS - p\,dv. \qquad (115)$$

If we differentiate F (equation 108) in the most general way, we obtain

$$dF = dE - T\,dS - S\,dT + p\,dv + v\,dp,$$

but by (115), $dE - T\,dS + p\,dv = 0$, so that we have

$$dF = -S\,dT + v\,dp. \qquad (116)$$

Therefore when the pressure is constant ($dp = 0$), we have

$$\left(\frac{dF}{dT}\right)_p = -S, \qquad (117)$$

and for constant temperature ($dT = 0$);

$$\left(\frac{dF}{dp}\right)_T = v. \qquad (118)$$

It obviously follows that since $F_2 - F_1 = \Delta F$,

$$\left(\frac{d(\Delta F)}{dT}\right)_p = -(S_2 - S_1) = -\Delta S. \qquad (119)$$

and

$$\left(\frac{d(\Delta F)}{dp}\right)_T = v_2 - v_1 = \Delta v. \qquad (120)$$

Now, by (108), $\Delta F = \Delta H - T\Delta S$,

and substituting the value of ΔS given by (119) in this equation, we have

$$\Delta F - \Delta H = T\left(\frac{d(\Delta F)}{dT}\right)_p. \qquad (121)$$

This equation will be familiar as the Gibbs-Helmholtz equation. It can be written in another form, which is sometimes convenient in practice. Differentiating the quotient $\Delta F/T$, we have

$$\frac{(\Delta F/T)}{dT}=\frac{1}{T}\left(\frac{d(\Delta F)}{dT}\right)-\frac{\Delta F}{T^2}.$$

Comparing this with (121), we see that

$$\left(\frac{d(\Delta F/T)}{dT}\right)_p=-\frac{\Delta H}{T^2}. \quad \text{......................(122)}$$

It can easily be shown by similar methods that

$$\left(\frac{d(F/T)}{dT}\right)_p=-\frac{H}{T^2}, \quad \text{......................(123)}$$

i.e. the rate of variation of (F/T) with the temperature, at constant pressure is equal to minus the heat content divided by the square of the absolute temperature.

* Again, if we differentiate A (equation 107), we obtain

$$dA=dE-TdS-S\,dT.$$

Therefore, substituting (115), we have

$$dA=-S\,dT-p\,dv. \quad \text{..................(124)}$$

Therefore we have

$$\left(\frac{dA}{dT}\right)_v=-S, \quad \text{..............................(125)}$$

and $$\left(\frac{dA}{dv}\right)_T=-p. \quad \text{..............................(126)}$$

Substituting in $A=E-TS$, the value of S given by (125), we have :

$$A-E=T\left(\frac{dA}{dT}\right)_v, \quad \text{.........................(127)}$$

from which it is easy to obtain the equation

$$\left(\frac{d(A/T)}{dT}\right)_v=-\frac{E}{T^2}. \quad \text{..............................(128)}$$

Similar equations can of course be written for ΔA and ΔE.

Examples.

1. The heat capacities of rhombic and monoclinic sulphur are given by the equations,

$$S_r, \; C_p = 4{\cdot}12 + 0{\cdot}0047T \; ; \quad S_m, \; C_p = 3{\cdot}62 + 0{\cdot}0072T.$$

The heat content change in the reaction $S_r = S_m$ is 77·0 cals. at 0° C.

Deduce expressions for (1) the variation of the heat content change with the temperature, (2) using (122), the variation of the free energy change with the temperature. The transition point is 95·0° C.

$$(\Delta F = 120 + 0{\cdot}50T \log T - 0{\cdot}00125T^2 - 2{\cdot}82T.)$$

2. Using Table I*a*, p. 18, find the entropy change of H_2 between 0° C. and 200° C., at constant pressure. (5·72 cals/°.)

CHAPTER XII

THE FREE ENERGIES OF PERFECT GAS REACTIONS

The Free Energy of Perfect Gases. By (120) the entropy change when a gram molecule of a perfect gas is expanded at constant temperature from unit pressure to a pressure p is

$$\Delta S = R \log 1/p = -R \log p.$$

If S° is its entropy at unit pressure, and S its entropy at the same temperature at the pressure p, we have therefore

$$S = S^\circ - R \log p. \quad \text{........................(129)}$$

The free energy, by (108), is

$$F = E - TS + pv,$$

and introducing this value of S, we have

$$F = E - TS^\circ + pv + RT \log p. \quad \text{........(130)}$$

Since the energy and the product $pv (= RT)$ for a perfect gas are not altered by a change of pressure at constant temperature, $E - TS^\circ + pv$ is the free energy of the gas at the temperature T and unit pressure. If we denote this quantity by F°, we have

$$F = F^\circ + RT \log p. \quad \text{..............(131)}$$

Similarly it is easy to show that

$$A = A^\circ + RT \log p, \quad \text{....................(132)}$$

where A° is the value of A for a gram molecule of the gas at the temperature T and unit pressure, and evidently

$$F^\circ = A^\circ + RT. \quad \text{.....................(133)}$$

A perfect gas mixture is one for which the total pressure is equal to the sum of the pressures which each constituent would exert if present by itself in the same space. Or since the total pressure may be regarded as the sum of the partial pressures of the different constituents, we may define a perfect gas mixture as one for which the partial pressure of each constituent is equal to the pressure it would exert if it occupied the same space alone, *i.e.* the partial pressure of each constituent is unaffected by the presence of the others. It follows that the free energy of a perfect gas mixture may be regarded as the sum of the free energies of the various constituents, each of which is equal to the free energy which this constituent would have if it occupied the same space by itself. Suppose that we have a perfect gas mixture at the temperature T, containing the substances A, B, C, D, at the partial pressures p_A, p_B, p_C, p_D. The free energies, per gram molecule, of these substances in the mixture are

$$\left.\begin{aligned} F_A &= F^\circ{}_A + RT \log p_A, \\ F_B &= F^\circ{}_B + RT \log p_B, \\ F_C &= F^\circ{}_C + RT \log p_C, \\ F_D &= F^\circ{}_D + RT \log p_D, \end{aligned}\right\} \quad \text{............(134)}$$

where $F^\circ{}_A$, $F^\circ{}_B$, $F^\circ{}_C$, $F^\circ{}_D$, are the free energies of the respective gases at the temperature T and at unit pressure.

Equilibrium in Perfect Gas Mixtures. Suppose that C and D can be formed out of A and B by the reaction

$$A + B = C + D.$$

The free energy change when a mol each of C and D at partial pressures p_C and p_D are formed from A and B at partial pressures p_A and p_B is

$$\Delta F = F_C + F_D - F_A - F_B$$
$$= \Delta F^\circ + RT \log \left(\frac{p_C\, p_D}{p_A\, p_B}\right), \quad \text{..............(135)}$$

where ΔF° stands for $F^\circ{}_C + F^\circ{}_D - F^\circ{}_A - F^\circ{}_B$, *i.e.* the free energy change in the reaction when all the substances taking part are at unit pressure.

Now when the products and the reactants are in equilibrium with each other the free energy change ΔF is zero. Writing the *equilibrium* pressures as $p^e{}_A$, $p^e{}_B$, $p^e{}_C$, $p^e{}_D$, we have therefore

$$0 = \Delta F^\circ + RT \log \frac{p^e{}_C\, p^e{}_D}{p^e{}_A\, p^e{}_B}. \quad \text{...........(136)}$$

The quantity $p^e{}_C\, p^e{}_D / p^e{}_A\, p^e{}_B$ is the equilibrium constant of the reaction, usually expressed as K_p; so that

$$\Delta F^\circ = -RT \log K_p. \quad \text{..................(137)}$$

Change of Equilibrium Constant with Temperature. By (122), we have

$$\left(\frac{d(\Delta F^\circ/T)}{dT}\right)_P = -\frac{\Delta H^\circ}{T^2}, \quad \text{...........(138)}$$

where ΔH° is the change of heat content corresponding to ΔF°, *i.e.* for the change of the reactants at unit pressure into the resultants at unit pressure. Introducing the value $\Delta F^\circ = -RT \log K_p$, we have

$$\frac{d(\log K_p)}{dT} = \frac{\Delta H^\circ}{RT^2}. \quad \text{..............(139)}$$

We have already seen (Part I, p. 98) how this equation can be integrated over a limited range of temperature over which ΔH° can be regarded as constant. It can be integrated over a wide range of temperature if the variation of ΔH° with the temperature is known. When equations similar to those in Table I*a* (p. 18) are known for the heat capacities of the gases concerned, the heat content change in the reaction can be formulated as in (3*a*) by a series of the form

$$\Delta H = \Delta H_0 + \alpha' T + \beta' T^2 + \gamma' T^3 + \delta' T^4 \ldots, \quad (140)$$

where ΔH_0 is the value of ΔH as determined by this equation when $T = 0$. (The heat content of a perfect gas does not vary with its pressure, so that ΔH°, the value for unit pressure, is the same as that determined for any convenient pressure. For actual gases at moderate pressures the distinction between ΔH, the heat content change for any given pressure, and ΔH° can be neglected.)

Introducing this value of ΔH into (139), we have

$$\frac{d(\log_e K_p)}{dT} = \frac{\Delta H_0}{RT^2} + \frac{\alpha'}{RT} + \frac{\beta'}{R} + \frac{\gamma' T}{R} + \frac{\delta' T^2}{R} + \ldots,$$

and integrating this :

$$\log_e K_p = -\frac{\Delta H_0}{RT} + \frac{\alpha'}{R}\log T + \frac{\beta' T}{R} + \frac{\gamma' T^2}{2R} + \frac{\delta' T^3}{3R} + \ldots + J, \quad (141)$$

where J is an integration constant. J can be evaluated when the value of K_p for one value of T is known. Since $\Delta F^\circ = -RT \log K_p$, we obtained by multiplying (141) through by $-RT$:

$$\Delta F^\circ = \Delta H_0 - \alpha' T \log T - \beta' T^2 - \frac{\gamma'}{2} T^3 - \frac{\delta'}{3} T^4 \ldots - IT \quad (142)$$

where $I = JR$.

This equation gives the variation of the free energy change with the temperature over the same range of temperature as that to which the heat capacity equations apply.

Examples.

1. We found (p. 19) that the heat content change in the reaction

$$H_2 + 1/2O_2 = H_2O\,(g) \quad \ldots\ldots\ldots\ldots\ldots\ldots\ldots\ldots (a)$$

can be represented for a range of temperature from 0° C. to over 1000° C. by the equation

$$\Delta H = -57410 - 0{\cdot}94T - 0\ 00165T^2 + 0{\cdot}00000074T^3.$$

Inserting this value into $(d \log K_p/dT) = \Delta H/RT^2$ and integrating, we have

$$\log K_p = \frac{57410}{RT} - \frac{0{\cdot}94}{R}\log T - \frac{0{\cdot}00165T}{R} + \frac{0{\cdot}00000074T^2}{2R} \ldots + J,$$

where J is the integration constant.

In order to evaluate J we may make use of Nernst and von Wortenberg's measurements of the dissociation of water vapour. They found that at 1480° K. the percentage dissociation of water vapour is 0·0184. The equilibrium constant at this temperature is thus

$$K_p = \frac{p_{H_2O}}{p_{H_2} \cdot p_{O_2}{}^{1/2}} = \frac{1}{0{\cdot}000184 \times (0{\cdot}000092)^{1/2}} = 5{\cdot}66 \times 10^5.$$

Introducing this figure, and the value of T into the equation, we find that $J = -1{\cdot}98$. Similarly

$$\begin{aligned}\Delta F^\circ &= -RT \log K_p \\ &= -57410 + 0{\cdot}94 \log T + 0{\cdot}00165T^2 \\ &\qquad + 0{\cdot}00000037T^3 + 3{\cdot}94T,\end{aligned}$$

where $3{\cdot}94 = -JR$. By means of this equation we can find ΔF° at any other temperature. Thus when $T = 298$ (25° C.), we have

$$\Delta F^\circ_{298} = -54590 \text{ calories.}$$

After an examination of all the available data for the free energy of formation of water vapour Lewis and Randall have given 3·92 as the best value of I.

2. It is of interest to calculate from this result the theoretical electromotive force of the reversible oxygen-hydrogen cell at 25° C.

The reaction

$$H_2(g) + 1/2O_2(g) = H_2O(l), \quad \ldots\ldots\ldots\ldots\ldots\ldots (b)$$

differs from that considered above in that the water formed is obtained as liquid water. To obtain ΔF for this reaction, we must add to ΔF° (the free energy change for gases at unit pressure), the free energy change in the change of water vapour at unit pressure (and 25°) to liquid water at the same temperature. The vapour pressure of liquid water at 25° is 23·8 mm. of mercury. Water vapour at this pressure must have the same free energy (per mol) as liquid water, so that we need only evaluate the free energy change in the isothermal expansion of water vapour from unit pressure (1 atmosphere) to a pressure of 23·8 mm. By (131) we have therefore

$$\Delta F_{298}(g \to l) = RT \log \frac{23{\cdot}8}{760} = -2053 \text{ calories.}$$

The total free energy change for the reaction (2) is therefore

$$\Delta F_{298} = -54590 - 2050 = -56640 \text{ calories.}$$

Two Faradays of electricity must pass through the oxygen-hydrogen cell in order to bring about the reaction represented by (*b*). Therefore if **E** is the reversible electromotive force

$$2\mathbf{EF} = 56640 \times 4{\cdot}182 \text{ joules,}$$

or

$$\mathbf{E} = \frac{56640 \times 4{\cdot}182}{2 \times 96490} = 1{\cdot}227 \text{ volts.}$$

3. From the heat capacity equations we can derive the equation

$$\Delta H = \Delta H_0 - 4{\cdot}96T - 0{\cdot}0006T^2 + 0{\cdot}0000017T^3,$$

for the heat content change in the reaction

$$1/2N_2(g) + 3/2H_2(g) = NH_3(g).$$

(See Chapter I, ex. 12.) By the use of thermochemical data it is found that $\Delta H_0 = -9500$ calories. Introducing this value of ΔH into (139), and integrating, we have

$$\log K_p = \frac{9500}{RT} - \frac{4 \cdot 96}{R} \log T - \frac{0 \cdot 000575T}{R} + \frac{0 \cdot 0000017T^2}{2R} + J,$$

and

$$\Delta F^\circ = -RT \log K_p$$
$$= -9500 + 4 \cdot 96T \log T + 0 \cdot 000575T^2 - 0 \cdot 00000085T^3 + IT.$$

From measurements of the equilibrium constant at various temperatures and pressures, Lewis and Randall conclude that the best value of I is $-9 \cdot 61$.

* **The Vapour Pressure Equation.** The equilibrium between a solid or liquid and its vapour can be similarly treated. Let F_s be the molar free energy of a solid at the temperature T, and F_g that of the vapour. For equilibrium it is necessary that $F_s = F_g$. If F°_g is the free energy of the vapour at this temperature, and at unit pressure, and p the vapour pressure, we have by (131), assuming that the vapour is a perfect gas,

$$F_g = F^\circ_g + RT \log p,$$

and therefore

$$F_s - F^\circ_g = RT \log p. \quad \text{..............(143)}$$

Therefore, by (122),

$$\frac{d \log p}{dT} = \frac{1}{R}\left(\frac{d(F_s/T)}{dT} - \frac{d(F^\circ_g/T)}{dT}\right)$$
$$= -\frac{H_s - H^\circ_g}{RT^2} = \frac{\Delta H}{RT^2}, \quad \text{...(144)}$$

where $\Delta H = H^\circ_g - H_s$ is the latent heat of vaporisation.

The dissociation equilibrium between solids and a gas can be similarly treated. Consider the reaction

$$CaCO_3 = CaO + CO_2.$$

It can easily be shown by the method previously used that the condition of equilibrium is

$$F_{CaCO_3} = F_{CaO} + F_{CO_2},$$

where F_{CaCO_3}, F_{CaO}, F_{CO_2}, are the free energies at a given temperature of the quantities of these substances which are represented in the chemical equation. Writing $F_{CO_2} = F^\circ_{CO_2} + RT \log p$, we thus have for equilibrium :

$$F_{CaCO_3} - F_{CaO} - F^\circ_{CO_2} = \Delta F^\circ = RT \log p,$$

and by the same method as above

$$\frac{d \log p}{dT} = \frac{\Delta H}{RT^2},$$

where ΔH is the heat content change in the reaction.

These expressions can be integrated similarly to (139), if ΔH is known as a function of T.

Examples.

1. The heat capacity change in the reaction

$$SO_2(g) + 1/2O_2 = SO_3(g)$$

can probably be taken as zero. The heat content change is thus independent of the temperature, and was found by Berthelot to be $\Delta H = -22600$. Formulate an expression giving $\log K_p$ as a function of the temperature. Given $\log_{10} K_p = 0{\cdot}268$ at 1000° K. the integration constant of this expression can be evaluated, hence ΔF° can be expressed as a function of the temperature.

$$(\Delta F^\circ = -22600 + 21{\cdot}37T.)$$

2. For the water-gas reaction :

$$CO_2(g) + H_2(g) = CO(g) + H_2O(g),$$

take the heat content equation from Chapter I, ex. 12, and write down an expression for the equilibrium constant. The integration constant can be evaluated by inserting the value $K_p = 0 \cdot 840$ at 1059° K. Formulate the expression for ΔF°.

$$(\Delta F^\circ = 10100 - 1 \cdot 81T \log T + 0 \cdot 00445T^2 - 0 \cdot 00000068T^3 - 0 \cdot 54T.)$$

3. The free energy change in the reaction

$$N_2(g) + O_2(g) = NO(g)$$

is expressed by $\Delta F^\circ = 21600 - 2 \cdot 50T$. Find the equilibrium constant when

$T = 1000$ and $T = 2000$. $(6 \cdot 8 \times 10^{-5}, 1 \cdot 5 \times 10^{-2}.)$

4. Write down an expression for ΔF° for the reaction

$$1/2H_2(g) + 1/2Br_2(g) = HBr(g).$$

Use the heat capacity equations of Table I. (p. 18) and the values

$$\Delta H_0 = -11970\ ;\ \log K_p = 2 \cdot 44 \text{ when } T = 1381^\circ \text{ K}.$$

$$(\Delta F^\circ = -11970 + 0 \cdot 45T \log T - 0 \cdot 000025T^2 - 5 \cdot 72T.)$$

5. The heat content change in the reaction, $3/2O_2 = O_3$ may be represented by

$$\Delta H = 34600 - 2 \cdot 75T + 0 \cdot 0028T^2 - 0 \cdot 0000062T^3.$$

Deduce an expression for the variation of the equilibrium constant of thermal equilibrium. $K_p = p_{O_3}/(p_{O_2})^{3/2}$ may be taken as roughly $0 \cdot 01$ at 2300° K.

$$(\Delta F^\circ = 34600 + 2 \cdot 75T \log T - 0 \cdot 0028T^2 + 0 \cdot 00000031T^3 - 22 \cdot 4T.)$$

CHAPTER XIII

THE THIRD LAW OF THERMODYNAMICS

In the last chapter we obtained equations giving the free energy change of gaseous reactions in terms of quantities which, with one exception, are derived from purely thermal data. The exception is the integration constant I, to evaluate which it is necessary to know the value of the equilibrium constant for at least one particular temperature. If I could be calculated or derived from thermal data, we should have in these equations the means of calculating the free energy changes from thermal data alone, *i.e.* from the measurements of the heat content change and of the heat capacities of the substances concerned. We should then be able to calculate outright the equilibrium constants of any reactions, for which these quantities are known.

The most general relation between the free energy change and the heat content change in a reaction at constant temperature and pressure is that given by

$$\Delta F = \Delta H - T\Delta S. \qquad (145)$$

The calculation of ΔF from ΔH is thus possible if we have an independent knowledge of ΔS, the entropy change in the reaction. The entropy change in a reaction could be determined if we had values of the entropies of the substances concerned. We have therefore to consider whether it is possible to assign values to the entropies of substances at any given temperature which can be used to determine the entropy changes in reactions.

Entropies Referred to Absolute Zero. In the first place we can evaluate the difference of entropy of a substance between the absolute zero and any given temperature T, if no change of state occurs between these temperatures, by integrating (21), *viz.* $dS = C_p/T \cdot dT$, between 0 and T. Thus if we denote this entropy difference by $S_0{}^T$, we have:

$$S_0{}^T = \int_0^T \frac{C_p}{T} dT = \int_0^T C_p d \log T.$$

The heat capacity of a solid at low temperatures is not a simple function of the temperature, and when the heat capacities down to very low temperatures are known the integration is best performed graphically. If C_p is plotted against $\log T$ the entropy change between any two temperatures T_1 and T_2 (Fig. 69) is equal to the area enclosed by the curve between the ordinates representing $\log T_1$ and $\log T_2$. To find $S_0{}^T$ we have to determine the area enclosed by the curve between the ordinate for $\log T$ and that for $T = 0$ ($\log T = -\infty$). This is usually

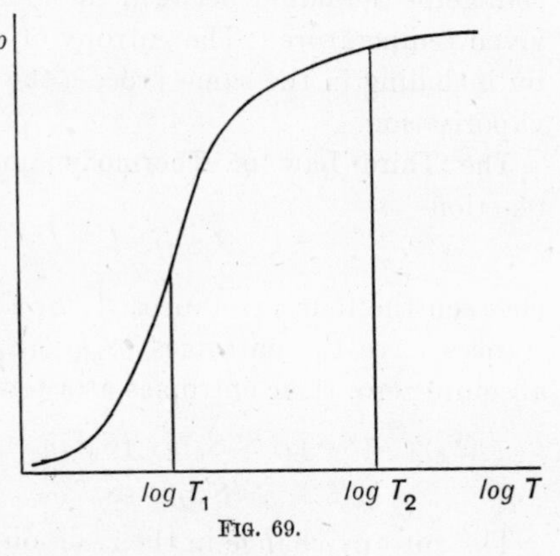

FIG. 69.

possible because the heat capacities of solids approach the value zero asymptotically in the vicinity of absolute zero. If the heat capacity is known down to about 40° K. usually the extrapolation to absolute zero can be made without any great error.

When, in passing from absolute zero to the given temperature the substance changes its state by passing from one allotropic modification to another, the entropy change in the change of state (q/T) must be added to the sum of the $\int C_p \,.\, d \log T$ terms. The entropy of a liquid at any given temperature may similarly be evaluated by determining the entropy change of the solid form of the substance from absolute zero to the melting point, and adding the entropy change on fusion and the entropy change of the liquid between the melting point and the given temperature. The entropy of a gas can be found by including in the same process the entropy change in vaporisation.

The Third Law of Thermodynamics. Consider the reaction

$$A + B = C + D$$

between the four substances A, B, C, D. If these substances have the entropies $(S_0)_A$, $(S_0)_B$, $(S_0)_C$, $(S_0)_D$ at absolute zero, their entropies at a temperature T are

$$(S_0)_A + (S_0{}^T)_A, \quad (S_0)_B + (S_0{}^T)_B, \quad (S_0)_C + (S_0{}^T)_C,$$
$$(S_0)_D + (S_0{}^T)_D.$$

The entropy change in the reaction at absolute zero is

$$\Delta S_0 = (S_0)_C + (S_0)_D - (S_0)_A - (S_0)_B,$$

and the entropy change at the temperature T is

$$\Delta S_T = \Delta S_0 + \Sigma S_0{}^T, \quad \text{..............(146)}$$

where ΣS_0^T is the difference between the sum of the values of S_0^T for the products C and D, and that for the reactants A and B. The values of S_0^T can be determined by heat capacity measurements, as described in the last section. In order to find ΔS_T we therefore need to know ΔS_0, the entropy change in the reaction at absolute zero.

The Third Law of Thermodynamics states that *the entropy change of a reaction between crystalline solids is zero at the absolute zero of temperature.** The justification of this law will be discussed later. If it is true, ΔS_0 is zero for a reaction between crystalline solids, and therefore

$$\Delta S_T = \Sigma S_0^T, \quad \ldots\ldots\ldots\ldots\ldots\ldots(147)$$

for such reactions. The entropy change in the reaction can now be determined by evaluating S_0^T for the substances concerned by heat capacity measurements.

This law can be expressed in another way. If the entropy changes of all reactions between crystalline solids are zero at absolute zero, the entropy of a crystalline compound must be the same as that of its crystalline elements at this temperature, so that if we take the entropies of the elements in the crystalline form to be zero, the entropies of crystalline compounds must also be zero at the absolute zero of temperature. We can therefore state the Third Law in the form :

If the entropy of each element in some crystalline form be taken as zero at the absolute zero, the entropy of any pure crystal at the absolute zero is zero.†

* Lewis and Gibson, *J. Amer. Chem. Soc.*, 39, 2554, 1917 ; Lewis, Gibson and Latimer, *ibid.* 44, 1008, 1922.

† In some special cases in which more than one arrangement of the atoms in the crystal can occur at absolute zero, a further qualification is necessary (see Appendix, p. 562).

The values of $S_0{}^T$, determined as described in the last section, starting with a crystalline form of the substance at absolute zero, can thus be taken as the real values of the entropy at the given temperature T. The following table gives the entropies of a number of substances, as determined in this way, at 25° C.

TABLE XXIV.

ENTROPIES AT 25° C. (IN CALORIES/DEGREES).

Elements.

Element	Entropy	Element	Entropy
Hydrogen ($1/2H_2$, *g*)	14·72	Chlorine ($1/2Cl_2$, *g*)	26·3
Carbon (C, *graphite*)	1·3	Iron (Fe, *s*)	6·71
Nitrogen ($1/2N_2$, *g*)	22·8	Cobalt (Co, *s*)	7·2
Oxygen ($1/2O_2$, *g*)	24·0	Nickel (Ni, *s*)	7·2
Sodium (Na, *s*)	12·2	Zinc (Zn, *s*)	9·83
Sulphur (S, *rhombic*)	7·6	Bromine (Br_2, *l*)	16·3
Sulphur (S, *monoclinic*)	7·8	Silver (Ag, *s*)	10·25
Cadmium (Cd, *s*)	11·80	Mercury (Hg, *l*)	17·8
Iodine (I_2, *s*)	13·19	Lead (Pb, *s*)	15·53
Iodine (I_2, *g*)	31·1		

Compounds.

Compound	Entropy	Compound	Entropy
$H_2O(l)$	15·9	$NH_3(g)$	46·7
$HCl(g)$	41·2	$NaCl(s)$	17·2
$HBr(g)$	44·9	$KCl(s)$	19·9
$HI(g)$	47·8	$CuO(s)$	9·76
$CH_4(g)$	43·4	$HgCl(s)$	22·8
$CO(g)$	45·9	$AgCl(s)$	23·1
$CO_2(g)$	51·1		

Origin and Development of the Third Law of Thermodynamics. The free energy change and heat content change in a chemical reaction are related, as we have seen, by the equivalent relations :

$$\Delta F = \Delta H + T\left(\frac{d\Delta F}{dT}\right)_p,$$

$$\Delta F = \Delta H - T\Delta S.$$

It was long suspected that some general relation between ΔF and ΔH might be found which would enable free energy changes to be determined from thermal data. T. W. Richards* in 1902 studied the free energy and heat content changes in a number of galvanic cells and found that they rapidly approached each other as the temperature was lowered. van't Hoff † further studied the matter in 1904, and in 1906 Nernst ‡ formulated the relations known as the "Nernst heat theorem."

According to these equations it is evident that unless $d\Delta F/dT$ (or ΔS) is infinite, $\Delta F = \Delta H$ when $T = 0$. Nernst postulated that not only are ΔF and ΔH equal at absolute zero, but they approach equality at this temperature asymptotically. Some of the possibilities are shown in Fig. 70.

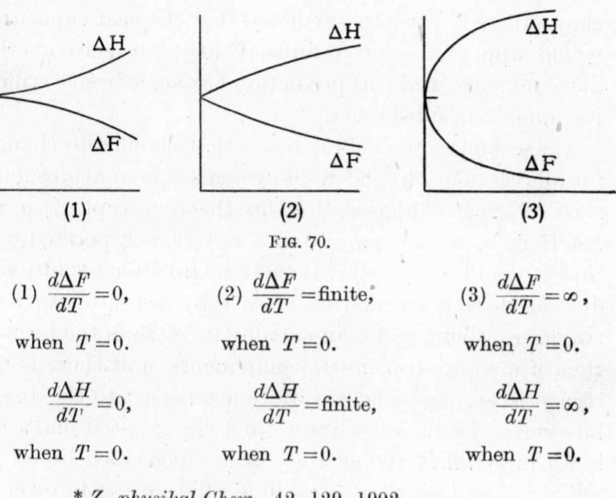

FIG. 70.

(1) $\dfrac{d\Delta F}{dT} = 0$, when $T = 0$. $\qquad$ (2) $\dfrac{d\Delta F}{dT} = \text{finite}$, when $T = 0$. $\qquad$ (3) $\dfrac{d\Delta F}{dT} = \infty$, when $T = 0$.

$\dfrac{d\Delta H}{dT} = 0$, when $T = 0$. $\qquad$ $\dfrac{d\Delta H}{dT} = \text{finite}$, when $T = 0$. $\qquad$ $\dfrac{d\Delta H}{dT} = \infty$, when $T = 0$.

* *Z. physikal Chem.*, 42, 129, 1902.

† Boltzmann *Festschrift*, p. 233, 1904.

‡ *Nachr. Kgl. Ges. Wiss.*, Göttingen; 1, 1906.

Nernst postulated that the actual behaviour of condensed systems (solids or liquids) was that of case (1), *i.e.*

$$(1)\ \frac{d\Delta H}{dT}=0, \text{ in the limit when } T=0, \quad \text{.........(148)}$$

$$(2)\ \Delta S=\frac{d\Delta F}{dT}=0, \text{ in the limit when } T=0. \quad \text{...(149)}$$

Since $\frac{d\Delta H}{dT}=\Delta C_p$, (148) implies that the heat capacity change for all reactions in condensed systems is zero when $T=0$. If this is the case the heat capacity of compounds must be equal to that of the elements from which they are formed. Nernst thought that the heat capacities of all liquids and solids approached the value $C_p=1{\cdot}5$ calories per gram atom in the vicinity of absolute zero. In 1907 Einstein predicted that the heat capacities would approach, not a finite value, but zero at the absolute zero, and this prediction has since been verified for numerous substances.

The second relation (149) means that the entropy change for all reactions of condensed systems is zero at absolute zero. Nernst supposed that his theorem applied to all reactions of condensed systems, but Planck pointed out that it could not apply to reactions involving solutions. Just as there is an increase of entropy in the mixture of two gases, there is also an entropy increase in the formation of a solution from its components, and there is no reason to suppose that this does not persist to the absolute zero. Lewis and Gibson, in 1920, pointed out that in all probability the entropy of a supercooled liquid is greater than that of a crystalline solid at absolute zero. There is no sharp dividing line between pure liquids and solutions, since liquids may contain more than one molecular species. A test of this point can be made by measuring the heat capacities of the solid and (supercooled) liquid forms of the substance from the melting point to the vicinity of absolute zero. If ΔS_T is the entropy change of fusion at the temperature T, and ΔS_0 the entropy difference between the solid and supercooled liquid at absolute zero, we have

$$\Delta S_T = \Delta S_0 + \Sigma S_0{}^T.$$

Gibson and Giauque* determined the heat capacities of glycerine as a solid and as a supercooled liquid and found that their results required that ΔS_0 should be an appreciable positive quantity. Simon and Lange † have also shown that amorphous silica has an appreciably greater entropy at absolute zero than the crystalline variety. It is therefore necessary to limit the scope of the law to crystalline substances.

Tests of the Third Law of Thermodynamics. The third law can be tested by comparing the entropy change in a reaction (measured independently) with the difference of the entropies of the products and reactants as calculated on the assumption that the entropies of crystalline solids are zero at absolute zero. The entropy change of a reaction at a temperature T can be determined if the changes of free energy and heat content are known by the equation

$$\Delta S = -\frac{\Delta F - \Delta H}{T}. \quad \text{...............(150)}$$

1. *The Conversion of White to Grey Tin.* The entropy change for the reaction at 25° C., calculated by (150), is $\Delta S_{298} = -1{\cdot}87$ units. From the heat capacities the entropy of white tin is $S_{298} = 11{\cdot}17$ and that of grey tin $S_{298} = 9{\cdot}23$, *i.e.* $\Delta S = -1{\cdot}94$.

* *J. Amer. Chem. Soc.*, 45, 93, 1923.

† *Z. Physik*, 38, 227, 1926.

2. The reaction $Ag + HgCl(s) = AgCl(s) + Hg$.

Accurate measurements of the free energy and entropy change of this reaction can be made by measurements of the cell

$$Ag \mid AgCl(s),\ KCl,\ HgCl(s) \mid Hg.$$

From the electromotive force measurements of Gerke,

$$\mathbf{E}_{298} = 0{\cdot}0455,\quad d\mathbf{E}/dt = 0{\cdot}00038.$$

The entropy change in the reaction as calculated from these measurements is $\Delta S = +7{\cdot}8$ cals./degs. The entropy change as determined from the specific heats of the substances, making use of the Third Law, is also $+7{\cdot}8$ units (see Table XXIV).

Uses of the Third Law of Thermodynamics. The direct determination of the free energy change of a reaction requires a knowledge of the state of equilibrium. There are many reactions, particularly those involving the formation of organic compounds, for which a state of equilibrium cannot be realised. A knowledge of the free energies of formation of organic compounds would be an extremely valuable aid in estimating the possibilities of effecting reactions. They can be determined indirectly by (145) if the heat contents and entropies of the substance concerned are known. The free energies of a number of compounds have been determined in this way by Parks, Kelley, Anderson, Huffman* and others. Some of their values are given in Table XXV. The second column gives the entropy of the compound at 25° C. and the third the entropy of formation from the elements at the same temperature. Knowing ΔH, ΔF for the formation of the compound from its elements can now be determined. By means of such a table we can find the free energy

* *J. Amer. Chem. Soc.*, 47, 338, 2094, 1925; 48, 1506, 2788, 1926.

changes of numerous reactions. For further details see *The Free Energies of Organic Compounds*, by Parks and Huffman, Chem. Cat. Co., 1932.

Example. From the free energies of glucose and liquid water we can find the free energy change in the reaction :

$$C_6H_{12}O_6\,(\text{glucose}) = 6C\,(\text{gr.}) + 6H_2O(l)$$
$$\Delta F \quad -219000 \qquad 0 \qquad -339360.$$

The ΔF for the reaction is thus

$$-339360 - (-219000) = -120360.$$

There is thus a large free energy decrease in this reaction, which should be easily effected. Sugars are easily decomposed by strong dehydrating agents such as sulphuric acid.

TABLE XXV.

ENTROPY AND FREE ENERGY OF FORMATION OF SOME ORGANIC COMPOUNDS AT 25°.

(Parks, Kelley and Huffman, *J. Amer. Chem. Soc.*, 51, 1972, 1929.)

	S.	ΔS.	$-\Delta H$.	$-\Delta F$.
Methyl alcohol	31·0	54·0	60300	44200
Ethyl alcohol -	38·4	77·5	66300	43200
n-Propyl alcohol	46·1	100·7	73300	43300
iso-Propyl alcohol	43·1	103·7	79000	48100
n-Butyl alcohol -	54·5	123·2	80000	43200
tert-Butyl alcohol -	43·3	132·4	89600	50100
Glycerol - -	49·7	146·1	159300	115700
Erythritol	39·8	211·4	215000	152000
Mannitol -	57·0	305·0	317000	226100
Dulcitol - -	56·0	306·0	318000	226800
Formic acid -	30·7	49·2	99900	85200
Acetic acid -	38·2	72·6	117000	95400
n-Butyric acid -	54·1	118·5	130400	95100
Oxalic acid -	28·7	101·3	196800	166500
Ethyl ether -	60·4	117·3	67300	32300
Acetone - -	47·8	69·4	57300	36600
Glucose - -	50·5	281·9	303000	219000

Entropy and Probability. There are two ways of dealing with large assemblies of molecules. One is the classical thermodynamical method, which we have been expounding, of deducing their behaviour from the laws of thermodynamics. In the other we could start with a knowledge of the laws of the behaviour of individual atoms and molecules and deduce therefrom the behaviour of large assemblages which we encounter in matter in bulk. This involves the use of statistics and, indeed, the laws of thermodynamics should follow as statistical consequences of the laws of energy and motion of atoms and molecules.

The student will have to consult treatises on statistical mechanics or the brief summary given in the Appendix for the development of this point of view. It is only necessary here to mention the significance which entropy has in the statistical theory. The basis of the application of statistics to collections of atoms and molecules is that of all the ways of distributing a given quantity of energy among a collection of atoms there is no inherent likelihood that a given atom will have any one quantity of energy rather than another. This is alternatively expressed by saying that, if the various components of the energy of the atom (or molecule) are indicated by the co-ordinates of its position in a *phase space* having a suitable number of dimensions, the atom (or molecule) is just as likely to be found in one part of the phase space as in another.

It follows that the most likely arrangement of an assembly of atoms is that in which the given distribution of energy between them can be arrived at in the greatest number of ways. The *statistical probability* of a given arrangement is defined as the number of different ways in which it can be arrived at by redistribution of its matter or energy. It can be shown that the logarithm of this quantity is proportional to the entropy of the system ; or, more exactly,

$$S = k \log_e W,$$

where S is the entropy per molecule in a system having the probability W and k is the gas constant per molecule $(= R/N_0)$.

Free Energies of Gaseous Reactions from Third Law. The entropy and therefore the free energy of a gas can be obtained from thermal data, starting with the substance in the form of a perfect crystal at 0° K., if we know the heat capacities and latent heats of liquefaction and vaporization absorbed in the process of bringing it from the crystalline state to the gaseous state at the desired temperature. Some examples of these calculations are given below :

(1) *Hydration of Ethylene.* $C_2H_4(g) + H_2O(g) = C_2H_5OH(g)$ (Aston ; *Ind. and Eng. Chem.*, 34, 516, 1942). To find $\Delta F°$ at 298·2° K.

Entropy of ethyl alcohol	ΔS
0° K.—16°, crystals by extrapolation	0·45
16°—158·5°, crystals from C_p - -	16·20
Fusion, 1200/158·5 - - - -	7·57
158·5—298·2, liquid from C_p - -	14·18
Entropy of liquid alcohol at 298·2°	38·4 ± 0·3
Vaporisation at 298·2° and 0·07763 atm. 10,120/298·2 - - -	33·94
Compression from 0·07763 atm. to 1 atm. - - - - - - -	−5·08
Entropy of ideal gas at 298·2° and 1 atm. - - -	67·26 ± 0·3 cals/deg.

Entropy of ethylene.

0° K—15° K., crystals by extrapolation - - - - - -	0·25
15—103·95°, from C_p of crystal -	12·23
Fusion 800·8/103·95 - - - -	7·70
103·95—169·40, from C_p of liquid -	7·92
Vaporisation 3237/169·4 - - -	19·11
Correction for gas imperfection - -	0·15
Entropy at boiling point - - -	47·36
169·40 to 298·2, from C_p gas - -	5·12
Entropy of gas at 298·2 and 1 atm. -	52·48 cals./deg.
Entropy of water vapour at 1 atm. and 298·2° - - - - -	45·10 cals./deg.

Hence $\Delta S_{298\cdot 2} = -30\cdot 3$ cals./deg.

The heat of reaction $\Delta H°$ is obtained from the following heats of formation :

	Ethylene	Water	Ethyl Alcohol
Heat of formation of gas at 298·2° - -	12,576	– 57,813	– 56,201

$\Delta H°_{298\cdot 2} = -56{,}201 - 12{,}576 - (-57{,}813) = -10{,}964$ cals.

$\Delta F°_{298\cdot 2} = \Delta H° - T\Delta S°$

$= -10{,}964 - 298\cdot 2 \times -30\cdot 3 = -1926$ cals.

(The accuracy of the last figure is estimated at ± 500 cals.)

(2) *Isomerization reaction, n-Butane→Isobutane.* The entropies of butane and isobutane were determined thermally by Aston, Kennedy, Messerley and Schumann (*J. Amer. Chem. Soc.*, 62, 1917, 2059, 1940).

n-Butane	ΔS
0—10° K. extrap. - - - - - -	0·15
10—107·55, C_p crystal I - - - - -	14·534
107·55 transition 494/107·55 - - -	4·593
107·55—134·89, C_p crystal II - - -	4·520
134·89, fusion 1113·7/134·87 - - -	8·255
134·89—272·66, C_p liquid - - - -	20·203
272·66, vaporisation 5351/272·66 - -	19·62
	71·88

Correction for gas imperfection	0·17
Entropy of ideal gas at 272·66° K. and 1 atm.	72·05 ± 0·2
Entropy of ideal gas at 298·16° K. and 1 atm.	74·0

Isobutane

	ΔS
0—12·53° extrap.	0·247
12·53°—113·74°, C_p crystal	16·115
113·74°, fusion 1085·4/113·74	9·543
113·74°—261·44, C_p liquid	22·030
261·44°, vaporization 5089·6/261·44	19·468
	67·52 ± 0·10
261·44° – 298·16°, C_p vapour	2·91
Entropy of ideal gas at 1 atm. and 298·16°	70·43 ± 0·15

Using the data

$$\Delta H^\circ_{298 \cdot 2} = -1630 \pm 280 \text{ cal.}$$

$$\Delta S^\circ_{298 \cdot 2} = -3 \cdot 6 \pm 0 \cdot 3 \text{ cals./deg.}$$

we obtain

$$\Delta F^\circ_{298 \cdot 2} = -557 \pm 370 \text{ cals.}$$

from which the equilibrium constant is obtained

$$K^\circ_{298 \cdot 2} = 2 \cdot 56.$$

This is not in very good agreement with the experimental value $K^\circ_{298 \cdot 2} = 5 \cdot 47 \pm 0 \cdot 5$, but the discrepancy is considered to be just within the possible errors arising from the data going into the calculation.

Thermodynamic Data of Hydrocarbons.

The following table gives thermodynamic data of liquid hydrocarbons at 25° C. ΔH_f° is the heat of formation, S° the entropy, and ΔS_f° the entropy of formation at 25°. ΔF_f° is the free energy of formation and $\Delta F_f^\circ/n$ the value of this quantity per carbon atom, which is of special interest in making comparisons of thermodynamic stability.*

* Parks, G. S., *Chem. Revs.*, 27, 75, 1940.

TABLE XXVa.

ENTROPY AND FREE ENERGY OF FORMATION OF HYDROCARBONS.

	ΔH_f°.	S°.	ΔS_f°.	ΔF_f°	$\Delta F_f^\circ/n$.
Hexane (*l*)	– 47,560	70·9	– 155·9	– 1,080	– 180
Heptane (*l*)	– 53,910	78·6	– 180·8	000	000
Octane (*l*)	– 60,250	86·2	– 205·8	+ 1,110	+ 139
Nonane (*l*)	– 66,450	94·0	– 230·5	+ 2,280	+ 253
Decane (*l*)	– 72,360	102·7	– 254·4	+ 3,490	+ 349
Undecane (*l*)	– 78,790	111·0	– 278·7	+ 4,310	+ 392
Dodecane (*l*)	– 84,110	118·3	– 304·0	+ 6,530	+ 544
Hexadecane (*l*)	– 109,780	148·6	– 404·1	+ 10,710	+ 668
Methylcylopentane (*l*)	– 33,730	59·3	– 136·2	6,880	+ 1,147
Ethylcyclopentane (*l*)	– 40,000	67·1	– 161·0	8,000	+ 1,143
Cyclohexane (*l*)	– 37,680	49·3	– 146·2	5,910	+ 985
Methylcycohexane (*l*)	– 46,020	59·4	– 168·7	4,280	+ 611
n-heptylcyclohexane (*l*)	– 84,960	106·8	– 316·9	9,530	+ 733
Benzene (*l*)	11,200	41·9	– 59·9	29,060	+ 4,843
Toluene (*l*)	3,520	52·4	– 82·0	27,970	+ 3,996
Ethyl benzene (*l*)	– 3,430	61·3	– 105·7	28,090	+ 3,511
n-Butyl benzene (*l*)	– 16,630	76·9	– 155·3	29,670	+ 2,967
Naphthalene (*s*)	18,030	39·9	– 98·6	47,430	+ 4,743
Anthracene (*s*)	26,740	49·6	– 125·6	64,190	+ 4,584
Phenanthrene (*s*)	16,940	50·6	– 124·6	54,090	+ 3,864

The most stable member of the C_6 series is hexane. Cyclohexane has a free energy some 7000 cals./mol. higher, and benzene is greater by a further 23,000 cals./mol. The free energy change in the isomerization reaction

$$\text{cyclohexane } (l) \rightarrow \text{methylcyclopentane } (l)$$

is $\Delta F_{25} = 970$ cals. Direct equilibrium measurements gave the figure 1150 cals., which agrees well.

***Entropy of Gases.** When the temperature of a gas is increased by a small amount dT at constant pressure, the heat absorbed is $dq = C_p dT$, and the entropy change is

$$dS = \frac{dq}{T} = C_p \frac{dT}{T}.$$

Integrating this we obtain, for a constant pressure,

$$S = S_0 + \int \frac{C_p}{T} . dT, \quad \ldots\ldots\ldots\ldots\ldots\ldots (151)$$

where S_0 is an integration constant.

When C_p is independent of the temperature, we have

$$S = S_0 + C_p \log T,$$

and combining this with the variation with the pressure which is given for a perfect gas by (129), we have

$$S = S_0 + C_p \log T - R \log p.$$

The entropy of a monatomic gas for which $C_p = 5/2R$ is thus given by

$$S = S_0 + 5/2R \log T - R \log p.$$

The value of S_0 for monatomic gases was first calculated by means of statistical mechanics by Sackur* and Tetrode.† The basis of this calculation cannot be given here, but the result is ‡

$$S_0 = R \log_e \frac{(2\pi)^{3/2} (ke)^{5/2}}{N_0^{3/2} h^3} + 3/2R \log_e M + R \log_e g_0,$$

where $k = R/N_0$ is the gas constant per molecule, N_0 the Avogadro number, h the Planck constant, e the base of natural logarithms, g_0 the weight factor due to electron

* *Ann. Physik*, (4), 40, 67, 1913.

† *Ibid.* (4), 38, 434, 1912 ; 39, 255, 1913 ; also Stern, *Physik. Z.*, 14, 629, 1913. See Kassel, *Chem. Revs.*, 18, 277, 1936 ; E. B. Wilson, *ibid.*, 27, 17, 1940.

‡ See Appendix, p. 555, equation 41.

spin, and M the atomic weight of the gas. When the pressure is expressed in atmospheres the result is

$$S_0 = -2{\cdot}31 + 3/2R \log_e M$$

and the entropy of a monatomic gas at 1 atmos. pressure is

$$S = -2{\cdot}31 + 3/2R \log_e M + 5/2R \log T + R \log g_0. \quad (152)$$

The following table shows the observed entropies of four monatomic gases at 298 K. and 1 atmos., compared with the values calculated by this equation.

ENTROPY OF MONATOMIC GASES AT 298 K. AND 1 ATMOS.

	S_{298} (Obs.).	S_{298} (Calc.).	g_0.
Helium - - -	30·4	30·1	1
Argon - - -	36·9	37·0	1
Mercury vapour - -	42·2	41·8	1
Sodium vapour - -	37·2	36·7	2

The heat capacity of a molecule which consists of more than one atom may be represented by

$$C_p = 5/2R + C_{rot.} + C_{vib.},$$

where $C_{rot.}$, $C_{vib.}$, represent the contributions of the rotational and vibrational energy of the molecule. It has been shown that the value of $C_{rot.}$ for diatomic gases is R. It is impossible to derive expressions for these quantities with the theoretical background available here and reference must be made for details to the Appendix.

Since however the student may encounter some of those expressions in his reading and may wish to use the results without necessarily understanding how they are arrived at, it may be useful to give some of the results of these calculations. The translational entropy is still given by (152).

Linear (including diatomic) molecules. The contribution of the rotations to the entropy is

$$S_r = R + R \log_e \left[\frac{8\pi^2 IkT}{\sigma h^2} \right],$$

where I is the moment of inertia of the molecule and σ a symmetry number representing the number of indistinguishable positions into which the molecule can be turned by simple rigid rotations, *e.g.*, for HCl, N_2, C_2H_2, C_2H_4, NH_3, C_2H_2 and C_2H_4, σ is 1, 2, 2, 4, 3 and 12 respectively. When the numerical values of the constants are inserted this gives

$$S_r = R(\log_e IT - \log_e \sigma + 89{\cdot}408).$$

The following table gives a few values of S for 298° and 1 atmos. as determined calorimetrically, and as calculated:

	$I \times 10^{40}$ g.cm.²	g_0.	σ.	S (obs.).	S (calc.).
O_2 - -	19·2	3	2	49·1	49·0
N_2 - -	13·8	1	2	43·9	45·8
HCl - -	2·64	1	1	44·5	44·6
CO - -	15·0	1	1	46·2	47·3

Rigid non-linear molecules.

$$S_r = 3/2R + R \log_e \frac{8\pi^2}{\sigma h^3} (8\pi^3 ABC)^{\frac{1}{2}} (kT)^{3/2},$$

where A, B, C are the principal moments of inertia of the molecule. When these are expressed in gm. cm.², this becomes

$$S_r = R(3/2 \log_e T + \tfrac{1}{2} \log_e ABC - \log_e \sigma + 134{\cdot}69)$$

Vibrational contributions. This involves a knowledge of the vibrational frequencies of the molecule. The contribution of a single vibration of frequency ν is

$$S_v = -R \log_e (1 - e^x) + \frac{Rx}{e^x - 1}, \text{ where } x = h\nu/kT.$$

This expression has to be summed for all the known vibration frequencies.

Examples.

The calculation for the linear molecule COS is shown below. I is taken as 137×10^{-40} gm. cm.^{2}.

ENTROPY OF CARBONYL SULPHIDE

Calorimetric	ΔS
0 – 15° K.	0·55
15 – 134·31° K.	14·96
Fusion 1129·8/134·31	8·41
134·31° – 222·87°	8·66
Vaporization 4423/222·87	19·85
Entropy at b. pt.	52·43 ± 0·10
Corr. for gas imperfection	0·13
Entropy of ideal gas at b. pt.	52·56

Statistical Calculation

$$S_{trans.} = 3/2R \log_e M + 5/2R \log_e T - 2{\cdot}300 \qquad = 36{\cdot}761$$

$$S_{rot.} = R \log IT + 177{\cdot}676 \qquad = 15{\cdot}19$$

$$S_{vib.} \qquad = 0{\cdot}711$$

Calculated entropy at 222·87° K. - - - - - 52·66

The following table shows the entropy of ethylene gas at its boiling point (169·40° K.), determined calorimetrically and by calculation.* A, B, C are taken as $33{\cdot}2 \times 10^{-40}$, $27{\cdot}5 \times 10^{-40}$ and $5{\cdot}70 \times 10^{-40}$ gm. cm.^{2}.

ENTROPY OF ETHYLENE

Calorimetric	ΔS
0 – 15° K.	0·25
15 – 103·95° K.	12·226
Fusion 800·8/103·95	7·704
103·95° – 169·40°	7·924
Vaporization 3237/169·40	19·11
Corr. for gas imperfection	0·13
Entropy of ideal gas at 169·40°	47·36

* Data from Egan & Kemp, *J. Amer. Chem. Soc.*, 59, 1264, 1937

Statistical Calculation

$$S_{trans.} = 3/2R \log_e M + 5/2R \log_e T - 2{\cdot}300 \qquad = 33{\cdot}1330$$

$$S_{rot.} = 3/2R \log ABC + 3/2R \log_e T - \mathrm{R} \log \sigma + 267{\cdot}649 \qquad = 14{\cdot}192$$

$$S_{vib.} = \qquad 0{\cdot}031$$

$$47{\cdot}35$$

Internal rotations. Any group, like $-CH_3$ or $-OH$ which can rotate freely within the molecule will contribute $R/2$ to the heat capacity and will make a contribution to the entropy which can be calculated. When such calculations were made it was found that the total calculated entropy was frequently a few units greater than the calorimetrically determined values. In order to account for the discrepancy it has been assumed that the free internal rotation of the groups in such cases is hindered by potential barriers. For details the reader must be referred to treatises on Statistical Mechanics, or to *Chemical Reviews*, vol. 27 (1940), where there is a Symposium on *The Fundamental Thermodynamics of Hydrocarbons.*

***Chemical Constants.** If ΔH is the heat content change in the vaporisation of a gram molecule of a solid at a temperature T, we have

$$\Delta H = \Delta H_0 + \int_0^T \Delta C_p \, . \, dT,$$

where ΔH_0 is the heat content change at absolute zero and ΔC_p, the difference of heat capacity between the vapour and the solid.

Introducing this value into (144), we have

$$\frac{d \log p}{dT} = \frac{\Delta H_0}{RT^2} + \frac{1}{RT^2} \int_0^T \Delta C_p \, . \, dT.$$

Integrating, we have

$$\log p = -\frac{\Delta H_0}{RT} + \int \left(\frac{\int_0^T \Delta C_p \, . \, dT}{RT^2} \right) dT + i, \quad \ldots\ldots(153)$$

where i is the integration constant. The second term can be integrated in parts by making use of the formula

$$\int A\,dB = AB - \int B\,dA\,;$$

putting $\quad A = \int_0^T \Delta C_p\,.\,dT,$ and $B = -1/RT,$

we have

$$\log p = -\frac{\Delta H_0}{RT} - \frac{\int_0^T \Delta C_p\,.\,dT}{RT} + \int \frac{\Delta C_p\,.\,dT}{RT} + i,$$

or, $\quad RT \log p = -\Delta H + T\int \frac{\Delta C_p\,.\,dt}{T} + iRT.$

Writing $RT \log p = -\Delta F^\circ$, we thus have

$$\Delta F^\circ = \Delta H - T\int \frac{\Delta C_p\,.\,dT}{T} - iRT, \quad \text{...........(154)}$$

where ΔF° is the difference between the free energy of the gas at unit pressure and that of the solid, both at the temperature T. We can compare this equation with

$$\Delta F^\circ = \Delta H - T\Delta S,$$

where ΔS is the corresponding entropy difference. Evidently

$$\Delta S = \int \frac{\Delta C_p\,.\,dT}{T} + iR.$$

Now $\quad \Delta S = S_{\text{gas}} - S_{\text{solid}} \quad$ and $\quad \Delta C_p = C_{p\,\text{gas}} - C_{p\,\text{solid}},$

so that $S_{\text{gas}} - S_{\text{solid}} = \int \frac{C_{p\,\text{gas}}}{T}\,.\,dT - \int \frac{C_{p\,\text{solid}}}{T}\,.\,dT + iR.$

By the Third Law, $S_{\text{solid}} = \int^T \frac{C_{p\,\text{solid}}}{T}\,.\,dT$, so that

$$S_{\text{gas}} = \int \frac{C_{p\,\text{gas}}}{T}\,dT + iR. \quad \text{..................(155)}$$

Comparing this with (151), we see that

$$iR = S_0, \quad \text{.........................(156)}$$

where S_0 is the entropy constant of the gas.

i is known as the *chemical constant* of the gas. It can be evaluated by (153) when the heat capacities are sufficiently well known. For monatomic gases it can also be calculated by using the value of S_0 given by (152),

$$\left(i=S_0=-\frac{2\cdot31}{R}+\frac{3}{2}\log_e M+\log_e g_0\right),$$

and for diatomic gases

$$i=\frac{S_0}{R}=-\frac{7\cdot67}{R}+\frac{3}{2}\log_e M+\log_e(10^{40}I)+\log_e\frac{g_0}{\sigma},$$

where it is understood that the unit of pressure in the vapour pressure equation is the atmosphere.

The following table gives a comparison of the values observed and calculated in this way.

CHEMICAL CONSTANTS OF MONATOMIC GASES.

	i (Calc.).	i (Obs.).
Hg - -	6·80	6·71 ±0·07
A - -	4·37	4·32 ±0·09
Na - -	4·24	4·3 ±0·2
Tl - -	7·52	8·0 ±0·7

The chemical constants of a number of diatomic gases as determined by experiment and calculated are given below.

CHEMICAL CONSTANTS OF DIATOMIC GASES.

	i (Calc.).	i (Obs.).
O_2 - -	4·72	4·77 ±0·05
N_2 - -	3·08	3·13 ±0·07
I_2 - -	10·48	10·6 ±0·1
HCl - -	2·53	2·58 ±0·07

(for I_2, $g_0=1$, $\sigma=2$)

In Chapter XII we integrated the reaction isochore, making use of empirical equations which represent the change of heat capacity with temperature over a wide range of temperature. This range does not extend to low temperatures in the neighbourhood of absolute zero, and the equations obtained for K_p or $\Delta F°$ cease to hold at these low temperatures. The integration constants J or I obtained are thus empirical. If the integration were extended to absolute zero, using the actual values of the heat capacities at low temperatures, we should obtain different values of the integration constant.

Making no assumption as to the way in which the heat capacities vary with the temperature, we can integrate the reaction isochore for a gas reaction in the same way as the vapour pressure equation is integrated in (153). Writing

$$\Delta H = \Delta H_0 + \int_0^T \Delta C_p \,.\, dT,$$

where ΔC_p is the heat capacity change in the reaction, and inserting this value of ΔH in (139), we have

$$\frac{d \log K_p}{dT} = \frac{\Delta H}{RT^2} = \frac{\Delta H_0}{RT^2} + \frac{1}{RT^2}\int \Delta C_p \,.\, dT.$$

ntegrating this, we have

$$\log K_p = -\frac{\Delta H_0}{RT} + \int \left(\frac{\int_0^T \Delta C_p \,.\, dT}{RT^2} \right) dT + J, \quad \text{......(157)}$$

where J is regarded as the true integration constant. Integrating by parts as before, this becomes

$$\log K_p = -\frac{\Delta H_0 + \int_0^T \Delta C_p \, dT}{RT} + \int \frac{\Delta C_p}{RT} \,.\, dT + J,$$

or, $$\Delta F^\circ = -RT \log K_p = \Delta H - T \int \frac{\Delta C_p}{T} \,.\, dT - JRT$$

Comparing this with

$$\Delta F^\circ = \Delta H - T\Delta S,$$

we see that

$$\Delta S = \int \frac{\Delta C_p}{T} \,.\, dT + JR.$$

Now by (155), we have for each gas concerned

$$S_{\text{gas}} = \int \frac{C_p}{T} \, dT + iR,$$

so that $$J = \Delta i, \quad \text{.......................................(158)}$$

where Δi is the difference between the sum of the chemical constants of the gases formed and of the reactants.

Alternatively, since $iR = S_0$, we have

$$J = \Delta S_0 / R, \qquad \text{(159)}$$

i.e. the true integration constants of a gaseous reaction is equal to the difference between the corresponding entropy constants of the gases, divided by R. Many of the values of i or J which are to be found in the earlier papers are incorrect, having been derived from too limited a range of temperature.

Examples.

1. The entropies of $N_2(g)$, $H_2(g)$, $NH_3(g)$ at 25 C., as determined by thermal measurements, are 45·6, 29·4, and 46·7 entropy units respectively. The heat content change in the reaction $1/2N_2 + 3/2H_2 = NH_3$ is $\Delta H_{298} = -10985$ cals. Find the free energy change at this temperature. Compare the value obtained with that given in Ex. 3 (p. 268);

($\Delta F = -4960$ cals., from Ex. 3 $= -3910$ cals.)

2. The heat content change in the reaction

$$Zn + 1/2O_2 = ZnO$$

is $\Delta H_{298} = -83000$ cals. The entropy of ZnO at 25° C., as determined by heat capacity measurements, is 10·4. Using the data in Table XXIV, find the free energy of formation of zinc oxide. The heat of formation of carbon monoxide being given by $C(gr.) + 1/2O_2 = CO$, $\Delta H_{298} = -26150$ cals., find also the free energy change in the reaction,

$ZnO + C(gr.) = Zn + CO$. ($\Delta F(ZnO) = -79600$; ΔF (reaction) $= +43700$.)

3. The entropy of benzene ($C_6H_6(l)$) at 25° C. is 44·5 cals./degrees. The heat of formation is

$$6C(gr.) + 3H_2 = C_6H_6(l), \quad \Delta H = 11700.$$

Find the free energy of formation of benzene from the elements at this temperature. ($\Delta F = 13950$.)

The free energy of formation of acetylene at 25° is $+50,840$ cals. Find the free energy change in the reaction

$$3C_2H_2(g) = C_6H_6(l).$$

4. From electromotive force measurements it has been proved that for the reaction

$$1/2Pb + AgCl(s) = 1/2PbCl_2(s) + Ag,$$

$\Delta F_{298} = -11306$, $\Delta H_{298} = -12585$ cals. Find the entropy change in the reaction, and using the values in Table XXIV, find the entropy of $PbCl_2$. The entropy of $PbCl_2$, from heat capacity measurements, is $S_{298} = 33{\cdot}2$.

($\Delta S = -4{\cdot}29$; $S(PbCl_2) = 32{\cdot}6$.)

CHAPTER XIV

THE PROPERTIES OF SOLUTIONS

The Components. A solution may be defined as a homogeneous phase of variable composition. It is distinguished from a mixture by its homogeneity, and from a compound by the variability of its composition. That is, we cannot distinguish in it parts which are different from other parts, and we can add small quantities, at least, of any of the substances contained in it without destroying its homogeneity (in some cases we may thereby obtain a supersaturated solution which is unstable). The composition of a solution is stated in terms of its *components*, which must be chosen in such a way that (1) the amount of each component in the solution may be independently varied, (2) every possible variation in the composition of the solution may be expressed in terms of them. It is often possible to choose alternative sets of components. For example, either SO_3 and H_2O or H_2SO_4 and H_2O might properly be chosen as the components of a solution of sulphuric acid in water. The amount of any one of these pairs of substances in the solution can be varied without affecting the amount of the other, and both pairs are adequate to express every possible variation in the composition of the solution. But although the solution contains sulphur, oxygen and hydrogen, none of these substances can be regarded as components, for their amounts are not *independently* variable. We cannot increase the quantity of sulphur in the solution without also increasing the quantity of oxygen (at least so long as the solution remains a solution of sulphuric acid in water), and we cannot increase the amount of hydrogen without also increasing the amount of oxygen.

It sometimes happens that the physico-chemical properties of solutions obey simpler relations when a particular set of components is chosen. This might be taken as evidence that these components are actually present in the solution as chemical individuals. For example, if it were found that the properties of hydrochloric acid solutions took a particularly simple form (for example, obeyed Raoult's law) when the components are taken as $HCl . H_2O$ and H_2O, this might be regarded as evidence that these are the actual molecular individuals present. But any set of substances which satisfy the conditions stated above may properly be chosen as components, and the choice of any particular set does not imply that these substances are believed to be present as molecules in the solution. For example, if we use SO_3 and H_2O as the components of a sulphuric acid solution, we do not postulate that SO_3 is present in the solution as such. The compounds are merely substances in terms of which all the possible variations of composition can be expressed.

Having chosen the components, the composition of the solution can be expressed in a number of ways. Consider a solution containing w_1 grams of a component A, and w_2 grams of a component B. The following are some of the more common ways of expressing the composition :

(1) *Weight fraction.* The weight fraction of A is $w_1/(w_1+w_2)$.

(2) *Molar fraction.* If M_1 is the molecular weight, according to its chemical formula, of A, and M_2 that of B, the number of mols of A is $w_1/M_1 = n_1$ and that of B, $w_2/M_2 = n_2$, and the molar fraction of A is $\frac{n_1}{n_1 + n_2}$. The molar fraction evidently depends on the molecular formula used.

(3) *Weight concentration.* For dilute solutions it is convenient to use as the concentration the amount of one component dissolved in a given weight of the second component. For example, if the solution contains w_2 grams of B in 1000 grams of A, we may use as the weight concentration $m_2 = w_2/M_2$ (sometimes called molar concentration).

(4) *Volume concentration.* Weight of substance expressed in mols in (say) 1 litre of the solution.

Partial quantities. Two kinds of quantities are employed in describing the state of a solution (or any other body).

(1) *Intensity factors.* Quantities like temperature, refractive index, density, viscosity are independent of the amount of the substance under consideration. They are the same whether we have a gram or a kilogram of the substance in question.

(2) *Capacity factors.* Quantities like volume, heat capacity, energy, free energy, which depend on the amount of the substance in question. If the quantity of matter is doubled, the value of each of these quantities is also doubled.

It should be observed that while volume is a capacity factor, the volume per gram (or density) is an intensity factor. The heat capacity is a capacity factor, but the heat capacity per gram (or specific heat) is an intensity factor.

The capacity factors of a solution can usually be directly measured. For example, we can determine the volume, heat capacity, etc., of a given mass of solution. For thermodynamical calculations it is necessary to know also how these quantities vary when the composition is varied. For example, when dealing with a sulphuric acid solution it is necessary to know not only the volume of a given mass, but also the change in volume produced by adding a little sulphuric acid or a little water.

Suppose that we have a solution containing w_1 grams of the component A and w_2 grams of the component B. Let us add a small quantity dw_1 grams of A, which is not sufficient to alter appreciably the relative amounts of A and B. Let the increase in the volume of the solution be dV. Then the increase of volume per unit mass of A added is

$$\frac{dV}{dw_1}=\bar{v}_1\,;$$

$\bar{v}_1$ is called the *partial specific volume* of A in the solution.

We can equally well make use of molar quantities. Consider a solution containing n_1 mols of A and n_2 mols of B. Suppose that when we add dn_1 mols of A the increase of volume is dV, then

$$\frac{dV}{dn_1}=\bar{V}_1$$

is the partial molar volume of A in the solution. Similarly, if we add dn_2 mols of B,

$$\frac{dV}{dn_2}=\bar{V}_2$$

is the partial molar volume of B. $\bar{V}_1$ and $\bar{V}_2$ are evidently intensity factors; they do not depend on the amount of the given solution, although of course they may vary with its composition.

If we start with a solution containing n_1 mols of A and n_2 mols of B, and add dn_1 mols of A and dn_2 mols of B, the increase of volume is

$$dV = \bar{V}_1 dn_1 + \bar{V}_2 dn_2.$$

Now if dn_1 and dn_2 are in the same proportion as n_1 and n_2, we may continue making additions of these quantities until we have added finite amounts of A and B, without altering the proportions of A and B in the solution, and therefore without altering $\bar{V}_1$ and $\bar{V}_2$. We can continue adding A and B in these proportions until we have added n_1 of A and n_2 of B, etc., until we have doubled the amount of the original solution. The increase in volume is then

$$V = \bar{V}_1 n_1 + \bar{V}_2 n_2,$$

so that if V is the original volume of the solution, we have

$$V = \bar{V}_1 n_1 + \bar{V}_2 n_2.$$

***Generalised Treatment of Solutions.** Consider a solution containing n_1 mols of A, n_2 mols of B, n_3 mols of C, etc. Let M be the value of any property which is a "capacity factor."* The change in M caused by adding dn_1 of A, dn_2 of B, dn_3 of C, etc., is given by

$$dM = \frac{\partial M}{\partial n_1} \cdot dn_1 + \frac{\partial M}{\partial n_2} \cdot dn_2 + \frac{\partial M}{\partial n_3} \cdot dn_3, \ \ldots\ldots (160)$$

where $\frac{\partial M}{\partial n_1} = \overline{M}_1$ represents the increase in M caused by the addition of ∂n_1 of A, when the amounts of B, C, etc., remain constant. Similarly, we may write

$$\frac{\partial M}{\partial n_2} = \overline{M}_2, \quad \frac{\partial M}{\partial n_3} = \overline{M}_3, \text{ etc.,}$$

* The symbol M in this section does not stand for molecular weight, as it does elsewhere.

and (160) becomes

$$dM = \overline{M}_1\,dn_1 + \overline{M}_2\,dn_2 + \overline{M}_3\,dn_3 + \ldots \qquad (161)$$

$\overline{M}_1$, $\overline{M}_2$, $\overline{M}_3$, etc., are the partial molar values of M for the components A, B and C in the solution.

This equation contains quantities of the two kinds. $\overline{M}_1$, $\overline{M}_2$, etc., are intensity factors, while n_1, n_2, etc., are capacity factors. If we double the amount of the solution, $\overline{M}_1$, $\overline{M}_2$, etc., are unaffected, while n_1 and n_2 are doubled. There is a mathematical theorem (Euler's theorem) which states that a change in the value of a quantity like M, in any small variation of the system, may be completely expressed by summing the products of the intensity factors with the corresponding capacity factors, *i.e.*

Change in M

= (Intensity factor × change of capacity factor).

Equation (161) is thus a *complete differential*. It represents completely the change in M produced by the infinitesimal additions dn_1, dn_2, etc. (Variations involving change of temperature and pressure are not taken into account here.)

Keeping $\overline{M}_1$, $\overline{M}_2$, $\overline{M}_3$, etc., constant by some such process as that described in the last section, we can integrate (161) for a change in which n_1 varies from 0 to n_1, n_2 from 0 to n_2, etc., and obtain

$$M = \overline{M}_1 n_1 + \overline{M}_2 n_2 + \overline{M}_3 n_3 + \ldots \qquad (162)$$

Differentiating this generally, without any regard for the significance of the quantities, we have

$$dM = \overline{M}_1\,dn_1 + n_1\,d\overline{M}_1 + \overline{M}_2\,dn_2 + n_2\,d\overline{M}_2 + \overline{M}_3\,dn_3 + n_3\,d\overline{M}_3 + \text{etc.}$$

But if $\quad dM = \overline{M}_1\,dn_1 + \overline{M}_2\,dn_2 + \overline{M}_3\,dn_3$, etc.

represents completely an infinitesimal change of M, the sum of the remaining terms must be zero, *i.e.*

$$n_1\,d\overline{M}_1 + n_2\,d\overline{M}_2 + n_3\,d\overline{M}_3 + \text{etc.} = 0. \qquad (163)$$

This is the generalised form of the Duhem-Margules equation.

As an illustration of the meaning of this equation let M be the volume V of a solution having two components. Then (163) becomes

$$n_1 d\bar{V}_1 + n_2 d\bar{V}_2 = 0 \quad \text{.................(164)}$$

for any variation. If the variation considered be a change dN_1 in the molar fraction of A, we have

$$n_1\left(\frac{d\bar{V}_1}{dN_1}\right) + n_2\left(\frac{d\bar{V}_2}{dN_1}\right) = 0,$$

or

$$\frac{d\bar{V}_1/dN_1}{d\bar{V}_2/dN_1} = -\frac{n_2}{n_1} = -\frac{N_2}{N_1}, \quad \text{.............(165)}$$

i.e. when the composition of the solution is varied, the changes in the values of $\bar{V}_1$ and $\bar{V}_2$ are *inversely proportional to the amounts* n_1 *and* n_2 *of the substances present, and of opposite signs, i.e.* if $d\bar{V}_1$ is positive, $d\bar{V}_2$ is negative, and *vice versa.* (See Fig. 73.)

Evaluation of Partial Molar Volumes. To illustrate the methods used for the determination of partial molar quantities we shall give here some methods employed for finding partial molar volumes from the densities of binary solutions.

(1) *Direct graphical method for dilute solutions.* Consider, for example, an aqueous solution of density d, containing m_2 mols of a solute (molecular weight M_2) in 1000 grams of water. The total weight of this solution is $1000 + m_2M_2$ grams and its volume,

$$V = (1000 + m_2M_2)/d.$$

Since the weight of the solvent is constant, the partial molar volume of the solute is $(dV/dm_2)_{1000}$, and this

* The remainder of this chapter can be omitted at first reading, as it contains nothing essential for the understanding of the unstarred parts of later chapters.

quantity may be determined for any given value of m_2 by plotting V against m_2 and taking the tangent to the curve at the point representing the given solution. Instead of V it is more convenient to plot $\Delta V = V - V_0$, where $V_0 = 1000/d_0$ is the volume of the solvent. Fig. 71 shows the values of ΔV for solutions of lithium chloride in several solvents plotted against m_2.

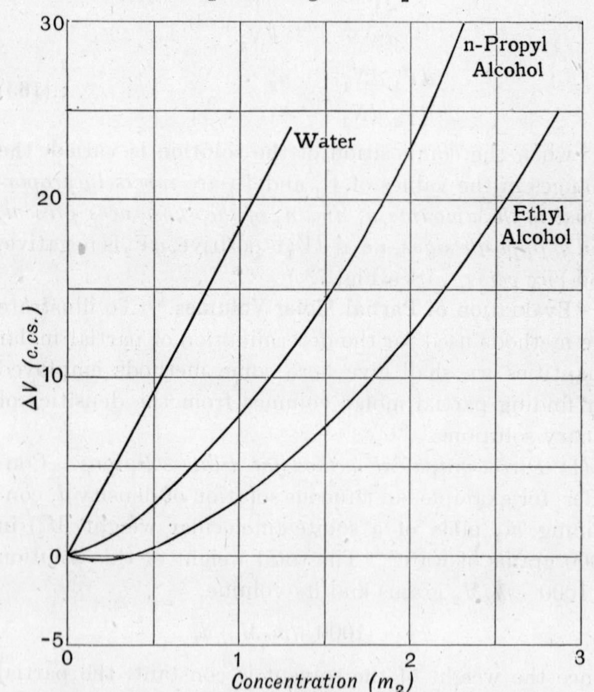

FIG. 71.—Volume changes on addition of lithium chloride (m) to various solvents at 25°.

(2) *From the apparent molar volume.* Let V be the volume of a solution containing m_2 mols of a solute in

1000 grams of water, and V_0 the volume of 1000 grams of pure water. The "apparent volume" of the solute is $V - V_0$ and its *apparent molar volume* is $\phi = (V - V_0)/m_2$. This quantity is not itself very useful in thermodynamical calculations, but it can be used in the determination of partial molar volumes.

Writing

$$\phi m_2 = V - V_0,$$

and differentiating with respect to m_2, we have

$$m_2 \cdot \frac{d\phi}{dm_2} + \phi = \frac{dV}{dm_2},$$

or

$$\frac{d\phi}{d \log m_2} + \phi = \bar{V}_2. \quad \text{..................(166)}$$

The partial molar volume can thus be found by plotting ϕ against $\log m_2$, and taking the slope of the curve at any point. If the value of ϕ at this point be added, we obtain the partial molar volume $\bar{V}_2$.

(3) *The method of intercepts.* Consider a solution of volume V, containing w_1 grams of A and w_2 grams of B. The specific volume $(1/d)$ is $v = V/(w_1 + w_2)$; *i.e.*

$$V = v(w_1 + w_2).$$

The partial specific volume of A is

$$\bar{v}_1 = \left(\frac{dV}{dw_1}\right)_{w_2} = v + (w_1 + w_2)\left(\frac{dv}{dw_1}\right)_{w_2} \quad \text{....... (167)}$$

If we write for the weight fraction of B,

$$W_2 = w_2/(w_1 + w_2),$$

we obtain by differentiation, when w_2 is constant:

$$dW_2 = -\frac{w_2 \, dw_1}{(w_1 + w_2)},$$

and therefore,

$$(w_1 + w_2)\left(\frac{dv}{dw_1}\right)_{w_2} = -W_2\left(\frac{dv}{dW_2}\right).$$

Substituting this in (167), we have

$$\bar{v}_1 = v - W_2\left(\frac{dv}{dW_2}\right). \quad \text{..............(168)}$$

The quantities on the right of this equation can be evaluated by plotting the specific volume v against the weight fraction W_2 (curve XY, Fig. 72).

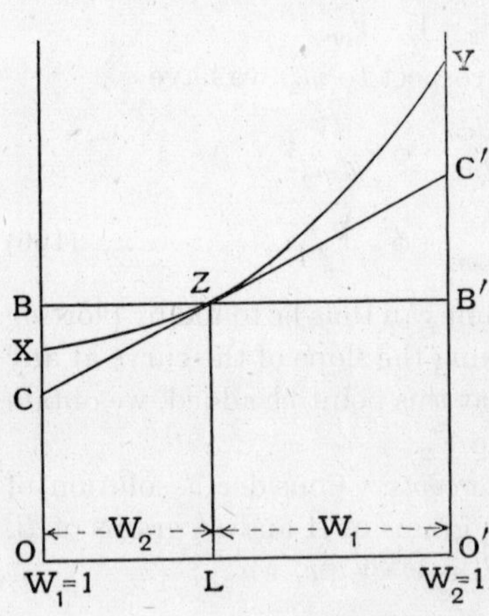

FIG. 72.—Method of Intercepts.

Let Z be the point of this curve representing the specific volume of the given solution, the composition of which is represented by the point L. BB' is a horizontal line through Z, so that $OB = v$. Let CC' be the tangent to the curve at the point Z. The slope of this tangent is equal to (dv/dW_2), so that the distance BC is equal to $W_2(dv/dW_2)$. Thus $OC = v - W_2(dv/dW_2)$, which by (101) is equal to $\bar{v}_1$. The partial specific volume of A in the given solution L is therefore equal to the intercept OC made by the tangent at Z on the axis representing pure A $(W_1 = 1)$. Similarly it can be shown that the partial specific volume of B in the given solution is equal to the intercept $O'C'$ made by the tangent on the axis representing pure $B(W_2 = 1)$.

The partial molar volumes can of course be found by multiplying the partial specific volumes by the molecular weights of the substances. They could alternatively be determined by plotting the molar volume of the solution against the molar fraction and taking intercepts as above. (If the volume of a solution containing n_1 mols of A and n_2 mols of B is V, the molar volume is V/n_1+n_2.)

Fig. 73 shows the differences between the partial molar volumes of water and alcohol in their solutions and

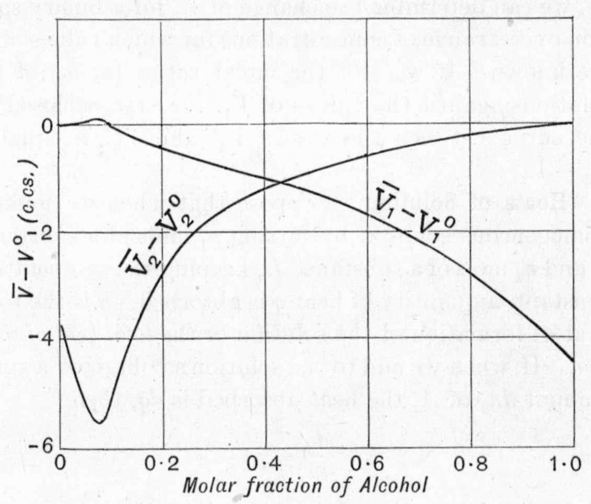

FIG. 73.—Partial molar volumes of water and alcohol in their solutions.

molar volumes V°_1 and V°_2 of the pure liquids. Notice that when $\bar{V}_1$ increases, $\bar{V}_2$ decreases, and vice versa. Also when N_2 is small compared with N_1, the change of $\bar{V}_2$ is large compared with that of $\bar{V}_1$, and when N_1 is small compared with N_2, the change of $\bar{V}_1$ is large compared with that of $\bar{V}_2$, as is required by (165).

(4) *Calculation of partial volumes of the second constituent from those of the first.* Writing (164) in the form

$$d\bar{V}_2 = -\frac{n_1}{n_2}\, d\bar{V}_1,$$

and integrating between the limits $V_1{}'$ and $V_1{}''$, we have

$$\bar{V}_2{}'' - \bar{V}_2{}' = -\int_{\bar{V}_1{}'}^{\bar{V}_1{}''} \frac{n_1}{n_2}\, d\bar{V}_1.$$

i.e. we can determine the change of $\bar{V}_2$ for a binary solution over a range of concentrations for which values of $\bar{V}_1$ are known. If we plot the molar ratios (n_1/n_2) of the solutions against the values of $\bar{V}_1$, the area enclosed by the curve between the values $\bar{V}_1{}'$ and $\bar{V}_1{}''$ is equal to $\bar{V}_2{}' - \bar{V}_2{}''$.

***Heats of Solution.** Suppose that when we make a homogeneous solution by mixing n_1 mols of a substance A and n_2 mols of a substance B, keeping the temperature constant, a quantity of heat q is absorbed. q is the total heat of formation of the solution or the *total heat of solution.* If, when we add to the solution so obtained a small amount dn_1 of A, the heat absorbed is dq, then

$$\frac{dq}{dn_1} = \bar{q}_1$$

is the *partial or differential heat of solution* of A in the given solution. Similarly

$$\frac{dq}{dn_2} = \bar{q}_2$$

is the partial heat of solution of B in the given solution. It is assumed of course that the quantities added are so small in comparison with the amount of the solution that they do not appreciably affect the concentration. The following table gives the partial molar heats of solution of water (*A*) and sulphuric acid, H_2SO_4 (*B*) in sulphuric acid solutions.

TABLE XXV.

PARTIAL HEATS OF SOLUTION IN SULPHURIC ACID SOLUTIONS AT 18° (calories).

Molar Fraction of H_2SO_4.	Partial Heat of Solution of H_2O.	Partial Heat of Solution of H_2SO_4.	Relative Partial Heat Content of H_2O.	Relative Partial Heat Content of H_2SO_4.
N_2	$\bar{q}_1$	$\bar{q}_2$	$\bar{L}_1$	$\bar{L}_2$
0·00	0·0	−20200	0	0
0·05	−43·7	−16070	−43·7	4130
0·10	−293·3	−12470	−293·3	7730
0·20	−1000	−9010	−1000	11190
0·30	−1910	−6230	−1910	13970
0·40	−3060	−4040	−3060	16160
0·50	−4850	−1890	−4850	18310
0·60	−6300	−670	−6300	19530
0·70	−7010	−290	−7010	19910
0·80	−7490	−102	−7490	20092
0·90	−7870	−47	−7870	20153
1·00	−8220	0	−8220	20200

The total heat of solution can easily be found when the partial heats of solution are known. The heat absorbed when small additions dn_1 and dn_2 are made to the solution is :

$$dq = \bar{q}_1 dn_1 + \bar{q}_2 dn_2, \qquad (169)$$

and therefore, we can obtain by integration, as in (162),

$$q = \bar{q}_1 n_1 + \bar{q}_2 n_2. \qquad (170)$$

Example. What is the total heat of formation of a solution containing 0·1 mols of sulphuric acid and 1 mol of water ? By (170), using the values given in Table XXV for $N_2 = 0·10$,

$$q = -293·3 - (0·1 \times 12470) = -1540 \text{ calories.}$$

Heats of dilution can also be calculated when the partial

heats of solution in the initial and final solutions are known. Suppose that we start with a solution of n_1 mols of A and n_2 mols of B and add n_3 mols of A. The total heat of dilution is evidently equal to the difference between the heats of formation of the final and that of the initial solution. Let $\bar{q}_1'$, $\bar{q}_2'$, be the partial heats of solution in the original solution. Then its heat of formation is

$$q' = n_1\bar{q}_1' + n_2\bar{q}_2'.$$

Similarly if $\bar{q}_1''$, $\bar{q}_2''$ be the partial heats of solution in the final solution, its heat of formation is

$$q'' = (n_1 + n_3)\bar{q}_1'' + n_2\bar{q}_2'',$$

and the heat absorbed in the dilution is

$$q'' - q' = (n_1 + n_3)\bar{q}_1'' + n_2\bar{q}_2'' - n_1\bar{q}_1' - n_2\bar{q}_2'.$$

Example. What is the heat absorbed if we start with a solution containing 0·1 mols of sulphuric acid and 1 mol of water and add 1 mol of water ?

The heat of formation of the original solution, as we have seen in the previous example, is $q' = -1540$ calories. The heat of formation of the final solution ($N_2 = 0{\cdot}05$) is

$$q'' = -2 \times 43{\cdot}7 - (0{\cdot}1 \times 16070) = -1694 \text{ calories}.$$

The heat of dilution is thus

$$-1694 - (-1540) = -154 \text{ calories},$$

i.e. 154 calories are evolved.

***Heat Contents of Solutions.** If H is the heat content of a solution containing n_1 mols of A and n_2 mols of B, and $H°_1$, $H°_2$ the molar heat contents of A and B at the same temperature and pressure, the heat absorbed in the formation of the solution is

$$q = H - n_1 H°_1 - n_2 H°_2. \quad \text{.................(171)}$$

The partial heat content of A in the given solution may be defined as

$$\bar{H}_1 = \left(\frac{dH}{dn_1}\right)_{n_2}, \quad \text{.................(172)}$$

i.e. the increase of H, caused by the addition of a small quantity of A to the solution, per mol of A added. The heat absorbed when dn_1 mols of A are added to the solution (at constant T and P) is equal to the increase in the heat content of the solution less the heat content of the substance added, *i.e.*

$$dq = \bar{H}_1 dn_1 - H^\circ{}_1 dn_1.$$

Since $\frac{dq}{dn_1} = \bar{q}_1$ is the partial heat of solution of A in the given solution, $\bar{q}_1 = \bar{H}_1 - H^\circ{}_1$, ...(173)

i.e. the partial heat of solution is equal to the difference between the heat content in the solution and the heat content of the pure substance.

The values of the partial heat contents of the components of solutions can conveniently be tabulated by giving the difference between the partial heat content in a given solution and the heat content of the substance in some suitable standard state at the same temperature and pressure. These quantities are called relative partial heat contents. For most purposes the use of one or other of the following standard states is sufficient.

(1) The standard state of a component is taken to be the pure substance in a specified form at the given temperature and pressure. Thus with aqueous solutions it is convenient to take as the standard state of water, pure liquid water at the same temperature and pressure. The relative heat content is then

$$\bar{L}_1 = \bar{H}_1 - H^\circ{}_1,$$

where H°_1 is the heat content of the pure substance, and thus by comparison with (106), it is evident that when this choice is made

$$\bar{L}_1 = \bar{q}_1, \quad \text{.........................(174)}$$

or, the relative heat content is equal to the partial heat of solution of the pure substance.

(2) The standard state of a substance is taken to be an infinitely dilute solution in the given solvent.

If $\bar{H}^\circ_2$ is the partial molar heat content of the substance S, at infinite dilution, the relative heat content according to this definition is

$$\bar{L}_2 = \bar{H}_2 - \bar{H}^\circ_2.$$

If H°_2 is the heat content of the same substance in a pure state, we may write,

$$\begin{aligned}\bar{L}_2 &= \bar{H}_2 - H^\circ_2 - (\bar{H}^\circ_2 - H^\circ_2)\\ &= \bar{q}_2 - \bar{q}_2^\circ, \quad \text{............................(175)}\end{aligned}$$

where $\bar{q}_2^\circ$ is its partial heat of solution in an infinitely dilute solution.

In many cases, particularly in dealing with dilute solutions, it is convenient to use the first standard state for one component (the solvent) and the second for the other. Table XXV shows the relative heat contents of water and sulphuric acid in their solutions, at 25° C., the standard states being (1) for water, the pure liquid; (2) for sulphuric acid, an infinitely dilute solution in water. The relative heat content of water in any solution is thus equal to its partial heat of solution, and that of H_2SO_4, by (175), is obtained by subtracting (-20200) calories from the partial heat of solution of sulphuric acid.

Applying (163) to a binary solution, we have

$$n_1 d\bar{H}_1 + n_2 d\bar{H}_2 = 0, \quad \text{..................(176)}$$

and if the relative heat contents as defined above be taken

$$n_1 \, d\bar{L}_1 + n_2 \, d\bar{L}_2 = 0. \quad \text{.................(177)}$$

When the partial heat contents of one component are known for a range of concentrations it is thus possible to determine the changes of the partial heat contents of the second component over the same range.

Partial molar heat capacities. If C_p is the heat capacity of a solution containing n_1 mols of a substance A, n_2 mols of B, etc., the partial molar heat capacity of A in the solution is defined as

$$\bar{C}_{p_1} = \left(\frac{dC_p}{dn_1}\right)_{n_2, n_3, \text{ etc.}} \quad \text{...............(178)}$$

The total heat capacity of the solution is

$$C_p = n_1\bar{C}_{p_1} + n_2\bar{C}_{p_2} + n_3\bar{C}_{p_3} + \text{etc.} \quad \text{............(179)}$$

and by (163) we have the following relation between the changes of the partial heat capacities of the different components:

$$n_1 \, d\bar{C}_{p_1} + n_2 \, d\bar{C}_{p_2} + n_3 \, d\bar{C}_{p_3} + n_4 \, d\bar{C}_{p_4} \ldots = 0. \quad \text{.....(180)}$$

By (11), the rate at which the heat content of the whole system changes with the temperature is equal to its heat capacity, or $\frac{\partial H}{\partial t} = C_p$. Differentiating this with respect to n_1 (n_2, n_3, etc., being constant), we have

$$\frac{\partial^2 H}{\partial t \,.\, \partial n_1} = \frac{\partial C_p}{\partial n_1} = \bar{C}_{p_1}.$$

But

$$\frac{\partial H}{\partial n_1} = \bar{H}_1 \quad \text{and} \quad \frac{\partial^2 H}{\partial n_1 \,.\, \partial t} = \frac{\partial \bar{H}_1}{\partial t},$$

therefore, comparing these two expressions, which only differ in the order of differentiation, we have

$$\frac{\partial \bar{H}_1}{\partial t} = \bar{C}_{p_1}. \qquad \text{(181)}$$

Since $\bar{L}_1 = \bar{H}_1 - H^\circ{}_1$,

we obviously have

$$\frac{d\bar{L}_1}{dt} = \frac{d\bar{H}_1}{dt} - \frac{dH^\circ{}_1}{dt} = \bar{C}_{p_1} - C^\circ{}_{p_1}, \qquad \text{(182)}$$

where $C^\circ{}_{p_1}$ is the corresponding heat capacity in the standard state. In order to find the variation of the partial (or relative) heat contents with the temperature, it is thus necessary to know the corresponding partial heat capacities.

Examples.

1. In a thallium amalgam in which the molar fraction of thallium is 0·400 the partial molar heats of solution of thallium and mercury are +715 cals. and −232 cals. respectively. Find the total heat of solution. The partial heat of solution of thallium in a very large quantity of mercury is −805 cals. Find the partial molar heat content of thallium in the given amalgam relative to an infinitely dilute amalgam. ($q = 147$ cals. ; $L_2 = +1520$ cals.)

2. The quantities of heat evolved (per mol) when small quantities of sulphuric acid and water are added to a solution containing 50 mols per cent. of each are 1890 and 4850 cals., and the same quantities for a solution containing 75 mols per cent. water are 7520 and 1450 cals. Find (1) the heat evolved when a mol of water and a mol of sulphuric acid are mixed ; (2) the heat evolved when two mols of water are added to the solution. (1) 6740 cals., (2) 5130 cals.)

3. The heat absorbed per mol when water is added to a large quantity of a saturated solution of sodium chloride is 11·5 cals., and that absorbed when salt is added to the solution obtained is 517 cals. per mol. Find the heat of solution of a mol of sodium chloride in sufficient water to make a saturated solution, 9·04 mols. (621 cals.)

***4.** Criticise the following suggested method of finding the "volumes of the constituents of a solution." In 100 volumes of a solution of x volumes of one substance A and y volumes of a substance B, where the sum of x and y are not a hundred, there must be some factor a by which the original volume x of A is expanded or contracted and another factor b by which the original volume y of B is contracted or expanded. Therefore we can write

$$ax + by = 100.$$

Similarly for another solution of A and B, which also occupies 100 volumes,

$$a'x' + b'y' = 100.$$

If x is very near x' and y very near y', no great error is made if we assume that $a = a'$ and $b = b'$; and thus $+a$ and b may be determined by solving the two equations. What are the quantities a and b ?

***5.** At 24·90° the density ($d_4^{24 \cdot 9}$) of methyl alcohol is 0·786624, and the following table gives the densities of some lithium chloride solutions in this solvent at the same temperature. Find the apparent molar volumes of lithium chloride in the solutions (m = mols LiCl in 1000 gms. methyl alcohol).

m.	d.
0·0638	0·788826
0·0834	0·789478
0·1079	0·790309
0·2183	0·793916

(See *J. Chem. Soc.*, p. 933, 1933, for results.)

CHAPTER XV

THE FREE ENERGY OF SOLUTIONS

Partial Molar Free Energies. Since the free energy of a solution is also a "capacity factor," the partial free energies of the components may be determined by the methods of Chapter XIV. Suppose that a solution contains n_1 mols of S_1, n_2 mols of S_2, n_3 mols of S_3, ... and n_n mols of S_n. The partial molar free energies are defined as

$$\bar{F}_1 = \left(\frac{dF}{dn_1}\right)_{T,\,p,\,n_2,\,\text{etc.}}$$

$$\bar{F}_2 = \left(\frac{dF}{dn_2}\right)_{T,\,p,\,n_1,\,n_3,\,\text{etc.}}, \text{ and so on.}$$

When dn_1 mols of S_1, dn_2 mols of S_2 ... dn_n mols of S_n are added to the solution the increase of its free energy can therefore be written

$$dF = \bar{F}_1\,dn_1 + \bar{F}_2\,dn_2 + \bar{F}_3\,dn_3 \ldots + \bar{F}_n\,dn_n. \quad \ldots.(183)$$

Applying (162) and (163), we have then

$$F = \bar{F}_1 n_1 + \bar{F}_2 n_2 + \bar{F}_3 n_3 \ldots + \bar{F}_n dn_n, \quad \ldots\ldots\ldots(184)$$

and $$n_1\,d\bar{F}_1 + n_2 d\bar{F}_2 + n_3 d\bar{F}_3 \ldots + n_n d\bar{F}_n = 0. \quad \ldots\ldots(185)$$

The partial free energies are fundamentally important in chemical thermodynamics because the conditions of equilibrium of the parts of a heterogeneous system are most conveniently stated in terms of them. It has been shown that the conditions of thermal and mechanical equilibrium of a material system are that the temperature and, provided that the system is not so large that the effect of gravitational forces becomes appreciable, the pressure must be the same throughout. The condition of chemical equilibrium is contained in the statement that *the partial free energy of each component must be the same in every phase in which it is actually present.* A proof of this proposition is given in the following section. Uninterested readers can pass straight on to page 322.

***Conditions of Equilibrium in Heterogeneous Systems.** Consider for simplicity the case of a system of two phases, both containing the components S_1, S_2, $S_3 \ldots S_n$. The quantities of these components in the first phase are n_1', n_2', n_3', etc., and the quantities in the second phase n_1'', n_2'', n_3'', etc. Then the variation of the free energy of the first phase when the quantities of its components are varied by small amounts $\delta n_1'$, $\delta n_2'$, etc., at constant temperature and pressure, is given by

$$\delta F' = \overline{F}_1' \delta n_1' + \overline{F}_2' \delta n_2' + \overline{F}_3' \delta n_3' \ldots \overline{F}_n' \delta n_n',$$

and similarly we may write for similar variations of the second phase

$$\delta F'' = \overline{F}_1'' \delta n_1'' + \overline{F}_2'' \delta n_2'' + \overline{F}_3'' \delta n_3'' \ldots + \overline{F}_n'' \delta n_n'',$$

where $\overline{F}_1'$ is the partial free energy of S_1 in the first phase, and $\overline{F}_1''$ its value in the second phase, etc. We shall suppose that the temperature and pressure are the same in both phases, since it has already been shown that this is a necessary condition. This being the case, it is necessary by (114) that the variation of the free energy of the system shall be zero or positive for all possible variations of the state of the system which do not alter its temperature and pressure, *i.e.*

$$(\delta F' + \delta F'') \geqq 0$$

for all such variations.

Let us consider what variations are possible. We will limit ourselves at first to the case in which none of the components can be formed out of other components. The possible variations are then those in which small quantities of the different components pass from one phase to the other. All such variations must be in accordance with the equations:

$$\left.\begin{array}{r}\delta n_1' + \delta n_1'' = 0,\\ \delta n_2' + \delta n_2'' = 0,\\ \cdots\cdots\cdots\cdots\cdots\cdots\\ \delta n_n' + \delta n_n'' = 0,\end{array}\right\} \qquad \text{(186)}$$

i.e. the total amount of each component is a constant. The change of free energy of the whole system in any variation in which the temperature and pressure remain unchanged is given by

$$\begin{aligned}\delta F &= \delta F' + \delta F'' \\ &= \bar{F}_1' \delta n_1' + \bar{F}_2' \delta n_2' + \bar{F}_3' \delta n_3 \ldots + \bar{F}_n' \delta n_n' \\ &\quad + \bar{F}_1'' \delta n_1'' + \bar{F}_2'' \delta n_2'' + \bar{F}_3'' \delta n_3'' \ldots + \bar{F}_n'' \delta n_n''. \qquad (187)\end{aligned}$$

This quantity must be zero or positive for all possible values of $\delta n_1'$, $\delta n_2'$, etc. Since, by (186), $\delta n_1' = -\delta n_1''$, etc., we may therefore write as the condition of equilibrium.

$$\begin{aligned}(\bar{F}_1' - \bar{F}_1'')\delta n_1' + (\bar{F}_2' - \bar{F}_2'')\delta n_2' \ldots \\ + (\bar{F}_n' - \bar{F}_n'')\delta n_n' \geqq 0. \qquad (188)\end{aligned}$$

If, as we have supposed, every component is present in both phases, its amount in either phase may either increase or decrease, *i.e.* dn_1', dn_2', etc., may be separately either positive or negative. (188) can therefore only be generally true if

$$\bar{F}_1' = \bar{F}_1'', \quad \bar{F}_2' = \bar{F}_2'', \ldots \bar{F}_n' = \bar{F}_n''. \qquad (189)$$

It is thus necessary for equilibrium that the partial free energy of each component shall be the same in both phases. It is easy to extend this argument to a system containing any number of distinct phases and to show that it is necessary for equilibrium that the partial free energy of each component shall have the same value in every phase in which it is actually present.*

We have supposed that every component is present in all the phases. It may happen that some of the components are entirely absent from certain phases. There is then no necessary equality like those in (189), but the partial free energy in this phase cannot be *less* than that in other parts of the system in which the component is present.†

Finally there is the case in which some components can be formed out of others. Suppose that the components C, D can be formed out of the components A, B according to the equation

$$aA + bB = cC + dD, \quad \text{..................(190)}$$

where a, b, c, d represent the numbers of formula weights of these substances which enter into the reaction. It is easy to prove as above, by considering variations in which the amount of each component remains constant that $\bar{F}_1' = \bar{F}_1''$, $\bar{F}_2' = \bar{F}_2''$, etc. (If (189) is satisfied for every possible variation it must be satisfied for any selection of the possible variations.) Thus (187) can be written

$$\bar{F}_A \Sigma\, \delta n'_A + \bar{F}_B \Sigma\, \delta n'_B + \bar{F}_C \Sigma\, \delta n'_C + \bar{F}_D \Sigma\, \delta n'_D = 0,$$

and where $\Sigma\, \delta n'_A$ is the total change in the amount of A throughout the system. Evidently the quantities $\Sigma\, \delta n_A'$, $\Sigma\, \delta n_B'$, $\Sigma\, \delta n_C'$, $\Sigma\, \delta n_D'$ must be such that (190) is satisfied,

* The partial free energy of a component in a phase which consists of that component only is of course equal to its molar free energy in that state.

† For if a component is absent from any phase its amount may be increased but cannot be decreased. δn for the given component in this phase may thus have positive but it cannot have negative values.

i.e. they must be proportional to $a, b, -c, -d$. We therefore have

$$a\overline{F}_A + b\overline{F}_B = c\overline{F}_C + d\overline{F}_D. \qquad (191)$$

The relation between the partial free energies is thus the same as that between the chemical formulae of the substances concerned.

The Phase Rule. Each distinct kind of body which is present in a heterogeneous system is called a *phase*, but bodies which differ only in amount or shape are regarded as examples of the same phase.

Consider a single phase containing the quantities n_1, $n_2, \ldots n_n$ of the independent components $S_1, S_2, \ldots S_n$, and having the entropy S and volume v. The phase is characterised by the $n+2$ intensity factors $t, p, \overline{F}_1, \ldots \overline{F}_n$. But these quantities are not all independent, for their variations are related by the equation

$$+S\,dT - v\,dp + n_1\,d\overline{F}_1 + n_2\,d\overline{F}_2 \ldots + n_n\,d\overline{F}_n = 0.* \qquad \ldots(192)$$

That is, if $n+1$ of the quantities $T, p, \overline{F}_1, \ldots \overline{F}_n$ are varied, the variation of the last is given by (192). A single phase is thus capable of only $n+1$ independent variations, or we may say that it has $n+1$ *degrees of freedom*.

Now suppose that we have two phases in equilibrium with each other, each containing the same n components $S_1, \ldots S_n$. It is necessary for equilibrium that $T, p, \overline{F}_1, \ldots \overline{F}_n$ shall be the same in the two phases. But there are now two equations like (192), one for each phase. It follows that only n of these quantities can be varied indepen-

* Combining (116), which gives the variation of F with T and p, with (183), which gives the variation of F with n_1, n_2, etc., at constant T and p, we obtain

$$dF = -S\,dT + v\,dp + \overline{F}_1 dn_1 + \overline{F}_2 dn_2 \ldots + \overline{F}_n dn_n.$$

Integrating this at constant T and p, we obtain

$$F = \overline{F}_1 n_1 + \overline{F}_2 n_2 \ldots + \overline{F}_n n_n. \qquad (184)$$

whence, instead of (185), in which T and p are supposed constant, we obtain

$$+S\,dT - v\,dp + n_1 d\overline{F}_1 + n_2 d\overline{F}_2 \ldots + n_n d\overline{F}_n = 0.$$

dently, the variations of the last *two* being given by the two equations. The two phases have thus $(n+2)-2=n$ degrees of freedom.

In general, if there are r phases each containing the same n components, there will be r equations like (192) between the variations of the $n+2$ quantities T, p, $\overline{F}_1$, $\overline{F}_2, \ldots \overline{F}_n$, which are the same throughout the system. Therefore only $n+2-r$ of the quantities can be varied independently, and the number of degrees of freedom of n components in r phases is thus

$$\mathcal{F}=n+2-r. \qquad (193)$$

This is the *Phase Rule* of Gibbs.

It does not matter if some of the components are absent from certain phases. Taking the system as a whole, we shall still have the $n+2$ quantities T, p, $\overline{F}_1, \ldots \overline{F}_n$ characteristics of the system and r relations like (192), which limit their variations. It is sometimes convenient to choose components which are not all independent of each other. Let n be the number of *independent* components, *i.e.* the minimum number of components in terms of which every variation of the system can be expressed. Let there be additional h components. These components can be formed out of the others by reactions similar to that represented in (190), and for each such relation between the components there is a corresponding relation between their partial free energies, similar to (191). There will thus be h relations between the partial free energies like (191). The total number of variable quantities is $n+h+2$, and the total number of relations between them $h+r$, so that the number of degrees of freedom is still

$$\mathcal{F}=n+2-r.$$

We will briefly survey the application of the phase rule to some typical systems. In the first place, a system of one component in one phase has, by (193), two degrees of freedom. That is, there is a single relation like (192), *viz.*

$$+S\,dT - v\,dp + v_1\,d\overline{F}_1 = 0$$

between the three quantities T, p and $\overline{F}_1$. Thus T and p can be varied at will, but for every value of T and p there is a corresponding value of F_1. Again, a single component in two phases has one degree of freedom, since there are two equations like (192) between the three quantities T p, $\overline{F}_1$. By means of these two equations we can get a relation between T and p. This relation is Clausius's equation. Finally, when a single component is present in three phases, there are three equations like (192) between dT, dp, and $d\overline{F}_1$, and therefore no variation is possible.

Again, a system of two independent components in a single phase has three degrees of freedom, *i.e.* if we give T and p certain values we cannot vary both $\overline{F}_1$ and $\overline{F}_2$ independently, but for every value of $\overline{F}_1$ there will be a corresponding value of $\overline{F}_2$. In two phases this system has two degrees of freedom. Therefore if we fix T and p no variation of the system is possible, *i.e.* so long as there are two phases $\overline{F}_1$ and $\overline{F}_2$ have constant values. Thus at a given T and p the two layers formed by water and ether have a definite composition and therefore definite values of $\overline{F}_1$ and $\overline{F}_2$.

If there are three phases the number of degrees of freedom is only one. We can no longer fix arbitrarily the temperature and the pressure, but for every temperature there will be a fixed pressure. Thus if our three phases are ice—aqueous solution—vapour, the vapour pressure is completely determined at each temperature, and the relation between dp and dT can be obtained by solving the three equations like (192) between the four quantities dp, dT, $d\overline{F}_1$, $d\overline{F}_2$.

Determination of the Partial Free Energy from the Vapour Pressure. When a liquid and its vapour are in equilibrium, the partial free energy of a volatile component must be the same in both phases, and its value in the liquid may be determined by finding its value in the vapour. Consider a binary solution containing the components S_1, S_2 whose partial pressures in the vapour are p_1, p_2. If the vapour has the properties of a perfect gas mixture, the partial molar free energy of S_1 in the vapour, by (131), is

$$\bar{F}_1 = (F^\circ{}_g)_1 + RT \log p_1,$$

and similarly if $p_1{}^\circ$ is the partial pressure of the pure liquid S_1 at the same temperature, its partial molar free energy is

$$F^\circ{}_1 = (F^\circ{}_g)_1 + RT \log p_1{}^\circ.$$

Combining these two equations, we have

$$\bar{F}_1 = F^\circ{}_1 + RT \log p_1/p_1{}^\circ. \quad \text{.............(194)}$$

Similarly for the second component,

$$\bar{F}_2 = F^\circ{}_2 + RT \log p_2/p_2{}^\circ. \quad \text{...........(195)}$$

It must be observed that in these equations the partial free energy obtained is that of a gram molecule in the *vapour phase*, and has nothing to do with the molecular weight in the liquid.

If the solution contains n_1 mols of S_1 and n_2 mols of S_2 (taking any convenient molecular weights), we have by (185), for a constant temperature variation :

$$n_1 d\bar{F}_1 + n_2 d\bar{F}_2 = 0,$$

or introducing the values of (194), (195),

$$n_1 d \log(p_1/p_1{}^\circ) + n_2 d \log(p_2/p_2{}^\circ) = 0,$$

or since $p_1{}^\circ$ and $p_2{}^\circ$ are constant, dividing by dn_2, we obtain,

$$n_1\left(\frac{d \log p_1}{dn_2}\right)_{n_1} + n_2\left(\frac{d \log p_2}{dn_2}\right)_{n_1} = 0. \quad \text{.........(196)}$$

It is evident from these equations, which are forms of the Duhem-Margules relation, that when a small quantity of S_2 is added to the solution :

(1) If $\log p_2$ increases, $\log p_1$ decreases.

(2) The magnitude of the change of $\log p_2$ is inversely proportional to the amount of S_2 in the solution. Thus if n_1 is large compared with n_2, the change of $\log p_1$ is small, and of the opposite sign to that of $\log p_2$.

Writing (196) in the form

$$d \log p_1 = -\frac{n_2}{n_1} d \log p_2,$$

and integrating from p_2 to p_2', we have

$$\log p_1' - \log p_1 = -\int_{p_2}^{p_2'} \frac{n_2}{n_1} d \log p_2. \quad \text{........(197)}$$

Thus if p_2 is known as a function of the molar ratio for a range of solutions the variation of p_1 over the same range can be calculated.

Variation of the Partial Free Energy with Composition in Very Dilute Solutions. This variation cannot be deduced *a priori* by thermodynamical arguments, but must in general be established by experimental study. Concentrated solutions exhibit a wide variety of behaviour, and no generalisation can be made, but in very dilute solutions the researches of van't Hoff, Raoult and others on the vapour pressures, freezing points, boiling points, osmotic pressures of these solutions established the law that equal numbers of solute molecules in a given quantity of a solvent cause the same change of all these magnitudes. Since no independent determination of the molecular weight in solution is available, this law depends on the fact that it has been shown to hold in a very considerable number of cases when the molecular weight is that required by the chemical formula. The evidence is so strong that in cases of apparent disagreement it may be assumed that the molecular weight employed is incorrect, and the law may be used to establish the molecular weights in solution.

Since all the properties listed above depend on the effect of the solute on the partial free energy of the solvent, we may state that in very dilute solutions equal numbers of solute molecules in a given quantity of solvent cause the same change in the partial free energy of the solvent. Since the change produced by a given amount of solute is obviously inversely proportional to the amount of solvent, we can therefore write

$$\frac{d\bar{F}_1}{dn_2} = -\frac{A}{n_1}, \quad \text{.....................(198)}$$

where n_2 is the number of mols of the solute, n_1 is the amount of the solvent * and A a constant.

Although for convenience we have expressed the amount of the solvent as a molar quantity n_1, and have used the corresponding molar free energy, $\bar{F}_1$, we are involved in no assumption as to the molecular weight of the solvent in the liquid state, for $n_1 d\bar{F}_1$ is independent of the unit of quantity employed. If the molecular weight used were doubled, $d\bar{F}_1$ would be doubled and n_1 halved and the product $n_1 d\bar{F}_1$ would be unchanged.

The experimental behaviour of dilute solutions shows that, provided the molecular weight of the solute is chosen properly, A is independent of the solvent and has the universal value RT. This identification of A with RT is the simplest and most general way of stating van't Hoff's analogy between the laws of dilute solutions and of gases. Writing $d\bar{F}_1/dn_2 = -RT/n_1$, we obtain by integration

$$\bar{F}_1 = \bar{F}^\circ_1 - RTn_2/n_1. \quad \text{..............(198}a\text{)}$$

* Expressed in terms of the same units as F_1.

Since by (185), $n_1 d\bar{F}_1 = -n_2 d\bar{F}_2$, we also have

$$\frac{n_2\, d\bar{F}_2}{dn_2} = \frac{d\bar{F}_2}{d \log n_2} = RT.$$

The integral of this equation may be written in the form

$$\bar{F}_2 = \bar{F}^\circ{}_2 + RT \log (n_2/n_1), \quad \text{.............(199)}$$

where $\bar{F}^\circ{}_2$ is a constant. If the quantity of the solvent is 1000 gms., n_2/n_1 may be replaced by m_2. Also in dilute solutions n_2/n_1 is practically equal to the molar fraction

$$N_2 = n_2/(n_1 + n_2).$$

Derivation of Raoult's Law. The change of vapour pressure, freezing point, etc., of the solvent produced by a solute can easily be derived from these equations. We will give the derivation of Raoult's Law as an example. Putting $d\bar{F}_1 = RT \,.\, d \log p_1 = RT \,.\, dp_1/p_1$, in (198) and giving A its value RT, we have

$$\frac{dp_1}{p_1} = -\frac{dn_2}{n_1}.$$

When n_2 is very small this may be written in the form

$$\frac{p_1{}^\circ - p_1}{p_1} = \frac{n_2}{n_1}, \quad \text{.....................(200)}$$

i.e. the fractional lowering of the vapour pressure of the solvent is equal to the ratio of the number of mols of solute to that of the solvent. In finding this molar ratio it is important to observe that while the molecular weight of the solute is that in the solution (which is fixed by the criterion that equal numbers of solute molecules must cause the same lowering of the free energy of the solvent), the molecular weight of the solvent is that in *the vapour phase.* This is the case because the equation $d\bar{F}_1 = RT \,.\, d \log p_1$ refers to the vapour. There is nothing in this equation which refers to the molecular weight of the solvent in the *liquid state*.

The Activity. The equations of the preceding sections only apply to extremely dilute solutions, and in more concentrated solutions very considerable deviations often occur. In such solutions it is convenient to express the partial free energies of the components in terms of their *activities*, which are defined by equations of the type:

$$\bar{F}_2 = \bar{F}^\circ_2 + RT \log a_2, \quad \text{.................(201)}$$

where $\bar{F}^\circ_2$, the partial free energy of S_2 in the solution for which the activity has been taken as unity, may be termed the standard free energy under the conditions defined. In different cases it is convenient to adopt different conventions.

(1) *Activity of the solvent.* In this case it is usually more convenient to take the activity of the solvent (S_1) as unity in the pure liquid. Then writing

$$\bar{F}_1 = F^\circ_1 + RT \log a_1, \quad \text{.................(201}a\text{)}$$

it can be seen that F°_1 is the molar free energy of the pure liquid. If the molecular weight employed is that in the vapour phase, we have by (194),

$$F_1 = F^\circ_1 + RT \log p_1/p_1{}^\circ,$$

or $a_1 = p_1/p_1{}^\circ$. Now Raoult's Law (200), can be written as

$$p_1/p_1{}^\circ = \frac{n_1}{n_1 + n_2} = N_1.$$

If the molecular weights are chosen according to the principles given above this holds accurately for very small concentrations of the solute. In some solutions it has been found experimentally to hold over a considerable concentration range. In such a case it is evident that

$$\bar{F}_1 = F^\circ_1 + RT \log N_1.$$

This equation is often taken as representing the behaviour of an "ideal" solution. The ratio $f_1 = a_1/N_1$, which is obviously unity in the pure liquid, is the *activity coefficient* and may be taken as a measure of the deviation from the ideal behaviour.

For two liquids which are miscible in all proportions, either can be regarded as the solvent. The activities and activity coefficients of both can be determined from the partial vapour pressures and it is convenient to take a and f as unity for each component in the pure liquid.

Fig. 74 shows the partial pressures in carbon disulphide—methylal mixtures and the activity coefficients derived therefrom. The deviations from Raoult's law are positive and evidently increase as the mol fraction diminishes. In Fig. 74(a) AC represents the partial pressure p_2 of CS_2 in a particular solution. AB represents the Raoult's law value for the same solution *i.e.* $p_2^\circ N_2$. The activity coefficient $p_2/p_2^\circ N_2$ is thus the ratio of AC to AB.

Table XXVI. shows the calculation of the activities and activity coefficients of n-propyl alcohol (S_2) and water (S_1) in mixtures extending over the whole range of composition from pure alcohol to pure water. a_1 and f_1, the activity and activity coefficient of water, are taken as unity in pure water; while a_2 and f_2, the activity and activity coefficient of alcohol, are unity in the pure alcohol.

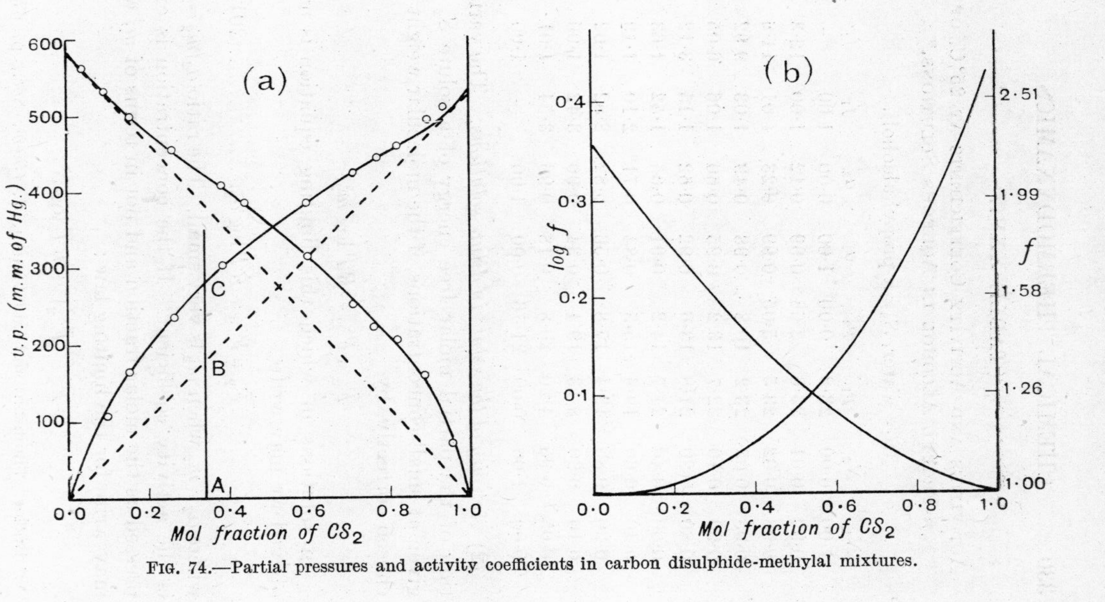

FIG. 74.—Partial pressures and activity coefficients in carbon disulphide-methylal mixtures.

TABLE XXVI.

ACTIVITIES AND ACTIVITY COEFFICIENTS AT 25° C. OF n-PROPYL ALCOHOL IN AQUEOUS SOLUTIONS.*

(S_1=water, S_2=n-propyl alcohol).

N_1	N_2	p_1	p_2	a_1	a_2	f_1	f_2
1·00	0·00	23·8	0·00	1·00	0·00	1·00	—
0·99	0·01	23·6	2·68	0·99	0·12	1·00	12·3
0·98	0·02	23·5	5·05	0·99	0·23	1·01	11·6
0·95	0·05	23·2	10·8	0·98	0·49	1·03	9·92
0·90	0·10	22·7	13·2	0·95	0·60	1·06	6·05
0·80	0·20	21·8	13·6	0·92	0·62	1·15	3·12
0·60	0·40	21·7	14·2	0·91	0·65	1·52	1·63
0·40	0·60	19·9	15·5	0·84	0·71	2·10	1·19
0·20	0·80	13·4	17·8	0·56	0·82	2·82	1·02
0·10	0·90	8·13	19·4	0·34	0·90	3·42	1·00
0·05	0·95	4·20	20·8	0·18	0·96	3·54	1·01
0·00	1·00	0·00	21·76	0·00	1·00	—	1·00

(2) *Activity of the solute in dilute solutions.* The variation of the partial molar free energy of a solute S_2 is given at small concentrations, if the molecular weight is chosen correctly, by

$$\bar{F}_2 = \bar{F}^\circ{}_2 + RT \log m_2.$$

In solutions in which this limiting equation is not obeyed we may write

$$\bar{F}_2 = \bar{F}^\circ{}_2 + RT \log a_2, \quad \text{...............(201}b\text{)}$$

where $a_2 = m_2$ when m_2 is very small. The ratio $a_2/m_2 = f_2$ is the activity coefficient. If the concentration is expressed as the molar fraction and not in terms of m, we may write for the limiting law :

$$\bar{F}_2 = (\bar{F}^\circ{}_2)' + RT \log N_2,$$

* Butler, Thomson and Maclennan, *J. Chem. Soc.*, p. 674, 1933.

and for actual solutions

$$\bar{F}_2 = (\bar{F}^\circ{}_2)' + RT \log a_2,$$

and the *activity coefficient* is $f_2 = a_2/N_2$. Evidently $f_2 = 1$, when m_2 (or N_2) is very small.

It is important to observe that it is only possible for a_2 to become equal to m_2 (or N_2) when m_2 is small if the molecular weight of the solute which is used in calculating the molecular concentrations is that which satisfies $d\bar{F}_1/dn_2 = -RT/n_1$.

(3) *Relation between activities determined by conventions* (1) *and* (2). When a complete range of solutions exists which extends from one pure liquid to the other, either convention may be adopted. It is of interest to compare the results of the two definitions. Consider the component S_2. According to the second definition, *i.e.* taking the activity as unity in the pure liquid S_2, the partial free energy in any given solution, since $a_2 = f_2 N_2$, is

$$\bar{F}_2 = F^\circ{}_2 + RT \log f_2 N_2.$$

In the same solution, by the first definition, we have

$$\bar{F}_2 = (F^\circ{}_2)' + RT \log f_2' N_2,$$

where $f_2' = 1$, when N_2 is very small. Comparing these equations it is evident that

$$(\bar{F}^\circ{}_2)' - F^\circ{}_2 = RT \log f_2/f_2'. \quad \text{..............(202)}$$

If the solution is so dilute that $f_2' = 1$, we may distinguish f_2 as f_2°, and we have then

$$(F^\circ{}_2)' - F^\circ{}_2 = RT \log f_2^\circ. \quad \text{...........(203)}$$

Thus if the activity coefficient is taken as unity in the pure liquid and f_2° is its value in an extremely dilute solution in another solvent, $RT \log f_2^\circ$ is equal to the difference between the standard free energy for dilute solutions of S_2 in the given solvent and its free energy in the pure liquid state.

Activity of a Solute from the Vapour Pressures of the Solvent. When the activity of one component of a binary solution is known over a range of concentration the variation of the activity of the second component over the same range can be found by the application of the Duhem-Margules equation. Putting

$$d\bar{F}_1 = RT \, . \, d \log a_1, \; d\bar{F}_2 = RT \, . \, d \log a_2,$$

in (185), we have

$$n_1 \, . \, d \log a_1 + n_2 \, . \, d \log a_2 = 0, \quad \text{.........(204)}$$

and since it can easily be shown that

$$n_1 \, . \, d \log N_1 + n_2 \, . \, d \log N_2 = 0 \, ;$$

it follows that

$$n_1 \, . \, d \log f_1 + n_2 \, . \, d \log f_2 = 0. \quad \text{.........(205)}$$

Therefore, integrating from the values for a solution A to those for a solution B:

$$(\log a_2)_B - (\log a_2)_A = -\int_A^B \frac{n_1}{n_2} \, . \, d \log a_1 \, ; \quad \text{...(206)}$$

and

$$(\log f_2)_B - (\log f_2)_A = -\int_A^B \frac{n_1}{n_2} \, . \, d \log f_1. \quad \text{...(207)}$$

The variation of a_2 (or f_2) between any two solutions can thus be found if a_1 (or f_1) is known as a function of the molar ratio (n_1/n_2) between these limits. The activity of an involatile solute can be determined in this way from the partial vapour pressure of the solvent. In some cases these equations can be conveniently integrated graphically by plotting n_1/n_2 against $\log a_1$ or $\log f_1$. When the range over which the integration is to be made includes the pure solvent $(n_1/n_2 = \infty)$ difficulties

* The remainder of this chapter is concerned with rather specialised material which most students may wish to omit on first reading.

arise, and it is better to make use of some empirical relation between n_1/n_2 and a_1 (or f_1) for dilute solutions.

The following table shows the activity coefficients of cane sugar in aqueous solutions at 50° as determined from the partial vapour pressures of water in this way.* In this case the solution remains practically ideal up to $n_2/n_1 = 0{\cdot}014$, and no difficulty arises over the extrapolation to infinite dilution.

TABLE XXVII.

ACTIVITY COEFFICIENTS OF CANE SUGAR IN AQUEOUS SOLUTIONS AT 50° C.

n_2/n_1.	N_1.	$f_1 = p_1/p_1^\circ N_1$.	N_2.	$f_2 = a_2/N_2$.
0·005993	0·9940	0·9999	0·0060	1·000
0·01382	0·9864	1·0071	0·0136	1·000
0·01773	0·9826	0·9974	0·0174	1·134
0·02435	0·9762	0·9933	0·0238	1·269
0·03472	0·9665	0·9950	0·0335	1·437
0·04615	0·9559	0·9914	0·0441	1·624
0·05939	0·9439	0·9852	0·0561	1·847
0·07259	0·9323	0·9699	0·0677	2·053
0·09906	0·9098	0·9626	0·0902	2·427
0·1222	0·8911	0·9347	0·1089	2·801

Variation of the Partial Free Energy with Temperature and Pressure. Let F be the free energy of a solution containing n_1 mols of S_1, n_2 mols of S_2, etc. By definition

$$F = E - TS + pv.$$

Differentiating with respect to n_1, we have

$$\frac{\partial F}{\partial n_1} = \frac{\partial E}{\partial n_1} - T\frac{\partial S}{\partial n_1} + p\frac{\partial v}{\partial n_1},$$

or

$$\bar{F}_1 = \bar{E}_1 - T\bar{S}_1 + p\bar{v}_1 = \bar{H}_1 - T\bar{S}_1, \quad\ldots\ldots\ldots\ldots(208)$$

* Perman, *Trans. Faraday Soc.*, 24, 330, 1928.

where $\bar{S}_1 = (dS/dn_1)_{t,p,n_2}$ etc., is the partial molar entropy defined in the same way as the partial molar energy or volume, etc. We can now find the change of $\bar{F}_1$ with temperature and pressure.

First differentiating F with respect to T, we have by (115),

$$\left(\frac{dF}{dT}\right)_{p,n} = -S,$$

and differentiating again with respect to n_1,

$$\left(\frac{d^2F}{dT \,.\, dn_1}\right)_p = -\frac{dS}{dn_1} = -\bar{S}_1.$$

Since
$$\left(\frac{d^2F}{dT \,.\, dn_1}\right)_p = \frac{d^2F}{dn_1 \,.\, dT} = \frac{d\bar{F}_1}{dT},$$

and introducing the value of $\bar{S}_1$ given by (208), we have

$$\frac{d\bar{F}_1}{dT} = -\bar{S}_1 = \frac{\bar{F}_1 - \bar{H}_1}{T}. \quad \text{..............(209)}$$

Dividing through by T, we thus find

$$\frac{1}{T} \cdot \frac{d\bar{F}_1}{dT} - \frac{\bar{F}_1}{T^2} = -\frac{\bar{H}_1}{T^2},$$

or
$$\frac{d(\bar{F}_1/T)}{dT} = -\frac{\bar{H}_1}{T^2}. \quad \text{..............(210)}$$

Similarly differentiating F with respect to p, we have by (116),

$$\left(\frac{dF}{dp}\right)_{t,n} = v,$$

and
$$\left(\frac{d^2F}{dp \,.\, dn_1}\right)_{t,n_2,\text{etc.}} = \frac{dv}{dn_1} = \bar{v}_1.$$

Since
$$\frac{d^2F}{dp \,.\, dn_1} = \frac{d^2F}{dn_1 \,.\, dp} = \frac{d\bar{F}_1}{dp},$$

we have
$$\frac{d\bar{F}_1}{dp} = \bar{v}_1, \quad \text{................(211)}$$

i.e. the rate of change of the partial free energy of a component with the pressure is equal to its partial volume.

***Determination of Activity from the Freezing Point of Solutions.** Consider an aqueous solution containing n_1 mols of water (S_1) and n_2 mols of a solute S_2. The partial molar free energy in (1) pure water, (2) ice, (3) the solution at the freezing point of pure water (t_0) and at the freezing point of the solution (t) are represented by the symbols given below.

	Water.		Ice.		Solution.
t_0	$(F^\circ_1)_{t_0}$	$=$	$(F_s)_{t_0}$		$(\bar{F}_1)_{t_0}$,
t	$(F^\circ_1)_t$		$(F_s)_t$	$=$	$(\bar{F}_1)_t$.

The conditions for the equilibrium of ice and water at its freezing point (t_0), and of ice and the solution at its freezing point (t) are given by the equalities in this scheme.

The variation of the free energy of ice with the temperature, according to (210), is

$$\frac{d(F_s/t)}{dt} = -\frac{H_s}{t^2},$$

where H_s is the molar heat content of ice. Integrating this equation between t and t_0, we have

$$(F_s)_{t_0}/t_0 - (F_s)_t/t = -\int_t^{t_0} H_s/t^2 \,.\, dt.$$

The variation of $\bar{F}_1$ between the same temperatures is similarly given by

$$\frac{(\bar{F}_1)_{t_0}}{t_0} - \frac{(\bar{F}_1)_t}{t} = -\int_t^{t_0} \frac{\bar{H}_1}{t^2} \,.\, dt,$$

where $\bar{H}_1$ is the partial molar heat content of water in the solution. Combining these equations and writing $(F_s)_t = (\bar{F}_1)_t$, it follows that

$$\frac{(\bar{F}_1)_{t_0} - (F_s)_{t_0}}{t_0} = -\int_t^{t_0} \frac{\bar{H}_1 - H_s}{t^2} \, . \, dt,$$

and since $(F_s)_{t_0} = (F^\circ{}_1)_{t_0}$, and by the definition of the activity of the solvent

$$(\bar{F}_1)_{t_0} = (F^\circ{}_1)_{t_0} + Rt_0 \log(a_1)_{t_0},$$

we have

$$\log(a_1)_{t_0} = -\int_t^{t_0} \frac{\bar{H}_1 - H_s}{Rt^2} \, . \, dt. \quad \text{.........(212)}$$

If the solution is so dilute, or its nature is such that the partial heat of water in the solution is negligible, instead of $\bar{H}_1$ we may write $H^\circ{}_1$ (*i.e.* the partial heat content of water in the solution is replaced by the heat content of pure water). $\Delta H = H^\circ{}_1 - H_s$ is the latent heat of fusion of ice, the variation of which over a considerable range of temperature may be expressed by the Kirchhoff equation

$$\Delta H = \Delta H_0 + \Delta C_p (t_0 - t),$$

where ΔC_p is the difference between the molar heat capacities of ice and water, and ΔH_0 the latent heat of fusion of ice at t_0. According to Lewis and Randall these quantities have the values

$$\Delta H_0 = 1438 \text{ calories}, \quad \Delta C_p = -9 \text{ calories}.$$

Introducing these values into (212), we have *

$$(\log a_1)_{t_0} = -\int_t^{t_0} \frac{1438 - 9(t_0 - t)}{Rt^2} \, . \, dt.$$

* The steps of this calculation are: writing $t^2 = t_0^2 - 2t_0\Delta t + (\Delta t)^2$, and neglecting $(\Delta t)^2$, we have to a first approximation

$$\frac{1438 - 9\Delta t}{Rt^2} = \frac{1}{Rt_0^2}\left\{(1438 - 9\Delta t)\left(1 + \frac{2t_0\Delta t)}{t_0^2}\right)\right\}$$

$$= \frac{1}{Rt_0^2}\left\{1438 + \left(\frac{2 \times 1438}{t_0} - 9\right)\Delta t.\right.$$

Writing $t = t_0 - \Delta t$, we obtain

$$\frac{1438 - 9(t_0 - t)}{Rt^2} = 0{\cdot}009696 + 0{\cdot}0000103\Delta t,$$

and $$(\log a_1)_{t_0} = -0{\cdot}009696\Delta t - \frac{0{\cdot}0000103\Delta t^2}{2}. \quad \ldots(213)$$

This gives the activity of the solvent at its freezing point as a function of the freezing point depression. In order to find the activity of the solute we can use the expression $d \log a_2 = -(n_1/n_2) d \log a_1$. If the solution contain m mols of the solute in 1000 gms. (55·51 mols) of water, we have

$$d \log (a_2)_{t_0} = \frac{0{\cdot}009696 \times 55{\cdot}51}{m} . d(\Delta t)$$

$$+ \frac{0{\cdot}0000051 \times 55{\cdot}51}{m} . 2\Delta t . d(\Delta t). \quad \ldots\ldots(214)$$

For a very dilute solution we can neglect the second term of this equation, and putting in that case $a_2 = m$,* we obtain

$$\frac{d(\Delta t)}{dm} = \frac{1}{0{\cdot}009696 \times 55{\cdot}51} = 1{\cdot}858.$$

This is the molecular lowering of the freezing point for very dilute solutions. Representing it by λ, (214) becomes

$$d \log (a_2)_{t_0} = \frac{d(\Delta t)}{\lambda m} + 0{\cdot}00057 \frac{\Delta t . d(\Delta t)}{m}. \quad \ldots(215)$$

In order to integrate this it is necessary to resort to graphical methods.

* Note that the correct choice of the molecular weight comes in at this point.

* *Integration formulae.* In order to integrate this expression, Lewis and Randall make use of the quantity j, which is defined by

$$\frac{\Delta t}{\lambda m} = 1 - j, \quad \text{or} \quad j = 1 - \frac{\Delta t}{\lambda m}.$$

Since at infinite dilution $\Delta t/m$ is equal to λ, j is a measure of the difference between the actual molecular depression of the solution and the value at infinite dilution. By differentiation, we have

$$\frac{d(\Delta t)}{\lambda m} - \frac{\Delta t \,.\, dm}{\lambda m^2} = -dj,$$

and
$$\frac{d(\Delta t)}{\lambda m} = (1-j)\frac{dm}{m} - dj = (1-j)\log m - dj.$$

Introducing this value into (215), it follows that

$$d\log(a_2)_{t_0} = (1-j)\,d\log m - dj + 0{\cdot}00057 \,.\, \frac{\Delta t}{m} \,.\, d(\Delta t),$$

and therefore,

$$\log\frac{(a_2)_{t_0}}{m} = -\int_0^m j \,.\, d\log m - j + \int_0^m 0{\cdot}00057 \,.\, \frac{\Delta t}{m} \,.\, d(\Delta t).$$

The first integral $A = \int_0^m \frac{j}{m} \,.\, dm$ can be obtained by plotting j/m against m and taking the area of the curve from 0 to m, the second B by plotting $\Delta t/m$ against Δt, and multiplying by 0·00057.

The following data for solutions of butyl alcohol in water, obtained by Harkins and Wampler,* illustrate this procedure. Table XXVIIA. gives the values of m, Δt, $\Delta t/m$, j and j/m for some of the solutions.

* *J. Amer. Chem. Soc.*, 53, 850, 1931.

TABLE XXVIIA.

FREEZING POINT DEPRESSIONS OF BUTYL ALCOHOL SOLUTIONS.

m.	Δt.	$\Delta t/m$.	j.	j/m (Interpolated).
0·004134	0·007669	1·855	0·00201	0·487
0·01140	0·02112	1·851	0·00525	0·460
0·01605	0·02957	1·842	0·00711	0·443
0·02420	0·04452	1·840	0·00997	0·412
0·04631	0·08470	1·829	0·01572	0·339
0·05206	0·09505	1·826	0·0174	0·325
0·06894	0·1255	1·821	0·0197	0·286
0·09748	0·1768	1·814	0·0238	0·245
0·1641	0·2956	1·801	0·0306	0·1864
0·2153	0·3863	1·794	0·0343	0·1593
0·4197	0·7442	1·773	0·0455	0·1084
0·7035	1·2310	1·750	0·0583	0·0804

Fig. 75 shows j/m plotted against m. A certain latitude in drawing the curve to zero concentration is obviously

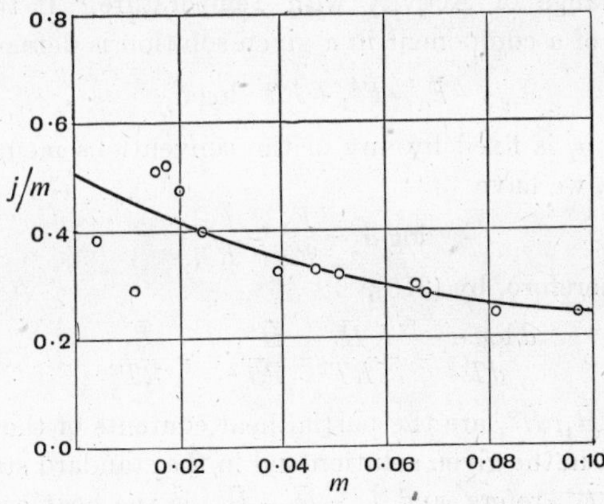

FIG. 75.—j/m for butyl alcohol solutions plotted against m

possible, but this makes very little difference to the result. The values of the integrals A and B and of a_2/m, obtained from the smoothed curves for round concentrations are given in Table XXVIII.

TABLE XXVIII.

m.	$-A$.	B.	a_2/m_2.
0·001	·000499	—	0·9990
·003	·001485	—	0·9971
·006	·002946	—	0·9942
·010	·004840	0·00001	0·9906
·020	0·009308	·00004	0·9823
·040	0·001710	·00008	0·9691
·070	0·02661	·00013	0·9546
·100	0·03442	·00019	0·9433
·200	0·05420	·00038	0·9161
·300	0·06991	·00054	0·8974
·400	0·08201	·00071	0·8817
·500	0·09252	·00089	0·8681
·600	0·1019	·00106	0·8563
·700	0·1104	·00123	0·8465

***Change of Activity with Temperature.** If the activity of a component in a given solution is defined by

$$\bar{F}_1 = \bar{F}^\circ_1 + RT \,.\, \log a_1,$$

where a_1 is fixed by any of the conventions mentioned above, we have

$$\log a_1 = \frac{\bar{F}_1}{RT} - \frac{\bar{F}^\circ_1}{RT},$$

and therefore, by (210),

$$\frac{d \log a_1}{dT} = -\frac{\bar{H}_1}{RT^2} + \frac{\bar{H}^\circ_1}{RT^2} = -\frac{\bar{L}_1}{RT^2}, \quad \text{........(216)}$$

where $\bar{H}_1$, $\bar{H}^\circ_1$ are the partial heat contents of the component in the given solution and in the standard state to which $\bar{F}^\circ_1$ refers, and $\bar{L}_1 = \bar{H}_1 - \bar{H}^\circ_1$ is the heat content relative to this standard state. The change of activity (and also of the activity coefficient, if the composition is expressed in a way which does not depend on the temperature) over a range of temperature can be obtained by integrating this equation. For a wide range of temperature it may be necessary to give $\bar{L}_1$ as a function of the temperature as in Kirchhoff's equation.

Activity from the freezing point when heat of dilution is not neglected. As before, (212), we have

$$\log (a_1)_{t_0} = -\int_t^{t_0} \frac{\bar{H}_1 - H_s}{Rt^2} \,.\, dt,$$

but we cannot now identify $\bar{H}_1$ with H°_1. Adding and subtracting H°_1/Rt^2, we obtain

$$\log (a_1)_{t_0} = -\int_t^{t_0} \frac{\bar{H}_1 - H^\circ_1}{Rt^2} dt - \int_t^{t_0} \frac{H^\circ_1 - H_s}{Rt^2} \,.\, dt,$$

but by (216), this becomes

$$\log (a_1)_{t_0} = \log (a_1)_{t_0} - \log (a_1)_t - \int_t^{t_0} \frac{H^\circ_1 - H_s}{Rt^2} \,.\, dt.$$

Therefore

$$\log (a_1)_t = -\int_t^{t_0} \frac{H^\circ_1 - H_s}{Rt^2} \,.\, dt. \qquad \ldots\ldots\ldots\ldots (217)$$

This integral thus really gives the activity of the solvent at the freezing point of the solution (t). This is equal to the activity at t_0 only when, as was previously supposed to be the case, the heat of dilution of the solution is negligible. When this is not so, the activity at any given temperature can be obtained by adding to the value of (217), the change of activity between t and the given temperature as determined by the integral of (216). This involves a knowledge of the relative heat contents of the solutions, and if the temperature interval is large, possibly also their variation with temperature.

*** Solubility of Solids.** Let F_s be the molar free energy of a solid, and $\overline{F}_2$ its partial free energy in a saturated solution in a given solvent. The condition of equilibrium is $F_s = \overline{F}_2$. Writing $\overline{F}_2 = \overline{F}^\circ_2 + RT \cdot \log m_2 f_2$, we have

$$\frac{F_s - \overline{F}^\circ_2}{RT} - \log f_2 = \log m_2,$$

and, differentiating with respect to the temperature, we obtain

$$-\frac{H_s - \overline{H}^\circ_2}{RT^2} - \left(\frac{d \log f_2}{dT}\right)_m - \left(\frac{d \log f_2}{dm_2}\right)_T \cdot \frac{dm_2}{dT} = \frac{d \log m_2}{dT},$$

or, since by (216),

$$\left(\frac{d \log f_2}{dT}\right)_m = -\frac{\overline{H}_2 - \overline{H}^\circ_2}{RT_2},$$

this becomes

$$\frac{\overline{H}_2 - H_s}{RT^2} = \left(\frac{d \log f_2}{dm_2}\right)_T \cdot \frac{dm_2}{dT} + \frac{d \log m_2}{dT}.$$

The variation of the activity coefficient of non-electrolytes with the concentration is probably often so small that the first term on the right can be neglected, and we then have

$$\frac{d \log m_2}{dT} = \frac{\overline{H}_2 - H_s}{RT^2}, \quad \text{..................(218)}$$

where $\overline{H}_2 - H_s$ is the partial heat of solution in the saturated solution.

Example. In the case of solutions of salts the term $(d \log f_2/dm_2)_T$ cannot safely be neglected. The heat of solution of slightly soluble salts can be determined in the following way. The reciprocals of the solubility products of a slightly soluble salt can be extrapolated to give an ideal value for the solubility product in an infinitely dilute solution (*i.e.* activity coefficient unity). (218) can be applied to the values so obtained to give the heat of solution of the salt at infinite dilution. Butler and Hiscocks found (*J. Chem. Soc.*, 2554, 1926) that for thallous chloride the values of $1/\sqrt{m^\circ_{Tl} \cdot m^\circ_{Cl}}$ at infinite dilution were 0°, 163·6 ;

25°, 72·1. The heat of solution of the salt as determined by $\frac{d \log (m^{\circ}_{\text{Tl}} m^{\circ}_{\text{Cl}})}{dT} = \frac{\Delta H^{\circ}}{RT^2}$ (since there are two ions), over this range of temperatures is thus $\Delta H = 10560$ calories.

***The Osmotic Pressure of Solutions.** When two phases are separated by a membrane which offers no resistance to the passage of one component and is completely impermeable to all others, the condition of equilibrium is that the partial free energy of the component which can pass freely through the membrane shall be the same in both phases, but there is no such condition for the components which cannot pass the membrane.

Consider a solution of a solute S_2 in a solvent S_1, separated from the solvent by a membrane which is permeable to S_1 only. Let the partial free energy of S_1 at the temperature T and the pressure P_0 be $(F^{\circ}_1)_{P_0}$ in the pure solvent and $(\bar{F}_1)_{P_0}$ in the solution. If the pressure on the solvent has the constant value P_0, it is necessary in order to establish equilibrium across the membrane to increase the pressure on the solution until the partial free energy of the solvent in the latter is equal to $(\bar{F}_1)_{P_0}$. The variation of $\bar{F}_1$ with pressure is given according to (211) by

$$d\bar{F}_1 = \bar{v}_1 \, dP.$$

Integrating this between the pressures P_0 and P, we have

$$(\bar{F}_1)_P - (\bar{F}_1)_{P_0} = \int_{P_0}^{P} \bar{v}_1 \,.\, dP. \quad \text{.............(219)}$$

We have to find the pressure which is required to make $(\bar{F}_1)_P$ equal to $(F^{\circ}_1)_{P_0}$. Writing

$$(F^{\circ}_1)_{P_0} - (\bar{F}_1)_{P_0} = -RT \log a_1,$$

(219) may therefore be replaced by

$$RT \log a_1 = -\int_{P_0}^{P} \bar{v}_1 \,.\, dP. \quad \text{.............(220)}$$

If $\bar{v}_1$ is taken as constant and independent of the pressure between P and P_0, we obtain by integration,

$$RT \log a_1 = -\bar{v}_1(P - P_0) \quad \text{.............(221)}$$

where $P - P_0$ is the osmotic pressure.

Introducing the value of (198*a*), viz.

$$RT \log a_1 = -RT n_2/n_1,$$

we obtain $$P - P_0 = \frac{RT}{\bar{v}_1} \cdot \frac{n_2}{n_1}. \quad \text{.................(221a)}$$

This will be recognized as van't Hoff's law of osmotic pressure, since n_2 is the number of mols of solute dissolved in a volume $n_1 \bar{v}_1$ of solvent.

The following table gives a comparison between the osmotic pressures of aqueous solutions of cane sugar and α-methyl glucoside at 0°, and the values calculated by this equation, taking for $\bar{v}_1$ a mean value between P_0 and P.* The activities of water in the solutions were obtained from its partial vapour pressures as $a_1 = p_1/p_1^\circ$.

TABLE XXIX.

CANE SUGAR.

Concentration gms. Sugar in 100 gms. Water.	$-\log_e a_1$.	$\bar{v}_1$. (per gram.)	$P-P_0$. (calc.)	$P-P_0$. (obs.).
56·50	0·03516	0·99515	43·91	43·84
81·20	0·05380	0·99157	67·43	67·68
112·00	0·07983	0·98690	100·53	100·43
141·00	0·10669	0·98321	134·86	134·71
α-METHYL GLUCOSIDE.				
35·00	0·03878	0·99810	48·29	48·11
45·00	0·05153	0·99709	64·22	63·96
55·00	0·06451	0·99579	80·50	81·00
64·00	0·09253	0·99254	115·74	115·92

* Berkeley, Hartley and Burton, *Phil. Trans.*, 218, 295, 1919; *Proc. Roy. Soc.*, *A*, 92, 483, 1916.

It is obvious that in a precise calculation of the osmotic pressure the variation of the partial volume of the solvent $\bar{v}_1$ with the pressure ought to be taken into account. Perman and Urry * have expressed $\bar{v}_1$ as a linear function of $P - P_0$ by the equation

$$\bar{v}_1 = \bar{v}_1^\circ(1 - s(P - P_0)).$$

Then (220) becomes

$$RT \log a_1 = -\int_{P_0}^{P} \bar{v}_1^\circ[1 - s(P - P_0)] \,.\, dP$$

$$= -\bar{v}_1^\circ(P - P_0)\left(1 - \frac{s(P - P_0)}{2}\right). \quad \ldots(222)$$

where the relatively small term sP_0^2 is neglected.

Table XXX gives a comparison of the observed osmotic pressures of a cane sugar solution containing 1 gm. mol sugar in 1000 gms. water, at a few temperatures, with the values calculated by (221), a_1 being determined from the partial vapour pressures by $a_1 = p_1/p_1^\circ$ (s is about 370×10^{-7}).

TABLE XXX.

OBSERVED AND CALCULATED OSMOTIC PRESSURES OF A SUCROSE SOLUTION.

Temperature.	$-\log_e a_1$.	v_1°.	$P - P_0$. (Calc.).	$P - P_0$. (Obs.).
40°	0·01940	1·006456	27·51	27·70
50°	0·01914	1·010650	27·88	28·21
60°	0·01839	1·016843	27·45	28·37
70°	0·01848	1·0195	28·34	28·62
80°	0·01809	1·0257	28·41	28·82

* *Proc. Roy. Soc., A*, 126, 44, 1930.

Examples.

1. The following are the measured partial pressures of solutions of water (S_1) and methyl alcohol (S_2) at 25° :

N_2	p_1	p_2	N_2	p_1	p_2
0·00	23·8	0·00	0·20	19·5	35·8
0·02	22·9	3·85	0·40	15·8	59·6
0·04	22·3	7·67	0·66	10·5	85·7
0·06	22·2	11·7	0·81	5·26	104·6
0·08	21·2	15·1	1·00	0·00	126·0

Find the activities and activity coefficients of the components.

2. The solubility of carbon tetrachloride in water at 20° C. is 0·080 gms. CCl_4 to 100 gms. H_2O. Assuming that carbon tetrachloride dissolves practically no water, and that its activity coefficient is 1 in the pure liquid, find its activity coefficient in the saturated aqueous solution. (10600.)

3. According to Bell (*J. Chem. Soc.*, 1932, p. 2907), the equilibrium molar fraction of water in chlorobenzene, when shaken with Na_2SO_4, $10H_2O$ and Na_2SO_4 is nearly 0·02 at 25°. The dissociation pressure of the salt hydrate is19·2 mm. and that of pure water 23·8 mm. at 25°. Find the activity coefficient of water in the chlorobenzene solution. (42.)

4. Find the activities and activity coefficients in chloroform (S_1) – acetone (S_2) solutions from the following partial pressures. which refer to 35·17°.

$100\,N_1$	p_1 (m.m.)	p_2 (m.m.)	$100\,N_1$	p_1 (m.m.)	p_2 (m.m.)
0	0	344·5	49·4	111·8	143·6
5·9	9·2	323·2	51·4	117·8	135·0
12·3	20·4	299·3	58·7	139·9	108·5
18·5	31·9	275·4	66·3	170·2	79·0
26·6	50·7	240·9	80·0	224·4	37·5
29·7	55·4	230·3	91·75	267·1	13·0
36·6	74·3	197·9	100·00	293·1	0·0
42·3	88·9	174·3			

CHAPTER XVI

SOLUBILITY AND MOLECULAR INTERACTIONS IN SOLUTION*

Activity coefficients and solubility. (*a*) *Mixed liquids.* Liquids which form ideal solutions with each other will clearly mix in all proportions. Usually deviations from Raoult's law are in the positive direction ; unless there is a definite affinity between the two substances which gives rise to an intermolecular compound or " complex " having some stability. The variation of the activity coefficient with concentration in the case of positive deviations was shown by van Laar to be represented by equations of the type :

$$\log_e f_2 = \beta_2 N_1^2 \,, \quad \text{(1·0)}$$

$$\log_e f_1 = \beta_1 N_2^2 \,; \quad \text{(1·1)}$$

where f_1, f_2 are the activity coefficients of the components A and B ; and N_1, N_2 their molar fractions. Thus the activity coefficient of B increases with the molar fraction of the *other* component. The limiting value of f_2 reached when its concentration is small and the molar fraction of the other component thus approaches unity ($N_1 \to 1$) is

$$\log f_2 \, (N_1 \to 1) = \beta_2, \quad \text{(2·0)}$$

and similarly $$\log f_1 \, (N_2 \to 1) = \beta_1. \quad \text{(2·1)}$$

* This chapter is entirely new and the equations are numbered independently of the rest of the book.

Fig. 76 shows the activities or partial pressures of B, calculated according to this equation for various values of β. It can be seen that when β is large the activity curve passes through a minimum and a maximum. This results in instability. There are now two solutions with the same partial free energy and solutions with vapour pressures above the *minimum* of the curve will break into two phases in which the partial pressures are the same and which can therefore exist in equilibrium with each other.

Note that in dilute solutions of B, where N_1 is practically unity, $\log f_2 = \beta_2$, or $f_2 = e^{\beta_2}$, so that

$$p_2/p_2^\circ = a_2 = f_2 N_2 = e^{\beta_2} N_2,$$

i.e. the partial pressure is again proportional to the molar fraction; the proportionality constant being e^{β_2}. This proportionality is Henry's law.

(*b*) *Solubility of solids.* A solid cannot exist above the melting point. Below the melting point its free energy is less than that of the pure liquid at the same temperature; hence it can exist in equilibrium with a solution. The condition of equilibrium between a solid and its solution is

$$F_2(s) = \bar{F}_2(l),$$

where $F_2(s)$ is the molar free energy of the solid and $\bar{F}_2(l)$ its partial free energy in the saturated solution. The latter can be written as

$$\bar{F}_2(l) = F_2^\circ(l) + RT \log f_2 N_2, \quad \text{...........(3·0)}$$

where $F_2^\circ(l)$ is the molar free energy of the pure liquid at the same temperature and f_2, N_2 the activity coefficient and molar fraction in the saturated solution.

If the solution is an ideal one, $f_2 = 1$, and we may write for the solubility in the ideal case:

$$RT \log N_2^{\text{ideal}} = F_2(s) - F_2^\circ(l). \quad \text{...........(3·1)}$$

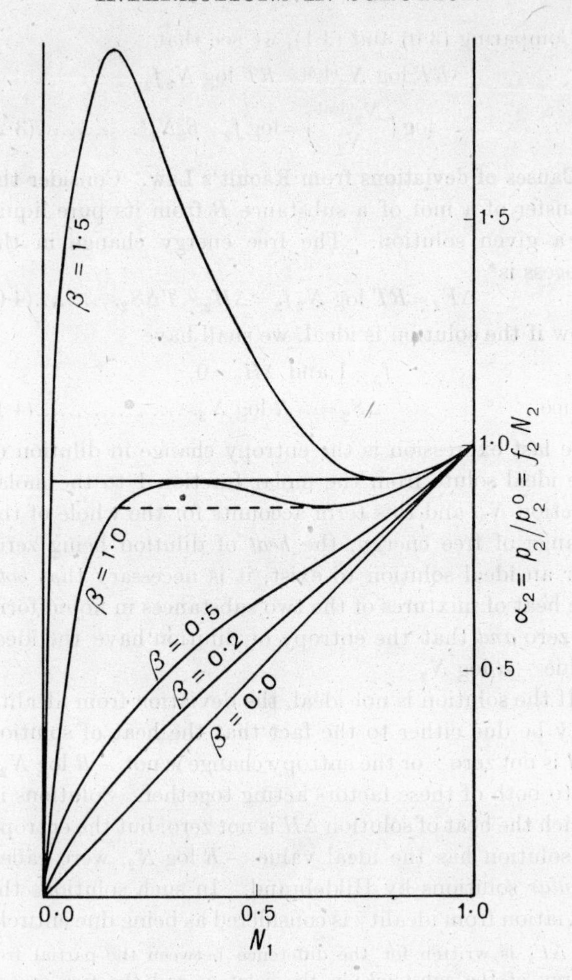

FIG. 76.—Partial pressure curves for various values of β calculated by $\log_{10} f_2 = \beta_2 N_1^2$.

Comparing (3·0) and (3·1), we see that

$$RT \log N_2^{\text{ideal}} = RT \log N_2 f_2,$$

or
$$\log\left(\frac{N_2^{\text{ideal}}}{N_2}\right) = \log f_2 = \beta_2 N_1^2. \quad \text{.........(3·2)}$$

Causes of deviations from Raoult's Law. Consider the transfer of a mol of a substance B from its pure liquid to a given solution. The free energy change in the process is*

$$\Delta F_2 = RT \log N_2 f_2 = \Delta H_2 - T\Delta S_2. \quad \text{.........(4·0)}$$

Now if the solution is ideal, we shall have

$$f_2 = 1 \text{ and } \Delta H_2 = 0,$$

hence,
$$\Delta S_2 = -R \log N_2. \quad \text{..................(4·1)}$$

The last expression is the entropy change in dilution of the ideal solute from the molar fraction 1 to the molar fraction N_2, and this term accounts for the whole of the change of free energy, the *heat* of dilution being zero. For an ideal solution to exist, it is necessary that *both* the heat of mixtures of the two substances in liquid form be zero *and* that the entropy of dilution have the ideal value $-R \log N_2$.

If the solution is not ideal, the deviation from ideality may be due either to the fact that the heat of solution ΔH is not zero ; or the entropy change is not $-R \log N_2$; or to both of these factors acting together. Solutions in which the heat of solution ΔH is not zero, but the entropy of solution has the ideal value $-R \log N_2$, were called *regular* solutions by Hildebrand. In such solutions the deviation from ideality is considered as being due entirely

*ΔF_2 is written for the difference between the partial free energy of the substance in the solution and the free energy of the pure liquid, *i.e.* for $\bar{F}_2(l) - F_2^{\circ}(l)$ in 3·0. ΔH and ΔS are the corresponding heats and entropy changes.

to the heat of transfer. Writing $\Delta F_2{}^i$ for the ideal value $RT \log N_2$, we shall have in such cases :

$$\Delta F_2 - \Delta F_2{}^i = \Delta H_2, \quad \text{.................(4·2)}$$

$$RT \log_e f_2 = \Delta H_2 = RT \, . \, \beta_2 \, . \, N_1{}^2. \quad \text{............(4·3)}$$

Heat of transfer of a molecule from its pure liquid to a solution. In order to perform this operation we have to do three things :

(1) remove the molecule B from its own pure liquid ; the heat required is the heat of vaporisation ;

(2) make a cavity in the solution large enough to hold it.

(3) introduce the molecule into the cavity.

In order to simplify the problem we will suppose (*a*) that the molecules of solute and solvent are of the same size, (*b*) that the concentration of B is small in the solution into which the substance B is transferred, *i.e.* it consists almost entirely of molecule A. Thus in this solution the molecule B will be surrounded almost entirely by A molecules and will be uninfluenced by other B molecules.

We will also suppose that the molecule B is in contact with x neighbouring B molecules in its own pure liquid and with x molecules in the solvent A. We will suppose that the intermolecular forces which determine the energy change are of short range, and that to a first approximation we need only consider the forces between a molecule and its neighbours.

The energy of transfer can then be simply formulated as follows :

(1) Energy of removal of a molecule from its own pure liquid. Let λ_{22} be the interaction energy between the given molecule and one of its neighbours. The energy

of removing the molecule completely from its place in the liquid is $x\lambda_{22}$; but this will leave a cavity in the liquid. When this cavity closes up, $x/2$ molecules on one side of it come into contact with $x/2$ molecules on the other side, releasing the energy $x/2 . \lambda_{22}$. The energy required to remove a molecule from its liquid, leaving no cavity (which is the ordinary energy of vaporisation), is therefore

$$\Delta E_2{}^v = x/2 . \lambda_{22}.$$

(2) Energy of making a cavity in the liquid A. This involves separating $x/2$ molecules to make one side of the cavity from their neighbouring $x/2$ molecules which form the other side. If the interaction between any two molecules is λ_{11}, the energy required to produce the cavity is

$$\Delta E_{\text{cav.}} = x/2 . \lambda_{11}.$$

(3) Energy of introducing the molecule B into the cavity. If λ_{12} is the interaction energy between a molecule B and a neighbouring molecule A, the total interaction energy yielded (since there are x neighbouring A molecules) is

$$\Delta E_{\text{solution}} = x\lambda_{12}.$$

The energy change in the transfer is therefore

$$\Delta E_{\text{transfer}} = x/2 . \lambda_{11} + x/2 . \lambda_{22} - x\lambda_{12}$$
$$= x/2 . (\lambda_{11} - 2\lambda_{12} + \lambda_{22}). \quad \text{.........(5·0)}$$

Internal pressure. Suppose a plane of unit area (1 cm.^{2}) is drawn within a liquid. The intermolecular attractions (or cohesive forces) of the molecules on one side of the plane with those on the other side, give rise to what is sometimes called the *internal pressure* of the liquid. Hildebrand took internal pressure as a generalised measure of the intermolecular forces within a liquid.

It cannot be measured directly, but indirect estimates can be made from the energy of vaporisation, from the surface energy and from the constant a of van der Waal's equation. For details Hildebrand's book *Solubility of non-electrolytes* (Reinhold Publ. Corp., 1936) may be consulted.

It is possible to arrange non-polar liquids in the order of their internal pressures. If two liquids have the same internal pressure, *i.e.* if the interaction of A molecules with each other is the same as that of B molecules with each other, it is probable that the interaction of molecule A with molecule B will be of the same order of magnitude. Thus in (5·0)

$$\Delta E = x/2 \,.\, (\gamma_{11} + \gamma_{22} - 2\gamma_{12})$$

will be zero. Hildebrand therefore concluded that two liquids with the same internal pressure might be expected to form ideal solutions ; whereas if they have not the same internal pressure the deviation from ideality is approximately proportional to the internal pressure difference between them.*

Nature of short range forces between molecules. In order to evaluate (5·0) more exactly, we must consider in more detail the nature of the forces between non-polar molecules. In the case of *polar* molecules (*i.e.* molecules in which the electric charges are not symmetrically arranged round the centre, giving rise to a permanent dipole) there are electrical forces between molecules, which, since they

* This means that if $\gamma_{11} > \gamma_{22}$, the interaction energy of unlike molecules will be closer to the smaller interaction energy than to the larger one. If γ_{12} approximates to γ_{22} rather than to γ_{11}, *i.e.* $\gamma_{12} \approx \gamma_{22}$, we have $\Delta E = x/2 \,.\, (\gamma_{11} - \gamma_{22})$, which is equivalent to Hildebrand's rule.

fall off comparatively slowly with the distance, are effective over comparatively long ranges. The same is true, of course, of the forces between ions.

That two non-polar molecules, even the inert gas atoms, attract each other has long been known. These forces give rise to the deviations from the perfect gas law at high pressures, which are represented by the term a/v^2 in the van der Waal's equation

$$(p + a/v^2)(v - b) = RT.$$

These forces are responsible for the transition to the liquid state at sufficient pressures below the critical temperature.

The origin of this attractive force has been discussed by London.* In the quantum-mechanical picture of molecular structure, the electrons are considered to be rapidly circulating round the atoms by virtue of their zero-point energy. London describes the effect of this as follows:

"If one were to take an instantaneous photograph of a molecule at any time, one would find various configurations of nuclei and electrons, showing in general dipole moments. In a spherically symmetrical rare gas molecule, as well as in our isotropic oscillators, the average over very many of such snapshots would of course give no preference for any direction. These very quickly varying dipoles, represented by the zero-point motion of a molecule, produce an electric field and act upon the polarisability of the other molecule and produce there induced dipoles, which are in phase and in interaction with the instantaneous dipoles producing them."

* *Trans. Faraday Soc.*, 33, 8, 1937.

London showed that to a first approximation this interaction gives rise to an attractive force between two molecules which varies inversely with the sixth power of the distance between them. The interaction between two like molecules at the distance r_{11} is shown to be given by

$$\lambda_{11} = -\frac{3}{4}\frac{h\nu_0 a^2}{r_{11}{}^6}, \quad \text{..................(6·1)}$$

where a is the polarisability of the molecule and ν_0 a characteristic frequency.

There are two other types of forces which have to be considered when the molecules are *polar, i.e.* possess permanent electric dipoles owing to the distribution of electric charges within them not being completely symmetrical.

(1) *Orientation effect.* The dipoles of one molecule will attract those of another. For a given position of the two dipoles the force arising varies with the inverse cube root of the distance; but the effect of the attraction will be to tend to bring the dipoles into an orientation with respect to each other which has the lowest energy. Averaging over all the positions and taking the agitation due to temperature into account, the energy of interaction of two molecules having dipole moments μ_1, μ_2 respectively is

$$\lambda_{\text{orient}} = -\frac{2\mu_1{}^2\mu_2{}^2}{3r^6}\cdot\frac{1}{kT}, \quad \text{..............(6·2)}$$

or for two like molecules,

$$\lambda_{\text{orient}} = -\frac{2\mu^4}{3r^6}\cdot\frac{1}{kT}\cdot \quad \text{....................(6·3)}$$

(2) *Induction effect.* The dipoles of a polar molecule will give rise by induction to induced dipoles in neighbouring molecules. The strength of the induced dipole is proportional to the polarisability a of the molecule. Thus a molecule of polarisability a has an induced moment $M = aK$ in an electric field of strength K and its energy, arising there-

from, is $E = -\frac{1}{2}aK^2$. The electric field near a dipole (1) is proportional to μ_1/r^3, and therefore the energy of interaction will contain the term $-\alpha\mu_1{}^2/r^6$. The total interaction energy of two molecules of dipole moments μ_1 and μ_2, arising from induction, is thus

$$\lambda_{\text{ind.}} = -\frac{1}{r^6}(\alpha_1\mu_2{}^2 + \alpha_2\mu_1{}^2), \qquad (6\cdot4)$$

or, if the molecules are alike,

$$\lambda_{\text{ind.}} = -\frac{2\alpha\mu^2}{r^6}. \qquad (6\cdot5)$$

The following table shows London's calculations of the relative magnitudes of the three types of forces. It can be seen that the orientation and induction effects are comparatively insignificant except for such highly polar molecules as water and ammonia. (The figures have to be divided by r^6 to get the interaction energies.)

TABLE XXXI.

THE THREE CONSTITUENTS OF THE VAN DER WAAL'S FORCES.

	$\mu\cdot10^{18}$.	$\alpha\cdot10^{24}$.	$h\nu_0$ volts.	Orientation effect $\frac{2}{3}\mu^4/kT$ $\times 10^{60}$ ergs. cm.^{6}.	Induction effect $2\mu^2\alpha$ $\times 10^{60}$ ergs. cm.^{6}.	Dispersion effect $\frac{3}{4}\alpha^2 h\nu_0$ $\times 10^{60}$ ergs. cm.^{6}.
CO	0·12	1·99	14·3	0·0034	0·057	67·5
HI	0·38	5·4	12	0·35	1·68	382
HBr	0·78	3·58	13·3	6·2	4·05	176
HCl	1·03	2·63	13·7	18·6	5·4	105
NH_3	1·5	2·21	16	84	10	93
H_2O	1·84	1·48	18	190	10	47

We may therefore express the interaction energy of the like molecules S_1 shortly as

$$\lambda_{11} = -\frac{k_{11}}{r_{11}{}^6}; \qquad (6\cdot6)$$

and similarly for the interaction of two like molecules S_2, we shall have

$$\lambda_{22} = -\frac{k_{22}}{r_{22}^{6}}; \quad \text{.......................(6·7)}$$

and for the two unlike molecules

$$\lambda_{12} = -\frac{k_{12}}{r_{12}^{6}}. \quad \text{.......................(6·8)}$$

We do not need to concern ourselves here with the evaluation of the constants k_{11} etc. from the structure of the molecules. All we need notice is that (1) the interaction is additive, *i.e.* the fact that a molecule interacts in this way with a second molecule does not affect its interaction with a third: (2) it was shown by London that the interaction constant between two unlike molecules is equal (or possibly smaller than) the geometrical mean of their interactions with each other; *i.e.* he writes

$$k_{12} \leqq (k_{11}\, k_{22})^{\frac{1}{2}}. \quad \text{.....................(6·9)}$$

For equal-sized molecules we see that

$$\lambda_{12} \leqq (\lambda_{11} \cdot \lambda_{22})^{\frac{1}{2}}.$$

If we take the equality as applying, we can put (50) in the form

$$\Delta E_{tr} = x/2 \cdot \{\lambda_{11} - 2(\lambda_{11} \cdot \lambda_{22})^{\frac{1}{2}} + \lambda_{22}\}$$

$$= x/2 \cdot (\lambda_{11}^{\frac{1}{2}} - \lambda_{22}^{\frac{1}{2}})^2$$

or,
$$\Delta E_{tr} = (\Delta E_1^{\frac{1}{2}} - \Delta E_2^{\frac{1}{2}})^2, \quad \text{.....................(7·0)}$$

where ΔE_1 and ΔE_2 are the energies of vaporisation of A and B from their own liquids.

The difference between ΔE and ΔH in such cases is negligible. Introducing this value of ΔE into (4·3) we have

$$RT \log_e f_2 = (\Delta E_1^{\frac{1}{2}} - \Delta E_2^{\frac{1}{2}})^2. \quad \text{.........(8·1)}$$

This, it will be remembered, is the activity coefficient for the transfer of the molecule B from its pure liquid into a dilute solution in the solvent A. Therefore, by (2), we have

$$\beta_2 = \frac{(\Delta E_1^{\frac{1}{2}} - \Delta E_2^{\frac{1}{2}})^2}{RT}. \quad \text{.........(8·2)}$$

These equations are completely symmetrical and apply equally to the transfer of molecule A from its pure liquid to a dilute solution in B; for which

$$RT \log_e f_1 = (\Delta E_1^{\frac{1}{2}} - \Delta E_2^{\frac{1}{2}})^2, \quad \text{.........(8·3)}$$

Example. Iodine and carbon disulphide have nearly the same molecular volumes. The energies of vaporisation are 11,300 cals. and 5970 cals. respectively at 25°. From this we get

$$[\Delta E_1^{\frac{1}{2}} - \Delta E_2^{\frac{1}{2}}]^2 = 840 \text{ cals.}$$

or

$$\beta_2 = 840/RT = 1{\cdot}55.$$

The solubility of iodine in carbon disulphide at 25° C. is $N_2 = 0{\cdot}058$ (corresponding to $N_1 = 0{\cdot}942$) which is 0·272 of the calculated ideal solubility at this temperature. By (3·2) we find

$$\log_e (N_2/N_2\text{ideal}) = -\log_e 0{\cdot}272 = -\beta_2 . N_1^2,$$

hence

$$\beta_2 = -\frac{2{\cdot}303 \log_{10} 0{\cdot}272}{(0{\cdot}942)^2} = 1{\cdot}47,$$

which is in quite good agreement with the calculated value.

***Mixtures of molecules having unequal volumes.** A more complete and accurate derivation of the heat of solution, which covers both the case of variable molar fractions and that in which the two molecules concerned have different volumes, has been given by Hildebrand

and Wood.* This derivation uses a probability function W which expresses the probability that a given molecule will be found in a particular element of volume. If dV is an element of the volume V of a liquid, the probability of finding the centre of a given molecule within the element is expressed as $W \,.\, dV/V$.

Consider a spherical shell of thickness dv at a distance r from a central molecule. The volume of this shell is $dV = 4\pi r^2 \,.\, dr$. If the solution contains n_1 mols of A and n_2 mols of B in a total volume V, the shell mentioned would contain, if the function W is unity,

$$\frac{n_1 N_0}{V} \,.\, dV \text{ mols of } A,$$

and

$$\frac{n_2 N_0}{V} \,.\, dV \text{ mols of } B.$$

At short distances from the central molecule the function W is not necessarily unity and the number of A molecules to be found in a shell at a distance r from a central molecule A is written as

$$\frac{n_1 N_0 W_{11} \, dV}{V} = \frac{n_1 N_0}{V} \,.\, 4\pi r^2 \,.\, W_{11} \,.\, dr.$$

The number of A–A *pairs* at this distance throughout the solution is thus

$$\frac{1}{2} \frac{n_1{}^2 N_0{}^2}{V} \,.\, 4\pi r^2 \,.\, W_{11} \,.\, dr.$$

If the energy of interaction of each AA pair is λ_{11} we have for the whole interaction energy of AA pairs in the solution

$$\frac{2\pi n_1{}^2 N_0{}^2}{V} \int_0^\infty \lambda_{11} W_{11} r^2 dr. \quad \ldots\ldots\ldots\ldots\ldots\ldots(9{\cdot}1)$$

* *J. Chem. Physics*, **1**, 817, 1933 ; Hildebrand, *J. Amer. Chem. Soc.*, **57**, 866, 1935 ; see also the book on *Solubility* quoted above.

Similarly for the interaction energy of all BB pairs we have

$$\frac{2\pi n_2^2 N_0^2}{V}\int_0^\infty \lambda_{22} W_{22} r^2\,dr, \quad \text{.................}(9{\cdot}2)$$

and for the energy of all AB and BA pairs (which are the same),

$$\frac{2\pi \,.\, n_1 n_2 N_0^2}{V}\int_0^\infty \lambda_{12} W_{12} r^2\,dr. \quad \text{...........}(9{\cdot}3)$$

The total energy of interaction in the solution is

$$E=\frac{2\pi N_0^2}{V}\left[n_1^2\int(11)+n_2^2\int(22)+2n_1 n_2\int(12)\right], \quad (9{\cdot}4)$$

where the integrals in (9·1), (9·2) and (9·3) are shortly written as $\int(11)$, $\int(22)$ and $\int(12)$.

The partial molar energy of A is obtained by differentiating this expression with respect to n_1, n_2 remaining constant.

Writing $V=n_1V_1+n_2V_2$, where V_1, V_2 are the molar volumes (strictly the *partial* volumes) of A and B, we find that $\Delta E_1=\overline{E}_1-E_1^\circ$

$$=2\pi N_0^2\left(\frac{n_2V_2}{n_1V_1+n_2V_2}\right)^2$$

$$\times V_1\left[\frac{2}{V_1V_2}\int(12)-\frac{1}{V_1^2}\int(11)-\frac{1}{V_2^2}\int(22)\right]. \quad (9{\cdot}5)$$

This expression can be simplified as follows. Firstly, $(n_2V_2/n_1V_1+n_2V_2)$ is evidently the *volume fraction* of the component A; which may be written as v_2. Secondly, it follows from (6·5) that the following is at least approximately true :

$$\int(12)=\int^{\frac{1}{2}}(11)\times\int^{\frac{1}{2}}(22).$$

Therefore (9·5) takes the form

$$\Delta\bar{E}_1 = 2\pi N_0{}^2 \,.\, v_2{}^2 \,.\, V_1 \left[\frac{1}{V_1}\int^{\frac{1}{2}}(11) - \frac{1}{V_2}\int^{\frac{1}{2}}(22)\right]^2. \quad (9{\cdot}6)$$

The same kind of argument applied to the vaporisation of pure liquid A gives

$$E_1{}^\circ = \frac{2\pi N_0{}^2}{V_1}\int(11),$$

and similarly for the evaporation of pure B,

$$E_2{}^\circ = \frac{2\pi N_0{}^2}{V_2}\int(22),$$

so that (9·6) can be written as

$$\Delta\bar{E}_1 = v_2{}^2 \,.\, V_1\left[\left(\frac{E_1{}^\circ}{V_1}\right)^{\frac{1}{2}} - \left(\frac{E_2{}^\circ}{V_2}\right)^{\frac{1}{2}}\right]^2, \quad \ldots\ldots(10{\cdot}1)$$

and similarly

$$\Delta\bar{E}_2 = v_1{}^2 \,.\, V_2 \,.\left[\left(\frac{E_1{}^\circ}{V_1}\right)^{\frac{1}{2}} - \left(\frac{E_2{}^\circ}{V_2}\right)^{\frac{1}{2}}\right]^2. \quad \ldots(10{\cdot}2)$$

This reduces to (7) for mixtures of two substances having equal molecular volumes.

For regular solutions, we may therefore write

$$RT \log_e f_2 = v_1{}^2 \,.\, V_2 \,.\, D^2, \quad \ldots\ldots\ldots\ldots(10{\cdot}3)$$

where D is written for the quantity in square brackets in (10·2). Since $E_1{}^\circ/V_1$ is the energy of vaporisation per c.c. of the pure liquid, *i.e.* the *energy density* of the intermolecular interaction energy, we see that D is proportional to the difference between the square root of the energy densities in the two liquids. We thus obtain a simple quantitative measure of " internal pressure ".

Table XXXII gives the energy densities of evaporation of a number of liquids.

TABLE XXXII.

ENERGIES OF VAPORISATION PER C.C.

	V c.c./mol.	$E°$ cals./mol.	$E°/V$ cals./c.c.	$(E°/V)^{\frac{1}{2}}$.
n-Butane	102·0	4440	43·5	6·60
n-Hexane	116·3	5700	51·8	7·20
n-Octane	124·6	9200	56·3	7·50
Ethyl ether	34·6	5800	55·5	7·45
Cyclohexane	108·6	6600	57·3	7·57
m-Xylene	123·3	8100	60·8	7·80
Toluene	106·9	7400	69·2	8·32
Carbon tetrachloride	97·1	7080	72·9	8·54
Chloroform	80·7	6430	79·7	8·93
Brombenzene	105·5	8450	80·0	8·95
Benzene	89·3	7220	80·9	9·00
Ethyl iodide	81·1	6630	81·8	9·05
Ethylene chloride	78·9	6940	82·3	9·08
Naphthalene	123	10700	87·2	9·34
Chlorbenzene	89·9	8140	90·6	9·52
Aniline	91·5	8780	96·0	9·80
Carbon disulphide	60·7	6040	99·6	9·98
Bromoform	87·8	8980	102·3	10·1
Bromine	51·2	6900	135	11·6
Iodine	59·2	11200	190	13·6

Example. Hildebrand gives the following data for iodine. The ideal solubility at 25° is calculated to be $N_2 = 0{\cdot}212$. From the actual solubilities, the activity coefficients can be obtained by (3·2), as $f_2 = N_2^{\text{ideal}}/N_2$. For regular solutions (10·3) takes the form

$$\log_e (N_2^{\text{ideal}}/N_2) = v_1^2 \,.\, V_2 \left[\left(\frac{E_1°}{V_1}\right)^{\frac{1}{2}} - \left(\frac{E_2°}{V_2}\right)^{\frac{1}{2}}\right]^2,$$

which, for dilute solutions, takes the form

$$\beta_2 = V_2 \,.\, D^2.$$

Hildebrand tested this equation by putting in the values of $E_1°/V_1$ for various solvents and finding the value of E_2/V_2 (for iodine) required to account for the measured solubility. The following table gives some of the results :

TABLE XXXIII.

CALCULATION OF $E_2°/V_2$ FROM SOLUBILITIES OF IODINE.

Solvent.	Solubility (N_2).	$(E_1°/V_1)^{\frac{1}{2}}$.	$(E_2°/V_2)^{\frac{1}{2}}$ calc.
n-Hexane - - -	0·00456	7·44	13·67
Carbon tetrachloride	0·0115	8·54	13·99
Chloroform - -	0·0228	8·93	13·71
Carbon disulphide -	0·0576	9·98	13·82
Bromoform - -	0·0616	10·1	13·78
Ideal - - -	0·212	—	13·79 (mean)

The observed value of $(E_2°/V_2)^{\frac{1}{2}}$ for iodine is 13·6.

The agreement between the observed and calculated deviations from Raoult's law is quite good in most cases and may be considered to be very satisfactory considering the approximations made in the derivation. Hildebrand * gives the following comparisons. The comparison is made by calculating the value of D required to account for the deviation and comparing it with that obtained from the energies of vaporisation.

TABLE XXXIV.

System.	D from energy of vap.	D from solubility.
$C_6H_6 - C_4H_{10}$ - - -	2·4	2·6
$C_6H_6 - C_6H_{12}$ (cyclo) - -	1·0	1·5
$C_6H_6 - CH_2$ - - - -	1·0	1·8
$CCl_4 - Br_2$ - - - -	3·1	2·8
$CCl_4 - S_1Cl_4$ - - - -	1·0	1·1
$CCl_4 - C_6H_6$ - - - -	0·6	1·0
$CCl_4 - C_7H_{16}(n)$ - - -	1·1	1·5
$SiCl_4 - SnI_4$ - - - -	1·8	3·7
$C_6H_6 - P_4$ - - - -	5·0	5·7
$S_1Cl_4 - I_2$ - - - -	6·0	6·1

* *Trans. Faraday Soc.*, 33, 149, 1937.

As may be expected when *polar* molecules are included greater differences are found.

* **Entropy of solution.** In the foregoing we have attempted to account for deviations from Raoult's law in non-ideal solutions by taking into account the heat of mixing, on the assumption that the entropy of solution has its normal values

$$\Delta S_2 = -R \log N_2. \qquad \text{..............(11·0)}$$

There is no doubt that the results of this assumption have a considerable measure of success. But the agreement between the observed and calculated activities is not perfect, indeed there are considerable quantitative discrepancies, although the order of magnitude of the deviations is accounted for. These discrepancies might be due to the approximations introduced into the calculations or to various factors which have been left out of the account. It is quite likely that the magnitude of the discrepancies may be reduced in this way; but there have been indications that the discrepancies may arise to some extent from the *entropy* of dilution.

Now, it will simplify matters if we limit the argument to two cases, viz. the pure liquid and a dilute solution of the substance in another solvent. The entropy of solutions which contain appreciable quantities of two kinds of molecules is very difficult to determine (if it differs from the ideal value). For if, for example, the molecule A attracts molecules B more strongly than other molecules A, there will be a tendency for B molecules to concentrate round A molecules. The proportions of A to B molecules will then differ from point to point in the solution, and the entropy will differ from the entropy of a perfect solution, which assumes perfectly random mixing.

In a very dilute solution of B in A this effect cannot occur, for A molecules will be so far apart that every B molecule will be surrounded entirely by A (solvent) molecules. We will therefore compare the entropy of a substance in a pure liquid with its entropy in a dilute solution in another solvent.

The activity coefficient in a dilute solution of molar fraction N_2 may be written as

$$f_2 = p_2/p_2^\circ N_2,$$

and the free energy of dilution corresponding to this quantity (*i.e.* to the *deviations* from Raoult's law) is

$$RT \log f_2 = RT \log (p_2/p_2^\circ N_2),$$

which may, again, be expressed as

$$\Delta F_2 = RT \log (p_2/N_2) - RT \log p_2^\circ.$$

$RT \log p_2^\circ$ is the free energy of evaporation from the pure liquid and $RT \log (p_2/N_2)$ may be regarded as the free energy of vaporisation from the dilute solution.* We will suppose that the solution is so dilute that p/N has its limiting value for great dilutions. We thus regard the free energy of dilution as the difference free energy of evaporation from the dilute solution and that from the pure liquid.

* If F_e° is the molar free energy of the pure liquid and F_g° that of the vapour at unit pressure, we have for equilibrium

$$F_e^\circ = F_g^\circ + RT \log p^\circ;$$

so that $RT \log p^\circ$ is the difference between the molar free energy of the liquid and that of the vapour at unit pressure. Similarly for a dilute solution

$$\overline{F}_s = \overline{F}_s^\circ + RT \log N = F_g^\circ + RT \log p,$$

if p is the partial pressure for the molar fraction, N. $RT \log (p/N)$ is thus the difference between the standard partial free energy for the dilute solution and the free energy of the vapour at unit pressure.

The corresponding entropy changes in these processes are obtained by differentiating the free energy with respect to temperature; *i.e.* the entropy of vaporisation from the pure liquid is

$$\Delta S_{N_2=1} = -d(RT \log p_2^{\circ})/dT, \quad \text{.........(11·1)}$$

and the entropy of vaporisation from the solution (excluding the part which is due solely to the concentration N_2)

$$\Delta S_{N_2} = -d[RT \log (p_2/N_2)]/dT. \quad \text{.........(11·2)}$$

Indications that the entropy of vaporisation varied with the heat of vaporisation were found by a number of authors. Bell * found that the accurate gas solubilities of Horiuti indicated an accurate linear relation between the heats and entropies of solution in each of five solvents. Evans and Polanyi suggested that the solubility curves indicated a similar relationship; but their conclusions were drawn from very approximate extrapolation formulae which may differ much from the actual curve.† Barclay and Butler ‡ found that there was a universal relationship which fitted both the entropies vaporisation of pure liquids and dilute solutions. The evidence for this is shown in Fig. 77, in which the entropy of vaporisation as defined above is plotted against the heat of vaporisation. It covers a wide variety of cases, (1) the vaporisation of pure liquids; (2) the vaporisation of several gases and vapours from their solutions in benzene, methyl acetate, chlorobenzene and carbon

* *Trans. Faraday Soc.*, 33, 496, 1937; see Butler and Reid, *J. Chem. Soc.*, 1936, 1171.

† The solubility curve of $\log N$ against $1/T$ in cases which show deviations from Raoult's law is usually an S-shaped curve, which can only be very approximately represented by a straight line.

‡ *Trans. Faraday Soc.*, 34, 1445, 1938.

tetrachloride ; and (3) various vaporisable solutes in acetone solution ; (4) the four lower alcohols from benzene.

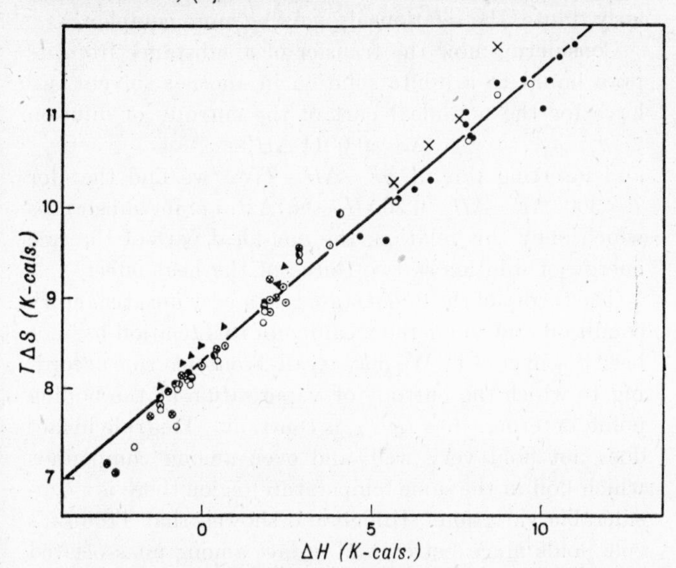

FIG. 77.—Heats and entropies of vaporisation from solutions and pure unassociated liquids at 25°.

KEY.

○ Gases and liquid solutes in acetone. ⊙ Gases in carbon tetrachloride.

⊗ Gases in benzene. × Alcohols in benzene.

◐ Gases in methyl acetate. ● Pure liquids.

▲ Gases in chlorobenzene.

The entropy of vaporisation in all these cases is represented with fair accuracy by

$$\Delta S_p = 0{\cdot}0277 + 0{\cdot}0011\Delta H.*$$

* Unit pressure is taken here as 1 mm. of mercury. The entropy of vaporisation to 1 atmos. pressure (760 mm.) is 13·19 cals./degs. less than the entropy of vaporisation to 1 mm. pressure, and at 25° C. $T\Delta S$ is 3·93 k-cals. less.

It must be remembered that this applies to pure liquids and dilute solutions. In solutions which are not particu larly dilute, the relationship may be more complex.

Considering now the transfer of a substance from its pure liquid to a dilute solution in another solvent, we have for the non-ideal part of the entropy of dilution

$$\Delta S = 0{\cdot}0011\ \Delta H,$$

and inserting this in $\Delta F = \Delta H - T\Delta S$, we find that for $T = 300$, $\Delta F = \Delta H - 0{\cdot}33\Delta H = 0{\cdot}67\Delta H$, *i.e.* for substances which obey this relation, the non-ideal part of the free energy of dilution is two-thirds of the heat effect.

The theory of the liquid state is in a very unsatisfactory condition and so far the meaning of this relation has not been discovered.† We may recall Trouton's rule according to which the entropy of vaporisation at the boiling point, determined as L_v/T_b, is constant. This rule in fact does not hold very well, and even among compounds which boil in the same temperature region there is a considerable variation. Hildebrand showed that Trouton's rule holds much better, and in fact among unassociated compounds with considerable exactness, if the comparison is made not at the boiling point, but at temperatures at which the vapours in equilibrium with the liquids have equal concentrations.*

*** Raoult's law and molecular size.** In Chapter XIV, Raoult's law was deduced in the limiting case of a very dilute solution. In more concentrated solutions it has been employed purely as an empirical law, justified only by its inherent plausibility. In mixtures of molecules having the same size it is natural to expect the partial

* Hildebrand. *J. Amer. Chem. Soc.*, 37, 970, 1915 ; 40, 45, 1918.

† See p. 376.

pressure of each species of molecule to be proportional to its molar fraction. In the earlier part of this chapter such deviations as do occur have been attributed to the heats of mixture arising from the molecular interactions in the solution. We must now enquire if there is really any reasonable basis for expecting Raoult's law to hold for mixtures of molecules of different sizes.

In the first place we must try to give a justification of the law for molecules of equal sizes. To do this, we have to go outside the strictly thermodynamical methods we have usually used. The argument is however a comparatively simple one. We shall use the expression giving entropy in terms of the thermodynamic probability, viz.

$$S = k \log W. \quad \text{.....................(12·0)}$$

This is a theorem in statistical mechanics and we shall only remark that the probability W has a special meaning, namely, it is defined as the number of distinct ways in which a given system can be arrived at.* Now the entropy of a homogeneous piece of matter arises from the parcelling of its energy among all the different energy states of the molecules. For our present purpose we need only consider the contribution to the entropy which arises from the different ways in which the molecules of a solution can be mixed, *i.e.* the configurational contribution to the entropy.

We will suppose that we have m_1 molecules of type A and m_2 molecules of type B, a total of $m_1 + m_2$.

We will suppose that these molecules are of the same size and that one can be substituted for another without any other change in the solution. In the solution we therefore have $(m_1 + m_2)$ " places " to be filled by the

* See Appendix, p. 539.

molecules. To simplify the problem these " places " can be supposed to be arranged regularly like in a lattice.

If all the molecules were different the number of ways in which the $(m_1 + m_2)$ places could be filled would be $(m_1 + m_2)!$.* The m_1 molecules of A are, however, all alike and indistinguishable, so that to get the number of distinguishable ways we must divide this result by the number of permutations of the m_1 molecules with each other; *i.e.* by $m_1!$. Performing the same operation for the m_2 molecules of B, we then get for the distinguishable ways of arranging $m_1 + m_2$ molecules among the available places:

$$W = \frac{(m_1 + m_2)!}{m_1!\, m_2!}, \qquad \text{(12·1)}$$

and therefore the entropy of mixing is

$$\Delta S = k \log \frac{(m_1 + m_2)!}{m_1!\, m_2!}. \qquad \text{(12·2)}$$

By Stirling's theorem, for large values of m_1, etc., we can write

$$\log (m_1 + m_2)! = (m_1 + m_2) \log (m_1 + m_2), \text{ etc.,}$$

and therefore

$$\Delta S = k[(m_1 + m_2) \log (m_1 + m_2) - m_1 \log m_1 - m_2 \log m_2]$$

$$= -k \left[m_1 \log \left(\frac{m_1}{m_1 + m_2} \right) + m_2 \log \left(\frac{m_2}{m_1 + m_2} \right) \right],$$

or writing $R = k/N_0$ and $m_1/N_0 = n_1$ for the corresponding molar quantities, we have the usual expression for the entropy of mixing when Raoult's law is obeyed:†

$$\Delta S = -R[n_1 \log N_1 + n_2 \log N_2]. \qquad \text{(12·3)}$$

* This is merely the total number of permutations of $m_1 + m_2$ objects taken all together. The first place can be filled in $(m_1 + m_2)$ ways, the second in $(m_1 + m_2 - 1)$ ways, etc.

† If $\Delta \overline{S}_1$ is the partial entropy of A, which by Raoult's law is $-R \log N_1$, the total entropy of mixing in a given solution is

$$\Delta S = n_1 \Delta \overline{S}_1 + n_2 \Delta \overline{S}_2 = -R\,(n_1 \log N_1 + n_2 \log N_2).$$

We can thus derive Raoult's law from simple considerations of the number of distinguishable ways in which molecules of equal sizes can be arranged to form a given mixture. When the molecules are of different sizes the calculation is much more complicated and has only been achieved in simple cases.* It is sufficient to say that entropies of mixing, which are in fact somewhat different to the Raoult's law value, are derived from arguments of this type. For example, when one of the molecules is twice the size of the other (to be exact, one molecule is made up of two units each the same size as the other), Chang found activity coefficients arising from the entropy of mixture between 0·7 and 0·8 for the larger molecule, depending on the type of arrangement assumed.

Long chain polymers. It has been known for some time that solutions of long chain polymers, such as rubber, in low molecular weight solvents, deviate from the laws of ideal solutions, at quite small concentrations, although the heat of mixing is small. For example, the osmotic pressure π should be accurately proportional to the concentration according to

$$\pi = c \,.\, RT/M, \quad \ldots\ldots\ldots\ldots\ldots\ldots (13{\cdot}0)$$

where c is the concentration of the solute in, say, grams per litre and M the molecular weight. It was found in practice that π/c is not constant even at quite small concentrations and increases comparatively rapidly with the concentration.†

* See Guggenheim, *Proc. Roy. Soc.*, **135A**, 181, 1932; **148A**, 304, 1935; Fowler and Rushbrooke, *Trans. Far. Soc.*, **33**, 1272, 1937; Chang, *Proc. Roy. Soc.*, **169A**, 512, 1939, *Proc. Camb. Phil. Soc.*, **35**, 265, 1939; Orr, *Trans. Faraday Soc.*, **40**, 320, 1944; Miller, *Proc. Camb. Phil. Soc.*, **38**, 109, 1942.

† See Gee, *Ann. Reports Chem. Soc.*, p. 8, 1942.

In order to account for this behaviour a statistical analysis of the entropy of mixture of long chain polymer molecules with simple solvent molecules of the same type has been made by various authors. K. H. Meyer * was the first to suggest that the calculation could be made by computing the number of ways of arranging a long flexible chain on an array of lattice " points ". Each point of the lattice might be occupied by either a solvent, molecule or a segment of the polymer having the same size as the solvent molecule. In counting the number of possibilities we take into account the fact that the successive segments of a polymer molecule must occupy adjacent lattice points.

Calculations of this kind were carried through by Flory † and Huggins ‡ and have been improved by others.§ The results of this analysis are most simply expressed in the following approximate equation for the partial entropy of the solvent :

$$\Delta S_1 = -R\left[\log v_1 + \left(1 - \frac{1}{x}\right) v_r\right], \quad \text{........(13·1)}$$

where v_1 is the *volume fraction* of the solvent v_r is the *volume fraction* of polymer, and x is the number of segments in the polymer molecule,|| or alternatively the

* *Helv. Chim. Acta*, 23, 1063, 1940.

† *J. Chem. Physics*, 9, 660, 1941 ; 10, 51, 1942 ; 13, 453, 1945.

‡ *Ibid.*, 9, 440, 1941 ; *J. Physical Chem.*, 46, 1, 1942 ; *J. Amer. Chem. Soc.*, 64, 1712, 1942 ; *Ind. and Eng. Chem.*, 35, 216, 1943.

§ Miller, *Proc. Camb. Phil. Soc.*, 39, 54, 1943 ; Orr, *Trans. Faraday Soc.*, 40, 320, 1944 ; Guggenheim, *Proc. Roy. Soc.*, 183A, 203, 213, 1945.

|| Miller's expression is

$$\Delta S = -R\left[\log v_1 + \frac{Z}{2}\log\left\{1 - \frac{2v_r}{Z}\left(1 - \frac{1}{x}\right)\right\}\right]$$

where Z is the co-ordination number of the lattice.

ratio of the volume of the polymer to that of the simple molecule.

Introducing this value into $\Delta F_1 = \Delta H_1 - T\Delta S_1$ and writing $\Delta F_1 = RT \log a_1$, we get

$$\log a_1 = \log v_1 + \left(1 - \frac{1}{x}\right) v_r, \quad \text{.........(13·2)}$$

when ΔH_1 is taken as zero. If however there is a heat of mixing, it may be expressed to the first approximation as

$$\Delta H_1 = k' v_r^2.$$

Introducing this value we get

$$\log a_1 = \log v_1 + (1 - 1/x) v_r + k_1 v_r^2. \quad \text{......(13·3)}$$

The osmotic pressure is obtained by using the equation

$$\pi = -\frac{RT}{v_1} \log a_1.$$

Expanding $\log v_1$ as

$$\log v_1 = \log (1 - v_r) = -v_r - \frac{v_r^2}{2} - \frac{v_r^3}{3}, \text{ etc.,}$$

we obtain

$$\pi = -\frac{RT}{v_1}\left[-\frac{1}{x} v_r + (k_1 + \tfrac{1}{2}) v_r^2\right].$$

When v_r is small, this reduces to

$$\pi = \frac{RT}{v_1} \cdot \frac{n_r}{n_1},$$

where n_r, n_1 are the number of mols of solvent and rubber.*

This is the usual form of van't Hoff's law of osmotic pressure, so that the molecular weight measurements obtained by extrapolation to very small concentrations with high molecular weight substances will be correct.

$$* \, v_r = \frac{n_r v_r}{n_1 v_1 + n_r v_r} \approx \frac{n_r v_r}{n_1 v_1} \quad \text{and} \quad x = \frac{v_r}{v_1}.$$

Fig. 78 shows a test of (13·3) for various types of rubber in toluene. The equation is written as

$$\frac{\log a_1 - \log v_1}{v_r} - 1 = -\frac{1}{x} + k_1 v_r.$$

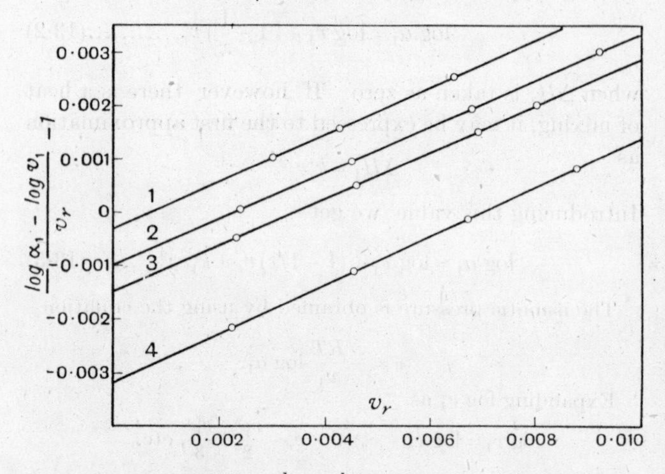

FIG. 78.—Plot of $\frac{\log a_1 - \log v_1}{v_r} - 1$ against v_r, for

(1) rubber treated with Al_2O_3; $k_1 = 0{\cdot}44$, $M_r = 395{,}000$.

(2) Crepe rubber, $k_1 = 0{\cdot}43$, $M_r = 102{,}000$.

(3) Masticated rubber, $k_1 = 0{\cdot}42$, $M_2 = 68{,}000$.

(4) Cyclic rubber made with $SnCl_4$, $k_1 = 0{\cdot}46$, $M_r = 32{,}000$.

(Huggins, *Ind. Eng. Chem.*, 35, 219, 1943.)

The left-hand side of this equation is plotted against v_r. The intercept made by the line on the axis $v_r = 0$ is equal to $-1/x$ and gives a measure of the molecular weight of the rubber; the slope is the constant k_1.

Finally we shall give a comparison of the activity calculated by this equation and that which would be required if Raoult's law holds over the entire concentration range. Fig. 79 shows a_1 plotted against the *molar* fraction of rubber (in benzene) and the values calculated by (13·3), taking molecular weights of the

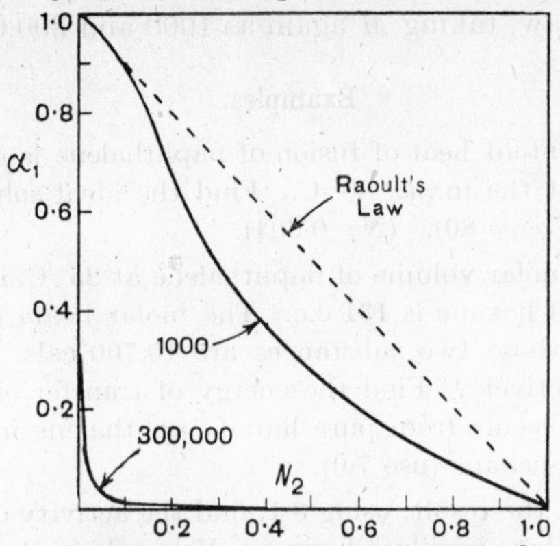

FIG. 79.—Activity as function of mol fraction for rubber-benzene system. (Huggins, *Ind. Eng. Chem.*, 35, 219, 1943.)

polymer as 1000 and 300,000 respectively, and taking k_1 as 0·43. Fig. 80 shows the reverse, the activity of

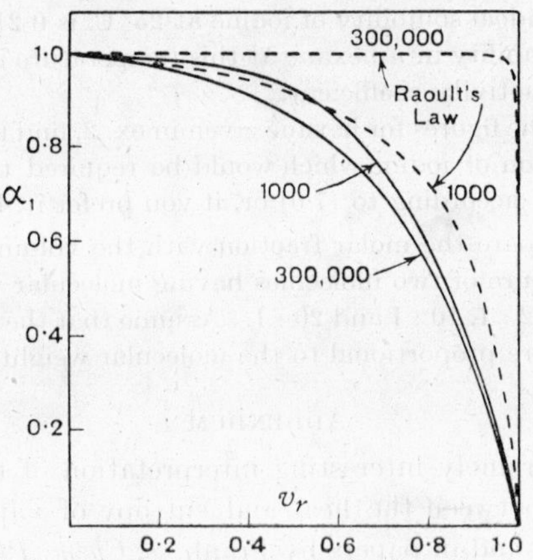

FIG. 80.—Activity as function of volume fraction for rubber-benzene system. (Huggins, *Ind. Eng. Chem.*, 35, 219, 1943.)

the solvent plotted against the *volume fraction* of the rubber according to the equation and according to Raoult's law, taking M again as 1000 and 300,000.

Examples.

1. The latent heat of fusion of naphthalene is 4540 cals. per mol. at the m.pt., 80° C. Find the ideal solubility at 25° C. (see page 80). ($N = 0{\cdot}304$).

2. The molar volume of naphthalene at 25° C. is 123 c.c. and that of hexane is 131 c.c. The molar heats of vaporisation of these two substances are 10,700 cals. and 6800 cals. respectively. Find the energy of transfer of a naphthalene molecule from pure liquid naphthalene into dilute solution in hexane (use 7·0).

3. From the result, using 8·1, find the activity coefficient of naphthalene in dilute hexane. Using this value and the ideal solubility found in ex. 1, find the solubility of naphthalene in hexane at 25°. The measured solubility is $N = 0{\cdot}121$.

4. The ideal solubility of iodine at 25° C. is 0·212, and its actual solubility in n-hexane at this temperature is 0·00456. Find the activity coefficient.

Using the figures for hexane given in ex. 2, find the heat of vaporisation of iodine which would be required to produce this result according to (7·0) or, if you prefer it, by (10·1).

5. Compare the molar fraction with the volume fraction for a mixture of two molecules having molecular weights in the ratios 2 : 1, 10 : 1 and 20 : 1. Assume that the molecular volumes are proportional to the molecular weights.

Addendum

An extremely interesting interpretation of the linear relation between the heat and entropy of vaporisation is to be found in papers by Frank, *J. Chem. Physics*, 13, 478, 493, 1945 ; Frank and Evans, *ibid.*, 13, 507, 1945.

CHAPTER XVII

SOLUTIONS OF NON-ELECTROLYTES IN WATER

We now come to consider solutions in water and similar liquids, which are extremely abnormal. The behaviour of these solutions differs markedly from that of the "non-polar" solutions considered in the last chapter. It may be said at once that the deviations from Raoult's law which are encountered are often of a much greater magnitude. This is shown, for example, by the low solubility of "non-polar" substances in water, which is to due the fact that their activity coefficients in dilute aqueous solutions are high. The following values of the activity coefficient in dilute aqueous solution (taking the value as unity in the pure liquid) may be quoted in support of this statement : ethyl chloride, *approx.* 2000 ; *di*-propyl ether, 2×10^5 ; carbon tetrachloride, *approx.* 10^6 ; *n*-octyl alcohol, 12,300.

Before we try to account for such values we must discuss the nature of water itself. This information is also a necessary basis for the understanding of the nature of solutions of electrolytes which follows in later chapters.

Structure of liquid water. The isolated water molecule was shown by Mecke to have a V-shaped structure, the two hydrogen nuclei (protons) being at a distance of 0·96 Ångstrom units from the oxygen units and the HOH angle being from 103° to 106°, which is very near the tetrahedral angle of 109°. The negative charge of the oxygen ion is not located at its centre, but as a result of the presence of the two protons within the molecule in the positions mentioned is concentrated particularly in two positions in a plane at right angles to the V made by HOH, and bisecting it (Fig. 81).

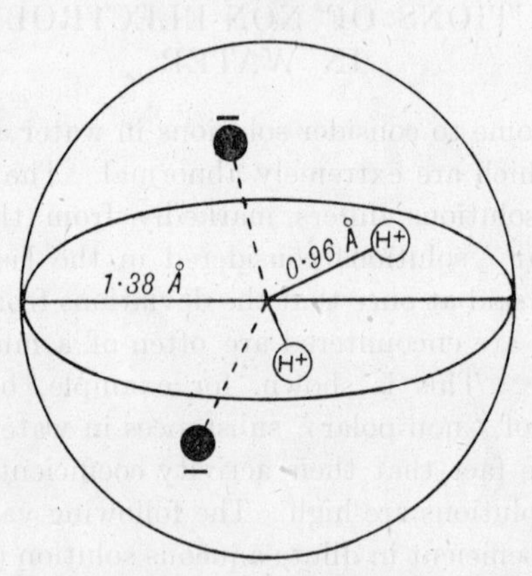

FIG. 81.—Distribution of charges in the water molecule.

The whole arrangement thus resembles a tetrahedron with positive charges at two corners and negative charges at the other two. The dipole moment of the isolated molecule is $1{\cdot}87 \times 10^{-18}$ e.s.u. The closest distance of approach of two molecules in ice is 2·76 Å and therefore we can consider the water molecule to be a sphere of radius 1·38 Å, in which positive and negative charges are situated as described.

In ice it has been shown that the water molecules are arranged in a tetrahedral structure ; that is, each oxygen atom is surrounded tetrahedrally by four others (Fig. 82) with the hydrogen ions on the lines joining the oxygen nuclei, *i.e.* the protons of one water molecule will face concentration of negative charge on two neighbouring molecules. The proton thus serves as a link, or "hydrogen bond", between two water molecules.

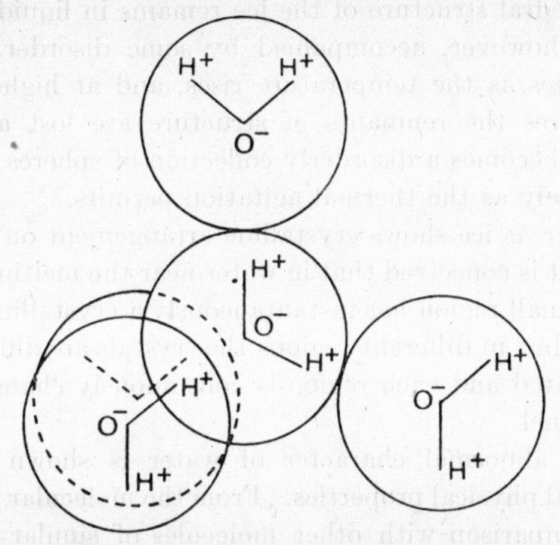

FIG. 82.—Tetrahedral arrangement of water molecules in ice.

There has been some discussion as to whether the proton is equidistant between the two oxygen atoms which it links together, or if it is closer to the one than the other. Pauling * has given reasons for believing that it is in fact closer to the one than the other and in fact remains in much the same position as in the isolated water molecules. It is possible that an occasional interchange from one nucleus to a neighbouring one occurs.

Liquid water is clearly a very anomalous substance. The tetrahedral structure of ice described above is a very open one and there is some collapse of structure when the ice melts as the water formed has a smaller volume. The volume diminishes further as the temperature rises,

* *J. Amer. Chem. Soc.*, 57, 2680, 1935.

reaching a minimum at 4° C. (the temperature of maximum density) and increasing at higher temperatures. Bernal and Fowler * suggested that much of the tetrahedral structure of the ice remains in liquid water. It is, however, accompanied by some disorder, which increases as the temperature rises, and at higher temperatures the remnants of structure are lost and the liquid becomes a disorderly collection of spheres packed as closely as the thermal agitation permits.

Whereas ice shows crystalline arrangement on a large scale, it is conceived that in water near the melting point each small region has instantaneously a crystalline character, but in different regions the crystals are differently orientated and each region is continuously changing its personnel.

The abnormal character of water is shown by its unusual physical properties. From the molecular weight, by comparison with other molecules of similar size, it would be expected that the melting and boiling points respectively would be about −100° C. and −80° C. The difference must be due mainly to possibility of the formation of hydrogen bonds. Of the simple hydrides, HF and NH_3 also have this power, though to a lesser extent, and it is reflected in their physical properties. In Table XXXV they are compared with methane, in which the ability to form hydrogen bonds are entirely absent and the only attraction between the molecules is that due to the van der Waals' (London) forces.

Of the heat of sublimation of ice (12·2 *k*-cals. per mol.) only about one-fourth can be attributed to the ordinary van der Waals' forces between the molecules. The

* *J. Chem. Physics*, 1, 515, 1933. Huggins, *J. Phys. Chem.*, 40, 723, 1936.

TABLE XXXV.

	CH_4.	NH_3.	OH_2.	HF.
Melting point, ° -	– 184	– 77·7	0·0	– 83
Boiling point, ° -	– 161·4	– 33·3	100·0	19·4
Heat of vaporisation (*k*-cals. per mol.) at b.pt., -	2·21	5·81	9·71	1·9

remainder, approximately 9 *k*-cals. must be attributed to the energy required to break the hydrogen bonds between the molecules. Each water molecule is held to its neighbours in ice by four such bonds ; but since each bond is shared by two water molecules the energy of vaporisation corresponds to the energy required to break two bonds, *i.e.* the electrostatic energy of each hydrogen bond may be estimated at about 4·5 *k*-cals.

Only 1·44 *k*-cals. per mol is absorbed in the melting of ice. If this were used entirely in breaking hydrogen bonds it would only be sufficient to break 15 per cent. of them. Even at the boiling point of water the heat of vaporisation is 10 *k*-cals. per mol, of which about 70 per cent. must be due to other than the van der Waals' forces. At these higher temperatures the molecules have a considerable amount of energy of rotation and vibration with respect to each other, and such bonds as exist between them must be made and broken at very short intervals. It is somewhat surprising that the energy of interaction under such conditions does not differ more from the static value of the crystal. It is probable that our knowledge of the state of these liquids is very rudimentary.*

* As a result of a careful X-ray analysis of liquid water, Morgan and Warren (*J. Chem. Physics*, VI, 667, 1938) conclude that " water is well described by the term ' broken down ice structure '. By this we mean a structure in which each water molecule is

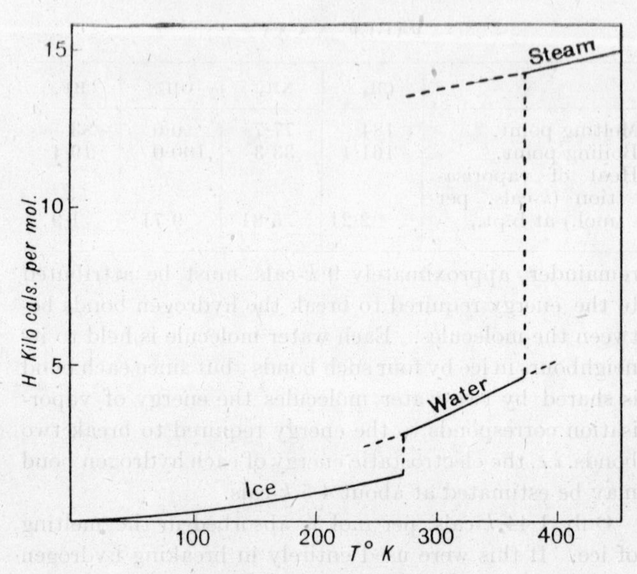

FIG. 83.—Heat content of forms of water.

Associated liquids. Water is a typical example of associated liquids, which may be defined as liquids in which the molecules are united by comparatively strong bonds, other than those arising from the van der Waals' attractions. These bonds are usually hydrogen bonds uniting two or more molecules. At one time attempts were made to determine the numbers of single, double

striving to bond itself tetrahedrally to four neighbouring molecules just as in ice, but in which the bonds are continually breaking and reforming, so that at any instant a molecule will be bonded to less than four neighbouring molecules, and have other neighbours at a continuous variety of distances ". Raman spectra studies (Katzoff, *J. Chem. Physics*, 2, 841, 1934; Cross, Burnham and Leighton, *J. Amer. Chem. Soc.*, 59, 1134, 1937) have led to a similar conclusion.

and triple molecules, etc., in these liquids. For example, it was thought that water was made up of hydrol, dihydrol, trihydrol, and so forth, as the single, double and triple molecules were called. This is probably much too definite a picture. There are many different degrees of bonding in these solutions and the actual state of every molecule is continuously changing.

Association can be detected by abnormal physical properties, especially boiling point and heat of vaporisation, which will be much higher than those of unassociated molecules of approximately the same molecular weights. Other tests are the entropy of vaporisation (L_v/T_b) which according to Trouton's rule is approximately constant for unassociated liquids and appreciably higher for associated liquids; and the molecular surface entropy which is measured by the temperature coefficient of the molecular surface free energy. If γ is the surface tension, the molecular surface energy is $\gamma V^{\frac{2}{3}}$, where V is the molecular volume. According to the rule of Eötvos, $d(\gamma V^{\frac{2}{3}})/dt$ is approximately constant for unassociated liquids and lower for associated liquids.*

Other liquids which show the phenomenon of association are HF and HCN (both of which are associated even in the vapour), NH_3, and organic compounds such as alcohols, phenols and carboxylic acids.

The hydroxyl groups of aliphatic alcohols can form a regularly continuing pattern only by forming hydrogen bonds with two other molecules, and in the crystalline

* It has been shown recently by Eley and Campbell (*Trans Faraday Soc.*, 36, 854, 1940) that the molecular surface entropy is a linear function of the molecular surface energy; a relation similar to that between the entropy and energy of vaporisation.

alcohols the molecules are arranged in chains united in this way :

```
      R             R             R
      |             |             |
      O             O             O
    /   \         /   \         /   \
   H     H       H     H       H     H
          \     /       \     /
             O             O
             |             |
             R             R
```

It has been estimated that the strength of these bonds is about 6·2 *k*-cals. per mol and the interatomic distance between adjacent O's is 2·70 Å.

Isolated groups of molecules may also satisfy their hydrogen bonding ability by combining with three others (when steric considerations permit), arranged tetrahedrally, as in :

```
   R
   |
   O    R
    \   |
     H  |
      \ |
        O
      /   \
     H     H     H
    /       \   /
   O          O
   |          |
   R          R
```

or in rings.

The carboxylic acids readily dimerise as

```
        O—H----O
      /          \
R—C               C—R,
      \          /
        O----H—O
```

and it has been found that the bond energy is from 7 to 8 *k*-cals. per bond. Acids, like benzoic acid, are usually in the dimeric form in non-polar solvents like benzene, carbon disulphide and carbon tetrachloride. In water and other hydroxylic solvents, the end groups satisfy their hydrogen bonding propensities by combination with water (or hydroxyl) and they then exist in the monomeric form.

Aqueous solutions. Non-polar substances are only slightly soluble in water. A cursory examination of solubilities in water indicates that in fact appreciable solubility is conferred by groups like —OH, —COOH, —SO_3H, etc., which can form hydrogen bonds in the water molecules and by ionisation as in the case of strong electrolytes. It has long been obvious that solubility in water depends on the ratio of the size of the non-polar part of the molecule to the number of " hydrophyllic " groups present. For example, in a series of aliphatic alcohols, amines, acids, etc., the lowest members may be soluble in water in all proportions and solubility then decreases regularly as the length of the hydrocarbon chain is increased. This behaviour is a consequence of increasing activity coefficients in dilute solutions.

Figs. 84 and 85 show the activity and activity coefficients of the four lower normal alcohols in aqueous solutions, taking the values as unity in the pure liquid alcohol—*i.e.* the activity is $p/p°$ and the activity coefficient p/p_0N. *n*-Butyl alcohol is not miscible in water in all proportions, consequently there is a gap in the values between the limits of miscibility. The figures for the more dilute solutions however can be worked out as if this gap does not exist and, in Fig. 85, the dotted part of the curve represents the region of immiscibility.

Table XXXVI shows the limiting values of the activity coefficients of the alcohols in dilute aqueous

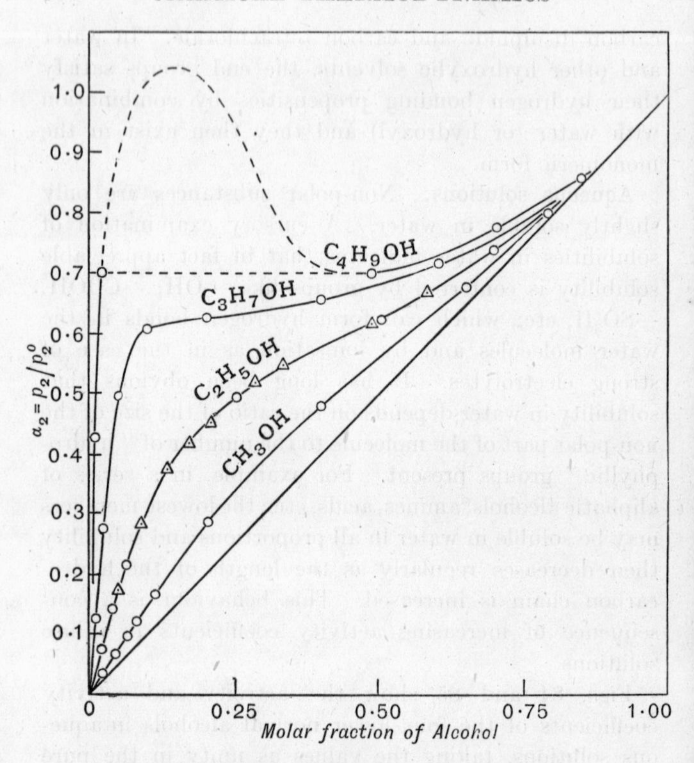

FIG. 84.—Activities of aliphatic alcohols at 25° in aqueous solutions.

solutions as determined in this way.* The activity coefficient increases approximately four times in going from one alcohol to its next higher homologue.

* Data from Butler, *Trans. Faraday Soc.*, 33, 229, 1937. The values for the higher members of the series are obtained from the solubility. The activity of the alcohol must be the same in both phases which are in equilibrium with each other. If the miscibility

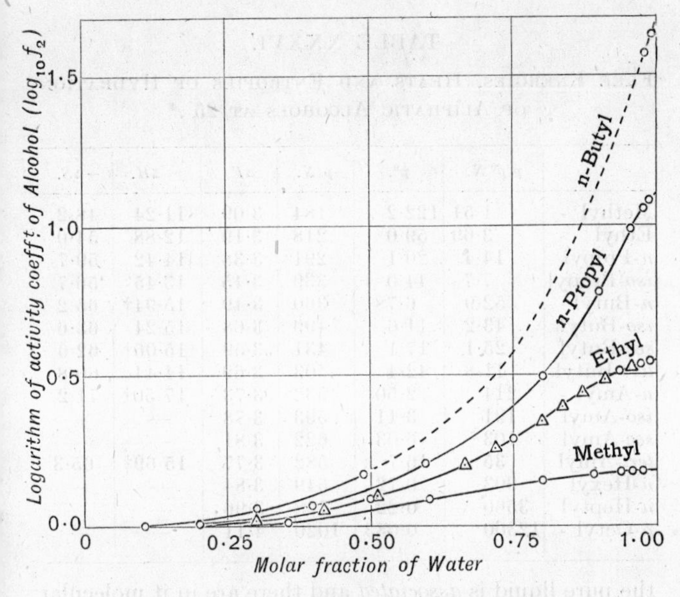

FIG. 85.—Activity coefficients of alcohols in aqueous solutions.

We now turn to consider the causes of this behaviour. In the first place we may note that $\Delta F = RT \log f$ is the free energy of transfer from the pure liquid alcohol to a dilute aqueous solution, over and above the "ideal" value $RT \log N$. In our previous calculations on solutions we took the pure liquid as the reference state. Now in the case of the alcohols and similar compounds,

of the two liquids is slight, the activity of the alcohol in the alcohol rich phase will be practically 1, while the activity in the dilute aqueous phase is $N_s f_s$, where N_s is the solubility expressed as a molar fraction. Hence $N_s f_s = 1$, or $f_s = 1/N_s$, which will not differ appreciably from the value for an infinitely dilute solution.

TABLE XXXVI.

FREE ENERGIES, HEATS AND ENTROPIES OF HYDRATION OF ALIPHATIC ALCOHOLS AT 25°.*

	$p/p^0 N$.	p^0.	p/N.	ΔF.	$-\Delta H$.	$-\Delta S$.
Methyl -	1·51	122·2	184	3·09	11·24	48·2
Ethyl -	3·69	59·0	218	3·19	12·88	54·0
n-Propyl	14·4	20·1	291	3·38	14·42	59·7
iso-Propyl	7·7	44·0	339	3·45	13·45	56·7
n-Butyl -	52·9	6·78	360	3·49	15·94†	65·2
iso-Butyl	43·2	11·6	499	3·68	15·24	63·6
sec-Butyl	25·1	17·1	431	3·59	15·06†	62·6
tert-Butyl	11·8	42·4	503	3·69	14·44	60·8
n-Amyl -	214	2·50	532	3·73	17·50†	71·2
iso-Amyl	191	3·11	593	3·78	—	—
sec-Amyl	103	6·03	622	3·81	—	—
tert-Amyl	35	16·7	582	3·77	15·69†	65·3
n-Hexyl	903	0·72	649	3·84	—	—
n-Heptyl	3560	0·22	798	3·96	—	—
n-Octyl -	12300	0·083	1020	4·11	—	—

the pure liquid is *associated* and there are in it molecular interactions that are difficult to define and evaluate in the present state of knowledge of such liquids. Accordingly it has been found convenient to use the vapour state of the substance as the reference state.

Thus for the partial molar free energy of the vapour, at partial pressure p, we may write

$$F_g = F_g{}^\circ + RT \log p,$$

and similarly the partial free energy in a dilute solution of molar fraction N may be expressed as

$$\bar{F} = \bar{F}^\circ + RT \log N,$$

* ΔF and ΔH in kilo-cals., ΔS in cals./degs. To get values referred to unit gas pressure of 1 atmos., subtract 13·2 from the values of ΔS and 3·9 from the values of ΔF.

where $\bar{F}^\circ$ is the standard free energy for the dilute solution. (This uses the definition $a = N$ in an infinitely dilute solution and it is assumed that the solutions considered are so dilute that this is still true.)

If the vapour of pressure p is in equilibrium with the solution of concentration N, we must have $F_g = \bar{F}$ and therefore

$$\bar{F}^\circ - F_g{}^\circ = RT \log (p/N).$$

The quantity $RT \log (p/N)$ is thus the difference of free energy of the substance in the standard state in the solution and at unit pressure in the vapour and may be termed the free energy of hydration.

Values of this quantity are shown in Table XXXVI. It varies in an additive fashion with the number and size of the hydrocarbon groups in the molecule. In order to ascertain the meaning of these variations, we will analyse it into the corresponding heat and entropy changes, by

$$\Delta F = \Delta H - T\Delta S,$$

where ΔH is the heat of hydration, *i.e.* the heat absorbed when a molecule of the solute is transferred from the vapour to a dilute aqueous solution and ΔS the entropy change in the same process. Table XXXVI shows the values of these quantities when known.

Heat of hydration. The heats of hydration of simple aliphatic compounds are an additive function of the groups in the molecule. The following calculation to account for them in terms of interactions of the various parts of the molecule with water, was given by Butler.*

The process of bringing a solute molecule into a solvent involves, as we have seen, two steps: (1) making a cavity in the solvent large enough to hold the solute

* *loc. cit.*

molecule, (2) introducing the solute molecule into the cavity so formed. In the case of water, the energy required to bring the solute molecule from the vapour into the solution can be expressed as

$$\Delta E = \Sigma\gamma_{W-W} - \Sigma\gamma_{A-W},$$

where $\Sigma\gamma_{W-W}$ is the energy required to separate the water molecules in order to make a cavity of the necessary size and $\Sigma\gamma_{A-W}$ is the energy of interaction of the solute molecule with the water molecules at the surface of the cavity. If there are m water molecules at the surface of the cavity, this can be written as

$$\Delta E = m/2 \cdot \gamma_{W-W} - \Sigma a\gamma_{A-W},$$

where γ_{A-W} is the energy of interaction of a group A of the solute molecule, with an adjacent water molecule, and a the number of water molecules adjacent to the group.

It was assumed for simplicity that water had on the whole the pseudo-crystalline tetrahedral arrangement of Bernal and Fowler. This simplifies the problem, but is not strictly necessary, as similar additive values would be obtained from other assumptions, provided only that only the energy of interaction of adjacent molecules, *i.e.* short range forces, need be considered.

On this assumption it is supposed, for example, that when a methane molecule, which does not differ greatly in size from a water molecule, is introduced into water, there are four water molecules at the surface of the cavity. The energy of solution of methane is thus

$$\Delta E_{CH_4} = 2\gamma_{W-W} - 4\gamma_{CH-W}.$$

Similarly, the cavity of ethane will have six water molecules, and therefore

$$\Delta E_{C_2H_6} = 3\gamma_{W-W} - 6\gamma_{CH-W}.$$

Similarly we can write the following formulae for more complex compounds :

$$\Delta E_{CH_3OH} = 3\gamma_{W-W} - 3\gamma_{CH-W} - 3\gamma_{OH-W}.$$

$$\Delta E_{C_2H_5OH} = 4\gamma_{W-W} - 5\gamma_{CH-W} - 3\gamma_{OH-W}.$$

$$\Delta E_{C_4H_9OH} = 6\gamma_{W-W} - 9\gamma_{CH-W} - 3\gamma_{OH-W}.$$

It is assumed here that a terminal —CH_3 is in contact with 3 water molecules, an intermediate —CH_2 group with 2 water molecules and a terminal —OH group with 3 water molecules.

In order to evaluate the constant we start with the value $\gamma_{W-W} = 5{\cdot}25$ *k*-cals., obtained from the heat of vaporisation of water. For ethane

$$\Delta E_{C_2H_6} = -4{\cdot}4 \text{ } k\text{-cals., hence } \gamma_{CH_2-W} = 3{\cdot}36.$$

Similarly for each additional —CH_2 group, the increment of ΔH is $-1{\cdot}58$ *k*-cals. This corresponds to

$$\Delta E_{CH_2} = \gamma_{W-W} - 2\gamma_{CH-W},$$

from which we obtain $\gamma_{CH-W} = 3{\cdot}42$ *k*-cals.

The energies of interaction which have been obtained in this way are given in Table XXXVII.

TABLE XXXVII.

ENERGIES OF INTERACTION OF VARIOUS GROUPS WITH EACH WATER MOLECULE. (kilo-cals.)

γ_{W-W}	5·5	γ_{OH-W}	5·6	γ_{O-W} (ether)	5·1
γ_{CH-W}	3·4	γ_{NH_2-W}	5·6	γ_{O-W} (ketone)	4·1

In the isomeric alcohols it is found that each *branching* of the hydrocarbon chain causes a decrease of about 0·8 *k*-cals. in $-\Delta E$. This can be accounted for if each branching of the chain reduces by one the number of water molecules at the surface of the cavity, in contact with hydrocarbon, which would indeed follow from the assumptions mentioned.

The following table shows the observed and calculated values of the heats of hydration of normal and isomeric hydrocarbons calculated in this way.

TABLE XXXVIII.

OBSERVED AND CALCULATED HEATS OF HYDRATION.*

	m.	$-\Delta H$ (obs.)	$-\Delta H$ (calc.)
$CH_3 . CH_2 . CH_2OH$	7	14·42	14·4
$(CH_3)_2CHOH$	6	13·45	13·6
$CH_3 . CH_2 . CH_2 . CH_2OH$	9	15·94	15·9
$CH_3 . CH_2 . CH(CH_3)OH$	8	15·06	15·1
$CH_3 . CH(CH_3)CH_2OH$	8	15·24	15·1
$C(CH_3)_3OH$	7	14·44	14·4
$CH_3(CH_2)_3CH_2OH$	11	17·50	17·5
$CH_3 . CH_2 . C(CH_3)_2OH$	9	15·69	15·9

Notwithstanding the good agreement between the observed and calculated values, the picture on which the theory is based should not be taken too literally. It would be possible to obtain agreement with the results in any calculation in which the energy of making the cavity is proportional to its size, and the energy of interaction of the solvent molecule is additive for its constituent groups. It is probable that the quantity

$$\gamma_{W-CH_2} = 3{\cdot}4 \ k\text{-cals.}$$

is too large to be accounted for as the London interaction between the water molecule and the hydrocarbon segment. If the energy of cavity formation were smaller than that estimated by the method used, a smaller value of γ_{W-CH_2} would suffice. It is quite possible that small

* The difference between ΔE and ΔH is ignored.

cavities can be made without such an extensive breakage of bonds as was visualised.

The heats of solution of the inert gases in water are negative (exothermic) and of a comparatively large order of magnitude (see Table XXXIX).*

Eley † therefore suggested that the energy required to make small cavities in water at low temperatures is zero, or small, since they either exist already or may be made by a small expansion of previously existing cavities. The heat of solution will then be mainly the London energy of interaction of the solute molecule with the surrounding water molecules. It must be noted that the exothermic heat of solution falls off rapidly with the temperature, especially for larger molecules, and is comparatively small at 80° C.

Entropy of hydration. It is somewhat surprising to find that although the simple gases dissolve in water with an evolution of heat (about 3·5 *k*-cals. per mol more heat is evolved when the inert gases dissolve in water than in organic solvents), they are nevertheless much less soluble in water than in organic solvents, like carbon tetrachloride, benzene, etc. This behaviour is due to the fact that the entropy of vaporisation of solutes from aqueous solutions is considerably greater than from the organic solvents. We have seen that there is a linear relation between the entropy and heat of vaporisation which applies both to pure liquids and to solutions in unassociated solvents. In aqueous solutions there is

* This will happen according to the theory whenever the energy of interaction of the solute with water is greater than *half* the energy of vaporisation of the water within the cavity, *i.e.* when $\Sigma a \gamma_{A-W} > \Sigma m/2 \, \gamma_{W-W}$.

† *Trans. Faraday Soc.*, 35, 1281, 1421 1939.

TABLE XXXIX.

HEATS AND ENTROPIES OF HYDRATION OF SOME GASES AT 25° C.*

	$-\Delta H$.	$-\Delta S$.		$-\Delta H$.	$-\Delta S$.
H_2	1·28	39·2	CO_2	4·73	43·8
He	1·02(0·53)†	40·0(38·6)†	COS	5·80	48·3
Ne	1·88(0·85)	42·0(39·4)	NO	2·68	42·6
A	2·73(2·63)	43·4(43·1)	N_2O	4·84	44·8
Kr	3·55	45·5	CH_4	3·18	45·0
X	4·49	46·8	C_2H_6	—	48·6
Rn	5·05	47·5	C_2H_4	3·79	44·5
N_2	2·14	43·0	C_2H_2	3·36	38·8
O_2	2·99	44·5	CH_3Cl	6·3	46·8
CO	3·91	43·0	(CCl_4	6·9	51)

also a similar approximate relation of this kind for solutes which do not form hydrogen bonds with water, the entropy of vaporisation from water being about 12 e.u. greater than from non-associated liquids for the same heat of vaporisation (Table XXXIX and Fig. 86).

We have here a feature of aqueous solutions which is clearly of great importance, but is as yet very imperfectly understood. If the entropy of vaporisation of a solute gas from water is greater than from an organic solvent, its entropy in the aqueous solution must be

* The figures for the entropy again refer to a standard state in the gas of 1 mm. pressure. If 1 atmos. pressure is chosen as the standard of reference, the values given for $-\Delta S$ should be diminished by 13·2 ($=R\ ln\ 760$).

† The bracketed figs. for the inert gases are from Lannung's measurements (*J. Amer. Chem. Soc.*, 1930, 52, 73), and the remainder from Valentiner's interpolation formulae (Landolt-Börnstein).

abnormally low. The partial entropy of a substance in solution (the change of entropy per mol caused by adding some of the solute to the solution) includes not only the entropy of the solute molecules, but also any changes of entropy which the solute molecules bring about in their action on the solvent. Thus the partial entropy of a solute in water may be abnormally low if the presence of a solute molecule diminishes the entropy of the solvent molecules about it. It might do this merely by the formation of the cavity which, by reducing the number of ways in which they can unite with each other, restricts the number of configurations open to the water molecules, or by reducing their ability to rotate.

The presence of groups which can form hydrogen bonds with the water still further increases the entropy of vaporisation and therefore results in a further diminution of the entropy of the solute molecule in the solution (Fig. 86). These entropy differences also have a predominating effect on the solubilities of a series of compounds. The heat of solution (exothermic) of the vapour increases with the length of the hydrocarbon chain. The solubility of the vapour (N/p) however diminishes in the same progress, and this is due to an increase in the entropy of vaporisation which is sufficiently large to make ΔF and ΔH change in opposite directions with the increase of the number of CH_2 groups.

The abnormal drop in entropy, however, diminishes rapidly as the temperature rises. Frank & Evans * have discussed these results and give the following interpretation. They suggest that " when a rare gas atom or a non-polar molecule dissolves in water at room temperature, it modifies the water structure in the direction of

* *J. Chemical Physics*, **13**, 507, 1945.

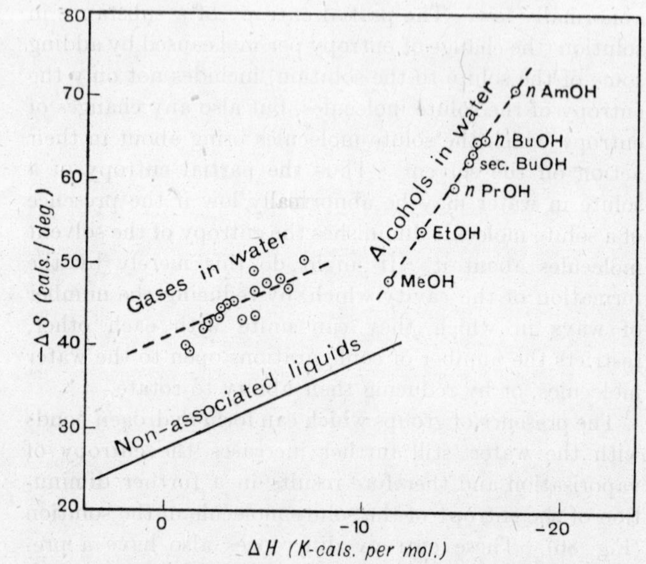

FIG. 86.—Entropies and heats of hydration.

greater 'crystallinity', the water, so to speak, builds a microscopic iceberg around it. The extent of this iceberg is the greater the larger the foreign atom. This 'freezing' of water produced by the rare gas atom causes heat and entropy to be lost, beyond what would have 'otherwise' have been expected. The heat adds on to the 'otherwise' smaller heat of solution of the gas, producing the rather considerable positive ΔH of vaporisation. The loss of entropy is what causes ΔS of vaporisation to be so remarkably large. As the temperature is raised these icebergs melt, giving rise to the enormous partial molar heat capacity of these gases in water, which may exceed 60 cal./deg./mol. The magnitude of this effect naturally depends on the size of the iceberg originally present, so it is greatest in Rn, and at the higher temperatures the order of ΔS for the rare gases has actually reversed itself, ΔS of vaporisation of Rn being smaller than that of He."

With regard to the alcohols, they point out that ΔS for MeOH is about the same as for C_2H_6. The entropy drop in the case of the MeOH is due to " iceberg " formation round CH_3 and hydrogen bonding round —OH, but the value of the entropy effect is about the same in each case. But the hydrogen bonding produces a considerably larger value of $-\Delta H$, so that the point for CH_3OH is shifted horizontally in Fig. 86 as compared with $C_2H_6(\Delta H = -4{\cdot}4$; $\Delta S = -48{\cdot}6)$. The relative importance of hydrogen bonding and iceberg formation shifts in favour of the latter as the hydrocarbon chain of the alcohol increases, and the points for the higher alcohols fall progressively closer and closer to the non-polar solute line, finally coming very near it for amyl alcohol. (The true line for non-polar solutes in water will therefore be steeper than that shown in Fig. 86 and will extend through the group of " gases " into the neighbourhood at the point for *n*-amyl alcohol.)

Examples.

1. The partial pressure of ethyl acetate over an aqueous solution of molar fraction $0{\cdot}97 \times 10^{-3}$ is 5·44 mm. Hg at 25°. The vapour pressure of pure ethyl acetate at the same temperature is about 93 mm. Find the activity coefficient of ethyl acetate in the solution and the non-ideal free energy of transfer from the pure liquid into the solution.

2. For acetone in dilute aqueous solution p/N is 1380 at 25° and 2380 at 35°, p being expressed in mm. of Hg. Find (1) the heat of vaporisation from this solution, (2) the entropy of vaporisation to 1 mm. of mercury.

CHAPTER XVIII

ACTIVITY COEFFICIENTS AND RELATED PROPERTIES OF STRONG ELECTROLYTES

Concentration Cells without Liquid Junctions. Consider a cell consisting of a hydrogen electrode and a silver electrode covered with solid silver chloride, in a hydrochloric acid solution of concentration m_1:

$$H_2 \left| \begin{array}{cc} HCl & AgCl_{(s)} \\ (m_1) & \oplus \end{array} \right| Ag.$$

$$\longrightarrow$$

When a current flows through the cell from left to right, hydrogen passes into solution as hydrogen ions at the left while silver ions are deposited at the right. Since solid silver chloride is present this does not reduce the amount of silver ions in the solution, for silver chloride dissolves so as to keep the silver ion concentration constant, and the result is an increase in the amount of chloride ion in the solution.

The reaction occurring when the circuit is closed is thus:

$$\tfrac{1}{2}H_2 + AgCl_{(s)} = HCl_{(m_1)} + Ag.$$

For the amount of chemical action represented by this equation, one faraday of electricity is produced, so that if $\mathbf{E}_1$ is the electromotive force (at open circuit) $\mathbf{E}_1\mathbf{F}$ is the net work obtainable or free energy decrease in this reaction, *i.e.*

$$\mathbf{E}_1\mathbf{F} = -\Delta F_{(m_1)}.$$

Similarly, if $\mathbf{E}_2$ is the electromotive force of another cell in which the concentration of hydrochloride acid is m_2, we may write :

$$\mathbf{E}_2\mathbf{F} = -\Delta F_{(m_2)}. \quad \text{.................(223)}$$

Now if we couple up these cells " back to back," thus :

	II		I	
H_2	HCl, AgCl	Ag - Ag	AgCl, HCl	H_2.
	m_2		m_1	

$$\longrightarrow$$

The result of the passage of one faraday of electricity in the direction shown is, in *II*, the reaction:

$$\tfrac{1}{2}H_2 + AgCl_{(s)} = HCl_{(m_2)} + Ag,$$

as before, and, in *I*, the reverse reaction :

$$Ag + HCl_{(m_1)} = AgCl + \tfrac{1}{2}H_2.$$

Thus the same amounts of hydrogen, silver chloride and silver which react in one cell are produced in the same form in the other, but the amount of hydrochloric acid in solution *II* increases by one equivalent, while that in solution *I* decreases by the same amount. The result is therefore the transfer of one equivalent of hydrochloric acid from a solution in which its concentration is m_1 to one in which its concentration is m_2. The electromotive force of the combination is $\mathbf{E}_1 - \mathbf{E}_2$, and $(\mathbf{E}_1 - \mathbf{E}_2)\mathbf{F}$ is equal to the net work or free energy decrease in this transfer, or

$$(\mathbf{E}_1 - \mathbf{E}_2)\,\mathbf{F} = -\Delta F_{m_1 \to m_2}. \quad \text{...........(223·1)}$$

It is thus possible in cells of this type, which are known as " concentration cells without liquid junction," to measure the free energy changes in the transfer of a strong electrolyte from one concentration to another. The free energy changes in the transfer of hydrochloric acid from a solution in which $m_1 = 0{\cdot}001$ to solutions of concentration m_2, as determined in this way, are given in Table XL.

TABLE XL.

FREE ENERGY CHANGES IN TRANSFER OF HCl FROM $m_1 = 0{\cdot}001$ TO m_2.

m_2.	ΔF Calories.	Degree of Dissociation (Conductivity).	"Apparent" Ion Concentration.	Mean Activity $a\pm$.	Activity Coefficient $f\pm$.
0·001	0	—	—	0·000984	0·984
0·01	2652	0·972	0·00939	0·00924	0·924
0·1	5227	0·925	0·0827	0·0814	0·814
0·5	7060	0·890	0·387	0·381	0·762
1	7972	0·845	0·836	0·823	0·823
2	9050	—	2·097	2·064	1·032
3	9861	—	4·12	4·05	1·35
4	10571	—	7·48	7·36	1·84
5	11204	—	12·75	12·55	2·51
10	13738	—	108·2	106·5	10·55
16	15955	—	702·6	691·0	43·2

How are these figures to be interpreted? In the first place, the transfer of an equivalent of hydrochloric acid may be regarded as the transfer of one equivalent each of hydrogen and of chloride ions. Thus, if the concentrations of hydrogen and of chloride ions in the two solutions are m_1' and m_2', and if the ions behave as perfect solutes, we have :

$$\left.\begin{aligned} w' = -\Delta F &= 2RT \log m_1'/m_2' \\ \text{or} \qquad \Delta F &= 2RT \log m_2'/m_1' \end{aligned}\right\} \quad \ldots\ldots\ldots(224)$$

The values of ΔF calculated by this equation, using the ion concentrations corresponding to the degree of dissociation as determined by conductivity measurements, do not by any means agree with the observed figures. This disagreement may be due either to deviations from the limiting law or to the incorrectness of the degree of dissociation given by conductivity measurements. In order to see if the second explanation is tenable we may suppose that at the concentration $m=0{\cdot}001$ hydrochloric acid is completely dissociated, so that in this solution the concentrations of the two ions are 0·001. Then assuming that (224) gives correctly the free energies of transfer of ions, we may work out the "apparent" ion concentrations in the other solutions. These "apparent" ion concentrations are given in the third column of the table. Up to $m=1$ the values might well correspond to the partial dissociation of the electrolyte, but at greater concentrations they cannot possibly be interpreted in this way. Thus in the solution $m=5$, the "apparent" ion concentration is 12·75 or more than twice as much as the total amount of electrolyte present. We are therefore forced to take the view that the solutions deviate widely from the requirements of the limiting law.

The Dissociation of Strong Electrolytes. It is necessary to recall briefly at this point the considerations on which the Arrhenius theory of electrolytic dissociation was based. Kohlrausch had observed that electrolytes fell into two classes, according to the behaviour of their aqueous solutions.

(1) *Strong electrolytes*, whose molecular conductivities in aqueous solution were large and tended towards a limiting value Λ_∞ at great dilutions.

(2) *Weak electrolytes*, having considerably smaller molecular conductivities, which did not tend to a limiting value at great dilutions.

Arrhenius postulated that at infinite dilution strong electrolytes are completely dissociated into ions. The decrease in the molecular conductivities as the concentration is increased might be due to either (1) a decrease in the number of ions given by a gram molecule of the electrolyte or (2) a decrease in the mobility of the ions, their number remaining constant. Arrhenius assumed that in fairly dilute solutions the mobilities of ions do remain constant and ascribed the change in the molecular conductivity to factor (1). Thus he regarded the ratio of the molecular conductivity at a dilution v, Λ_v, to that at infinite dilution, Λ_∞, as equal to the ratio of the number of ions given by one gram-molecule of the electrolyte at the dilution v to the corresponding quantity at infinite dilution, *i.e.* to the degree of dissociation :

$$\gamma = \Lambda_v / \Lambda_\infty .$$

The data by means of which he supported this theory are no doubt known to the reader. Although the theory gave in the early days a fairly adequate explanation of the known facts, and gave a great impetus to the study of electrolytes, in the course of time grave difficulties were encountered.

Thus, it was found that in some of their properties the behaviour of salt solutions was more uniform than the varying degrees of dissociation calculated from conductivity measurements, according to Arrhenius' theory, would lead us to expect. For example, A. A. Noyes found in 1904 that the optical rotatory powers of α-bromcamphoric acid and its metallic salts in solutions of equivalent strengths were almost identical, although conductivity measurements indicated degrees of dissociation varying from 70 to 93 per cent. In connection with these results Noyes remarked, " If there were not other evidence to the contrary these facts would almost warrant the conclusion that these salts are completely ionized up to the concentration in question."

Again, Ostwald had found that the change of the dissociation of weak electrolytes with concentration was in accordance with the law of mass action, but with strong electrolytes no such relation could be obtained.

It was therefore questioned whether the Arrhenius expression gave correct values of the degree of dissociation, even when corrections were made for the change of the mobilities of the ions caused by the effect of the dissolved substance on the viscosity of the solution.

Activity and Activity Coefficient of Strong Electrolytes. Before seeking an explanation of the properties of ionic solutions, it is necessary to determine and state them accurately. The activity coefficient is very suitable for this purpose.

A strong electrolyte, such as sodium chloride in aqueous solution, is regarded as being largely dissociated because its effect on the partial free energy of the water (and therefore on the freezing point, osmotic pressure and similar properties of the solution) is approximately twice that of the same number of molecules of a neutral substance. In very dilute solutions the change of the free energy of water becomes in fact exactly twice that produced by an equal number of molecules of, say, sugar, and in such a case we are justified in regarding the salt as completely dissociated.

Consider the salt AB which dissociates as

$$AB = A^+ + B^-.$$

Let $\bar{F}_+$, $\bar{F}_-$, $\bar{F}$ be the partial molar free energies of A^+,

B^- and AB in the solution. We can define the activities of the ions by

$$\left.\begin{aligned}\bar{F}_+ &= \bar{F}^\circ_+ + RT \log a_+,\\ \bar{F}_- &= \bar{F}^\circ_- + RT \log a_-,\end{aligned}\right\} \quad \text{.............(225)}$$

and since in dilute solutions each ion produces the same change of the free energy of the solvent as a separate molecule, it is possible to adopt the conventions that $a_+ = m_+$ and $a_- = m_-$, when m_+ (or m_-) $= 0$, where m_+, m_- are the concentrations of the ions. We may also write

$$\bar{F} = \bar{F}^\circ + RT \log a, \quad \text{.................(226)}$$

where a is the activity of the salt, AB, but since a molecule of the salt does not cause the theoretical molecular lowering of the partial free energy of the solvent, it is *not* possible to identify a with m in very dilute solutions.

The partial free energy of a gram molecule of the salt AB must be the sum of the molar free energies of A^+ and B^- (see p. 319), or $\bar{F} = \bar{F}_+ + \bar{F}_-$,* and therefore

$$\bar{F}^\circ + RT \log a = \bar{F}^\circ_+ + \bar{F}^\circ_- + RT \log a_+ a_-.$$

If the activity of the salt is so defined that $\bar{F}^\circ = \bar{F}^\circ_+ + \bar{F}^\circ_-$ we have then

$$a = a_+ a_-,$$

and writing $a_\pm = \sqrt{a_+ a_-}$, it follows that

$$\bar{F} = \bar{F}^\circ + 2RT \log a\pm. \quad \text{..............(227)}$$

$a\pm$ is called the *mean activity* of the salt.

The activity coefficients of the ions are $f_+ = a_+/m_+$ and $f_- = a_-/m_-$, and by definition they obviously become equal to unity in very dilute solutions. If we took the

* This also follows from the consideration that the partial free energy of the salt must be the same whether we regard it as the component AB, or as the components A_+, B_-.

activity coefficient of the salt as the ratio of its activity to its concentration, i.e. $f = a/m = a_+a_-/m$, we should obviously obtain a quantity which cannot become equal to unity at small concentrations. If, however, we write

$$f_{\pm} = a_{\pm}/m_{\pm} = \sqrt{f_+f_-},$$

where $m_{\pm} = \sqrt{m_+m_-}$, we obtain a quantity called the mean activity coefficient which evidently becomes equal to unity when f_+ and f_- are unity.

In a *saturated* salt solution, the partial free energy in the solution must be equal to the free energy of the solid salt, F_s; therefore writing (227) in the form

$$F_s = \bar{F}^{\circ} + 2RT \log a_{\pm},$$

we see that $a_{\pm}$ must be constant in a saturated solution, *i.e.* the activity product of the ions is constant so long as the solid is present. This relation may be used to find the *activity coefficients* of slightly soluble salts in solutions containing other salts. Since $a_{\pm}$ is a constant in all saturated solutions, the activity coefficient,

$$f_{\pm} = a_{\pm}/m_{\pm},$$

is inversely proportional to $m_{\pm}$.

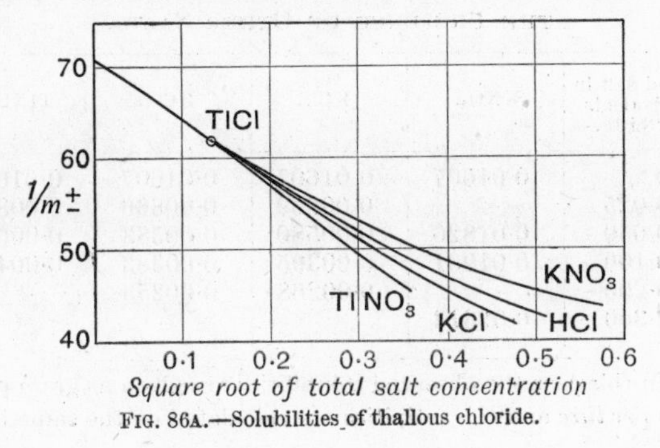

FIG. 86A.—Solubilities of thallous chloride.

Table XLA gives the solubilities of thallous chloride in the presence of a number of other salts at 25° C. From these figures it is possible to find m_+ (the total thallium ion concentration) and m_- (the total chloride ion concentration) in the different solutions, and hence

$$m_{\pm} = \sqrt{m_+ \cdot m_-}.$$

The reciprocal of this $1/m_{\pm}$ is plotted in Fig. 86A against the total salt concentration in the saturated solutions. This figure is proportional to the corresponding activity coefficient to thallous chloride. The smallest concentration in a saturated solution, that of thallous chloride in water, contains 0·01607 equivalents of thallous chloride per litre.* We cannot take the activity coefficient in this solution as one, but by extrapolating to zero concentration we find that the value of $1/m_{\pm}$ in a (fictitious) saturated solution of zero salt concentration, in which $f_{\pm} = 1$, is 70·3. Hence the activity coefficients in the other solutions is given by

$$f_{\pm} = \frac{1/m_{\pm}}{70 \cdot 3}.$$

TABLE XLA.

SOLUBILITIES OF THALLOUS CHLORIDE AT 25° C. IN THE PRESENCE OF OTHER SALTS.

Added Salt in Equivalents per Litre.	KNO_3.	KCl.	HCl.	$TlNO_3$.
0	0·01607	0·01607	0·01607	0·01607
0·025	—	0·00869	0·00866	0·00880
0·050	0·01826	0·00580	0·00583	0·00624
0·100	0·01961	0·00395	0·00383	0·00422
0·200	—	0·00268	0·00253	—
0·300	0·02313	—	—	—

* In this case the observed solubilities are given as gram-molecules per *litre* and the activities are calculated on the same basis.

Example. In a solution containing 0·050 equivalents of hydrochloric acid, the concentration of thallous chloride is 0·00583. Thus the thallium ion concentration is

$$m+ = 0\cdot00583,$$

and the chloride ion concentration

$$m_- = 0\cdot00583 + 0\cdot050 = 0\cdot05583.$$

Thus $$m_\pm = \sqrt{0\cdot05583 + 0\cdot00583} = 0\cdot0180.$$

Therefore $$f_\pm = \frac{1/0\cdot0180}{70\cdot3} = 0\cdot788.$$

In solutions of strong electrolytes, which are certainly very largely dissociated, it is usual to take m_+, m_- as the total stoichiometrical concentration of the ions, without having regard to the degree of dissociation of the salt. Thus in a sodium chloride solution, m_{Na^+}, m_{Cl^-} are taken as the total concentrations of sodium and chloride in the solution, without distinguishing to what extent they are present as ions or as undissociated molecules. The activity coefficient obtained in this way has been called the *stoichiometrical activity coefficient.*

*The activity of other types of electrolytes can be similarly defined. Suppose we have a salt $A_{\nu_1} B_{\nu_2}$ which dissociates into ν_1 ions A and ν_2 ions B, as in the equation

$$A_{\nu_1} B_{\nu_2} = \nu_1 A^+ + \nu_2 B^-.$$

The partial molar free energies of the ions are given by (225) as before, and the partial molar free energy of the salt is equal to

$$\overline{F} = \nu_1 \overline{F}_1 + \nu_2 \overline{F}_2,$$

so that if the activity of the salt is defined by

$$\overline{F} = \overline{F}^\circ + RT \log a, \quad \text{.................}(228)$$

where $\overline{F}^\circ = \nu_1 \overline{F}_1{}^\circ + \nu_2 \overline{F}_2{}^\circ$, we have

$$\log a = \nu_1 \log a_+ + \nu_2 \log a_-,$$

or $$a = a_+^{\nu_1} a_-^{\nu_2}. \quad \text{....................}(229)$$

The mean activity of the salt is defined as

$$a_{\pm} = (a_+^{\nu_1} a_-^{\nu_2})^{\frac{1}{\nu_1+\nu_2}}, \qquad \text{.................(230)}$$

and the mean activity coefficient as

$$f_{\pm} = a_{\pm}/m_{\pm}$$

where $\qquad m_{\pm} = (m_+^{\nu_1} \, . \, m_-^{\nu_2})^{1/\nu_1+\nu_2},$

$f_{\pm}$ obviously becomes unity when

$$f_1 = a_+/m_+ \quad \text{and} \quad f_2 = a_-/m_-$$

become unity. Finally, comparing (228) and (229), it can be seen that $\quad \overline{F} = \overline{F}^{\circ} + (\nu_1 + \nu_2)RT \log a_{\pm}. \quad$ ....(231)

Activity Coefficients. We are now in a position to determine the mean activity coefficients of hydrochloric acid in aqueous solutions from the data given in Table XL. In the most dilute solution given ($m = 0{\cdot}001$) hydrochloric acid is not yet behaving quite as an ideal solute. We may therefore in the first place determine the activities relative to this solution (*i.e.* take its activity as 0·001) and the corresponding activity coefficients. Plotting these activity coefficients against the concentrations and extrapolating to zero concentration, we find that the activity coefficient at $m = 0{\cdot}001$ is 0·984 times the value at zero concentration, so that multiplying the " relative " activity coefficients by this factor we obtain the true activity coefficients, referred to an infinitely dilute solution as the standard state.

Example. According to the table the free energy change in the transfer of hydrochloric acid from $m = 0{\cdot}001$ to $m = 0{\cdot}5$ is 7060 calories, hence

$$7060 = 2RT \log a''_{\pm}/a'_{\pm}.$$

If $a'_{\pm}$ be taken as 0·001, we have

$$\log_{10} a''_{\pm} = \frac{7060}{2 \times 1{\cdot}99 \times 298{\cdot}1 \times 2{\cdot}303} + \log_{10} 0{\cdot}001,$$

and the activity "relative to the 0·01 solution" is

$$a''_{\pm}=0{\cdot}387 \quad \text{and} \quad f''_{\pm}=0{\cdot}774.$$

Correcting for the activity coefficient in the $m=0{\cdot}001$ solution, we find that the true value of $f''_{\pm}$ is

$$f''_{\pm}=0{\cdot}774\times 0{\cdot}984=0{\cdot}762.$$

The following table gives the activity coefficients of a few typical uni-univalent salts. The values are also

TABLE XLI.

ACTIVITY COEFFICIENTS OF STRONG ELECTROLYTES.

m.	HCl.	LiCl.	KOH.	NaCl.	KCl.	H_2SO_4.
0·01	0·924	0·922	0·920	0·906	0·903	0·617
0·05	0·860	0·843	0·822	0·834	0·816	0·397
0·1	0·814	0·804	0·792	0·792	0·779	0·313
0·2	0·783	0·774	0·763	0·745	0·723	0·244
0·5	0·762	0·754	0·740	0·682	0·659	0·178
1·0	0·823	0·776	0·775	0·652	0·613	0·150
2·0	1·032	0·936	—	0·672	0·566	0·147
3·0	1·35	1·20	1·136	0·722	0·575	0·166
4·0	1·84	—	—	0·794	—	0·203
5·0	2·51	—	—	0·892	—	0·202
10·0	10·65	—	—	—	—	—

plotted against the concentrations in Fig. 87. It will be seen that the activity coefficients initially decrease with increasing concentration. In most cases they subsequently rise, becoming greater than one at high concentrations.

The more important methods for the determination of activity coefficients from the partial free energy of the solvent, which can be applied with only slight modification to solutions of electrolytes, have already been described. As an illustration of the determination of the activity coefficient of an electrolyte from the partial free energy of the solvent, consider a solution containing

n_1 mols of the solvent and n_2 mols of a salt a molecule of which dissociates into ν_1 positive and ν_2 negative ions.

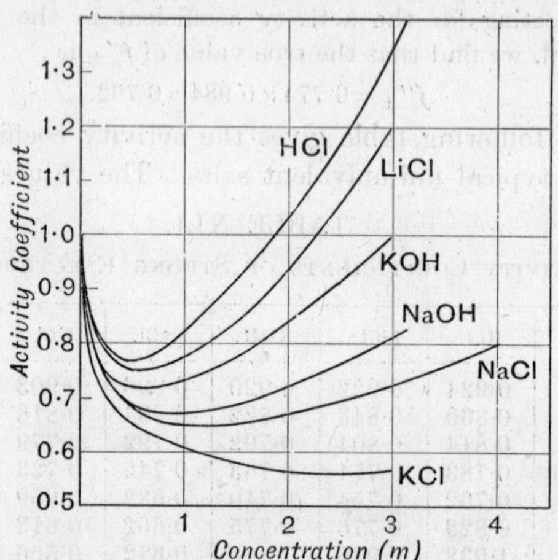

FIG. 87.—Activity coefficients of strong electrolytes.

If $\bar{F}_1$, $\bar{F}_2$ are the partial molar free energies of the solvent and salt in the given solution, we have by (185), $d\bar{F}_2 = -n_1/n_2 \,.\, d\bar{F}_1$, or writing $\bar{F}_2 = \bar{F}^\circ_2 + RT \,.\, \log a_2$, where a_2 is the activity of the salt as defined by (226), we have

$$RT \,.\, d(\log a_2) = -n_1/n_2 \,.\, d\bar{F}_1,$$

and by integrating, we get

$$\log a_2 = -\frac{1}{RT}\int \frac{n_1}{n_2}\, d\bar{F}_1.$$

Instead of $\log a_2$ we may use $(\nu_1 + \nu_2) \log a_\pm$, and we then have for the mean activity of the salt,

$$\log a_\pm = -\frac{1}{(\nu_1 + \nu_2)RT}\int \frac{n_1}{n_2} \,.\, d\bar{F}_1,$$

or

$$\log a_\pm = -\frac{1}{(\nu_1 + \nu_2)}\int \frac{n_1}{n_2} \,.\, d\log a_1. \quad \text{......(232)}$$

Similarly it is easy to obtain a corresponding equation for the activity coefficient (see 207), viz.:

$$\log f_{\pm} = -\frac{1}{\nu_1 + \nu_2}\int \frac{n_1}{n_2} \, . \, d \log f_1 .$$

These equations can be used in the ways which have already been described for the determination of the mean activities or activity coefficients.

Activity Coefficients in Dilute solutions of Single Salts and in Mixed Solutions. The variation of the activity coefficients of some typical salts with the concentration is shown in Fig. 87. In dilute solutions the activity coefficient decreases as the concentration is increased, but in most cases it reaches a minimum and increases again at higher concentrations. In very dilute solutions the activity coefficients of salts of the same ion type (*e.g.* uni-univalent) are very nearly the same. Lewis and Linhart * showed in 1919 that the activity coefficients in very dilute solutions could be represented by equations of the type $\log f_{\pm} = -\beta c^{\alpha'}$, and later Lewis and Randall and also Brönsted suggested that $\alpha' = 0{\cdot}5$. This equation is only adequate in very dilute solutions. In stronger solutions another term, with a positive sign, becomes important. Harned † showed that the equation

$$\log f_{\pm} = -\beta c^{\alpha'} + ac, \qquad (233)$$

gave good agreement with the experimental values for many salts over a considerable range of concentration, when α' is close to 0·5.

In mixed solutions the following cases can be distinguished.

* *J. Amer. Chem. Soc.*, 41, 1951, 1919.

† *Ibid.*, 42, 1808, 1920.

(*a*) *Mixtures of salts of the same ion type.* The activity coefficient of any salt of the mixture depends on the total salt concentration, and in very dilute solutions is the same in all solutions of the same total normality. In stronger solutions the activity coefficient of a salt is influenced by the individual behaviour of all the various ions present.

(*b*) *Mixtures of salts of different ion types* (*e.g.* HCl and K_2SO_4). In 1921 Lewis and Randall found that the effect of a bivalent ion on the activity coefficient of a salt was four times that of a univalent ion. In general, since the effect produced by an ion is proportional to the square of its valency, they introduced a quantity called the ionic strength.* This is obtained by multiplying the concentration of each ion by the square of its valency and dividing the sum of these products by two. Thus if m is the concentration of a given ion and z its valency, the ionic strength is

$$\mu = \Sigma mz^2/2.$$

(The factor two is inserted so that for uni-univalent salts the ionic strength is equal to the total molar concentration.) Lewis and Randall stated the rule that in very dilute solutions the activity coefficient of a salt is the same in all solutions of the same ionic strength. It should be emphasized that this only holds in extremely dilute solutions ($\mu < 0{\cdot}01$) and is to be regarded as the limiting law; in stronger solutions the activity coefficients are influenced by the individual characters of the various ions present.

The Debye-Hückel Calculation of the Activity Coefficient of a Strong Electrolyte. The possibility that strong electrolytes are completely dissociated, and that the

* *J. Amer. Chem. Soc.*, 43, 1112, 1921.

behaviour which was ascribed in the Arrhenius theory to variations of the degree of dissociation was caused by the electric forces between the ions was suggested at various times by van Laar, Sutherland, Bjerrum and others. S. R. Milner * in 1912 made the first serious attempt to calculate the effect of the electric forces on the thermodynamic properties of salt solutions. Assuming that the electrolyte was completely dissociated into ions and that the distribution of the ions was determined by the electric forces between them, he attempted to calculate the electric potential energy of the solution by summing the potential energy of every pair of ions. Effectively this determines the electrical work which must be done in separating the ions to an infinite distance from each other, *i.e.* the electrical work done in an infinite dilution of the solution. This calculation is very complicated and its result will be referred to later.

In 1923 Debye and Hückel † devised a comparatively simple mathematical treatment of the problem, the essential parts of which are given below.

It is assumed that strong electrolytes are completely dissociated. This is an obvious necessity, for until the properties of a completely dissociated solution have been calculated it is impossible to tell whether there is any discrepancy which might be ascribed to incomplete dissociation. The calculation is concerned with two interrelated effects, (1) the average distribution of ions round a given ion, (2) the electrical potential near the surface of the given ion due to this distribution.

* *Phil. Mag.*, 23, 551, 1912 ; 25, 743, 1914 ; 35, 214, 352, 1918.

† *Physikal. Z.*, 24, 185, 305, 1923. A simplified version is given by Debye, *ibid.*, 25, 97, 1924.

Consider a solution containing n_1 ions of valency z_1, n_2 ions of valency z_2, n_3 ions of valency z_3, etc., per c.c. Let ψ be the electric potential at a certain point in the vicinity of a given ion (*i.e.* the electric work which is done in bringing a unit charge to this point from an infinite distance). The work done in bringing an ion of charge $z_i\epsilon$ (where ϵ is the electronic charge) to the point in question is therefore $z_i\epsilon\psi$. If the concentration (per c.c.) of these ions at a great distance from the given ion ($\psi=0$) is n_i, according to *Boltzmann's equation* the concentration at the point where the potential is ψ is $n_i e^{-z_i\epsilon\psi/kT}$, where k is the gas constant per molecule. The electric charge carried by these ions is thus

$$n_i(z_i\epsilon)e^{-z_i\epsilon\psi/kT}$$

per c.c. Summing this for all the ions present in the solution we therefore find that the total charge density (*i.e.* charge per c.c.) at a point where the electric potential is ψ is

$$\rho=\Sigma n_i(z_i\epsilon)e^{-z_i\epsilon\psi/kT}. \quad\ldots\ldots\ldots\ldots\ldots\ldots(234)$$

Now an equation in electrostatics, *viz. Poisson's equation*, gives a relation between the variation of the electric potential at a point and the charge density. It is

$$\frac{\partial^2\psi}{\partial x^2}+\frac{\partial^2\psi}{\partial y^2}+\frac{\partial^2\psi}{\partial z^2}=-\frac{4\pi\rho}{D}, \quad\ldots\ldots\ldots\ldots\ldots(235)$$

where x, y, and z represent the rectangular co-ordinates of the point and D is the dielectric constant of the medium. The expression on the left of this equation is represented shortly by $\nabla^2\psi$.

Substituting the value of ρ given by (234), we obtain

$$\nabla^2\psi=-\frac{4\pi}{D}\Sigma n_i z_i\epsilon e^{-z_i\epsilon\psi/kT}. \quad\ldots\ldots\ldots\ldots\ldots(236)$$

An approximation to this equation can be made when $z_i \epsilon \psi$ is small compared with kT by substituting

$$1 - z_i \epsilon \psi / kT \text{ for } e^{-z_i \epsilon \psi / kT}.$$

Then (165) becomes

$$\nabla^2 \psi = -\frac{4\pi}{D}(\Sigma n_i z_i \epsilon - \Sigma n_i z_i^2 \epsilon^2 \psi / kT).$$

Since, when $\psi = 0$, there are as many positive as negative charges at any point, $\Sigma n_i z_i \epsilon$ is zero, and we are left with

$$\nabla^2 \psi = \kappa^2 \psi, \qquad (237)$$

where

$$\kappa^2 = \frac{4\pi \epsilon^2}{DkT} \Sigma n_i z_i^2. \qquad (238)$$

A solution of this equation giving ψ as a function of the distance r from the centre of the given ion can be written in the form

$$\psi = \frac{z\epsilon}{D} \cdot \frac{e^{-\kappa r}}{r} = \frac{z\epsilon}{Dr} - \frac{z\epsilon}{D} \cdot \frac{1 - e^{-\kappa r}}{r},$$

where $z\epsilon$ is the charge on the central ion. By electrostatic theory the first term $z\epsilon / Dr$ is the electric potential which is produced at the distance r by the charge $z\epsilon$ of the ion itself (it is assumed that the ion is spherical). The second term, which can be approximated to

$$\psi' = -\frac{z\epsilon\kappa}{D},$$

when κr is small compared with 1, is the potential at the given point produced by the surrounding distribution of ions (or ionic atmosphere). The potential at a point near the ion is thus

$$\psi = \frac{z\epsilon}{Dr} - \frac{z\epsilon\kappa}{D}, \qquad (239)$$

We may observe at this stage that ψ' is the potential

at the surface of a sphere having the charge $-z\epsilon$ and the radius $1/\kappa$ in a medium of dielectric constant D. Accordingly $1/\kappa$ can be regarded as the equivalent radius of the ionic atmosphere (*i.e.* if the whole ionic atmosphere were concentrated at the radius $1/\kappa$ the potential produced would be the same). The value of $1/\kappa$ obtained by inserting the values of the universal constants in (238) for a uni-univalent electrolyte in aqueous solution is $1/\kappa = 3 \times 10^{-8}/\sqrt{c}$ cm., where c is the concentration in gram molecules per litre. For a $0{\cdot}01N$ solution $1/\kappa$ is thus 30×10^{-8} cm., while the average distance between the ions in this case is 44×10^{-8} cm. It may also be observed that κ^2 is proportional to the ionic strength of the solution.

We now have to find the electric work done in transferring an ion from an infinitely dilute solution to a given solution. This can be regarded as the difference between the energy required to charge the ion in (1) an infinitely dilute solution, and (2) the given solution. In order to calculate these quantities it is supposed that it is possible to start with an uncharged ion and to build up the charge by infinitesimal amounts in such a way that at every stage the ion atmosphere adjusts itself so as to correspond with the amount of charge actually present.

If the potential at the surface of the ion (radius r_0) at any stage in this process is ψ, the work done in bringing up an element of charge de is $\psi\, de$, and the total work done in giving the ion its charge $z\epsilon$ is given by the integral

$$w = \int_0^{z\epsilon} \psi\, de.$$

When the ion has the charge e the potential at its surface is by (239), $\psi = e/Dr_0 - e\kappa/D$.

In an infinitely dilute solution the second term disappears, since κ is then zero, and the work done in charging the ion is

$$w_0 = \int_0^{z\epsilon} \frac{e}{Dr_0} . de = \frac{z^2\epsilon^2}{2Dr_0}.$$

Similarly the work done in charging the ion in the given solution is

$$w = \int_0^{z\epsilon} \frac{e}{Dr_0} . de - \int_0^{z\epsilon} \frac{e\kappa}{D} . de = \frac{z^2\epsilon^2}{2Dr_0} - \frac{z^2\epsilon^2}{2D} . \kappa.$$

The work done in transferring the ion from an infinitely dilute solution to the given solution is thus

$$W = w - w_0 = -z^2\epsilon^2\kappa/2D. \quad \text{...........(240)}$$

Now if there were no electric forces and the solutions were otherwise ideal, the free energy transfer of a single ion from a very dilute solution of concentration m_0 to a solution of concentration m would be

$$\Delta F_i = kT . \log(m/m_0).*$$

Adding the work done on account of the electric forces (which is a free energy quantity since it was evaluated by a reversible process) we thus obtain, when there are no other effects which contribute to the free energy charge,

$$\Delta F_i = kT . \log(m/m_0) + W.$$

But by definition,

$$\Delta F_i = kT . \log(a/a_0) = kT . \log(mf_i/m_0),$$

where f_i is the activity coefficient in the given solution, and the activity coefficient in the very dilute solution is 1. Comparing these equations it is evident that

$$kT . \log f_i = W = -z_i^2\epsilon^2\kappa/2D,$$

or

$$\log f_i = -z_i^2\epsilon^2\kappa/2DkT. \quad \text{.........(241)}$$

* $k = R/N°$, where $N°$ is the Avogadro number or the number of molecules in the gram molecule, is the gas constant per molecule.

In order to obtain the activity coefficient of a complete salt in a more practical form we may first observe that if n_i is the number of ions of species i per c.c., the number of gm. ions per litre is $c_i = n_i \cdot 1000/N_0$, where N_0 is the Avogadro number. Therefore

$$\Sigma n_i z_i^2 = \Sigma c_i z_i^2 \cdot N_0/1000.$$

The value of κ^2 can thus be written as

$$\kappa^2 = \frac{4\pi\epsilon^2}{DkT} \cdot \frac{N_0}{1000} \Sigma c_i z_i^2,$$

and introducing this into (170), we have

$$\log f_i = -z_i^2 \left(\frac{\epsilon^2}{2DkT} \sqrt{\frac{4\pi\epsilon^2}{DkT} \cdot \frac{N_0}{1000}} \right) \sqrt{\Sigma c_i z_i^2},$$

$$= -z_i^2 B \sqrt{\Sigma c_i z_i^2}, \quad \text{......................(242)}$$

where B is the quantity within the brackets. The mean activity coefficient of a salt $A_{\nu_1} B_{\nu_2}$ is

$$\log f_\pm = (1/\nu_1 + \nu_2)(\nu_1 \log f_1 + \nu_2 \log f_2),$$

and therefore

$$\log_e f_\pm = -\sum \frac{\nu_1 z_1^2}{\nu_1 + \nu_2} \cdot B \sqrt{\Sigma c_i z_i^2}, \quad \text{......(243)}$$

where ν_1 is the number of ions of valency z_1 in the salt and the summation extends over all the ions.

The valency factor $\Sigma \nu_1 z_1^2/(\nu_1 + \nu_2)$ has the values:

for uni-univalent electrolytes, $\nu_1 = 1$, $\nu_2 = 1$; $z_1 = 1$, $z_2 = 1$; $\sum \frac{\nu_1 z_1^2}{\nu_1 + \nu_2} = 1$
e.g. KCl;

for uni-bivalent electrolytes, $\nu_1 = 1$, $\nu_2 = 2$; $z_1 = 2$, $z_2 = 1$; $\sum \frac{\nu_1 z_1^2}{\nu_1 + \nu_2} = 2$
e.g. $CaCl_2$, K_2SO_4;

for uni-trivalent electrolytes, $\nu_1 = 1$, $\nu_2 = 3$; $z_1 = 3$, $z_2 = 1$; $\sum \frac{\nu_1 z_1^2}{\nu_1 + \nu_2} = 3$
e.g. $LaCl_3$, $K_3Fe(CN)_6$

for bi-bivalent electrolytes, $\nu_1 = 1,\ \nu_2 = 1;$ *e.g.* $CaSO_4$; $z_1 = 2,\ z_2 = 2;$ $\left.\right\} \sum \frac{\nu_1 z_1^2}{\nu_1 + \nu_2} = 4$

for bi-trivalent electrolytes, $\nu_1 = 2,\ \nu_2 = 3;$ *e.g.* $Fe_2(SO_4)_3$; $z_1 = 3,\ z_2 = 2;$ $\left.\right\} \sum \frac{\nu_1 z_1^2}{\nu_1 + \nu_2} = 6$

Tests of the Debye-Hückel Equation. In very dilute solutions it is often convenient to use the weight concentration (m) instead of c. If d is the density of the solvent, we can write for dilute solutions, without appreciable error, $c_i = m_i/d$; or $\Sigma c_i z_i^2 = \Sigma m_i z_i^2/d$, and since

$$\Sigma m_i z_i^2 = 2\mu,$$

we have
$$\log_e f_\pm = -\sum \frac{\nu_1 z_i^2}{\nu_1 + \nu_2} \cdot \frac{B}{\sqrt{d}} \sqrt{2\mu},$$

or
$$\log_{10} f_\pm = -\sum \frac{\nu_1 z_i^2}{\nu_1 + \nu_2} \cdot \frac{\sqrt{2}B'}{2{\cdot}303} \cdot \sqrt{\mu}, \quad \text{...(244)}$$

where $B' = B/\sqrt{d}$.

Using the constants,

$$\epsilon = 4{\cdot}77 \times 10^{-10} \text{ e.s.u.}, \quad N^\circ = 6{\cdot}06 \times 10^{23},$$

$k = 1{\cdot}371 \times 10^{-16}$ ergs, the value of $\sqrt{2}B'/2{\cdot}303$ for water is found to be 0·489 at 0°, 0·504 at 25°, 0·526 at 50°. We can take its value as 0·50 at 25°, with sufficient accuracy. The following equations are then obtained for the activity coefficients of electrolytes of various types at 25°.

Uni-univalent : $\log_{10} f_\pm = -0{\cdot}5\sqrt{\mu}$.

Uni-bivalent : $\log_{10} f_\pm = -1{\cdot}0\sqrt{\mu}$.

Uni-trivalent : $\log_{10} f_\pm = -1{\cdot}5\sqrt{\mu}$.

Bi-bivalent : $\log_{10} f_\pm = -2{\cdot}0\sqrt{\mu}$.

Bi-trivalent : $\log_{10} f_\pm = -3{\cdot}0\sqrt{\mu}$.

On account of the approximations which have been made in the derivation and of certain factors which will be considered later, these equations can only be expected to apply at very small concentrations ($\mu < 0{\cdot}01$).

Brönsted and La Mer * have made a test of these equations by determining the activity coefficients of some complex cobaltammine salts of various ion types in salt solutions, by the solubility method. Their curves, which are shown in Fig. 88, are in excellent agreement

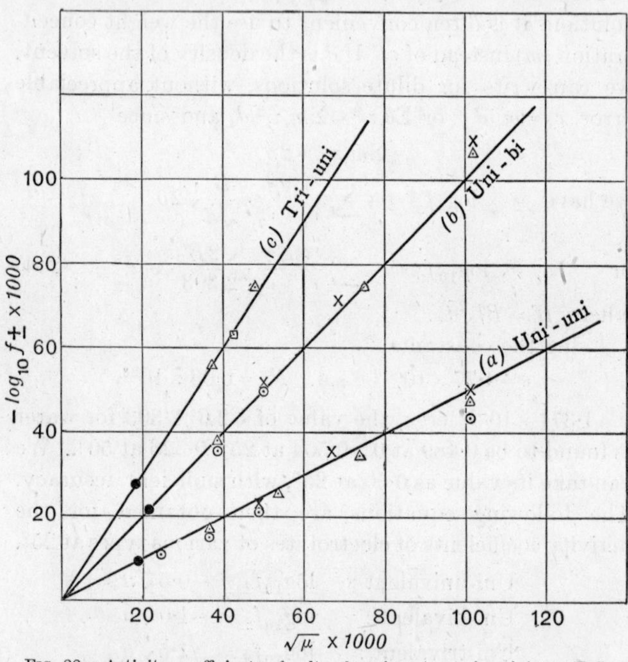

FIG. 88.—Activity coefficients of salts of various types in mixtures (Brönsted and La Mer):

(a) $[Co(NH_3)_4NO_2 . CNS]^+[Co(NH_3)_2(NO_2)_2C_2O_4]^-$. Uni-univalent.

(b) $\left[Co(NH_3)_4C_2O_4\right]_2^+\left[S_2O_6\right]^=$. Uni-bivalent.

(c) $[Co(NH_3)_6]^{+++}\left[Co(NH_3)_2(NO_2)_2C_2O_4\right]_3^-$. Tri-univalent.

Added salt; —⊙—NaCl, —△—KNO₃, —×—$K_3Co(CN)_6$, —⊡—$BaCl_2$, —●— none.

* *J. Amer. Chem. Soc.*, 46, 555, 1924.

with the requirements of the theory. Nonhebel * determined the activity coefficients of hydrochloric acid at very small concentrations in aqueous solutions and found that the results were best represented by the equation $\log f = -0{\cdot}39\sqrt{c}$, which is considerably different from the result of the Debye calculation, but quite close to that of Milner. Carmody obtained appreciably different results,† working in silica vessels, but Wynne-Jones has shown ‡ that if a correction is made in Nonhebel's data for the solution of alkaline impurities from the glass used, good agreement between the two sets of values is obtained, and the slope of the activity coefficient curve at very small concentrations is then in excellent agreement with Debye and Hückel's calculation.

Numerous other tests have been made of the theoretical equation. According to (242) B should be proportional to $1/(DT)^{3/2}$. This has been tested by measurements in aqueous solutions at temperatures other than 25°. For example, Baxter determined the activity coefficients of silver iodate in salt solutions at 75° and found agreement with the theory.§ The dielectric constant of the medium can also be varied by adding neutral substances, such as sugar, alcohol, etc. It is necessary to interpret the results in such solutions with caution for, as will be shown later, substances having a dielectric constant less than water are "salted out" from the vicinity of the ions. The addition of alcohol to a salt solution will thus affect the dielectric constant of the medium only at an appreciable distance from the ions. It has, however, been shown by Pauling || that variations of the dielectric

* *Phil. Mag.*, 2, 586, 1926.

† *J. Amer. Chem. Soc.*, 54, 188, 1932. ‡ *Ibid.*, 54, 2130, 1932.

§ *J. Amer. Chem. Soc.*, 48, 615, 1926.

|| *J. Amer. Chem. Soc.*, 47, 2129, 1925.

constant of the medium very near the ions have very little effect on the limiting equation. Numerous measurements of the value of B in the presence of non-electrolytes have been made, *e.g.* with hydrogen chloride in aqueous glycerol solutions by Lucasse,* and in sucrose solutions by Scatchard,† in which reasonable agreement with the theory has been obtained. Butler and Robertson ‡ determined the activity coefficients of hydrogen chloride in water-ethyl alcohol solvents extending from pure water to pure alcohol, and found that B varied approximately linearly with $1/(DT)^{3/2}$ over the whole range of solvents. A similar result was obtained by Åkerlöf § with hydrochloric and sulphuric acids in water-methyl alcohol solutions.

Extension to Concentrated Solutions. In estimating the potential at the surface of an ion due to the ionic atmosphere, the following approximation has been made:

$$\psi' = \frac{z\epsilon}{D} \cdot \frac{1 - e^{-\kappa r}}{r} \rightarrow \frac{z\epsilon}{D}\kappa.$$

When κr is not very small this needs amendment. A closer approximation is given by the equation

$$\psi' = \frac{z\epsilon}{D} \cdot \frac{\kappa}{1 + \kappa r},$$

If r_i is the radius of the ion, the potential at its surface is obtained by substituting r_i in this expression, and we then obtain

$$\log f_i = -\frac{z_i^2\epsilon^2}{2DkT} \cdot \frac{\kappa}{1 + \kappa r_i} = -\frac{z_i^2 B\sqrt{c_i z_i^2}}{1 + Ar_i\sqrt{c_i z_i^2}}, \quad \ldots(245)$$

where

$$A = \sqrt{\frac{4\pi\epsilon^2}{D\kappa T} \cdot \frac{N^\circ}{1000}}.$$

* *Ibid.*, 48, 626, 1926. † *Ibid.*, 48, 2026, 1926.

‡ *Proc. Roy. Soc.*, *A*, 125, 694, 1929.

§ *J. Amer. Chem. Soc.*, 52, 2353, 1930.

For aqueous solutions $A = 0{\cdot}232 \times 10^8$. This expression will apply to a uni-univalent salt if it be assumed that the ionic radius is the same for both ions, or that r_i is the mean ionic radius. Using reasonable values for the ionic radii, this expression fits the experimental data to a higher concentration than the original equation. That it fails in more concentrated solutions is obvious from the fact that in many cases the activity coefficient passes through a minimum and increases, becoming greater than unity in strong solutions, *i.e.* $\log f$ becomes positive and (245) is incapable of giving positive values. Fig. 89 shows the calculated and observed values of $\log f_{\pm}$ for NaCl. $\operatorname{Log} f'$ is the original equation (242) which represents the limiting slope at small concentrations ; $\log f''$ represents equation (245), using $r = 2{\cdot}35 \times 10^{-8}$ cm., while the dashed line represents the observed behaviour. It is evident that in strong solutions we need a positive term, which, according to the empirical equation (233), should be linear with the concentration.*

Hückel's theory of concentrated solutions. So far, the problem has been regarded as the calculation of the mutual electrical energy of charged particles in a medium of uniform dielectric constant. The medium only enters into the calculation in so far as it provides the dielectric constant D. In water and similar solvents, the molecules of the solvents carry electric dipoles and are themselves attracted by the ions. The electric forces in the immediate vicinity of ions are extremely powerful, *e.g.* it can be calculated, taking the dielectric constant of water

* A close examination of the approximations made in the Debye-Hückel theory and the effect of the ionic radii has been made by Gronwall, La Mer and Sandved (*Physikal. Z.*, 29, 558, 1928 ; *J. Physical Chem.*, 35, 2245, 1931).

as 80, that at 3×10^{-8} cm. from the centre of a univalent ion the electric field is 2×10^{6} volts/cm. This intense field has two consequences. In the first place, the

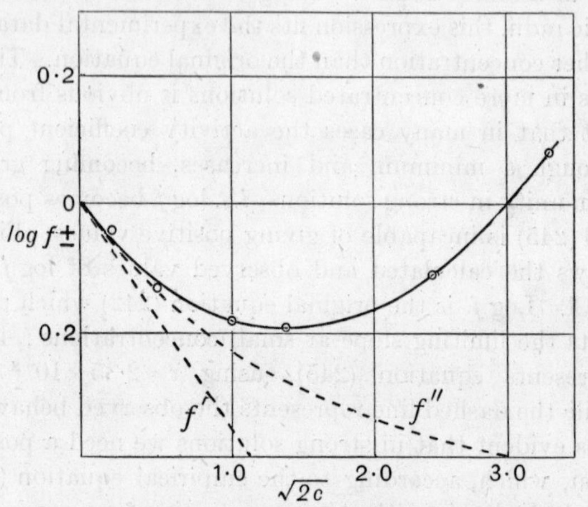

FIG. 89.—Calculated and observed activity coefficients of sodium chloride.

attraction of fields of this strength on the molecules of the solvent may be of the same order as that on oppositely charged ions. Consequently there will be a tendency for ions to be " crowded out " from the immediate vicinity of an ion, *i.e.* there will be superimposed on the " coulomb forces," which have already been considered, an effective repulsive force which must be taken into account in order to obtain the distribution of ions round a given ion. Secondly, it has been assumed that the dielectric constant has a uniform value throughout the solution. The dielectric constant is a measure of the polarisation produced in a medium by an applied electric field, and is due partly to the orientation in the direction of the field of the permanent dipoles which may be present in the molecules, and partly to the electric charges within the molecule under the influence of the applied field. In the intense fields of force near the ions the permanent dipoles become completely orientated and the induced polarisation is so great that the effect of any increase in the applied field is no longer proportional to its amount. Under these circumstances the solvent near the ions becomes "electrically saturated," and its dielectric constant may be considerably less than the normal value.* The dielectric constant of the medium in a salt solution will thus vary from point to point, and the average value for the whole of the solvent will be less than that of the pure solvent.

A precise calculation of the effect of these phenomena on the activity coefficients of ions is extremely difficult. Hückel † assumed that both effects might be introduced into the equations by regarding the average dielectric constant of the medium as a function of the salt concentration. The lowering of the dielectric constant by the factors mentioned above should be proportional to the number of ions, and we may write

$$D = D_0 - \delta_1 c_1 - \delta_2 c_2, \text{ etc.,}$$
$$= D_0 - \delta c,$$

where c_1, c_2, etc., are the concentrations of ions of different kinds (mols per litre of solution), and δ_1, δ_2, etc., the coefficients of the dielectric constant lowering produced by them.

This variation of the dielectric constant affects the

* Herweg (*Z. f. Physik*, 3, 36, 1922) demonstrated that the dielectric constant of water diminishes in intense electric fields.

† *Physikal. Z.*, 26, 93, 1925.

work of charging the ion on account of the potential due to its own charge, as well as the work done on account of the potential of the ionic atmosphere. The work of charging the ion in an infinitely dilute solution is $w_0 = z^2\epsilon^2/2D_0r_i$, and the work of charging the ion in the given solution, apart from the terms arising from the ionic atmosphere, is $w_0' = z^2\epsilon^2/2Dr_i$. The quantity

$$w' = z^2\epsilon^2/2Dr_i - z^2\epsilon^2/2D_0 r_i$$

must thus be added to the term arising from the potential of the ionic atmosphere, viz. $\psi' = \frac{z\epsilon}{D} \cdot \frac{\kappa}{1+\kappa r_i}$. In evaluating $\int_0^{z\epsilon} \psi' de$ it is also necessary to regard D as a function of the concentration. Hückel obtained the result of this calculation in the form

$$\log f_i = \frac{z_i^2\epsilon^2}{2D_0kT} \frac{\kappa_0}{1+\kappa_0 r_i} + f(\kappa),$$

where κ_0 is the value of κ corresponding to D_0, and $f(\kappa)$ is a complicated function which was found to be nearly proportional to the ionic concentration. For a uni-univalent salt we thus obtain

$$\log f_{\pm} = -\frac{B\sqrt{2c}}{1+A\bar{r}\sqrt{2c}} + C \,.\, 2c, \quad \text{........(246)}$$

i.e. as the result of assuming a lowering of the dielectric constant of the medium which is proportional to the concentration of the salt, we obtain an additional positive term for $\log f_{\pm}$ which is proportional to the concentration.

* In very dilute solutions the *ideal* equation for the partial free energy of a salt may be written equally well in terms of the molar ratio of the salt to solvent molecules (or the related quantity m) or the molar fraction of the salt, for n_2/n_1 does

not differ appreciably from n_2/n_1+n_2 when n_2 is small. But in concentrated solutions these quantities may differ appreciably. Hückel thought that the ideal equation for the partial free energy of a salt was properly expressed in terms of the molar fraction of the ions, *i.e.* for a binary electrolyte

$$\bar{F}_2=\bar{F}^\circ{}_2+2RT\,.\log\frac{\Sigma n_2}{\Sigma n_2+n_1},$$

where Σn_2 is the total number of ions and n_1 the number of solvent molecules. If we use an expression of the kind

$$\bar{F}_2=\bar{F}^\circ{}_2+2RT\,.\log(\Sigma n_2/n_1)$$

it is therefore necessary to make a correction which is equal to the difference between these expressions. This correcting term is $2RT\log(n_1/(n_1+\Sigma n_2))$. If the solution contains m gram molecules of salt to 1000 grams of the solvent, of molecular weight M_1, we have

$$\frac{n_1}{n_1+\Sigma n_2}=\frac{1000/M_1}{(1000/M_1)+2m}=1\bigg/\left(1+\frac{2mM_1}{1000}\right).$$

Inserting this correction into the activity coefficient (246) we thus have

$$\log f\pm=-\frac{B\sqrt{2c}}{1+A\bar{r}\sqrt{2c}}+C\,.\,2c-\log\left(1+\frac{2mM_1}{1000}\right). \quad (247)$$

This equation is similar in form to Harned's empirical equation, and by a suitable choice of the constants a and C can be made to fit the experimental data over a considerable range of concentration. There are two adjustable constants $\bar{r}$ and C (A and B are absolute constants which can be calculated), $\bar{r}$ being the mean ionic radius for the salt and C a function of the dielectric constant lowering coefficient $\bar{\delta}$. Fig. 90 shows curves of $\log f$ calculated by Hückel for various values of $\bar{\delta}$.

The values of the Debye-Hückel constants for a

number of salts, as determined by Harned and Åkerlöf,* are given in Table XLII.

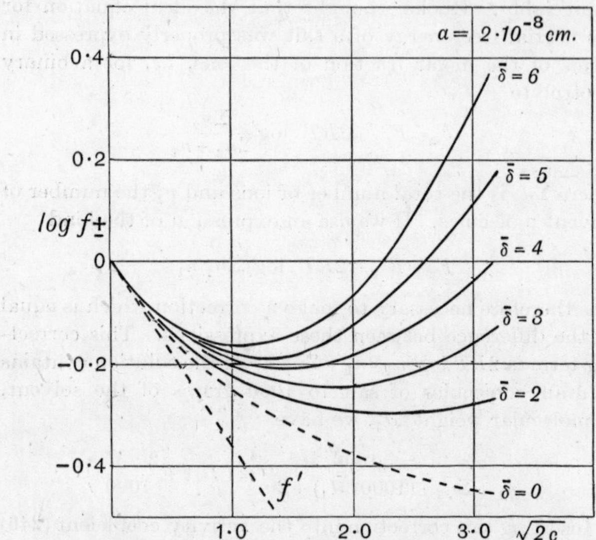

FIG. 90.—Theoretical curves of activity coefficients for various values of $\bar{\delta}$ (Hückel).

TABLE XLII.

Salt.	$\bar{r} \times 10^8$.	C.	$\bar{\delta}$.
KCl	3·38	0·017	3·2
NaCl	3·62	0·028	5·5
LiCl	3·62	0·0698	11·5
HCl	3·38	0·0805	11·8
KOH	3·35	0·0632	9·65
NaOH	2·87	0·050	6·45
LiOH	2·15	0·0215	2·2
$BaCl_2$	3·83	0·0285	7·14
$SrCl_2$	4·39	0·030	8·93
$CaCl_2$	4·35	0·060	14·61

* *Physikal. Z.*, 27, 411, 1926.

Although Hückel's theory succeeds in deriving a linear term in the expression for $\log f_{\pm}$, it is not known whether the values of $\bar{\delta}$ which are required to give agreement with the experimental data actually correspond with the effect of the salt on the dielectric constant of the solvent.* It is doubtful if the large values of δ required in certain cases can have a real physical meaning. It might also have been expected that the values of δ would be additive for the different ions, but it can be seen that whereas in the chlorides the values of δ are in the order Li>Na>K, in the case of the hydroxides the reverse order, K>Na>Li, is obtained.

***Solvation of Ions.** Many lines of evidence indicate that ions are solvated in solution, *i.e.* they carry with them a sheath of the solvent, which is firmly attached either by the attraction of the electric field of the ions on the dipoles of the solvent molecules or possibly by some kind of electronic interaction. A linear term in the equation for $\log f_{\pm}$ can be derived in a very simple way as a result of this solvation.† The solvent molecules which are attached to the ions are effectively withdrawn from the solution and the real concentration of the ions is thereby increased. For the purpose of computing this effect the concentration of an ion is best expressed as its molar ratio. If the solution contains n_1 molecules of the solvent and n_i ions of the ith kind, the apparent molar ratio of the ions to the solvent is n_i/n_1, and in the absence of solvation the partial free energy of these ions, neglecting the effect of the interionic forces, would be represented by

$$\bar{F}_i = \bar{F}^\circ_i + RT \log n_i/n_1.$$

* Walden, Ulich and Werner, *Z. phys. Chem.*, **116**, 261, 1926.
† Cf. Bjerrum, *Z. anorg. Chemie*, **109**, 278, 1920.

But if each ion is, on the average, solvated by h solvent molecules the effective number of the latter in the solution is $n_1 - \Sigma n_i h$, where the summation extends over all the ions present. (178) must therefore be replaced by

$$\bar{F}_i = \bar{F}^\circ_i + RT \,.\, \log \frac{n_i}{n_1 - \Sigma n_i h}$$

$$= \bar{F}^\circ_i + RT \log \frac{n_i}{n_1(1 - (\Sigma n_i h/n_1))}$$

$$= F^\circ_i + RT \,.\, \log n_i/n_1 - RT \,.\, \log(1 - (\Sigma n_i h)/n_1).$$

The additional factor may be written as $RT \log f_i{*}$, where $f_i{*}$ is that part of the activity coefficient which arises from solvation. To a first approximation we may write

$$\log f_i{*} = -\log(1 - (\Sigma n_i h)\, n_1) = (\Sigma n_i h)/n_1. \quad \text{...(248)}$$

If m_i is the molar (weight) concentration per 1000 grams of solvent, we have $n_i/n_1 = m_i M_1/1000$, where M_1 is the molecular weight of the solvent. Then (248) becomes

$$\log_e f_i{*} = \Sigma m_i h M_1/1000.$$

$f_i{*}$ is the same for all the ions present in the solution, so that the mean value of $f_i{*}$ for the salt is also given by

$$\log_{10} f_\pm{*} = \Sigma m_i h M_1/2{\cdot}3 \times 1000. \quad \text{.........(249)}$$

We can equate this with the final term of (246), which may be written for this purpose in the form :

$$\log f_\pm{*} = C \,.\, \Sigma m_i z_i^2,$$

and we then obtain

$$C = \frac{\Sigma m_i}{\Sigma m_i z_i^2} \cdot \frac{M_1 \,.\, h}{2{\cdot}3 \times 1000}. \quad \text{...........(250)}$$

The following table gives the values of h (the average effective hydration per ion) which would be required to account for the observed values of C in aqueous solutions.

TABLE XLIII.

KCl	2·2	KOH	8·1	$BaCl_2$	7·3
NaCl	3·6	NaOH	6·4	$SrCl_2$	7·7
LiCl	8·9	LiOH	2·7	$CaCl_2$	15·3
HCl	10·3				

While in most cases these are fairly reasonable magnitudes, the difficulty again arises that the values are not additive for the different ions as we should expect hydration values to be. A complete solution of the problem thus awaits a more complete mathematical treatment of the forces between the ions and the solvent.*

***Activity Coefficients in Mixtures of Strong Electrolytes.** While in very dilute solutions of a mixture of salts the activity coefficient of a salt is determined, at least approximately, by the ionic strength rule, in concentrated solutions it depends on the nature of the other ions present. In order to determine the activity coefficient of a salt in such a solution it is generally necessary to resort to electromotive methods. For example, the partial free energy of hydrogen chloride in the presence of other chlorides can be determined from the electromotive forces of cells of the type

$$H_2 \mid HCl(m_1),\ MCl(m_2),\ AgCl(s) \mid Ag.$$

* Butler (*J. Phys. Chem.*, 33, 1015, 1929) attempted to account for the linear term in the expression for log f as a consequence of the "salting out" of the ions by each other (see p. 464). Dielectric constant lowering, solvation, mutual "salting out" are only different ways of regarding the same phenomenon. This calculation does, however, demand somewhat smaller dielectric constant lowerings than Hückel's.

The activity coefficient of HCl in this cell can be determined by comparison with the cell :

$$H_2 \mid HCl(m),\ AgCl(s) \mid Ag,$$

for which the activity coefficient of HCl is known. Extensive measurements of cells of this type have been made by Harned and his co-workers,* and by others. Their main conclusions are summarised below.

(1) *Salt mixtures of constant total concentration.* When the total electrolyte concentration $(m_1 + m_2)$ remains

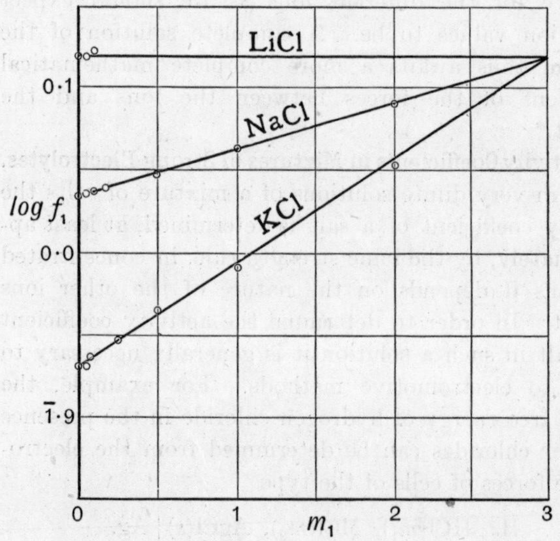

FIG. 91.—Activity coefficients of HCl in alkali chloride solutions at constant total concentration $(m_1 + m_2 = 3)$. (Harned and Åkerlöf.)

constant it is found that $\log f_1$ varies linearly with m_1. Fig. 91 shows the values of $\log f_1$ in lithium, sodium and potassium chloride solutions of total concentration

* Summaries by Harned and Åkerlöf, *Physikal. Z.*, 27, 411, 1926 ; Harned, *Trans. Far. Soc.*, 23, 462, 1927.

$(m_1 + m_2) = 3$. Similar results have also been obtained in more dilute solutions, *e.g.* Güntelberg obtained a similar relation for a total concentration $\Sigma m = 0{\cdot}1$.* The curves shown in Fig. 92 are obtained when f_1 is plotted against log m_1. It can be seen that when the concentration of hydrogen chloride is very small its activity coefficient is practically independent of m_1 and depends only on the nature and concentration of the solution in which it is dissolved.

(2) *Acid concentration constant, salt concentration variable.* When m_1 is kept constant and m_2 varied, the

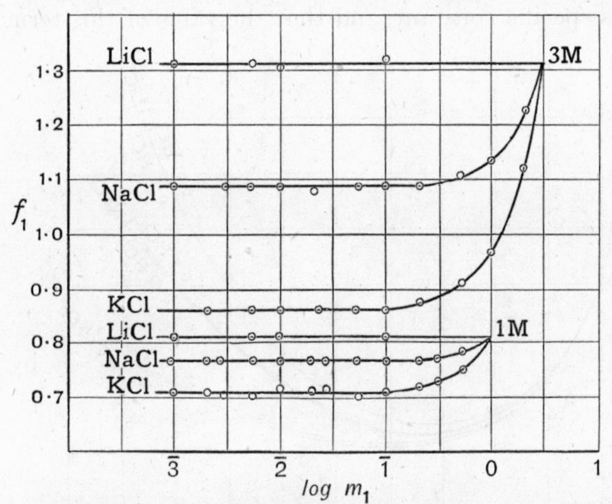

FIG. 92.—Activity coefficients of HCl in alkali chloride solutions at constant total concentrations $m_1 + m_2 = 1$ and $m_1 + m_2 = 3$ (Harned and Åkerlöf.)

curves obtained are very similar to the curves for the single salts. Fig. 93 shows the activity coefficients of hydrogen chloride at $m_1 = 0{\cdot}01$ and $0{\cdot}1$ in solutions of lithium, sodium and potassium chlorides.

* *Z. physikal. Chem.*, 123, 199, 1926.

This behaviour is in good agreement with the requirements of the Debye-Hückel theory. Writing the equation for the mean activity coefficient of a salt in the semi-empirical form

$$\log f_{\pm} = -\beta\sqrt{\Sigma m_i z_i^2} + \Sigma\lambda m_i,$$

it can be seen that the first term which represents the effect of the interionic forces will be constant in solutions of constant total ionic strength and the variation of $\log f_{\pm}$ will depend on the linear term $\Sigma\lambda m_i$. According to Hückel's theory we should expect that each kind of ion has its specific constant, and that the value of this term

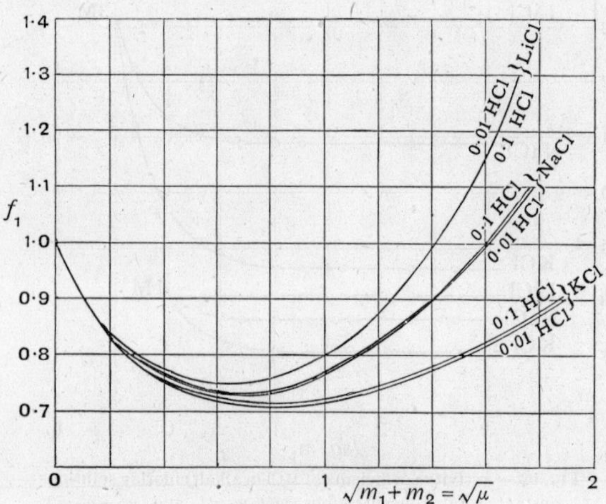

FIG. 93.—Activity coefficients of hydrogen chloride in alkali chloride solutions.
m_1 = const., m_2 = variable. (Harned and Åkerlöf.)

for a mixed solution is made up of the sum of the terms for the various ions present. Thus, in solutions of $HCl(m_1)$ and $KCl(m_2)$, we have (*a*) $m_1 + m_2 = \text{constant } (m)$.

$$\log f_1 = -\beta\sqrt{\Sigma m_i z_i^2} + \lambda_1 m_1 + \lambda_2 m_2$$
$$= (\lambda_1 - \lambda_2) m_1 + \lambda_2 m + \text{constant};$$

i.e. $\log f_1$ varies linearly with m_1.

(*b*) m_1 constant; m_2 variable.

$$\log f_1 = -\beta\sqrt{\Sigma m_i z_i^2} + \lambda_1 m_1 + \lambda_2 m_2.$$

When m_1 is small, the variation of $\log f_1$ will be determined mainly by the interionic term $-\beta\sqrt{\Sigma m_i z_i^2}$ and by $\lambda_2 m_2$. The curve for f_1 will thus be very similar to the curve for $\log f_2$ in a pure solution of the salt. In pure solutions of a series of salts of the same ion type, $\log f_2$ will be greater at a given concentration the greater the value of λ_2. It therefore follows that the activity coefficient of HCl, when present at a small constant concentration in a series of salt solutions of the same strength, should be greatest in that solution for which $\log f_2$ has the greatest value. Thus, since for a given concentration the activity coefficients of the alkali metal chlorides are in the order

$$f_{LiCl} > f_{NaCl} > f_{KCl},$$

we should find for the activity coefficients of HCl in the same solutions

$$f_{HCl\,(LiCl)} > f_{HCl\,(NaCl)} > f_{HCl\,(KCl)}.$$

Fig. 93 shows that this is the case. The same is also true for hydrogen chloride in solutions of the alkaline earth chlorides, and for sulphuric acid in the alkali sulphates.

Anomalous behaviour of hydroxides. The reverse, however, is the case for the strong hydroxides. It has been observed already that these electrolytes are anomalous in pure aqueous solution. At a given concentration in pure water their activity coefficients are in the order

$$f_{\text{KOH}} > f_{\text{NaOH}} > f_{\text{LiOH}}.$$

Similarly, in mixed solutions containing salts of a given ion type, it is found that, at a given hydroxide and total concentration, the activity coefficients of the strong hydroxides are less in the solution of the salt which has the higher activity coefficient itself. Thus, Harned and his co-workers found that

$$f_{\text{KOH (KCl)}} > f_{\text{NaOH (NaCl)}} > f_{\text{LiOH (LiCl)}},$$

and $f_{\text{KOH (KCl)}} > f_{\text{KOH (KBr)}} > f_{\text{KOH (KI)}}$;

while $f_{\text{LiCl}} > f_{\text{NaCl}} > f_{\text{KCl}}$,

and $f_{\text{KI}} > f_{\text{KBr}} > f_{\text{KCl}}$.

This is the reverse of what would be expected by Hückel's theory, or on any theory in which the linear term is additive for the various ions. Harned has suggested as a possible cause of this behaviour the highly unsymmetrical nature of the hydroxide ion, which will therefore be easily deformed by an electric field. The extent of this deformation will be greater the greater the field intensity, and in the presence of lithium ions the hydroxide ion will thus be less symmetrical than in the presence of sodium ions.

*** The Apparent Molar Volumes of Salts.** It has been found that the apparent molar volumes of salts in aqueous solution increase linearly with the square root of the concentration,* *i.e.* $\phi = \phi_0 + a\sqrt{c}$, where ϕ_0 is the apparent molar volume at infinite dilution, a a constant and c the concentration (mols per litre). In Fig. 94, which shows the data for a number of salts, it can be

* Masson, *Phil. Mag.*, 8, 218, 1929; Geffcken, *Z. physikal. Chem.*, *A*, 155, 1, 1931; Scott, *J. Physical Chem.*, 35, 2315, 1931.

seen that this relation holds over a considerable range of concentration. This is true of many salts in aqueous solution.

A similar relation can easily be derived for the partial molar volumes. In dilute aqueous solutions the weight

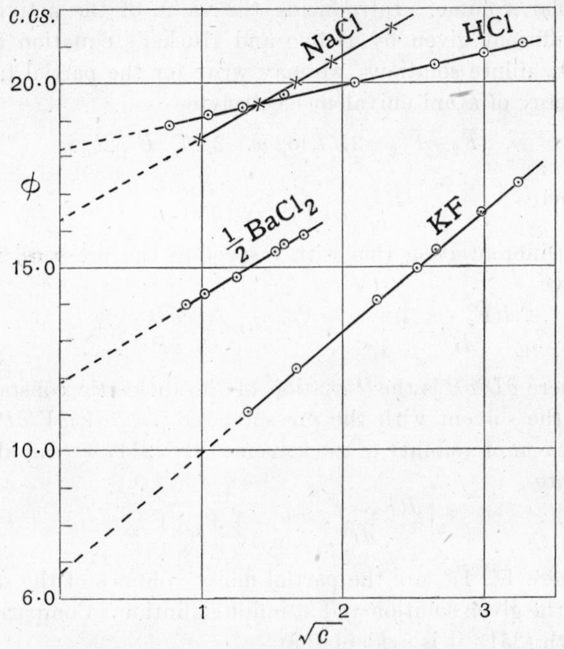

FIG. 94.—Apparent molar volumes of salts in aqueous solution at 25°.

concentration m_2 does not differ very greatly from c, and we may write $\phi = \phi_0 + a\sqrt{m_2}$. Substituting this value of ϕ in (99), viz. $d\phi/d \log m_2 + \phi = \bar{V}_2$, where $\bar{V}_2$ is the partial molar volume of the salt, we obtain

$$\bar{V}_2 = \phi_0 + 3a/2\sqrt{m_2}. \quad \text{..................(251)}$$

A derivation of the value of a in dilute solutions from the Debye-Hückel equation for the free energy of strong electrolytes has been given by Redlich and Rosenfeld.* By (211) the variation of the partial free energy of a component with the pressure is equal to its partial molar volume. Introducing the value of the activity coefficient given by Debye and Hückel's equation for very dilute solutions, we may write for the partial free energy of a uni-univalent electrolyte

$$\bar{F}_2 - \bar{F}^\circ_2 = 2RT \log m - 2RT \,.\, B\sqrt{2c},$$

where $$B = \frac{\epsilon^3}{(DkT)^{3/2}}\sqrt{\frac{\pi N_0}{1000}}.$$

Differentiating this with respect to the pressure, we have

$$\left[\frac{d(\bar{F}_2 - \bar{F}^\circ_2)}{dP}\right]_{T,m} = RT \,.\, B\left(\frac{3}{D}\cdot\frac{\partial D}{\partial P} - \beta\right)\sqrt{2c},$$

where $\partial D/\partial P$ is the variation of the dielectric constant of the solvent with the pressure, and $\beta = (1/V)\partial V/\partial P$ is the compressibility of the solvent. By (211) we can also write

$$\left[\frac{d(\bar{F}_2 - \bar{F}^\circ_2)}{dP}\right]_{T,m} = \bar{V}_2 - \bar{V}^\circ_2,$$

where $\bar{V}_2$, $\bar{V}^\circ_2$ are the partial molar volumes of the salt in the given solution and at infinite dilution. Comparing with (251), it is evident that

$$a = \frac{2RT\sqrt{2}B}{3}\left(\frac{3}{D}\cdot\frac{\partial D}{\partial P} - \beta\right). \quad \text{............(252)}$$

Using the available measurements of the variation of the dielectric constant of water with the pressure, and its compressibility, Redlich and Rosenfeld calculated

* *Z. physikal. Chem.*, *A*, 155, 65, 1931.

$a = 1{\cdot}8 \pm 0{\cdot}6$. Considering the uncertainty of $\partial D/\partial P$, this is in reasonable agreement with the observed values, a few of which are given in Table XLIV.

TABLE XLIV.

APPARENT MOLAR VOLUMES OF SALTS IN WATER AND METHYL ALCOHOL.

$(\phi = \phi_0 + a\sqrt{c})$.

		LiCl.	NaCl.	KCl.	NaI.	KI.	RbCl.
In H_2O*	ϕ_0	17·1	16·3	26·4	35·0	45·2	31·7
	a	1·4	2·2	2·4	1·4	1·6	2·3
In CH_3OH†	ϕ_0	−3·8	−3·3	(5·2)?	11·8	21·9	—
	a	9·2	11·4	—	12·0	10·8	—

In methyl alcohol the apparent molar volumes of salts are considerably less than in water, and in some cases become negative in very dilute solutions. In such a case, when the salt is added to the methyl alcohol the total volume of the solution is less than the original volume of the solvent. It is therefore evident that the solvent has undergone a contraction as the result of the presence of the ions. A contraction also occurs in aqueous solutions, though less clearly marked. For example, at 18° the molar volume of solid lithium chloride is 20·5 c.c., and its partial molar volume at $m = 1$ is 18·6 c.c.

In the intense electric fields near the ions very considerable pressures are produced in the solvent which are sufficient to cause an appreciable contraction. T. J. Webb has given a somewhat elaborate calculation of the contraction or electrostriction produced in this way.‡

* Geffcken, *Z. physikal. Chem.*, 155, 1, 1931.

† Vosburgh, Connell and Butler, *J. Chem. Soc.*, p. 933, 1933.

‡ *J. Amer. Chem. Soc.*, 48, 2589, 1926.

Table XLV. gives the pressures in megadynes/cm.² at various distances r from the centre of a univalent ion in water and methyl alcohol, as calculated by Webb's equations * (which refer to infinite dilution), and also the fractional contraction of the solvent, which is given as $-\Delta V_r/V$, where ΔV_r is the change of volume of a small mass of the solvent at the distance r, and V the final volume. The total contraction produced by a gm. molecule of ions of radius r_0 is given by the integral

$$C = N_0 \int_{r_0}^{\infty} -(\Delta V_r/V)\, 4\pi r^2 \,.\, dr.$$

TABLE XLV.

WATER.

r, Å.	4·26	3·24	2·50	2·13	1·71	1·25	1·00
p_r	26	169	713	1470	3520	11500	39100
$-\Delta V_r/V$	0·012	0·064	0·196	0·301	0·456	0·729	1·151
C, c.c.	1·97	5·0	10·4	14·1	18·3	22·8	25·6

METHYL ALCOHOL.

r, Å.	4·47	3·44	2·61	2·20	1·75	1·27	0·91
p_r	35·7	220	640	1290	3060	9160	36400
$-\Delta V_r/V$	0·034	0·140	0·268	0·377	0·565	0·905	1·60
C, c.c.	7·6	15·8	27·6	33·2	39·1	44·8	49·4

The apparent molar volume is obtained by adding the intrinsic volumes of the ions themselves, viz.

$$N_0 \,.\, 4\pi/3 \,.\, r_0^3.$$

The following table gives the mean radii of the ions of several salts which are required to give agreement of the observed with the calculated values of ϕ_0.

* Vosburgh, Connell and Butler, *loc. cit.*

TABLE XLVI.

MEAN ATOMIC RADII OF IONS FROM APPARENT MOLAR VOLUMES.

Salt.	LiCl.	NaCl.	KCl.	NaI.	KI.
Mean radius, Å, H_2O	2·09	2·08	2·19	2·28	2·38
Mean radius, Å, CH_3OH	2·28	2·29	2·37	2·43	2·51

The fact that the radii required in the two solvents approximate to each other may be taken as evidence that the contraction is mainly electrostatic in origin.* It can be seen from Table XLV. that the pressures at a given distance in the two solvents are not very different, and the greater contraction in methyl alcohol arises from its greater compressibility.

The slope a (Table XV.) for uni-univalent salts in methyl alcohol is approximately six times that in water. This is also in accordance with Redlich and Rosenfeld's equation (183), for taking $D = D_0(1 + 1{\cdot}0 \times 10^{-4}P)$, $\beta = 1{\cdot}2 \times 10^{-4}$, we obtain $a = 14$, which is in reasonable agreement with the observed values. It must be noted, however, that while according to Redlich and Rosenfeld's equation all uni-univalent salts should have the same value of a in a given solvent, the observed values of a in both water and methyl alcohol certainly differ among themselves by more than the experimental error. It must be remembered that the Debye-Hückel limiting equation, which is the basis of the calculation, is only valid in extremely dilute solutions—in fact at lower concentrations than those at which the accurate measure-

* These radii are, however, considerably greater than those derived from measurements of crystals. It is probable that Webb's theory requires some modification in respect to the water molecules which are in actual contact with the ions.

ment of apparent molar volumes is feasible. It is surprising that the relation $\phi = \phi_0 + a\sqrt{c}$ holds over a much more extensive concentration range than the equation $\log f_\pm = -B\sqrt{2c}$, from which the former can be derived.

A more complete equation for $\bar{V}_2$ would be obtained by differentiating with respect to the pressure the complete Debye-Hückel expression :

$$\log f_\pm = -\frac{B\sqrt{2c}}{1 + A\bar{r}\sqrt{2c}} + C \, . \, 2c.$$

The pressure variation of C is unknown, but the fact that $\phi = \phi_0 + a\sqrt{c}$ holds in many cases even in concentrated solutions indicates that it is probably negligible. That this should be so can readily be understood, for C depends upon the interaction of the ions and the solvent in the region where the pressure due to the electric field is extremely high and the effect of a small increase in the applied pressure will therefore be small. The variations in the actual value of a might be accounted for if the ionic radius term $A\bar{r}$ were taken into account.

*** Heats of Dilution of Strong Electrolytes.** By (210),

$$\left[\frac{d\left(\frac{\bar{F}_2 - \bar{F}^\circ_2}{T}\right)}{dT}\right]_{P,m} = -\frac{\bar{H}_2 - \bar{H}^\circ_2}{T^2},$$

where $\bar{F}_2$, $\bar{H}_2$ are the partial free energy and heat content in a given solution, and $\bar{F}^\circ_2$, $\bar{H}^\circ_2$ the corresponding values in the standard state ($f_2 = 1$). For dilute solutions the partial free energy of a uni-univalent strong electrolyte, according to the Debye-Hückel limiting equation, is

$$\bar{F}_2 - \bar{F}^\circ_2 = 2RT \log m - 2 \times RT \, . \, B\sqrt{2c},$$

and therefore (since m is independent of the temperature),

$$\left[\frac{d(2B\sqrt{2c})}{dT}\right]_{P,m} = \frac{\bar{H}_2 - \bar{H}^\circ_2}{RT^2} = \frac{\Delta\bar{H}_2}{RT^2}.$$

Differentiating with respect to the temperature (at constant P), we have

$$\frac{d(B\sqrt{2c})}{dT} = \frac{dB}{dT}\sqrt{2c} + B\frac{d(\sqrt{2c})}{dT},$$

and
$$\frac{dB}{dT} = -\frac{3}{2}\cdot\frac{B}{T}\left[1 + \frac{T}{D}\left(\frac{dD}{dT}\right)\right]$$

and
$$\frac{d\sqrt{2c}}{dT} = -\frac{1}{2}\sqrt{2c}\cdot\frac{1}{V}\left(\frac{dV}{dT}\right)_P,$$

where $V = 1/c$ is the volume of solvent containing 1 mol of the salt, and $1/V\left(\frac{dV}{dT}\right)_P$ can for dilute solutions be taken as the coefficient of thermal expansion of the solvent at constant pressure. Therefore

$$\left[\frac{d(B\sqrt{2c})}{dT}\right]_{P,m} = -\frac{3}{2}\frac{B}{T}\left[1 + \frac{T}{D}\left(\frac{dD}{dT}\right)_P + \frac{T}{3V}\left(\frac{dV}{dT}\right)_P\right]\sqrt{2c},$$

and therefore

$$\Delta\bar{H}_2 = -3RT\,.\,B\left[1 + \frac{T}{D}\left(\frac{dD}{dT}\right)_P + \frac{T}{3V}\left(\frac{dV}{dT}\right)_P\right]\sqrt{2c}.* \quad (253)$$

This gives the partial molar heat content of the salt in the given solution (*i.e.* the heat content change in the transfer of the salt from an infinitely dilute solution to the given solution, per mol). The total heat content of the given solution, taking the heat contents of the pure solvent and of the salt at infinite dilution as zero, can easily be shown to be $2/3\Delta\bar{H}_2$, and this is equal to the heat evolved when a quantity of the solution containing

* An equivalent expression containing the first two terms in the square bracket was obtained by Bjerrum (*Z. physikal. Chem.*, **109**, 145, 1926). The third term was added by Gatty (*Phil. Mag.*, **11**, 1082, 1931) and a little later by Scatchard (*J. Amer. Chem. Soc.*, **53**, 2037, 1931).

a mol of the salt is diluted with an infinite volume of the pure solvent. The heat of an infinite dilution is thus equal to

$$Q_c^\infty = 2RT \, . \, B\left[1 + \frac{T}{D}\left(\frac{dD}{dT}\right)_P + \frac{T}{3V}\left(\frac{dV}{dT}\right)_P\right]\sqrt{2c}. \quad (254)$$

Writing $Q_c^\infty = b\sqrt{c}$, the value of b calculated by (254), taking $1 + \frac{T}{D} \cdot \left(\frac{dD}{dT}\right)_P = -0{\cdot}379$, is 492 for uni-univalent salts in water at 25°. Lange and Leighton * found for KCl solutions the limiting value $b = 376$, which differs appreciably from that calculated. The temperature

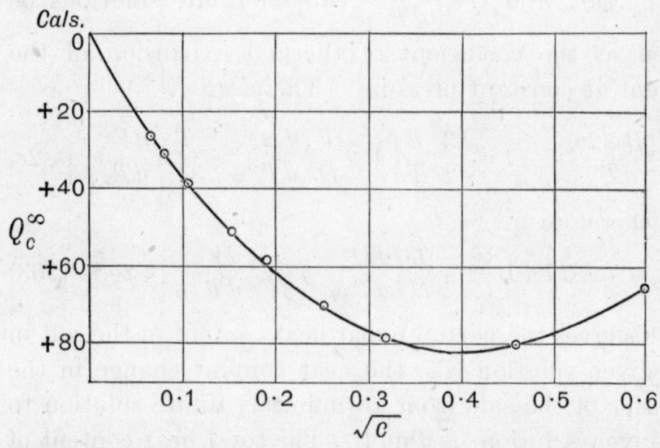

FIG. 95.—Heat of infinite dilution of KCl solutions (Lange and Leighton).

coefficient of the dielectric constant of water is, however, not known with certainty, and the discrepancy may be due to the inaccuracy of the value employed. In more concentrated solutions considerable deviations from the limiting equation occur,† the nature of which is shown in Fig. 95.

* *Z. f. Electrochem.*, 34, 566, 1928.

† See Lange and Robinson, *Chemical Reviews*, 9, 89, 1931.

Further Reading. In a short chapter it is only possible to cover the salient points. For fuller accounts of the voluminous researches on strong electrolytes, the student should consult one of the more specialised text-books or monographs, such as Harned and Owen's "Physical Chemistry of Electrolytic Solutions" (Reinhold Publ. Corp., 1943); Glasstone's "Electrochemistry of Solutions" (Methuen, 1937); Davies's "Conductivity of Solutions" (Chapman & Hall, 1933); "Theoretical Electrochemistry by N. A. McKenna (Macmillan, 1939); Falkenhagen's "Electrolytes" (Oxford, 1934). Harned and Owen, in particular, might be consulted on *ion-association* (or lack of complete dissociation) in solvents of low dielectric constant and on the variation of conductivity with frequency and field strength.

Examples.

1. The free energy in the transfer of HCl from $m = 0{\cdot}001$ to $m = 0{\cdot}1$ (in aqueous solution) is 5227 calories at 25°. If the mean activity in the first solution be 0·00098, find its mean activity at $m = 0{\cdot}1$. (0·0801.)

2. Given the following electromotive forces of the cell

$$H_2 \left| \begin{matrix} HCl(m)\ AgCl(s) \\ (\text{in } 50 \text{ mols } \%\ H_2O,\ 50 \text{ mols } \%\ C_2H_5OH) \end{matrix} \right| Ag:$$

m	25°
0·1	0·3034
0·01	0·4033

(1) find the free energy change in the transfer of HCl from 0·01 m to 0·1 m; (2) if the activity coefficient in the 0·01 m solution is 0·803, find its value in the 0·1 m solution. ((1) 2306 cals per mol.; (2) 0·561.)

3. The electromotive force of the cell:

$Ag \mid AgNO_3 m = 0{\cdot}1 \mid KNO_3 0{\cdot}1N \mid KCl\ 0{\cdot}1N, Hg_2Cl_2 \mid Hg$,

after correcting for the liquid junction potential differences, is **E** = $+0{\cdot}3985$ volts at 25°. Find the standard electrode potential of Ag/Ag^+. The activity coefficient of $AgNO_3$ at $m = 0{\cdot}1$ is 0·77. (+0·799.)

4. From the standard potentials of the Ag | AgCl(*s*), Cl^- and Ag | Ag^+ electrodes, find the activity product of silver chloride in saturated solutions. ($10^{-9\cdot7}$.)

5. The electromotive force of the cell

$$Hg \mid Hg_2SO_4(s), CuSO_4(m = 0{\cdot}05 \mid Cu$$

is +0·3928 volts at 25°. If the activity coefficient of $CuSO_4$ in this solution is 0·216, find the standard electrode potential of copper. (+0·345).

6. The electromotive force of a cell made up of two thallium amalgams in which the molar fractions of thallium were 0·00326 and 0·2071 respectively, with an electrolyte containing a little thallous chloride, was 0·1541 volts at 20°. Assuming that the activity of thallium in the more dilute solution is equal to its molar fraction, find activity in the more concentrated solution. (1·607.)

7. The free energy increase in the transfer of a gram atom of barium from an amalgam in which its molar fraction is $0{\cdot}155 \times 10^{-3}$ to a second in which its molar fraction is $3{\cdot}45 \times 10^{-3}$ is 2079 calories at 25° C. If the activity coefficient in the first amalgam is 1·019, find its activity coefficient in the second. (1·526.)

8. The solubility of thallous chloride in a solution of barium chloride containing 0·100 equivalents ($\frac{1}{2}BaCl_2$) per litre is 0·00416 equivalents per litre. Find the mean activity coefficient of thallous chloride in this solution (Table XLA, p. 406). (0·683.)

CHAPTER XIX

IONIC EQUILIBRIA IN SOLUTION AND SALTING-OUT

Electrical Conductivity of Solutions of Strong Electrolytes. The conductivity of a solution depends on the number of ions it contains and on their mobility. In the Arrhenius theory it was assumed that the mobility was independent of the concentration, and variations in the molecular conductivity were ascribed to changes in the number of ions. Debye and Hückel, in their second paper,* made a calculation of the effect of the interionic forces on the mobility of ions. In their calculation of the partial free energy of ions the central ion was supposed to be at rest, and the ionic atmosphere was symmetrical round about it, but if the ion is in motion under the influence of a potential gradient in the solution, the ionic atmosphere will no longer be symmetrical. The formation and disappearance of the atmosphere occupies a finite time which Debye and Hückel expressed in terms of a quantity τ called the time of relaxation. τ is approximately equal to the time in which the effective radius of the ionic atmosphere becomes twice its original value when the central ion is suddenly removed. For a uni-univalent electrolyte it is given by

$$\tau = \rho / \kappa^2 kT,$$

* *Physikal. Z.*, 24, 305, 1923.

where ρ is the frictional constant of an ion, defined as the force opposing an ion moving with unit velocity. For a tenth normal solution of KCl in water at 25°, $\tau = 0{\cdot}55 \times 10^{-9}$ seconds.

When an ion is moving through the solution the atmosphere in front of it has to be built up continuously, while the atmosphere behind dies away. On account of the finite time of relaxation the atmosphere in front of the ion never reaches its equilibrium density, while that behind is always a little greater than the equilibrium value. Consequently the average centre of charge of the ionic atmosphere is always a little behind the ion, and since the total charge of the ionic atmosphere is equal and opposite to that of the ion the motion of the latter will be retarded. The actual amount of dissymmetry, which is proportional to the velocity of the ion, is small, but on account of the relatively large electronic charge it produces an appreciable retardation of the ion.

The ionic atmosphere also influences the ionic mobility because of the increased viscous resistance caused by the movement of the ionic atmosphere with the ion. Taking both these effects into account Debye and Hückel obtained the equation

$$\frac{\Lambda_0 - \Lambda_c}{\Lambda_0} = \left\{ \frac{k_1}{(DT)^{3/2}} \cdot w_1 + \frac{k_2}{(DT)^{1/2}} \cdot w_2 b \right\} \sqrt{2c},$$

where Λ_0, Λ_c are the molecular conductivities at infinite dilution, and in the solution of concentration c; k_1, k_2 universal constants, w_1, w_2 valency factors, and b the average radius of the ions. The first term on the right expresses the result of the dissymmetry of the ionic atmosphere; the second, which they called the cataphoretic term, the result of the motion of the ionic atmosphere. This equation is evidently equivalent to Kohlrausch's empirical equation* $\Lambda = \Lambda_0 - x\sqrt{c}$, which fits the results for very dilute solutions of strong electrolytes in water and similar solvents with considerable accuracy (Fig. 96).

It was pointed out by Onsager † that in calculating the dissymmetry term Debye and Hückel had assumed the uniform motion of the ion under the applied field, and that if the Brownian movement of the ion is taken into account a factor $(2 - \sqrt{2})$ is introduced. He also showed that the mean radius of the ions could be eliminated from the equation, which was then obtained in the form

$$\Lambda_c = \Lambda_0 - \left[\frac{0{\cdot}986 \times 10^6}{(DT)^{3/2}}(2 - \sqrt{2})z^2\Lambda_0 + \frac{58{\cdot}0z}{(DT)^{1/2}D}\right]\sqrt{2zc} \quad (255)$$

for a z-valent binary electrolyte. For uni-univalent electrolytes in water at 25° this reduces to

$$\Lambda_c = \Lambda_0 - (0{\cdot}228\Lambda_0 + 59{\cdot}8)\sqrt{c}.$$

Comparing the values of x in the Kohlrausch equation with those calculated by equation (255), he found good agreement for uni-univalent salts in aqueous solution, the average deviation being only 7%. On the other hand in the case of bi-bivalent salts the experimental values of x are often considerably greater than the calculated values. While agreement of the experimental with the calculated value of x must be regarded as good evidence for the complete dissociation of the salt, when the observed value is considerably greater than the theoretical (*i.e.* the observed molecular conductivity falls off with increase of concentration more rapidly than that

* *Z. f. Electrochemie*, 13, 333, 1907.

† *Physikal. Z.*, 27, 388, 1926 ; 28, 277, 1927.

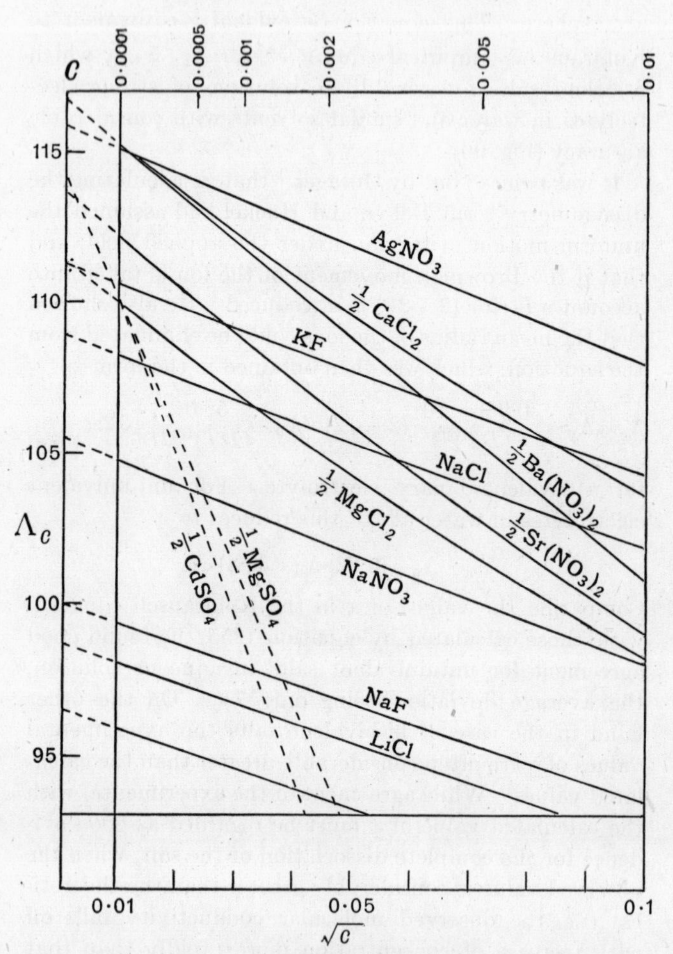

FIG. 96.—Part of Kohlrausch's diagram. Λ_c at 18° plotted against $\sqrt{c}$, for aqueous solutions of salts.

calculated), it is probable that the salt is incompletely dissociated. The degree of dissociation may be determined by $\gamma = \Lambda_c/\Lambda'$, where Λ' is the conductivity calculated by the Onsager equation for the given concentration. The Onsager equation gives such good agreement with many uni-univalent salts that in cases of non-agreement considerable reliance may be placed upon the degree of dissociation calculated in this way. It is necessary to state, however, that the Onsager equation applies only to very dilute solutions ($\sqrt{c} < 0{\cdot}02$). In concentrated solutions other factors enter which have not been elucidated.

Numerous determinations of the conductivities of salts in non-aqueous solvents have been made. Hartley and his co-workers in particular have made measurements of a large number of salts in methyl and ethyl alcohols and in other solvents. In methyl alcohol * they found that while all uni-univalent salts obey the square root relation and in many cases the experimental values of x agree well with those calculated by the Onsager equation, the individual differences were often greater than in the case of water. In ethyl alcohol, also, all uni-univalent salts obey the square root relation, but the observed and calculated values of x differ to a somewhat greater extent than in methyl alcohol. A greater variety of behaviour in these solvents is shown by acids (Fig. 97).† Hydrochloric, perchloric, ethyl sulphuric and benzenesulphonic acids are strong acids in water and both alcohols. The deviation from Onsager's equation, indicating lack of complete dissociation, is greatest in ethyl alcohol.

* *Proc. Roy. Soc.*, *A*, **109**, 351, 1925 ; **127**, 228, 1930 ; *J. Chem. Soc.*, 2488, 1930.

† Murray-Rust and Hartley, *Proc. Roy. Soc.*, *A*. **126**, 84, 1929.

Nitric and thiocyanic acids, which are strong acids in water, are weak in ethyl alcohol, while iodic acid, which

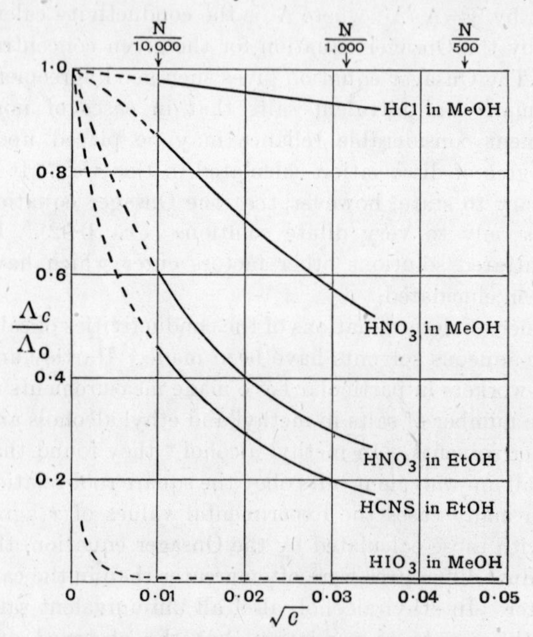

FIG. 97.—Electrical conductivities of acids in methyl and ethyl alcohols (Murray-Rust and Hartley).

is not completely dissociated in aqueous solution, is weak in methyl alcohol, having a dissociation constant about 10^{-8}.

Salts of a higher valence type, particularly salts of metals of the transitional series, are often incompletely ionised in these solvents. For example, cadmium and mercuric chlorides are incompletely ionised even in water and are weaker electrolytes in methyl alcohol. Zinc chloride, although a strong electrolyte in water, is incompletely ionised in methyl alcohol and is scarcely ionised at all in ethyl alcohol.

In non-hydroxylic solvents such as nitromethane, acetonitrile, nitrobenzene, acetone, a much greater variety of behaviour is encountered and even uni-univalent salts are in some cases weak electrolytes. In general it is found that salts are much less completely dissociated in these solvents than in the hydroxylic solvents mentioned above. This is not due solely to differences of dielectric constant, since nitromethane, nitrobenzene and acetonitrile all have greater dielectric constants than methyl alcohol. It has to be admitted that the dissociation of electrolytes is not determined solely by the dielectric constant of the medium. The chemical nature of the latter plays an important part, the nature of which is at present largely unknown.

True Dissociation Constant of a Weak Electrolyte. Consider a weak acid which dissociates as $HX = H^+ + X^-$. The partial free energies of HX, H^+, X^- can be represented by the following equations :

$$\bar{F}_{H^+} = \bar{F}^\circ_{H^+} + RT \log a_{H^+},$$

$$\bar{F}_{X^-} = \bar{F}^\circ_{X^-} + RT \log a_{X^-},$$

$$\bar{F}_{HX} = \bar{F}^\circ_{HX} + RT \log a_{HX}.$$

Since for equilibrium $\bar{F}_{HX} = \bar{F}_{H^+} + \bar{F}_{X^-}$, we have

$$\log \frac{a_{H^+} \cdot a_{X^-}}{a_{HX}} = \frac{\bar{F}^\circ_{HX} - \bar{F}^\circ_{H^+} - \bar{F}^\circ_{X^-}}{RT},$$

or

$$\frac{a_{H^+} \cdot a_{X^-}}{a_{HX}} = K. \qquad (256)$$

K is the true dissociation constant of the acid, and its value in a given solvent is thus fixed by the values of $\bar{F}^\circ_{H^+}$, $\bar{F}^\circ_{X^-}$ and $\bar{F}^\circ_{HX}$.

The Ostwald dissociation constant was defined as

$$K = \frac{c_{H^+} \cdot c_{X^-}}{c_{HX}} = \frac{\gamma^2 c}{1-\gamma},$$

where c is the total concentration of the acid and γ its degree of dissociation, which was determined by the Arrhenius expression $\gamma = \Lambda/\Lambda_0$. Two corrections are required in this calculation.* In the first place, the variation of the mobilities of the ions with their concentration must be taken into account in finding the degree of dissociation. Instead of $\gamma = \Lambda/\Lambda_0$, we must use $\gamma = \Lambda/\Lambda_e$, where Λ_e is the sum of the equivalent conductivities of the ions at their actual concentration. This can be obtained by $\Lambda_e = \Lambda_0 - x\sqrt{\gamma c}$, where the constant x is given by Onsager's equation. Since γ is initially unknown, in the first instance the value of γ given by Λ/Λ_0 can be used, and from it a new value of $\gamma = \Lambda/\Lambda_e$ is then obtained. A short series of approximations of this kind is sufficient to fix the corrected value of γ. Secondly, in finding the dissociation constant it is necessary to use activities instead of concentrations. Since very small concentrations of ions will not appreciably affect the activity of a neutral molecule, it can be assumed that the activity of the undissociated part of the acid is the same as its concentration. We can then write (256) as

$$\frac{c_{H^+} \cdot c_{X^-} \cdot f_{H^+} \cdot f_{X^-}}{c_{HX}} = K,$$

where f_{H^+}, f_{X^-} are the activity coefficients of the ions. These can be calculated by the Debye-Hückel limiting expression

$$\log(f_{H^+} \cdot f_{X^-}) = -2B\sqrt{c_i}.$$

* First made by Noyes and Sherrill, *J. Amer. Chem. Soc.*, 48, 1861, 1926 ; MacInnes, *ibid.*, 48, 2068, 1926.

We thus obtain

$$\log\left(\frac{c_{H^+}\,.\,c_{X^-}}{c_{HX}}\right)=\log\left(\frac{\gamma^2c^2}{(1-\gamma)c}\right)=\log K+2B\sqrt{c_i}, \quad (257)$$

where c is the total concentration of the acid, γ the true degree of dissociation and c_i the sum of concentrations of the ions. The following table gives the data of MacInnes and Shedlovsky* for acetic acid, as calculated by C. W. Davies.†

TABLE XLVII.

DISSOCIATION OF ACETIC ACID AT 25° IN AQUEOUS SOLUTION.

$$\Lambda_e = 390{\cdot}59 - 148{\cdot}61\sqrt{\gamma c}.$$

$c\times 10^3$.	Λ.	$\gamma c\times 10^3$.	$\gamma^2c^2/1-\gamma c$.
0·02801	210·32	0·01511	1·7682
0·11135	127·71	0·03649	1·7787
0·15321	112·02	0·04405	1·7775
0·21844	96·466	0·05410	1·7810
1·02831	48·215	0·12727	1·7974
1·36340	42·215	0·14803	1·8030
2·41400	32·208	0·20012	1·8090
3·44065	27·191	0·24092	1·8140
5·91153	20·956	0·31929	1·8230

The values of $\log(\gamma^2c^2/1-\gamma c)$ are plotted against $\sqrt{c_i}$ in Fig. 98. They are in good agreement with the straight line, having the slope 1·01 which is the value of $2B$ in (257), according to Debye and Hückel. The value of K, which is given by the intercept made by this line on the axis at zero concentration, is equal to $1{\cdot}753\times10^{-5}$.

Determination of the Dissociation Constant of a Weak Acid by Electromotive Force Measurements. Galvanic

* *J. Amer. Chem. Soc.*, 54, 1429, 1932.

† *Conductivity of Electrolytes*, 2nd ed., p. 105.

cells have been devised by Harned and his co-workers * by means of which the dissociation constants of weak

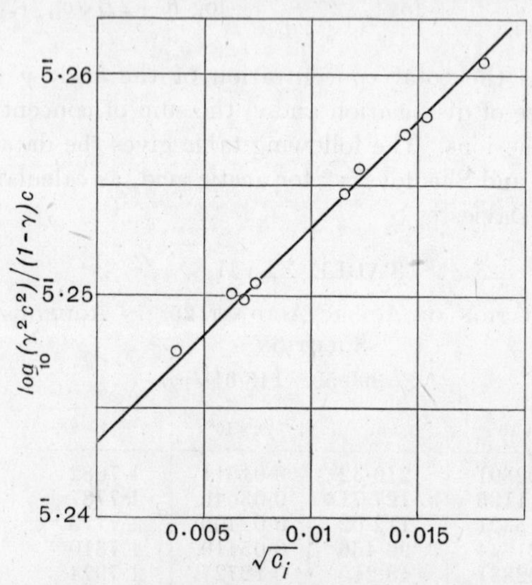

FIG. 98.—Apparent dissociation constants of acetic acid in aqueous solution (Davies).

acids and bases can be determined. For example, the dissociation constant of acetic acid (HAc) can be determined by means of the cell

$$H_2 \mid HAc(m_1),\ NaAc(m_2),\ NaCl(m_3),\ AgCl(s) \mid Ag.$$

Since the cell reaction is $\frac{1}{2}H_2 + AgCl(s) = Ag + HCl$, the electromotive force is determined by the activity of hydrogen chloride in the solution and is given by

$$E = E_0 - \frac{RT}{F}\log f_{H^+} f_{Cl^-} m_{H^+} m_{Cl^-}, \quad \ldots\ldots\ldots (258)$$

* Harned and Robinson, *J. Amer. Chem. Soc.*, 50, 3157, 1928; Harned and Owen, *ibid.*, 52, 5079, 1930; Harned and Ehlers, *ibid.*, 54, 1350, 1932.

where E_0 is the electromotive force of a cell made of similar electrodes in a solution containing hydrochloric acid of unit activity. This can be determined by measurements of the cell

$$H_2 \mid HCl(m),\ AgCl(s) \mid Ag,$$

according to which E_0 has the value 0·22239 at 25°. We may substitute for $f_{H^+}m_{H^+}$ in (258) by means of

$$K = \frac{f_{H^+}f_{Ac^-}}{f_{HAc}} \cdot \frac{m_{H^+}m_{Ac^-}}{m_{HAc}}$$

and we obtain

$$E - E_0 + \frac{RT}{F}\log\frac{m_{HAc}m_{Cl^-}}{m_{Ac^-}}$$

$$= -\frac{RT}{F}\log\frac{f_{H^+}f_{Cl^-} \cdot f_{HAc}}{f_{H^+}f_{Ac^-}} - \frac{RT}{F}\log K. \quad \ldots(259)$$

All the quantities of the left side of this equation are known.* The first term on the right becomes zero at infinite dilution, so that if the values of the left side of the equation are extrapolated to infinite dilution we obtain $RT/F \log K$. This extrapolation can be made by plotting the left side of the equation against the ionic strength of the solution, since in dilute solutions both $\log(f_{H^+}f_{Cl^-}/f_{H^+}f_{Ac^-})$ and $\log f_{HCl}$ vary linearly with the total ionic concentration. In this way Harned and Ehlers found that the value of K for acetic acid at 25° is $1{\cdot}754 \times 10^{-5}$, which is in excellent agreement with the corrected value derived from conductivity measurements.

Variation of equilibrium constant of weak acids with temperature. Careful measurements of the equilibrium constants in water over a range of temperature showed

* $m_{Cl^-} = m_3$, $m_{Ac^-} = m_2 + m_{H^+}$, $m_{HAc} = m_1 - m_H$, where m_{H^+} is the concentration of hydrogen ions formed by the dissociation of acetic acid.

that in most cases they reach a maximum between 270° K and 310° K. Occasionally the temperature of the maximum lies outside these limits, but the phenomenon of the maximum is general. Harned and Embree * showed that the curve was close to a parabola which could be represented empirically by

$$\log K - \log K_m = p(T - T_m)^2,$$

where K_m is the maximum value at the temperature T_m. Using the equation

$$\frac{d \log K}{dT} = \frac{\Delta H}{RT^2}, \quad \text{..................(260)}$$

we see that at the maximum point of the curve ΔH, the heat of dissociation, is zero ; the phenomenon therefore indicates a strong temperature dependence of ΔH.

Since $$\frac{d(\Delta H)}{dT} = \Delta C_p,$$

it follows that ΔC_p, the difference of the partial molar heat capacity in the dissociation reaction, is comparatively large. Values of ΔC_p have been worked out by Everett and Wynne-Jones † and some of their figures are given in Table XLVIII. It was found that ΔC_p was practically independent of the temperature over the temperature range considered. We may therefore write

$$\Delta H = \Delta H_0 + \Delta C_p . T,$$

and introducing this into (260) and integrating, we find that

$$\log K = -\frac{\Delta H_0}{RT} + \frac{\Delta C_p}{R} \log T + B. \quad \text{........(261)}$$

This equation fits the data with considerable accuracy.

* *J. Amer. Chem. Soc.*, **56**, 1050, 1934. See also Harned & Owen, *Chem. Revs.*, **25**, 31, 1939.

† *Trans. Faraday Soc.*, **35**, 1380, 1939.

The values of ΔC_p are of the order of -40 cals./deg., *i.e.* there is a drop in heat capacity of this amount in the ionisation process which involves the disappearance of a neutral molecule and the formation of a hydrogen ion and an anion closely similar to the neutral molecule in all respects except that it carries a charge.

Part of this figure will be due to the electrical energy of the ions. Instead of a neutral molecule, the ionisation process gives rise to two ions, and the electrical energy of these ions in a medium of dielectric constant D is by the Born calculation

$$E = \frac{N_2^2}{2D}\left(\frac{1}{r_+} + \frac{1}{r_-}\right),$$

where r_+, r_- are the ionic radii.* Since D varies with the temperature, this energy will also vary and thus give rise to a heat capacity. Probably the value of ΔC_p which can be accounted for in this way is not more than about $\Delta C_p = -10$ cals./deg. Everett and Wynne-Jones suggest that the main factor is a " freezing " of the water molecules round the ions. In the electric field near the ions, water molecules will lose their ability to rotate and this contribution to the heat capacity is thereby diminished.†

Table XLVIII. also gives the entropy of dissociation. This is obtained from the difference of the heat and free energy of dissociation, by

$$\Delta S^\circ = \frac{\Delta H - \Delta F^\circ}{T},$$

where $$\Delta F^\circ = RT \log K.$$

* This quantity is strictly the free energy of charging.

† The separation of the dissociation energy into electrical and other terms was first discussed by Gurney (*J. Chem. Physics*, 6, 499, 1938, and Baughan, *ibid.*, 7, 951, 1939.

TABLE XLVIII.

Constants of Ionisation of Weak Acids.*

Acid.	ΔC_p.	$\Delta S°_{298·1}$.	$\Delta F°_{298·1}$.	$\Delta H_{298·1}$.	$-A$.	B.	T_m.
Water	−51·0	−18·9	19122	13490	6274·0	70·4940	564·0
Formic	−41·4	−17·3	5114	−40	2684·1	56·7186	297·0
Acetic	−36·6	−22·1	6483	−100	2358·9	47·6856	295·3
Propionic	−35·4	−22·9	6644	−170	2265·9	46·7696	293·2
Butyric	−34·6	−24·4	6570	−700	2098·0	45·2729	278·0
Chloracetic	−39·0	−16·9	3898	−1150	2286·4	53·3068	268·7
Lactic	−40·2	−17·2	5259	−174	2578·0	54·7716	294·0
Glycollic	−40·2	−17·2	5222	100	2660·0	55·0749	302·0
Benzoic	−36·2	−18·9	5682	40	2362·6	48·7922	300·0
Salicylic	−47·7	−10·2	4055	1000	3327·8	67·5734	320·0
Anisic	−49·7	−17·8	6110	800	3405·0	68·7824	314·0
o-Toluic	−30·6	−22·4	5284	−1400	1683·5	39·8765	252·0
m-Toluic	−32·6	−19·2	5785	70	2135·0	43·4995	300·0
p-Toluic	−36·6	−18·9	5923	300	2449·9	49·3867	306·0
Ammonium ion	0·0	−0·54	12562	12400	2706·0	−0·139	—
Anilinium ion	0·0	+ 2·8	6265	7105	1553·0	0·614	—

*** Dissociation Constant and Degree of Dissociation of Water.** The dissociation of water may be represented by the equation, $H_2O = H^+ + OH^-$. The partial free energies of water and of the hydrogen and hydroxyl ions may be expressed by

$$\bar{F}_W = \bar{F}°_W + RT \log a_W,$$

$$\bar{F}_{OH^-} = \bar{F}°_{OH^-} + RT \log a_{OH^-},$$

$$\bar{F}_{H^+} = \bar{F}°_{H^+} + RT \log a_{H^+};$$

where a_W is taken as unity in pure water, and a_{OH^-}, a_{H^+} are made equal to the ionic concentrations m_{H^+}, m_{OH^-} in solutions which contain very small concentrations of

* A is the constant $\Delta H_0/R$ of (261) and T_m is the temperature at which the dissociation constant has its maximum value.

these and of other ions. Since $\bar{F}_W = \bar{F}_{OH^-} + \bar{F}_{H^+}$, it follows that

$$a_{H^+} a_{OH^-} / a_W = K_W, \quad \text{.................(262)}$$

where

$$\log K_W = \frac{\bar{F}^\circ_{H^+} + \bar{F}^\circ_{OH^-} - \bar{F}^\circ_W}{RT}.$$

K_W is the true dissociation constant of water. In order to evaluate it, it is necessary to determine the three quantities a_{H^+}, a_{OH^-} and a_W in the same solution. Harned and his co-workers have devised methods of determining these quantities by means of reversible galvanic cells without liquid junctions. Their first method involved the use of amalgam electrodes.* Later they devised a simpler method, of which the following is an example.† Consider the cell

$$H_2 \,|\, KOH(m_0),\ KCl(m),\ AgCl(s) \,|\, Ag. \quad \text{.......(A)}$$

Since the electromotive force is determined by the activity of hydrogen chloride in the solution, we have

$$E_A = E_0 + \frac{RT}{z\mathbf{F}} \log f_{H^+} f_{Cl^-} m_{H^+} m_{Cl^-}, \quad \text{.....(263)}$$

where E_0 is the electromotive force of a cell made of similar electrodes in a solution containing hydrochloric acid of unit activity.

We can substitute for $f_{H^+} m_{H^+}$ in (263) by means of the equation $K_W = f_{H^+} f_{OH^-} m_{H^+} m_{OH^-} / a_W$, and we thus obtain

$$E - E_0 + \frac{RT}{z\mathbf{F}} \log \frac{m_{Cl^-}}{m_{OH^-}} = \frac{RT}{z\mathbf{F}} \log \frac{f_{H^+} f_{OH^-}}{a_W} - \frac{RT}{z\mathbf{F}} \log K_W - \frac{RT}{z\mathbf{F}} \log f_{H^+} f_{Cl^-}. \quad (264)$$

* Harned, *J. Amer. Chem. Soc.*, 47, 930, 1925 ; Harned and Swindells, *ibid.*, 48, 126, 1926 ; Harned and James, *J. Physical Chem.*, 30, 1060, 1926.

† Harned and Schupp, *J. Amer. Chem. Soc.*, 52, 3892, 1930 ; Harned and Mason, *ibid.*, 54, 3112, 1932 ; Harned and Hamer, *bid.*, 55, 2194, 1933 ; Harned and Capson, *ibid.*, 55, 2206, 1933.

The activity coefficients of the ions f_{H^+}, f_{OH^-}, f_{Cl^-} all become unity when the salt concentration becomes very small and a_W also becomes equal to unity in pure water. The quantity on the left of this equation therefore becomes equal to $RT/z\mathbf{F} \log K_W$ at zero salt concentration. Harned plots this quantity against the ionic strength of the solution, and a short extrapolation to $\mu = 0$ gives the value of $RT/z\mathbf{F} \log K_W$. In this way it is found that the value of K_W at 25° is $1{\cdot}008 \pm 0{\cdot}001 \times 10^{-14}$.

Since $K_W = f_{OH^-} f_{H^+} . m_{H^+} m_{OH^-}/a_W$, it follows that the ionic product of the concentrations $m_{H^+} m_{OH^-}$ increases as $f_{OH^-} f_{H^+}$ decreases. In dilute solutions the activity coefficients of the hydrogen and hydroxyl ions, like those of other ions, decrease with increasing ionic strength of the solution and the ionic concentration product therefore increases. The extent of this increase can be calculated in very dilute solutions by means of the Debye-Hückel limiting expression. In such solutions we have by (242), $\log (f_{H^+} f_{OH^-}) = -2B\sqrt{\Sigma c_i z_i^2}$, and taking a as unity it follows that $\log (m_{H^+} m_{OH^-}) = \log K_W + 2B\sqrt{\Sigma c_i z_i^2}$.

In concentrated solutions the activity coefficients of the H^+ and OH^- ions will be influenced specifically by the nature of the other ions present in the solution. The value of $f_{H^+} f_{OH^-}/a_W$ can, however, be determined experimentally from (193) if we know $f_{H^+} f_{Cl^-}$.

The determination of this quantity in barium chloride solutions may be quoted as an example. The activity coefficients of HCl in $BaCl_2$ solutions can be determined (see p. 431) by cells of the type

$$H_2 \mid HCl(m_1),\ BaCl_2(m_2),\ AgCl \mid Ag.$$

It has been pointed out that when the concentration of hydrogen chloride is very small, its activity coefficient depends only on the nature and concentration of the solution in which it is dissolved and not on its concentration (m_1). In a mixed solution of $Ba(OH)_2(m_0)$ and $BaCl_2(m_2)$ it can be assumed if m_0 is small that the activity coefficient of hydrogen chloride is the same as in a pure barium chloride solution of the same total ionic strength. In Table XLIX the second column gives the values of $E - E_0 + 0{\cdot}05915 \log \frac{m_{Cl^-}}{m_{OH^-}}$ determined from the cells

$$H_2 \mid Ba(OH)_2(m_0),\ BaCl_2(m_2),\ AgCl(s) \mid Ag.$$

The third column gives the activity coefficients of HCl in these solutions and the fourth the calculated values of $f_{H^+} f_{OH^-} / a_W$. When the activity of water is

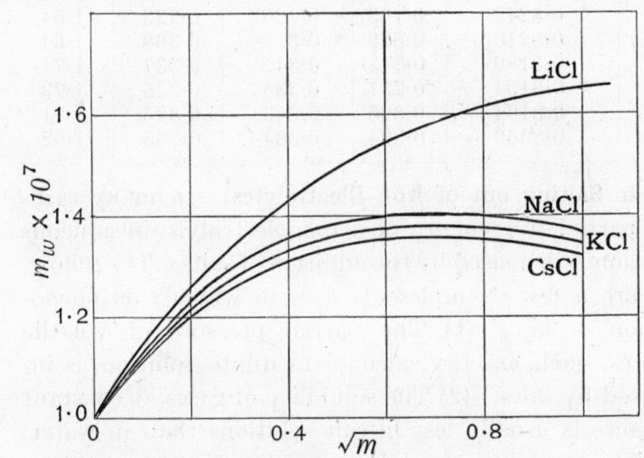

FIG. 99.—Dissociation of water in some salt solutions (Harned and Schupp).

known it is thus possible to find the products of the activities of the hydrogen and hydroxyl ions $f_{H^+} f_{OH^-}$ which are given in the fifth column. Finally, the ionic concentration product of water can be determined by $m_{H^+}m_{OH^-} = K_W a_W / f_{H^+} f_{OH^-}$. Values of $m_W = \sqrt{m_{H^+}m_{OH^-}}$ are given in the last column. Fig. 99 shows the values of this quantity in a number of chloride solutions.

TABLE XLIX.

ACTIVITY COEFFICIENT PRODUCT AND DISSOCIATION OF WATER IN BARIUM CHLORIDE SOLUTIONS AT 25°.

$H_2 \mid Ba(OH)_2(m_0),\ BaCl_2(m),\ AgCl(s) \mid Ag.$

μ.	$E - E_0 + 0{\cdot}05915 \log m/m_0$.	$f_{H^+}f_{Cl^-}$.	$f_{H^+}f_{OH^-}/a_W$.	$f_{H^+}f_{OH^-}$.	$m_W \times 10^7$.
0·01	0·8279	9·891	0·792	0·793	1·13
0·05	0·8276	0·818	0·660	0·659	1·23
0·1	0·8272	0·776	0·582	0·581	1·31
0·2	0·8264	0·739	0·514	0·512	1·40
0·5	0·8242	0·702	0·426	0·423	1·54
1·0	0·8210	0·699	0·373	0·368	1·64
1·5	0·8180	0·713	0·345	0·337	1·71
2·0	0·8154	0·737	0·335	0·325	1·73
3·0	0·8104	0·825	0·343	0·325	1·71
4·0	0·8069	0·934	0·384	0·355	1·62

The Salting out of Non-Electrolytes. In many cases the partial free energy of a non-electrolyte in aqueous solution is increased by the addition of salts. The following are a few examples of cases in which this phenomenon occurs. (1) The partial pressure of volatile solutes, such as ethyl alcohol in dilute solution, is increased by salts. (2) The solubility of gases at constant pressure is usually less in salt solutions than in water. (3) The solubility of solids, *e.g.* iodine,* is decreased by salts. Since the partial free energy of the solid is the same in all saturated solutions, this means that the saturation value is reached at a smaller concentration in

* Carter, *J. Chem. Soc.*, 127, 2861, 1925.

the presence of a salt, *i.e.* the partial free energy of the solute at constant concentration is increased by the salt. (4) The presence of salts also often reduces the mutual miscibility of partially miscible liquids. The addition of a salt to a saturated solution of ether may cause its separation into two layers.* (5) When the distribution of a solute such as acetic acid between aqueous solutions and a nearly immiscible solvent like amyl alcohol (which does not dissolve salts to any appreciable extent) is studied, it is found that the distribution ratio $c_{(\text{water})}/c_{(\text{alcohol})}$ is decreased in most cases by the addition of salts to the aqueous solution.† (6) The depression of the freezing point produced by a salt and a non-electrolyte together is greater than the sum of the depressions produced by each singly at equivalent concentrations.‡

If $\bar{F}_2$ is the partial free energy of a non-electrolyte in dilute aqueous solution of concentration m_2, we may write

$$\bar{F}_2 = \bar{F}^\circ_2 + RT \log m_2 f_2 \; ; \quad \text{.............(265)}$$

and if $\bar{F}_2'$ is its partial free energy in a similar solution containing a salt at the concentration m, we have

$$\bar{F}_2' = \bar{F}^\circ_2 + RT \log m_2 f_2' . \quad \text{.............(266)}$$

The change in the partial free energy of the non-electrolyte produced by the salt is thus

$$\bar{F}_2' - \bar{F}_2 = RT \log (f_2'/f_2).$$

It has been found that this quantity varies approximately linearly with the salt concentration, *i.e.*

$$\log (f_2'/f_2) = km_3 . \quad \text{..................(267)}$$

* Thorne, *J. Chem. Soc.*, 119, 262, 1921.

† J. N. Sugden, *ibid.*, p. 174, 1926.

‡ Tammann and Abegg, *Z. physikal. Chem.*, 9, 108, 1892 ; 11, 259, 1893.

This relation was first observed by V. Rothmund,* in his studies of the effect of salts on the solubilities of sparingly soluble non-electrolytes.

A theory of the salting-out effect has been given by Debye and McAulay.† It has already been pointed out that the molecules of a polarisable solvent are strongly attracted by the intense electric fields in the vicinity of ions. If the solution contains " solvent " molecules of two kinds, the more polarisable ones will be more strongly attracted and will tend to congregate round the ions. Near the ions there will thus be a greater proportion of the more polarisable molecules than in the bulk of the solution, and the proportion of the less polarisable molecules in the solution at a distance from the ions will be increased. The activity of the less polarisable molecules in the solution will thus be increased by the presence of ions, and the effect will be approximately proportional to the number of ions present. Water, on account of its high dielectric constant, is much more polarisable than most organic substances, and these are " salted out " in aqueous solutions. The reverse should be the case, however, with solutes which are more polarisable than water. This has been confirmed with aqueous solutions of hydrocyanic acid, which is " salted in ", *i.e.* its partial free energy is decreased by the presence of salts.‡

*The quantitative calculation of the effect of a salt on the partial free energy of a non-electrolyte is somewhat difficult.

* *Z. physikal. Chem.*, **33**, 401, 1900 ; **69**, 523, 1909 ; cf. Setschenov, *ibid.*, **4**, 117, 1889.

† *Physikal, Z.*, **26**, 22, 1925 ; *see also* McAulay, *J. Physical Chem.*, **30**, 1202, 1926 ; Debye, *Z. physikal. Chem.*, **30**, 56, 1927.

‡ P. Gross and Schwarz, *Monatsch.*, **55**, 287, 1930 ; P. Gross and Iser, *ibid.*, **55**, 329, 1930.

Debye and McAulay gave an indirect calculation which depended on evaluating the electric energy of the solution, taking into account the lowering of the dielectric constant produced by the non-electrolyte, and then separating the partial free energy of the latter. A more direct derivation of a similar equation was given by Butler.*

According to simple electrostatic theory, the field strength at a distance r from the centre of a spherical ion of charge e is $E = -e/Dr^2$. The electric work done in bringing a molecule B from infinity to a point near the ion where the field strength is E is $\int_0^E P_B \,.\, \delta v_B \,.\, dE$, where P_B is the polarisation produced in unit volume of B by the field and δv_B the volume of the molecule.† The polarisation is the electric moment produced in a medium by the action of an electric field, either by the orientation of the permanent dipoles or by induction. Except in intense fields, where electric saturation may occur, it is proportional to the field strength, and we have $P_B = \alpha_B \,.\, E$, where $\alpha_B = (D-1)/4\pi$, D being the dielectric constant of the element of material, *i.e.* the molecule B. The work done in bringing the molecule to the distance r is thus

$$\int_0^E P_B \,.\, \delta v_B \,.\, dE = -\frac{\alpha_B e^2}{2D^2 r^4} \cdot \delta v_B .$$

Now when a molecule of the solute (B) is moved, *an equal volume* of the solvent (A) is displaced in the opposite direction and the work done in this process is similarly

$$+\alpha_A e^2 \,.\, \delta v_B / 2D^2 r^4,$$

so that the total work done in moving the given molecule A is

$$w = (\alpha_A - \alpha_B) \frac{e^2}{2D^2 r^4} \cdot \delta v_B .$$

If $n_B{}^\circ$ is the concentration of B at a great distance from the

* *J. Physical Chem.*, 33, 1015, 1929.

† Livens, *Theory of Electricity*, 2nd edition (1926), p. 82.

ion, its concentration at a distance r is therefore, by Boltzmann's theorem,

$$n_B = n_B^\circ e^{-\frac{\alpha_A - \alpha_B}{kT} \cdot \frac{e^2}{2D^2r^4} \cdot \delta v_B}$$

or to a first approximation, if the exponent is small,

$$n_B^\circ - n_B = n_B^\circ \left(\frac{\alpha_A - \alpha_B}{kT} \cdot \frac{e^2}{2D^2r^4} \cdot \delta v_B \right).$$

The total deficit in the amount of B round an ion, *i.e.* the amount salted out by a single ion, is obtained by integrating this over all the space round the ion. This is given by the integral

$$\int_a^\infty (n_B^\circ - n_B) \, . \, 4\pi r^2 \, . \, dr = n_B^\circ \, . \, \frac{\alpha_A - \alpha_B}{kT} \cdot \frac{4\pi \, \delta v_B}{2D^2} \cdot \frac{e^2}{a},$$

where a is the radius of the ion. If the solution contains c_1 gram ions of charge e_1, c_2 gram ions of charge e_2, etc., per litre, the number of molecules of B salted out per c.c. of solution is

$$\Gamma_B = n_B^\circ \cdot \frac{\alpha_A - \alpha_B}{kT} \cdot \frac{4\pi \, \delta v_B}{2D^2} \cdot \sum \frac{e_1^2 c_1}{a_1} \cdot \frac{N_0}{1000}.$$

Thus if the original solution contains n_B° molecules of B per c.c., its average effective concentration after the addition of the salt is $n_B^\circ + \Gamma_B$. Its activity coefficient will thus be increased by the salt in the ratio

$$f_B'/f_B = \frac{n_B^\circ + \Gamma_B}{n_B^\circ} = 1 + \frac{\Gamma_B}{n_B^\circ}.$$

If Γ_B/n_B° is small, we may make the approximation

$$\log (f_B'/f_B) = \Gamma_B/n_B^\circ = \frac{\alpha_A - \alpha_B}{kT} \cdot \frac{4\pi \, \delta v_B}{2D^2} \sum \frac{e_1^2 c_1}{a_1} \cdot \frac{N_0}{1000}. \quad (268)$$

This equation is equivalent to that of Debye and McAulay. $4\pi(\alpha_A - \alpha_B)$ is the difference between the dielectric constants of the substances A and B in the solution * and therefore $4\pi(\alpha_A - \alpha_B)\delta v_B$ is the dielectric constant lowering produced

* This statement is intended to give a concrete idea of the meaning of this term. It cannot be interpreted strictly since we cannot assign dielectric constants to the components of a solution.

by a molecule of B in a c.c. of the solution. We thus have $D = D_0 - 4(\alpha_A - \alpha_B)\delta v_B . n_B^\circ$, which permits the evaluation of this term.

It is evident that according to this equation the salting out is proportional to the dielectric constant lowering produced by the solute, and inversely proportional to the radius of the ions. Randall and Failey,* as a result of an examination of the available evidence, came to the conclusion that " there seems to be a qualitative agreement with these demands, but not a quantitative one ". The available evidence, however, is neither very extensive nor exact.

***Salting out in Concentrated Solutions.** The effect of salts on the partial free energies of non-electrolytes in concentrated solutions is more complicated. Thus although in dilute aqueous solutions the addition of a salt increases the partial vapour pressure of alcohol, in pure alcohol it must obviously cause a lowering. There must be a transition from the one kind of behaviour to the other. Figs. 100–101 show the effect of lithium chloride on the partial pressures of water and alcohol in solutions extending from pure water to pure alcohol.† Here p_1, p_2 are the partial pressures of alcohol and water in solutions containing no lithium chloride, and p_1', p_2' the corresponding values for a given concentration of the latter, and the ratios p_1'/p_1 and p_2'/p_2 are plotted against the concentration of lithium chloride (m). It can be seen that while the partial pressure of alcohol is increased by the salt in dilute solutions, it is decreased in concentrated solutions, and the partial pressure of water is decreased in the alcoholic solutions to a greater extent than in pure water.

* *Chem. Reviews*, 4, 285, 1927, see also P. M. Gross, *Chem. Reviews*, 13, 91, 1933.

† Shaw and Butler, *Proc. Roy. Soc., A*, 129, 519, 1930.

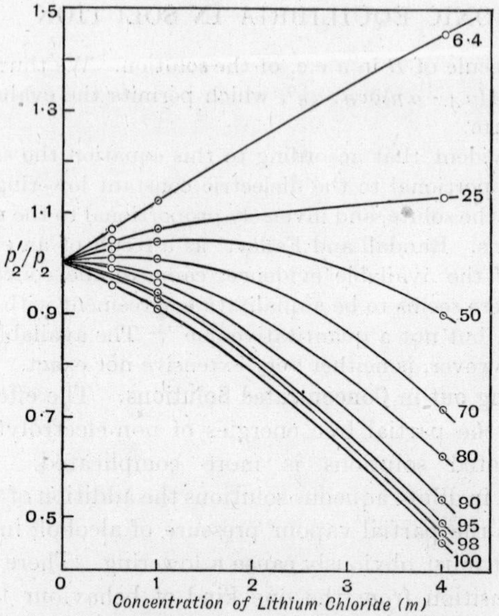

FIG. 100.—Effect of LiCl on partial pressures of alcohol in water-alcohol solutions.
(Numbers on right are molar fractions of alcohol in the solvent.)

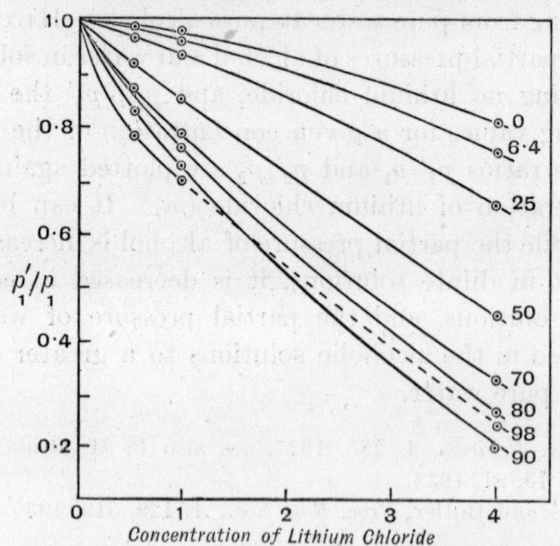

FIG. 101.—Effect of LiCl on partial pressures of water in water-alcohol solutions.

The thermodynamics of ternary solutions is considerably more complex than that of binary solutions, and it would take too much space to consider the detailed analysis of these effects.* It will be sufficient to say that the results indicate that the ion is surrounded entirely by water until at least 20 mols. % of alcohol is present, *i.e.* the alcohol is salted out. At higher alcohol concentrations, alcohol molecules begin to reach the zones nearest the ions, but at all concentrations there is relatively more water close to the ion than in the bulk of the solution. This conclusion was supported by measurements of the partial molar volumes and refractivities † and electrical conductivities ‡ of salts in water-alcohol mixtures. Fig. 102 shows the partial molar volumes

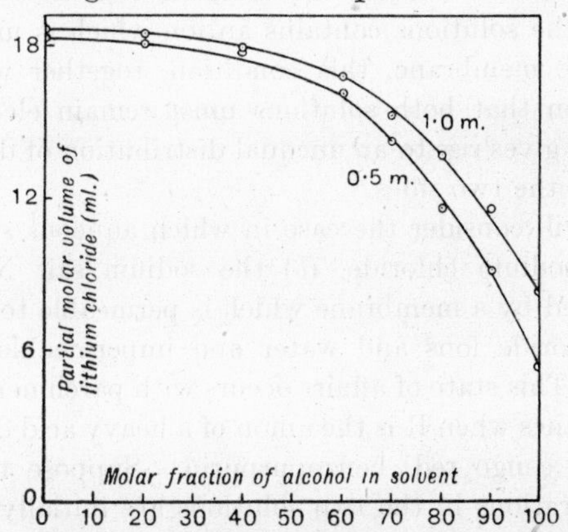

FIG. 102.—Partial molar volumes of lithium chloride in water-alcohol solvents.

of lithium chloride in water-alcohol solvents. This property indicates the composition of the immediate

* See Butler and Thomson, *Proc. Roy. Soc.*, A, **141**, 86, 1933.
† Butler and Lees, *ibid.*, **131**, 382, 1931.
‡ Connell, Hamilton and Butler ; *ibid.*, **147**, 418, 1934.

surroundings of the ions, for only in the intense electric field very near the ions is the volume much affected. The results show that the partial molar volume of lithium chloride is scarcely varied from the value in water until the molar fraction of alcohol is 0·3 or more, and it then falls off. At this concentration alcohol molecules begin to reach the inner sheath of the ions; and since they are more compressible than water there is a diminution of volume, which shows up in the partial molar volume of the salt.

Donnan's Membrane Equilibrium. When two solutions are separated by a membrane the equilibrium is determined by the condition that the partial free energy of every neutral component which can freely pass through the membrane must be the same on both sides. When one of the solutions contains an ion which is unable to pass the membrane, this condition, together with the condition that both solutions must remain electrically neutral, gives rise to an unequal distribution of diffusible salts on the two sides.*

We will consider the case in which aqueous solutions of (*a*) sodium chloride, (*b*) the sodium salt NaR are separated by a membrane which is permeable to sodium and chloride ions and water and impermeable to the ion *R*. This state of affairs occurs with parchment paper membranes when R is the anion of a heavy acid dyestuff, such as congo red, benzopurpurin. Suppose that the concentrations in the two solutions are initially

$$\begin{array}{cc|cc} Na^+ & R^- & Na^+ & Cl^- \\ c_2 & c_2 & c_1 & c_1 \end{array}$$

* Donnan, *Z. Electrochem.*, 17, 572, 1911; experimental investigations by Donnan and Harris, *J. Chem. Soc.*, **99**, 1559, 1911; Donnan and Allmand, *ibid.*, **105**, 1941, 1914; Donnan and Garner, *ibid.*, **115**, 1313, 1919; Donnan and Green, *Proc. Roy. Soc.*, *A*, **90**. 450, 1914.

The final state of equilibrium is determined by the following considerations :

(1) The two solutions must remain electrically neutral, *i.e.* equal quantities of sodium and chloride ions must diffuse from one solution to the other. If we suppose that the volumes of the two solutions are equal, and that the concentrations of sodium and chloride ions on the right are reduced by diffusion to $c_1 - x$, the concentrations of sodium and chloride ions on the left will be $c_2 + x$, x. The equilibrium state may therefore be represented by

Na^+	R^-	Cl^-	⋮	Na^+	Cl^-
$c_2 + x$	c_2	x	⋮	$c_1 - x$	$c_1 - x$

(2) For equilibrium, the partial free energy of sodium chloride must be the same in the two solutions, *i.e.*

$$a_{Na^+}' \, . \, a_{Cl^-}' = a_{Na^+}'' \, . \, a_{Cl^-}'', \qquad \text{............(269)}$$

where a_{Na^+}', a_{Na^+}'', are the activities of sodium ion in the two solutions, etc.

In the ideal case when the activities of the ions may be supposed to be the same as their concentrations, we have

$$(c_2 + x)x = (c_1 - x)^2,$$

or

$$x = \frac{c_1^2}{c_2 + 2c_1}.$$

The ratio

$$\frac{x}{c_1} = \frac{c_1}{c_2 + 2c_1}$$

gives the proportion of the amount of sodium chloride originally present which has diffused through the membrane. Table L gives some values of this quantity. It can be seen that the proportion of NaCl which diffuses decreases as the proportion c_2/c_1 increases, and when this ratio is large the distribution is very unequal.

TABLE L.

Initial Conc. of NaR (c_2).	Initial Conc. of NaCl (c_1).	Initial Ratio c_2/c_1.	Percentage of NaCl diffused, $x/c_1 \times 100$.	Ratio of Cl^- in two solutions, $x/c_1 - x$.
0·01	1	0·01	49·7	1·01
0·1	1	0·1	47·0	1·1
1	1	1	33	2
1	0·1	10	8·3	11
1	0·01	100	1	99

(3) It is necessary for equilibrium that the free energy of water on the two sides of the membrane shall be equal. Since in the equilibrium state the total salt concentrations are unequal, this can only be secured by a difference of hydrostatic pressure. This difference of hydrostatic pressure is obviously equal to the difference of the osmotic pressure of the two solutions.

(4) For the equilibrium of the ions Na^+ and Cl^- it is necessary that

$$\bar{F}_{Na^+}' - \bar{F}_{Na^+}'' = \mathbf{F}(V'' - V'),$$

and

$$\bar{F}_{Cl^-}' - \bar{F}_{Cl^-}'' = -\mathbf{F}(V'' - V').$$

There is thus a potential difference across the membrane which is given by

$$V'' - V' = \frac{RT}{\mathbf{F}} \log \frac{a_{Na^+}'}{a_{Na^+}''} = \frac{RT}{\mathbf{F}} \log \frac{a_{Cl^-}''}{a_{Cl^-}'}. \quad \ldots(270)$$

This potential difference is equal and opposite to the difference between the potential differences of two electrodes, reversible with respect to the sodium or chloride ion, placed in the two solutions.*

* A comprehensive discussion of the thermodynamics of membrane equilibria is given by Donnan and Guggenheim, *Z. phys. Chem.*, 162, 346, 1932.

CHAPTER XX

THE STANDARD FREE ENERGIES AND ENTROPIES OF IONS

Standard Free Energies of Ions in Aqueous Solutions. The partial molar free energy of an ion in solution is represented by:

$$\bar{F}_i = \bar{F}^\circ_i + RT \log a_i,$$

where a_i is the activity of the ion. For the solution of many problems concerning the equilibrium of solutions with other phases it is necessary to know the standard free energies $\bar{F}^\circ_i$ as well as the activities of the ions. Since it is usually unnecessary to have absolute values of $\bar{F}^\circ_i$, it is sufficient to take the free energies of the elements in a given state (in the case of gases at unit pressure) as zero. The value $\bar{F}^\circ_i$ depends on the way in which the activity is defined. As before, we shall suppose that the activity of an ion in any solvent becomes equal to its concentration (m) when the concentrations of the ion (and of other solutes) are very small. Since all methods of measuring partial free energies in solutions depend on the transfer from one phase to another of equivalent quantities of positive and negative ions, or the replacement of an ion by an equivalent quantity of ions of the same sign, it is only possible to determine directly either the sum of the values of $\bar{F}^\circ_i$ of equivalent quantities of ions of opposite sign, or the corresponding difference for equivalent quantities of ions of the same sign.

Determination from Standard Electrode Potentials. Consider the reversible cell:

$$H_2 \mid HCl(aq.) \mid Cl_2. \quad \ldots\ldots\ldots\ldots\ldots\ldots (a)$$

When positive electricity flows through the cell from left to right the reaction which takes place is

$$\tfrac{1}{2}H_2 + \tfrac{1}{2}Cl_2 = HCl(aq.).$$

If the sign of the electromotive force (E) is taken as that of the electrode on the right, **EF** is the electrical work yielded by this reaction, and this is equal to the free energy decrease, *i.e.*

$$\mathbf{EF} = -\Delta F.$$

Taking the free energy of the elements as zero, the free energy change in the reaction is

$$\Delta F = \bar{F}^\circ_{H^+} + \bar{F}^\circ_{Cl^-} + RT \log a_{H^+} . a_{Cl^-},$$

and therefore

$$\mathbf{EF} = -(\bar{F}^\circ_{H^+} - \bar{F}^\circ_{Cl^-}) - RT \log a_{H^+} . a_{Cl^-}.$$

Writing $$\mathbf{EF} = \mathbf{E}^\circ\mathbf{F} - RT \log a_{H^+} . a_{Cl^-},$$

where $\mathbf{E}^\circ$ is the standard electromotive force of the cell, we see that

$$-\mathbf{E}^\circ\mathbf{F} = \bar{F}^\circ_{H^+} + \bar{F}^\circ_{Cl^-}.$$

The value of $\bar{F}^\circ_{H^+} + \bar{F}^\circ_{Cl^-}$ can thus be determined by measuring the electromotive force of the cell in a solution in which the activity of hydrogen chloride is known. It is not possible to determine the separate values of $\bar{F}^\circ_{H^+}$ and $F^\circ_{Cl^-}$ in this way, but no inconvenience arises in practice if we arbitrarily take $\bar{F}^\circ$ as zero for one particular ion. If we take $\bar{F}^\circ_{H^+}$ as zero, we have

$$-\mathbf{E}^\circ\mathbf{F} = \bar{F}^\circ_{Cl^-}. \quad \ldots\ldots\ldots\ldots\ldots\ldots (271)$$

Since **E** is the electromotive force of a chlorine electrode measured against a hydrogen electrode in the same solution, $\mathbf{E}^\circ$ is the standard potential of the chlorine electrode measured against the standard hydrogen electrode. This quantity is taken as the standard electrode potential of chlorine for the given solvent. To obtain $\bar{F}^\circ_{Cl^-}$ according to our conventions

$$(F_{H_2}=0,\ F_{Cl_2}=0,\ \bar{F}^\circ_{H^+}=0),$$

the standard electrode potential is multiplied by $-\mathbf{F}$, *i.e.*

$$\bar{F}^\circ_{Cl^-} = -\mathbf{E}^\circ_{Cl_2}\mathbf{F} = -23074E^\circ \text{ calories.}$$

The standard free energies of positive ions can also be determined by means of suitable cells, and it is usually possible to devise cells without a liquid junction which will give the desired information. Since the chlorine electrode is not suitable for general use as a reference electrode, the calomel or similar electrode is usually employed as the electrode which is reversible with respect to the negative ion. Thus when a positive current passes from left to right through the cell

$$H_2 \mid HCl(aq.),\ HgCl(s) \mid Hg, \quad \ldots\ldots\ldots\ldots(b)$$

the reaction

$$\tfrac{1}{2}H_2 + HgCl(s) = H^+ + Cl^- + Hg$$

takes place, and therefore if E is the electromotive force, taking the sign as that of the electrode on the right, and ΔF the free energy change in this reaction,

$$\mathbf{EF} = -\Delta F.$$

The free energy change in the reaction, taking $\bar{F}^\circ_{H^+}$, F_{H_2}, F_{Hg} as zero, is

$$\Delta F = \bar{F}^\circ_{Cl^-} - F_{HgCl(s)} + RT \log a_{H^+} . a_{Cl^-},$$

so that

$$\mathbf{EF} = -(\bar{F}^\circ_{Cl^-} - F_{HgCl(s)}) - RT \log a_{H^+} . a_{Cl^-}.$$

Writing

$$\mathbf{EF} = \mathbf{E}^\circ_c\mathbf{F} - RT \log a_{H^+} . a_{Cl^-},$$

where E_c° is the standard electromotive of the cell, it follows that

$$\mathbf{E}^\circ_c F = -(F^\circ_{\text{Cl}^-} - F_{\text{HgCl}(s)}). \quad \text{.........(271}a\text{)}$$

Consider now the cell

$$\text{Hg} \mid \text{HgCl}(s),\ \text{LiCl} \mid \text{Li}. \quad \text{..................(}c\text{)}$$

When a positive current passes through the cell from left to right the reaction is

$$\text{Hg} + \text{Cl}^- + \text{Li}^+ = \text{HgCl} + \text{Li},$$

and the free energy in this reaction is

$$\Delta F = F_{\text{HgCl}(s)} - \bar{F}^\circ_{\text{Cl}^-} - \bar{F}^\circ_{\text{Li}^+} - RT \log a_{\text{Cl}^-} \,.\, a_{\text{Li}^+}.$$

If $\mathbf{E}$ is the electromotive force of the cell, taking the sign as that of the right-hand side, we thus have

$$\mathbf{EF} = -\Delta F,$$

or $$\mathbf{EF} = -F_{\text{HgCl}(s)} + \bar{F}^\circ_{\text{Cl}^-} + \bar{F}^\circ_{\text{Li}^+} + RT \log a_{\text{Cl}^-} \,.\, a_{\text{Li}^+},$$

and if $\mathbf{E}^\circ$ is the standard electromotive force of the cell defined by

$$\mathbf{EF} = \mathbf{E}^\circ\mathbf{F} + RT \log a_{\text{Cl}^-} \,.\, a_{\text{Li}^+},$$

it is evident that

$$\mathbf{E}^\circ\mathbf{F} = -F_{\text{HgCl}(s)} + \bar{F}^\circ_{\text{Cl}^-} + \bar{F}^\circ_{\text{Li}^+}.$$

Comparing with (206), it follows that

$$(\mathbf{E}^\circ + \mathbf{E}^\circ_c)\mathbf{F} = \bar{F}^\circ_{\text{Li}^+}. \quad \text{...............(272)}$$

$(\mathbf{E}^\circ + \mathbf{E}^\circ_c)$ is the standard electromotive force of the combination

$$H_2 | \text{HCl(aq.)}\ \text{HgCl}(s) | \text{Hg} - \text{Hg} | \text{HgCl}(s)\ \text{LiCl(aq.)} | \text{Li}, \quad (d)$$

which is the same as that of the cell

$$H_2 \mid H^+ \vdots \text{Li}^+ \mid \text{Li}$$

when any liquid-liquid junction potential is eliminated.

$(\mathbf{E}^\circ + \mathbf{E}^\circ_c) = E^\circ_{\text{Li}^+}$ is thus the standard potential of the lithium electrode measured against the standard hydrogen electrode, and we have

$$\mathbf{E}^\circ_{Li^+}\mathbf{F} = \bar{F}^\circ_{Li^+}. \qquad \ldots\ldots\ldots\ldots\ldots\ldots(273)$$

We can derive this relation directly from cell (d). The reaction which occurs in this cell when a positive current passes from left to right is

$$\tfrac{1}{2}H_2 + Li^+ + Cl^- = Li + H^+ + Cl^-$$

and the standard free energy change in this reaction is

$$\Delta F^\circ = F_{Li} + \bar{F}^\circ_{H^+} + \bar{F}^\circ_{Cl^-} - (\tfrac{1}{2}F_{H_2} - \bar{F}^\circ_{Li^+} - \bar{F}^\circ_{Cl^-}),$$

or, taking F_{H_2}, F_{Li} and $\bar{F}^\circ_{H^+}$ as zero.

$$\Delta F^\circ = -\bar{F}^\circ_{Li^+}.$$

Since $\mathbf{E}^\circ_{Li^+}\mathbf{F} = -\Delta F^\circ$, we have as before

$$\mathbf{E}^\circ_{Li^+}\mathbf{F} = \bar{F}^\circ_{Li^+}.$$

In general, the standard free energy of a positive elementary ion M^{+z} is really the standard free energy change of the reaction,

$$M + zH^+(aq.) = M^{+z}(aq.) + z/2H_2\ ;$$

and is measured by $z\mathbf{E}_M{}^\circ\mathbf{F} = \bar{F}^\circ_{M^{+z}}$. The standard free energy of a negative elementary ion X is the standard free energy change of the reaction,

$$\tfrac{1}{2}H_2 + X = zH^+ + X^{-z},$$

and is measured by $-z\mathbf{E}^\circ_X\mathbf{F} = \bar{F}^\circ_{X^{-z}}$. Values of the standard free energies of the elementary ions are given in Table LI. (p. 485).

Standard Free Energy of Hydroxyl Ion. By (262)

$$\bar{F}^\circ_{OH^-} + \bar{F}^\circ_{H^+} = \bar{F}^\circ_W + RT \log K_W.$$

Taking $\bar{F}^\circ_{H^+}$ as zero, we can thus find $\bar{F}^\circ_{OH^-}$ if we know $\bar{F}^\circ_W$, which is equal to the free energy of formation from its elements of pure liquid water, and its dissociation constant K_W.

The former may be determined (p. 268) from the equilibrium constant of the gaseous reaction, combined with the free energy of vaporisation of water. We thus obtained

$$H_2 + \tfrac{1}{2}O_2 = H_2O\ (1), \quad \Delta F^\circ_{298} = -56640.$$

It can also be determined indirectly from the free energy changes of such reactions as

$$(a)\ Hg(1) + \tfrac{1}{2}O_2 = HgO,$$
$$(b)\ H_2 + HgO = Hg + H_2O\ (1).$$

The free energy change in reaction (*a*) can be determined by measurements of the dissociation pressure of mercuric oxide. In this way it has been found that

$$\Delta F^\circ_{298} = -13786 \text{ cals.}$$

The free energy change of reaction (*b*) can be determined from the electromotive force of the cell

$$H_2 \mid KOH(aq.),\ HgO \mid Hg.$$

Except for small differences due to the effect of the potassium hydroxide on the activity of water, the electromotive force of this cell is independent of the concentration of the solution. Brönsted found that the electromotive force, corrected to unit activity of water, was $\mathbf{E}^\circ = 0{\cdot}9268$ at 25°, corresponding to the free energy change for reaction (*b*), $\Delta F^\circ_{298} = -z\mathbf{E}^\circ\mathbf{F} = -42752$ calories. Adding together the free energy changes in reactions (*a*) and (*b*), we find

$$H_2 + \tfrac{1}{2}O_2 = H_2O(1),\ \Delta F^\circ = -56540.$$

Lewis and Randall give as the means of several independent methods of determination, $\Delta F^\circ = F^\circ_W = -56560$.

Using this value and $K_W = 1{\cdot}008 \times 10^{-14}$, we obtain

$$\bar{F}^\circ_{OH^-} = -56560 - (-19110) = -37440 \text{ calories.}$$

Determination from Standard Oxidation Potentials. When a positive current passes from left to right through the cell

$$H_2 \mid H^+,\ Fe^{++},\ Fe^{+++} \mid Pt$$

the reaction is $\frac{1}{2}H_2 + Fe^{+++} = H^+ + Fe^{++}$, and if E is the electromotive force, taken with the sign of the right-hand side, $\mathbf{EF} = -\Delta F$, where $-\Delta F$ is the free energy decrease in the reaction. Thus if $\mathbf{E}^\circ$ is the standard potential of the ferrous-ferric electrode, referred to the standard hydrogen potential, $\mathbf{E}^\circ\mathbf{F} = -\Delta F^\circ$, where

$$\Delta F^\circ = \bar{F}^\circ_{H^+} + \bar{F}^\circ_{Fe^{++}} - \bar{F}^\circ_{Fe^{+++}} - \tfrac{1}{2}F_{H_2}.$$

Taking F_{H_2} and $\bar{F}^\circ_{H^+}$ as zero, we thus have

$$\mathbf{E}^\circ\mathbf{F} = \bar{F}^\circ_{Fe^{+++}} - \bar{F}^\circ_{Fe^{++}}. \quad \text{............(274)}$$

Taking $\mathbf{E}^\circ = 0{\cdot}748$,* $\mathbf{E}^\circ\mathbf{F} = 17260$ cals., and

$$\bar{F}^\circ_{Fe^{++}} = -20240 \text{ cals.},$$

we find that $\qquad \bar{F}^\circ_{Fe^{+++}} = -2980$ cals.

Example. Another example is the determination of the standard free energy of the bromate ion from the potential of the bromine-bromic acid electrode.

In the cell $\quad H_2 \mid H^+ \vdots\ HBrO_3, Br_2(1) \mid Pt$

when a positive current passes from left to right, the reaction is $\frac{5}{2}H_2 + H^+ + BrO_3^- = \frac{1}{2}Br_2(1) + 3H_2O$,

and the standard free energy change is

$$\Delta F^\circ = 3F_{H_2O} - \bar{F}^\circ_{BrO_3^-}. \quad \text{.............(275)}$$

If $\mathbf{E}^\circ$ is the standard electromotive force, $z\mathbf{E}^\circ\mathbf{F} = -\Delta F$, where z, the number of equivalents in the reaction, is in this case 5. According to the measurements of Sammet, the value of $\mathbf{E}^\circ_{291}$, when the liquid junction potential is subtracted, is $+1{\cdot}491$.†

Then $\quad \Delta F^\circ = -5 \times 1{\cdot}491 \times 23074 = -172000$ cals.,

and $\quad \bar{F}^\circ_{BrO_3^-} = 172000 - 3 \times 56560 = 2300$ cals.

* Popoff and Kunz, *J. Amer. Chem. Soc.*, 51, 382, 1929.

† Calculated by Lewis and Randall, *Thermodynamics*, p. 521.

This quantity represents the standard free energy change in the reaction

$$\tfrac{1}{2}Br_2(l) + \tfrac{1}{2}H_2 + \tfrac{3}{2}O_2 = H^+ + BrO_3^-.$$

Determination from Equilibrium in Solution. Noyes and Braun * determined the equilibrium reached when silver reacts with ferric nitrate solution to form ferrous nitrate and silver nitrate, according to the reaction :

$$Ag + Fe^{+++} = Ag^+ + Fe^{++}.$$

If $\overline{F}_{Fe^{+++}}$, $\overline{F}_{Ag^+}$, $\overline{F}_{Fe^{++}}$ are the partial free energies of the ions in the equilibrium solution, the condition of equilibrium is

$$F_{Ag} + \overline{F}_{Fe^{+++}} = \overline{F}_{Ag^+} + \ _{Fe^{++}}.$$

Writing
$$\overline{F}_{Fe^{+++}} = \overline{F}^\circ_{Fe^{+++}} + RT \log a_{Fe^{+++}},$$
$$\overline{F}_{Fe^{++}} = \overline{F}^\circ_{Fe^{++}} + RT \log a_{Fe^{++}},$$
$$\overline{F}_{Ag^+} = \overline{F}^\circ_{Ag^+} + RT \log a_{Ag^+},$$

we have

$$F_{Ag} + \overline{F}^\circ_{Fe^{+++}} - \overline{F}^\circ_{Fe^{++}} - \overline{F}^\circ_{Ag^+} = RT \log\left(\frac{a_{Fe^{++}} \cdot a_{Ag^+}}{a_{Fe^{+++}}}\right)$$
$$= RT \log K_0.$$

Noyes and Braun determined the concentration ratios

$$K = m_{Fe^{++}} \cdot m_{Ag^+} / m_{Fe^{+++}}$$

and plotting them against the total concentration they obtained by extrapolation to infinite dilution $K_0 = 0{\cdot}128$.

Therefore $\quad RT \log K_0 = -1218.$

Putting

$$F_{Ag} = 0, \quad \text{and} \quad \overline{F}^\circ_{Fe^{++}} = -20240, \quad \overline{F}^\circ_{Ag^+} = 18450,$$

we thus obtain

$$\overline{F}^\circ_{Fe^{+++}} = -3008.$$

Determination from Solubility and Other Measurements. If F_s is the free energy of a solid salt which gives in

* *J. Amer. Chem. Soc.*, 34, 1016, 1912.

solution ν_1 positive and ν_2 negative ions, and $(a\pm)_s$ its mean activity in the saturated solution, since the partial free energy in the saturated solution must be equal to F_s, we have

$$F_s = \nu_1 \bar{F}^\circ_+ + \nu_2 \bar{F}^\circ_- + (\nu_1 + \nu_2)\, RT \log (a\pm)_s. \quad \ldots(276)$$

If F_s and $(a\pm)_s$ are known, the sum of the standard free energies of the ions in solution can be determined. Alternatively, if we know $\bar{F}^\circ_+$ and $\bar{F}^\circ_-$ and $(a\pm)_s$ we can find the free energy of the solid salt.

Example. In a saturated solution of sodium chloride at 25°,

$m = 6{\cdot}12$ and $f_\pm = 1{\cdot}013$; $\bar{F}^\circ_{Na^+} = -62588$, $\bar{F}^\circ_{Cl^-} = -31367$; therefore :

$$F_s = -62588 - 31367 + 2RT \log_e (6{\cdot}12 \times 1{\cdot}013) = -91792 \text{ cals.}$$

This is the free energy change in the formation of solid sodium chloride from sodium and chlorine at unit pressure at 25°, *i.e.*

$$Na + \tfrac{1}{2}Cl_2(g) = NaCl(s)\,;\ \Delta F^\circ_{298{\cdot}1} = -91792 \text{ cals.}$$

The determination of the standard free energy of the ammonium ion in solution may be given as a case in which the solubility of a gas is used as one step in the calculation.

Example. The free energy of formation of gaseous ammonia, as determined from the study of the gas reaction (p. 268) is

$$\tfrac{1}{2}N_2 + 3/2H_2 = NH_3(g)\,;\ \Delta F^\circ_{298} = -3910 \text{ cals.,}$$

i.e. the free energy of gaseous ammonia at unit pressure at 25°, taking the free energies of the elements as zero, is $F^\circ(g) = -3910$ cals. Its free energy at a pressure p (atmos.) is $F(g) = F^\circ(g) + RT \log p$. Similarly, if $\bar{F}^\circ_{NH_3}$ is the standard free energy in aqueous solution, its partial free energy in a dilute solution of concentration m is

$$\bar{F}^\circ_{NH_3} + RT \log m,$$

and the condition of equilibrium between the gas and the solution is

$$F^\circ(g) + RT \log p = \bar{F}^\circ_{NH_3} + RT \log m,$$

or
$$\bar{F}^\circ_{NH_3} - F^\circ(g) = -RT \log (m/p).$$

It has been found * that the limiting value of (m/p) at small concentrations is $(m/p)_0 = 59{\cdot}2$. Using this value, we find that

$$\bar{F}^\circ_{NH_3} - F^\circ(g) = -2420 \text{ cals.},$$

and therefore
$$\bar{F}^\circ_{NH_3} = -6330 \text{ cals.}$$

The standard free energy of NH_4OH is obtained by adding the free energy of water in the solution to $\bar{F}^\circ_{NH_3}$, *i.e.*

$$F^\circ_{NH_4OH} = \bar{F}^\circ_{NH_3} + \bar{F}_{H_2O}$$
$$= -6330 - 56560 = -62890 \text{ cals.}$$

Finally, if K is the dissociation constant of ammonium hydroxide, we have (p. 155),

$$\bar{F}^\circ_{NH_4OH} - \bar{F}^\circ_{NH_4^+} - F^\circ_{OH^-} = RT \log K.$$

Taking $\bar{F}^\circ_{OH^-}$ as -37440 and K as $1{\cdot}79 \times 10^{-5}$,

i.e.
$$(RT \log_e K = -6480 \text{ cals.}),$$

we have
$$\bar{F}^\circ_{NH_4^+} = -18970 \text{ cals.}$$

This quantity actually represents the standard free energy change in the reaction

$$1/2N_2 + 3/2H_2 + H^+(aq.) = NH_4^+(aq.).$$

A complete tabulation of data from which the free energies of ions can be determined is given in Latimer's *Oxidation States of the Elements and their Potentials in Aqueous Solutions.* (Prentice-Hall, New York, 1938). The following table gives a selection of the most commonly used values. These may in some cases not agree completely with the other data used in examples in this chapter.

* de Wijs, *Rec. Trav. Chem.*, 44, 655, 1925.

TABLE LI.

STANDARD FREE ENERGIES OF IONS RELATIVE TO $F°_{H^+}=0$ IN AQUEOUS SOLUTION AT 25° (CALS.)

Ion	$F°$	Ion	$F°$	Ion	$F°$
Al^{+++}	-115500	I^-	-12333	$H_2PO_4^-$	-267100
Ba^{++}	-133850	Fe^{++}	-20310	K^+	-67430
Be^{++}	-78700	Fe^{+++}	-2530	Rb^+	-68800
Br^-	-24578	Pb^{++}	-5810	Ag^+	18441
Cd^{++}	-18550	Li^+	-70700	Na^+	-62590
Ca^{++}	-132700	Mg^{++}	-107780	Sr^{++}	-133200
$C_2O_4^=$	-158660	Mn^{++}	-48600	HS^-	2950
CN^-	39740	Hg_2^{++}	36850	$S^=$	23420
Cs^+	-70280	Hg^{++}	39415	HSO_3^-	-125905
Cl^-	-31330	Ni^{++}	-11530	$SO_3^=$	-116400
Cr^{+++}	-49000	NO_2^-	-8450	$SO_4^=$	-176100
$CrO_4^=$	-171400	NO_3	-26250	Tl^+	-7760
Co^{++}	-12800	OH^-	-37585	Sn^{++}	-6275
Cu^{++}	15910	$PO_4^{\equiv}$	40970	Zr^{++}	-35176
F^-	-65700	$HPO_4^=$	-257270	NH_4^+	-18960

Standard Entropies of Ions in Aqueous Solutions. If $\bar{F}$ and $\bar{H}$ are the partial free energy and heat content of a salt in a solution, the partial entropy is

$$\bar{S}=\frac{\bar{H}-\bar{F}}{T}.$$

In very dilute solutions $\bar{F}=\bar{F}°+(\nu_1+\nu_2)\,RT\log m_{\pm}$, and $\bar{H}$ is equal to the partial heat content for an infinitely dilute solution $\bar{H}°$, so that

$$\bar{S}=\frac{\bar{H}°-\bar{F}°}{T}-(\nu_1+\nu_2)\,R\log m_{\pm}. \quad \text{.........(277)}$$

The quantity $\frac{\bar{H}°-\bar{F}°}{T}=\bar{S}°$ is called the standard entropy of the salt. It can be readily determined when $\bar{H}°$ and $\bar{F}°$ are known.

The absolute values of the standard entropies of a

considerable number of salts have been calculated by Latimer and Buffington.* In the previous sections we evaluated the standard free energies of salts in aqueous solution at 25°, taking the free energies of the elements as zero at this temperature. The value of $\bar{H}°$ can easily be determined with reference to the same standard (*i.e.* $\bar{H}°$ is then the heat content change in the formation of a mol of the salt at infinite dilution from the elements).

We thus obtain by $(\bar{H}° - \bar{F}°)/T$ the standard entropy relative to the entropies of the elements. If we add the entropies of the elements at the given temperature, we obtain the absolute standard entropy of the salt in the solution. Some examples of this calculation are given in Table LII.

TABLE LII.

	$\bar{H}°$. Heat Content at $m=0$, relative to Elements.	$\bar{F}°$. Standard Free Energy relative to Elements.	$(\bar{H}°-\bar{F}°)/T$. Standard Entropy relative to Elements.	Entropy of Elements at 25° C.	$\bar{S}°$ (Absolute).
$CuCl_2$ -	$-62{\cdot}6$†	$-46{\cdot}9$†	-52	$8+51$	7
$CuBr_2$ -	$-40{\cdot}6$	$-33{\cdot}2$	-25	$8+36$	19
$FeCl_3$ -	$-127{\cdot}7$	$-96{\cdot}8$	-104	$7+76$	-21
$FeBr_3$ -	$-95{\cdot}5$	$-76{\cdot}0$	-65	$7+55$	-3
$TlBr_3$ -	$-56{\cdot}4$	$-27{\cdot}3$	-98	$18+55$	-25

† In kgm. cals.

It is often convenient to start with the entropy of the solid salt and to determine the entropy of solution. Since the free energy of the solid salt (F_s) is equal to its partial free energy in a saturated solution, we have

$$F_s = \bar{F}° + RT \log a_s,$$

where a_s is the activity in the saturated solution. We can thus evaluate $\Delta F° = \bar{F}° - F_s$, when the activity of the

* *J. Amer. Chem. Soc.*, 48, 2297, 1926.

salt in the saturated solution is known. Similarly, the heat of solution of the salt in an infinitely dilute solution gives $\Delta H^\circ = \bar{H}^\circ - H_s$.

$\Delta S^\circ = (\Delta H^\circ - \Delta F^\circ)/T$, which may be called the entropy of solution, is thus the difference between the standard entropy in the solution and the entropy of the solid salt. If we add the value of the latter we obtain the absolute value of $\bar{S}^\circ$. The details of this calculation for a number of salts are given in Table LIII.

TABLE LIII.

STANDARD ENTROPIES OF SALTS DETERMINED FROM THE ENTROPY OF THE SOLID SALT AND THE ENTROPY OF SOLUTION AT 25°.

	Entropy of Substance.	ΔH°. kgm. cals.	ΔF°. kgm. cals.	ΔS°.	$\bar{S}$ (Absolute).
HCl -	+44·5	−17·3	−8·7	−28·9	+15·6
HBr -	47·0	−19·9	−12·0	−26·4	20·6
HI -	49·0	−19·2	−12·7	−21·9	27·1
NaCl -	18·5	+1·0	−2·2	+10·6	29·1
KCl -	19·7	4·4	−0·9	18·0	37·7
AgCl -	24·0	16·0	+13·3	9·0	33·0
AgBr -	25·0	20·1	16·6	11·8	36·8
AgI -	26·8	26·4	21·8	15·6	42·4
MgF_2 -	15·7	−2·8	10·7	−45·0	−29·3
CaF_2 -	17·2	+2·7	13·9	−37·3	−20·1
PbF_2 -	22·0	+2·2	10·1	−26·3	−4·3
$BaSO_4$ -	38·0	5·6	13·1	−25·0	13·0

Finally, the difference between the standard entropies of two ions may be obtained from the consideration of replacement reactions. The standard entropy change in the reaction $Na + H^+ = Na^+ + \frac{1}{2}H_2$ is given by

$$\Delta S^\circ = (\Delta H^\circ - \Delta F^\circ)/T,$$

where ΔH° is the heat of solution (at infinite dilution) in very dilute solutions of hydrogen ions, and ΔF° is obtained in calories by multiplying the standard electrode potential of sodium, referred to the standard hydrogen electrode by 23,074. Since

$$\Delta S^\circ = \bar{S}^\circ_{Na^+} + \tfrac{1}{2}S_{H_2} - S_{Na} - \bar{S}^\circ_{H^+},$$

we obtain the absolute value of $\bar{S}^\circ_{Na^+} - \bar{S}^\circ_{H^+}$ by adding to ΔS° the absolute value of $S_{Na} - \tfrac{1}{2}S_{H_2}$ (Table LIV.).

TABLE LIV.

ENTROPY CHANGES IN REPLACEMENT OF H^+ BY OTHER IONS AT 25°.

Ion.	ΔH°. kgm. cals.	ΔF°. kgm. cals.	ΔS°	Entropy of Element.	$\bar{S}^\circ_{M^{+z}} - z\bar{S}^\circ_{H^+}$.
$\tfrac{1}{2}H_2$	—	—	—	14·7	—
Li	− 66·0	− 68·3	7·7	7·6	0·5
Na	− 56·8	− 62·6	19·3	12·3	16·8
K	− 61·5	− 67·4	19·9	16·6	21·8
Rb	− 60·8	− 67·5	22·4	17·4	25·8
Cu	− 129·0	− 131·9	9·7	10·6	− 9·1
Zn	− 36·3	− 35·0	− 4·3	9·8	− 23·9
Cd	− 17·1	− 18·3	4·0	11·8	− 13·6
Fe	− 20·7	− 20·3	− 0·1	7·7	− 21·8
Sn	− 4·5	− 6·3	6·0	11·2	− 12·2

It is not possible to determine the standard entropies of individual ions from these values. It is sufficient, however, for thermodynamical calculations to know relative values, taking that of one particular ion as zero. In finding the relative standard free energies we adopted the convention that $\bar{F}^\circ_{H^+} = 0$. Similarly the relative standard entropies of the ions are determined taking $\bar{S}^\circ_{H^+} = 0$. The values of these quantities so far determined are given in Table LV.*

* Latimer, Schutz and Hicks, *J. Chem. Physics*, 2, 82, 1934 ; Latimer, Pitzer and Smith, *J. Amer. Chem. Soc.*, 60, 1829, 1938 ; Keleey, *U.S. Bur. of Mines Bull.*, 394, 1935 ; Latimer, *Oxidation States of the Elements* (N.Y., 1938).

TABLE LV.

STANDARD ENTROPIES OF IONS IN AQUEOUS SOLUTION AT 25° RELATIVE TO $\bar{S}^{\circ}_{H^+}=0$ (CALS./DEG.).

Ion	Entropy	Ion	Entropy	Ion	Entropy
H^+	0·0	Ca^{++}	−11·4 ± 0·3	Br^-	19·7 ± 0·2
Li^+	4·7 ± 1·0	Sr^{++}	−7·3 ± 1·5	I^-	25·3 ± ·5
Na^+	14·0 ± 0·4	Ba^{++}	2·3 ± 0·3	ClO^-	10 ± 2
K^+	24·2 ± 0·2	Fe^{++}	−25·9 ± 1·0	ClO_2^-	24·1 ± 0·5
Rb^+	28·7 ± 0·7	Cu^{++}	−26·5 ± 1·0	ClO_3^-	39·4 ± ·5
Cs^+	31·8 ± 0·6	Zn^{++}	−25·7 ± 1·0	ClO_4^-	43·6 ± ·5
Ag^+	17·54 ± 0·15	Cd^{++}	−16·4 ± 1·5	BrO_3^-	38·5 ± 1·0
NH_4^+	26·4 ± 0·5	Hg_2^{++}	17·7 ± 3	IO_3^-	28·0 ± 1·0
Tl^+	30·5 ± 0·4	Sn^{++}	−4·9 ± 1·0	$SO_3^{=}$	3 ± 3
OH^-	−2·49 ± 0·06	Pb^{++}	3·9 ± ·9	$SO_4^{=}$	4·4 ± 1
F^-	−2·3 ± 2	Al^{+++}	−76 ± 10	NO_3^-	35·0 ± 0·2
CN^-	25 ± 5	Fe^{+++}	−61 ± 5	$H_2PO_4^-$	28·0 ± 1·5
MnO_4^-	46·7 ± 0·4	$CO_3^{=}$	−13·0 ± 1	$HPO_4^{=}$	−2·3 ± 1·5
$CrO_4^{=}$	10·5 ± 1·0	$C_2O_4^{=}$	9·6 ± 1	$PO_4^{\equiv}$	−45 ± 2
Mg^{++}	−31·6 ± 3	Cl^-	13·50 ± 0·10		

Applications. (1) *Calculation of standard potential of the fluorine electrode.* The heat of formation of sodium fluoride in aqueous solution at infinite dilution, from the elements, is

$$Na + \tfrac{1}{2}F_2 = Na^+(aq.) + F^-(aq.)\,;$$
$$\Delta H^{\circ}_{298} = -136000 \text{ calories.}$$

Taking the entropy of Na as 12·3 and of $\frac{1}{2}F_2$ as 23·5, and the standard entropies of the ions as given in Table LV., we have

$$\Delta\bar{S}^{\circ} = \bar{S}^{\circ}_{Na^+} + \bar{S}^{\circ}_{F^-} - S_{Na} - \tfrac{1}{2}S_{F_2} = -24{\cdot}1,$$

and therefore the standard free energy change is

$$\Delta\bar{F}^{\circ} = \Delta H^{\circ} - T\Delta S^{\circ} = -128900 \text{ calories.}$$

Taking the free energies of the elements as zero, we have

$$\Delta F^{\circ} = \bar{F}^{\circ}_{Na^+} + \bar{F}^{\circ}_{F^-}.$$

Since $\bar{F}^{\circ}_{Na^+} = -62600$, we have $\bar{F}^{\circ}_{F^-} = -66170$.

The standard potential of the fluorine electrode is thus

$$\mathbf{E} = -\frac{\overline{F}^\circ_{F^-}}{\mathbf{F}} = +2\cdot85 \text{ volts.}$$

(2) *Standard potential of the magnesium electrode.* The heat content change in the reaction

$$Mg + 2H^+ = Mg^{++} + H_2$$

as determined by the heat of solution of magnesium in dilute hydrochloric acid is $\Delta H^\circ_{298} = -110200$ cals. The standard entropy change is

$$\Delta S^\circ = \overline{S}^\circ_{Mg^{++}} + S_{H_2} - S_{Mg} - 2\overline{S}^\circ_{H^+}.$$

Taking $\overline{S}^\circ_{Mg^{++}} = -31\cdot6$, $S_{H_2} = 29\cdot4$, $S_{Mg} = 8\cdot3$, and $\overline{S}^\circ_{H^+} = 0$, we have $\Delta S_0 = -10\cdot5$ and $\Delta F^\circ = -107050$ cals. Since $2\mathbf{E}^\circ\mathbf{F} = \Delta F^\circ$, where $\mathbf{E}^\circ$ is the standard potential of the magnesium electrode, we have $\mathbf{E}^\circ = -2\cdot40$ volts. (See Coates, *J. Chem. Soc.*, 1945, p. 478, for a more exact calculation.)

(3) *Standard potential of the aluminium electrode.* Direct measurements of this potential have given extremely discordant values. It may be calculated from the free energy change in the reaction

$$Al + 3H^+ = Al^{+++} + 3/2H_2.$$

This can be determined if the heat of the reaction and the standard entropy of Al^{+++} are known. The latter could be determined as in Table LIII. from the entropy and entropy of solution of a suitable salt, but none of the simple salts of aluminium are suitable for the purpose. Latimer and Greensfelder * therefore used the caesium alum $CsAl(SO_4)_2 . 12H_2O$. They determined the entropy of the solid salt by heat capacity measurements, finding $S_{298\cdot1} = 163\cdot85$. The heat of solution of the salt in water at 25° is $\Delta H^\circ = \overline{H}^\circ - H_s = 13560$ calories. The free energy of solution $\Delta F^\circ = \overline{F}^\circ - F_s = -RT \log a_s$ can be determined when the concentration in the saturated solution and the activity coefficient are known. It was found that the concentration

* *J. Amer. Chem. Soc.*, 50, 2202, 1928.

of the saturated solution at 25° was $m = 0{\cdot}01403$, and $f_{\pm} = 0{\cdot}217$. Hence $\bar{F}^{\circ} - F_s = +12910$ calories. The entropy of solution is thus

$$\Delta S^{\circ}_{\text{soln.}} = \bar{S}^{\circ} - \bar{S}_s = (\Delta H^{\circ} - \Delta F^{\circ})/T = +2{\cdot}18,$$

and the absolute value of $S^{\circ}_{\text{soln.}} = 163{\cdot}85 + 2{\cdot}18 = 166{\cdot}03$.

Since $\quad \bar{S}^{\circ} = \bar{S}^{\circ}_{Cs^+} + \bar{S}^{\circ}_{Al^{+++}} + 2\bar{S}^{\circ}_{SO_4^=} + 12S_{H_2O}$,

taking $\bar{S}^{\circ}$ as 27·9, $\bar{S}^{\circ}_{Cs^+SO_4^=}$ as 9, S_{H_2O} as 15·9, we find that

$$\bar{S}^{\circ}_{Al^{+++}} = -70{\cdot}9.$$

The standard entropy change in the reaction

$$Al + 3H^+ = Al^{+++} + 3/2H_2,$$

taking $S_{Al} = 6{\cdot}8$, $3/2S_{H_2} = 43{\cdot}8$, $\bar{S}^{\circ}_{H^+} = 0$, is thus $-33{\cdot}9$.

ΔH° for the reaction, as given by the heat of solution of aluminium in dilute hydrochloric acid, is -127000 cals. Therefore the standard free energy change is

$$\Delta F^{\circ}_{298} = \Delta H^{\circ} - T\Delta S^{\circ} = -116900 \text{ cals.}$$

Writing $\Delta F^{\circ}_{298} = +3\mathbf{F}\mathbf{E}^{\circ}$, we have for the standard electrode potential of aluminium $\mathbf{E}^{\circ} = -1{\cdot}69$ volts.

(4) *Standard free energy of the sulphate ion.* The entropy of solid barium sulphate ($BaSO_4$), as determined by heat capacity measurements, is 31·5 at 25° C. Its heat of solution in water is $\Delta H^{\circ}_{298} = 5455$ cals. The free energy of solution is $\Delta F^{\circ} = F_0 - \bar{F}_s = 2RT \log (mf_{\pm})$. Taking the solubility as $m = 0{\cdot}957 \times 10^{-5}$ and $f_{\pm} = 0{\cdot}977$, we obtain $\Delta F^{\circ} = 13718$ cals. The entropy of solution

$$\Delta S^{\circ} = (\Delta H^{\circ} - \Delta F^{\circ})/T$$

is thus $\Delta S^{\circ} = -27{\cdot}7$, and combining this with the entropy of the solid, we have

$$\bar{S}^{\circ}_{Ba^{++}} + \bar{S}^{\circ}_{SO_4^=} = 31{\cdot}5 - 27{\cdot}7 = 3{\cdot}8 \text{ cals./deg.}$$

The value of $\bar{S}^{\circ}_{Ba^{++}}$ (determined similarly to $\bar{S}^{\circ}_{Mg^{++}}$ in (2)) is 0·8, and therefore $\bar{S}^{\circ}_{SO_4^=} = 3{\cdot}0$. As a result of measurements of this kind with several sulphates, Latimer, Hicks and Schutz * gave $\bar{S}^{\circ}_{SO_4^=} = 3{\cdot}8$ as the best value.

* Latimer, Hicks and Schutz, *J. Chem. Physics*, 1, 424, 622, 1933.

The heat of formation of pure sulphuric acid from its elements is

$$S_{rh} + H_2 + 2O_2 = H_2SO_4(l), \quad \Delta H^\circ_{298\cdot1} = -194120,$$

and the heat of solution of H_2SO_4 in water at infinite dilution is

$$H_2SO_4(l) = H_2SO_4(aq.), \quad \Delta H^\circ_{298\cdot1} = -20900.$$

The heat of formation of sulphuric acid in aqueous solution at infinite dilution is thus

$$S_{(rh)} + H_2 + 2O_2 = 2H^+ + SO_4^=, \quad \Delta H^\circ_{298\cdot1} = -215000 \text{ cals.}$$

The entropy change in this reaction, taking the following values for the entropy, $H_2 = 31\cdot23$, $S = 7\cdot6$, $O_2 = 49\cdot03$, $SO_4^= = 3\cdot8$, is $\Delta S^\circ = -133$.

The free energy change in the reaction,

$$\Delta F^\circ = \Delta H^\circ - T\Delta S^\circ,$$

is thus -175300 cals., which is equal to the free energy of formation of the sulphate ion $F^\circ_{SO_4^=}$, taking $F^\circ_{H^+}$ as zero.

The hydration energy of ions. Any discussion of the free energies of ions in aqueous solution will involve a consideration of the interaction of the ions with water. The energy of this interaction, *i.e.* of the solution of the isolated gaseous ion, is called the hydration energy. These quantities can be determined by the following process, in which NaCl is taken as an example :

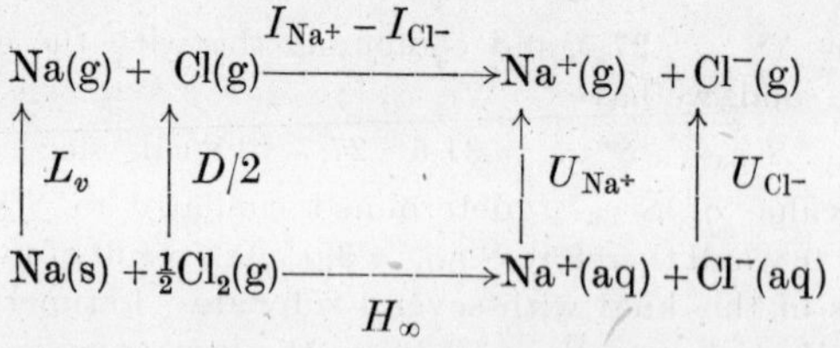

$$\begin{array}{ccccc}
Na(g) + Cl(g) & \xrightarrow{I_{Na^+} - I_{Cl^-}} & Na^+(g) + Cl^-(g) \\
\uparrow L_v \quad \uparrow D/2 & & \uparrow U_{Na^+} \quad \uparrow U_{Cl^-} \\
Na(s) + \tfrac{1}{2}Cl_2(g) & \xrightarrow[H_\infty]{} & Na^+(aq) + Cl^-(aq)
\end{array}$$

(1) An atomic weight of Na is vaporised (L_v) and half a mol. of chlorine is dissociated into its atoms ($D/2$).

(2) The sodium atoms are ionised into Na^+ and ϵ, and the chlorine atoms are ionised by taking up the electrons $Cl^+ + \epsilon \rightarrow Cl^-$. The energy required is $I_{Na^+} - I_{Cl^-}$, where I_{Cl^-} is the ionisation energy of Cl^-.

(3) The gaseous ions are dissolved in water, giving the hydration energies U_{Na^+} and U_{Cl^-}.

The total energy change in this process is the same as the heat of formation of Na^+Cl^- from its elements in dilute aqueous solution ; *i.e.*

$$\Delta H_{\infty} = L_v + D/2 + I_{Na^+} - I_{Cl^-} - (U_{Na^+} + U_{Cl^-}),$$

from which $(U_{Na^+} + U_{Cl^-})$ can be determined.*

Table LVI. shows a few values of the sum of the hydration energies of the two ions of a salt as determined in this way. There is no simple way of dividing these sums into the hydration energies of the separate ions. It has been found, however, by comparing a series of salts with the same anion, etc., that the hydration energies are approximately proportional to the ionic radius as measured crystallographically. It may therefore be assumed that if a salt can be found in which the positive and negative ions have the same radius (and charge), the hydration energy will be equally divided between them.

TABLE LVI.

$U_+ + U_-$ FOR IONS OF SOME SALTS (K-CALS. AT 25°).

LiF	241·8	LiCl	208·6	LiBr	197·6
NaF	214·7	NaCl	181·5	NaBr	175·3
KF	193·1	KCl	159·9	KBr	148·0

* The most inaccessible quantity in this expression is I_{Cl^-}, which cannot be directly determined. Indirect estimates have been obtained from the lattice energies of salts.

Such a pair occurs in KF and we can therefore divide the total hydration energy (193·1 k-cals.) into $U_{K^+}=96{\cdot}5$, $U_{F^-}=96{\cdot}5$ k-cals. Bernal and Fowler * have given reasons for believing that owing to the different orientations of water molecules round positive and negative ions the hydration energy of a negative ion will be about 2 % greater than that of a positive ion of the same size. On this basis we would assign 98 k-cals. to F^- and 95 k-cals. to K^+. Table LVII. shows some individual hydration energies obtained in this way.

TABLE LVII.

Hydration Energies of Ions (k-cals.)

H^+	280	Be^{++}	713	F^-	98
Li^+	441	Mg^{++}	498	Cl^-	65
Na^+	117	Ca^{++}	421	Br^-	53
K^+	95	Sr^{++}	383	I^-	46
Tl^+	95	Ba^{++}	347	Al^{+++}	1151
Ag^+	132	Zr^{++}	523	Cr^{+++}	1062
NH_4^+	97	Te^{++}	507	Cu^{++}	542

The simplest way of accounting for these values would be as the difference between the energy of charging the ion in vacuum and in a medium having the dielectric constant of water. The Born expression gives this as

$$U=\frac{z^2\epsilon^2}{2r}\left(1-\frac{1}{D}\right),$$

where $z\epsilon$ is the charge on the ion of radius r and D the dielectric constant of the medium.† In addition to this there will be a term representing the energy of solu-

* *J. Chem. Physics*, 1, 515, 1933.

† Strictly this gives the *free energy* of hydration. We can ignore the difference at present.

tion of the uncharged ion, but this can be taken to be comparable to that of the nearest inert gas and is a comparatively small quantity.

It is assumed in this calculation that the water very near the ion state has the dielectric constant D of water in bulk. As we have seen, the first layer of water molecules round the ion is probably electrically saturated, *i.e.* the dipoles are completely orientated by the electric field of the ion. An attempt to improve the calculation by taking this saturation effect into account was first made by Webb,* who found that he could account for the values on the basis of fairly reasonable ionic radii. Bernal and Fowler † made a more elaborate calculation. They supposed the hydration energy to be made up of three quantities :

(1) The energy of interaction of the ion with the water molecules in contact with it. If P is the interaction energy with a single water molecule and n the number of molecules in the inner hydration sheath, this term will be nP. P will be a function of the combined radii of the ion and the water molecule, which can be approximately represented by $P=\frac{\mu\epsilon z}{(r_i+r_w)^2}$; but there will be a slight difference for positive and negative ions owing to the different aspects presented by the water molecule in these cases.

(2) The electrical energy of the water outside this sphere, which may be found by the Born equation : $\frac{z^2\epsilon^2}{2R}\left(1-\frac{1}{D}\right)$, where R is the radius of the " saturation " sphere.

* *J. Amer. Chem. Soc.*, 48, 2589, 1926.

† *loc. cit.*

(3) A term u representing the disorientation of water produced by the ion, which is approximately constant We thus get

$$U = uP + \frac{z^2 \epsilon^2}{2R}\left(1 - \frac{1}{D}\right) - u.$$

Reasonable agreement can be obtained for many ions —particularly those having inert gas structures—in this way. Improvements in the calculation have been made by Eley and Evans,* and Eley and Pepper have also made similar calculations for methyl alcohol.†

***Entropy of Solution of Simple Gas Ions.** The entropy of monatomic ions in the gaseous state can be calculated by means of Sackur's equation (p. 287),

$$S_{\text{gas}} = 25{\cdot}7 + 3/2R \log (\text{atomic wt.}).$$

Subtracting the standard entropy of the ion in aqueous solution from this quantity, we obtain the entropy of solution of the gaseous ion. Some values are given in Table LVIII. Since the standard entropies in solution are relative to $\bar{S}_{H^+}{}^\circ = 0$, the values of the entropy of solution differ from their absolute values by the absolute value of $z\bar{S}_{H^+}{}^\circ$.

TABLE LVIII.

ENTROPIES OF SOLUTION OF SIMPLE GAS IONS.

	S_g.	ΔS of Solution of Gas Ion.		S_g.	ΔS of Solution of Gas Ion.		S_g.	ΔS of Solution of Gas Ion.
Li^+	31·5	31	F^-	34·5	39	Fe^{++}	37·7	59
Ag^+	39·7	24	Cl^-	36·4	21	Sn^{++}	39·9	52
Na^+	35·1	20	Br^-	38·8	19	Mg^{++}	35·2	53
Tl^+	41·6	15	I^-	40·1	13	Ca^{++}	36·7	46
K^+	36·6	15	Zn^{++}	38·3	62	Ba^{++}	40·4	36
Rb^+	39·0	14	Cu^{++}	38·2	61			

* *Trans. Faraday Soc.*, 34, 1093, 1938. † *ibid.*, 37, 581, 1941.

Latimer and Buffington* found that the entropy of solution varied inversely with the radius of the ion as determined by the crystal measurements of Bragg, and the values for uni- and bivalent positive ions are fairly closely represented by the equations:

$$\Delta S_{M^{+}} = -12{\cdot}6 + 58{\cdot}6(1/r),$$
$$\Delta S_{M^{++}} = -9{\cdot}5 + 94{\cdot}5(1/r).$$

These equations can be used, in conjunction with the Sackur equation, to obtain an estimate of the entropy in solution of ions for which no direct determination is available.†

The theoretical derivation of the entropy of hydration of ions has been discussed by Eley and Evans,‡ on the basis of Bernal and Fowler's picture of aqueous solutions. The entropy varies linearly with the heat of hydration for each type of ions. It is accounted for in part by the restriction of rotation of water molecules in the electric field of the ions.

The free energy of hydration of ions can be determined from the heats and entropies of hydration. It will be clear from this analysis that the free energy of *formation* of the ions in dilute solution from their elements is a somewhat complex quantity into which many factors enter. These quantities determine the electrode potentials of the elements. It will be obvious that it is not possible to give a simple explanation of the electrochemical series, *e.g.* why the alkali metals give highly negative electrode potentials and silver, copper, etc.,

* *J. Amer. Chem. Soc.*, 48, 2297, 1926. See also Latimer, *Chem. Revs.*, 18, 349, 1926.

† If the ionic radii of Goldschmidt are employed the agreement with this linear relation is not good.

‡ *loc. cit.*

relatively positive potentials. A full discussion of these factors is given in the author's *Electrocapillarity. The Chemistry and Physics of Electrically Charged Surfaces* (Methuen 1940), Chapter 3.

***Standard Free Energies of Ions in Other Solvents.** Very little information is available as to the standard free energies of ions in single solvents other than water. The difference between the standard free energies of a slightly soluble salt in two solvents can be estimated from the solubilities. Since the partial free energy of a salt in a saturated solution is equal to the free energy of the solid salt, we have for a salt giving ν_1 positive and ν_2 negative ions:

$$F_s = \bar{F}^{\circ\prime} + (\nu_1 + \nu_2) RT \log a'_{\pm},$$

$$F_s = \bar{F}^{\circ\prime\prime} + (\nu_1 + \nu_2) RT \log a_{\pm}'',$$

or

$$\bar{F}^{\circ\prime\prime} - \bar{F}^{\circ\prime} = (\nu_1 + \nu_2) RT \log a_{\pm}'/a_{\pm}'', \quad \ldots\ldots(278)$$

where $a_{\pm}'$, $a_{\pm}''$ are the mean activities of the ions in saturated solutions in the two solvents, and $\bar{F}^{\circ\prime}$, $\bar{F}^{\circ\prime\prime}$ the standard free energies. The mean activity can be determined from the concentration, using the activity coefficient calculated by the Debye-Hückel expression, if the solubility is sufficiently low. $a_{\pm}'/a_{\pm}''$ is the corrected distribution ratio of the salt between the two solvents. Table LIX. shows the values of these quantities for some saturated solutions of perchlorates in water and methyl alcohol.*

It is not, however, possible to determine the separate values of the ratios a_1'/a_1'', etc., since in no operation which is practically possible can we transfer a single ion from one phase to another. It is therefore impossible to split $(\bar{F}^{\circ\prime} - \bar{F}^{\circ\prime\prime})$ into the values of the separate ions.

* Brönsted, Delbanco and Volqartz, *Z. phys. Chem.*, *A*, 162, 128, 1932.

TABLE LIX.

ACTIVITIES OF PERCHLORATES IN SATURATED SOLUTIONS IN WATER AND METHYL ALCOHOL AT 20.

Cation.	$a_\pm$ in Water.	$a_\pm$ in Methyl Alcohol.	$(a_\pm)W/(a_\pm)MeOH.$
K^+	0·111	0·00436	25·4
Rb^+	0·057	0·00203	28·0
Cs^+	0·0664	0·00253	26·2
$[Co(NH_3)_4(NO_3)_2]^+$	0·0247	0·00143	17·3
$(Co(NH_3)_4 . NO_2 . CSN)^+$	0·0212	0·00343	6·2

The mean activity of the salt is related to the individual ion activities by $(a_\pm)^{\nu_1+\nu_2} = a_1^{\nu_1} a_2^{\nu_2}$, so that

$$\left(\frac{a_\pm'}{a_\pm''}\right)^{\nu_1+\nu_2} = \frac{a_1'^{\nu_1} a_2'^{\nu_2}}{a_1''^{\nu_1} a_2''^{\nu_2}}. \quad \ldots\ldots\ldots\ldots\ldots(279)$$

However, if we arbitrarily give a'/a'' a definite value for one particular ion, it is possible to determine the relative values of other ions by (279).

Taking the ratio of the activities of the chloride ion in water and methyl alcohol as 100 ($(a_{Cl})_W/(a_{Cl})_{Me} = 100$), Brönsted, Delbanco and Volqartz obtained the following values of the distribution ratios a_W/a_{Me} for other ions.

TABLE LX.

RELATIVE DISTRIBUTION RATIOS OF IONS BETWEEN WATER AND METHYL ALCOHOL AT 25°.

Cl^-	Br^-	I^-	NO_3^-	ClO_3^-	BrO_3^-	IO_3^-	ClO_4^-	$C_2H_3O_2^-$	$SO_4^=$
100	39·1	5·3	28·8	45·2	354	2790	5·8	224	2160

K^+	Rb^+	C_s^+	$[Co(NH_3)_4(NO_2)_2]^+$	$[Co(NH_3)_4 . NO_2 . CSN)]^+$
122	143	131	4	8·3

According to the Debye-Hückel theory the difference between the standard free energy of a salt in two solvents is equal to the difference between the electrical work of charging the ions in these media. By the simple electrical theory the work of charging an ion of radius r in a medium of dielectric constant D is $e^2/2rD$, and the difference of the standard free energies for a gram molecule of salt in media having dielectric constants D' and D'' is therefore

$$\bar{F}^{\circ\prime} - \bar{F}^{\circ\prime\prime} = N_0 \sum \frac{\nu_1 e^2}{2r_1}\left(\frac{1}{D_1'} - \frac{1}{D''}\right), \quad \ldots\ldots(280)$$

where N_0 is the Avogadro number, and the summation extends over all the ions. Bjerrum * has suggested that a term should be added to this representing the free energy difference of similar neutral molecules in the two solvents, viz.,

$$\bar{F}^{\circ\prime} - \bar{F}^{\circ\prime\prime} = (\bar{F}^{\circ}{}_n{}' - \bar{F}^{\circ}{}_n{}'') + N_0 \sum \frac{\nu_1 e_1{}^2}{2r_1}\left(\frac{1}{D'} - \frac{1}{D''}\right).$$

In this equation the term $N_0 \sum \frac{\nu_1 e_1{}^2}{2r_1}\left(\frac{1}{D'} - \frac{1}{D''}\right)$ represents that part of the standard free energy which arises from the electrical charges on the ions and $(\bar{F}^{\circ}{}_n{}' - \bar{F}^{\circ}{}_n{}'')$ that which arises from interactions of other kinds between the ions and the solvents. Thus for potassium and chloride ions $\bar{F}^{\circ}{}_n{}' - F^{\circ}{}_n{}''$ will be taken as the standard free energy difference of the similar uncharged atoms of argon in the two solvents. This is equal to $RT \log a''/a'$, where a''/a' is the distribution ratio of argon between the two solvents. It appears to be possible to account approximately for the solubilities of salts in this way.

It is necessary to point out that the expression $e^2/2rD$ is probably only a very rough approximation to the work of charging ions in actual media. Webb † has made a

* Bjerrum and Larrson, *Z. phys. Chem.*, *A*, **127**, 358, 1927; Bjerrum and Josefovicz, *ibid.*, *A*, **159**, 194, 1932.

† *J. Amer. Chem. Soc.*, **48**, 2589, 1926.

careful calculation of this quantity, taking into account the electric saturation due to dipole orientation near the ions, and has obtained values which differ widely from the simple expression.

A number of investigations have been made of the variation of the standard free energies of salts in aqueous solutions produced by the addition of non-electrolytes which lower the dielectric constant of the solution. According to (280) the difference between the standard free energy in water (D_0) and in a solution of dielectric constant D is given by $\Delta\bar{F}^\circ = -N_0 \sum \frac{e_1^2 \nu_1}{2r_1}\left(\frac{1}{D_0} - \frac{1}{D}\right)$ *i.e.* $\Delta\bar{F}^\circ$ should vary linearly with $1/D$. This has been found to be the case for lithium, sodium and potassium chloride in water and aqueous methyl alcohol solutions up to about 60 mols % alcohol;* and the same relation holds for lithium chloride in ethyl alcohol solutions.† Hydrochloric acid shows a considerable deviation when the proportion of alcohol is large, which is probably due to the ion H_3O^+ being replaced by $C_2H_5OH_2^+$ in such solutions.‡

For a more recent discussion, see Latimer and Slansky, *J. Amer. Chem. Soc.*, 62, 2019, 1940. See also Frank and Evans, *J. Chem. Physics*, 13, 507, 1945.

* Åkerlöf, *J. Amer. Chem. Soc.*, 52, 2353, 1930.

† Butler and Thomson, *Proc. Roy. Soc.*, *A*, 141, 86, 1933.

‡ Butler and Robertson, *Proc. Roy. Soc.*, *A*, 125, 694, 1929.

Examples.

1. The standard free energy of Zr^{++} is given in Table LI. as -35176 cals. What reaction is this the free energy change of. Find the standard electrode potential of Zr/Zr^{++}.

2. From the data in Table LI. find the free energy change in the reaction $2H^+ + C_2O_4^{=} = H_2 + 2CO_2$. Is oxalic acid stable in aqueous solution? (The free energy of formation of CO_2 at 25° is -94450 cals.).

3. From the data in Table LI. (1) find the free energy change in the reaction $SO_3^{=} + \frac{1}{2}O_2 = SO_4^{=}$. (2) Would you expect a sulphite solution to be able to reduce a silver salt solution to metallic silver?

4. The heat of solution of magnesium in a dilute acid solution is $\Delta H = -110230$ cals. per gm.-atomic wt. Taking the entropy of Mg as 7·76, and Mg^{++} as $-31·6$ cals./deg. at 25°, find the standard electrode potential of magnesium.

5. The free energy of formation of ammonia in dilute aqueous solution is -6330 cals. Find the free energy change in the reaction

$$NH_3(aq.) + 2O_2 = H^+ + NO_3^- + H_2O.$$

6. From Table LV. find the entropy change in the reaction $\frac{1}{2}Br_2^- + 3H_2O \rightarrow BrO_3^- + 6H^+ + 5\epsilon$ ($S_{H_2O} = 16·75$). The heat of formation of the bromate ion is -11200 cals. at 25°. Find the free energy of the reaction and the electrode potential of the bromine-bromate electrode.

7. The solubility of KH_2PO_4 (to form K^+ and $H_2PO_4^-$) in aqueous solution at 25° is 1·85 *m*, and the mean activity coefficient in the saturated solution is $f_\pm = 0·315$. Find the difference between the free energy of the solid and standard free energies of the ions. The heat of solution at infinite dilution is $\Delta H° = 4697$ cals. Find the entropy of solution. If the entropy of $KH_2PO_4(s)$ is 32·2 and that of $K^+(aq.)$ is 24·2, find the standard entropy of $H_2PO_4^-(aq.)$. (Data from Stevenson, *J. Amer. Chem. Soc.*, 66, 1436, 1944).

CHAPTER XXI

THE THERMODYNAMICS OF SURFACES

Surface Tension and Surface Energy. We have hitherto regarded the energy or free energy of a system as the sum of the energies or free energies of its homogeneous parts, neglecting any additional energy which might be associated with the surfaces of contact between the phases. It is known that energy is associated with such surfaces, because work has to be expended to increase the surface area.

We will consider a system of two phases, separated by a boundary of area s. Let $\bar{F}_1$ be the partial free energy of any component, which is the same in the two phases, and n_1 the total amount present in the system. If there were no surfaces of contact the total free energy would be $F = \Sigma \bar{F}_1 n_1$, where the summation is extended over all the components. If the additional free energy associated with unit area of the surface of contact is ρ, the total free energy of the system is

$$F* = \Sigma \bar{F}_1 n_1 + \rho s. \quad \ldots\ldots\ldots\ldots\ldots\ldots(281)$$

$\rho = \partial F* / \partial s$ is thus equal to the work which must be performed in creating unit area of new surface under reversible conditions.

Since the free energy of a system always tends to reach the smallest possible value, a mobile surface will tend to assume the minimum area which is consistent with the conditions, if ρ is positive. ρ therefore manifests itself as a contractile force, which is called the surface tension, and is usually measured in dynes per cm.[2] For thermodynamical purposes, however, ρ must be regarded as the surface free energy, the corresponding value of which is in ergs per cm.[2]

We will suppose that both phases have the same temperature T and pressure p. It will be shown below that the latter can only be the case when the radius of curvature of the surfaces is comparatively large, *i.e.* we assume that the surfaces are approximately plane. Then we may write

$$F = E - TS + pv,$$

and $$F* = E* - TS* + pv* ;$$

where $E*$, $S*$ and $v*$ are the energy, entropy and volume of the actual system, and E, S and v the values of these when the surface area between the phases is very small. Introducing these values into (281), we have

$$F* = F + \rho s,$$

or $$E* - E = T(S* - S) - p(v* - v) + \rho s,$$

or $$E^s = TS^s - pv^s + \rho s. \qquad (282)$$

Here $E^s = E* - E$ is the increase in the energy of the system consequent on the formation of the area s of surface, and S^s, v^s are similarly the corresponding increases of the entropy and volume of the system. TS^s is the heat absorbed in the reversible formation of the surface s and is the latent heat of formation of this surface. E^s, S^s and v^s may be called the surface energy, entropy and volume.

Now S^s, v^s and s n (282) are all capacity factors and

T, p and ρ are intensity factors. By Euler's theorem (p. 302) it follows that the *complete* differential of E^s is

$$dE^s = TdS^s - p\,dv^s + \rho\,ds,$$

and also that the sum of the products of the capacity factors by the differentials of the intensity factors is zero, *i.e.*

$$S^s\,dT - v^s\,dp + s\,d\rho = 0,$$

and therefore

$$\left(\frac{d\rho}{dT}\right)_p = -\frac{S^s}{s} \quad \text{.....................(283)}$$

and

$$\left(\frac{d\rho}{dp}\right)_T = \frac{v^s}{s}, \quad \text{........................(284)}$$

i.e. the rate of change of the surface tension with the temperature is equal to minus the surface entropy of unit surface, and its rate of change with the pressure is equal to the change in volume in the formation of unit surface.

Introducing this value of S^s into (282), we have

$$\frac{E^s + pv^s}{s} = \rho - T(d\rho/dT)_p. \quad \text{...............(285)}$$

The quantity $\rho - T(d\rho/dT)$ is usually regarded as the total surface energy, although strictly it is the "surface heat content." By (284), $pv^s/s = p(d\rho/dp)_T$, but little is known of the change of surface tension with pressure. Probably pv^s is comparatively small at low pressures. Values of the surface free energy, and the total surface energy $\rho - T(d\rho/dT)_p$ for the liquid-vapour interface of some liquids are given in Table LXI. Since the surface tension decreases roughly linearly with the temperature, the total surface energy $\rho - T(d\rho/dT)_p$ remains approximately constant over a considerable range of temperature. This is illustrated by the data for benzene in Table LXII.

TABLE LXI.

SURFACE TENSION AND TOTAL SURFACE ENERGY OF SOME LIQUIDS AT 0° C.

	ρ.	$-T\left(\frac{d\rho}{dT}\right)_p$.	$\rho - T\left(\frac{d\rho}{dT}\right)$.
Water - - -	75·87	42·25	118·1
Methyl alcohol - -	23·5	19·4	42·9
Ethyl alcohol - -	23·99	22·39	46·4
n-Propyl alcohol -	25·32	22·01	47·3
Hexane - - -	21·31	28·15	49·5
Chloroform - -	28·77	30·94	59·7
Carbon tetrachloride -	29·35	32·84	62·2

TABLE LXII.

TOTAL SURFACE ENERGY OF BENZENE.

Temp. °*K*.	ρ.	$d\rho/dT$.	$\rho - T\,d\rho/dT$.
353	20·28	−0·111	59·5
383	16·85	−0·1155	61·1
413	13·45	−0·111	59·4
453	9·15	−0·104	56·1
513	3·41	−0·087	48·1

*** Equilibrium at Curved Surfaces.** The equilibrium of systems containing interfaces is most conveniently investigated by means of Gibbs's second criterion of equilibrium, viz.,

$$(\delta E)_s \geqq 0 ;$$

i.e. the system is in equilibrium when none of the possible changes it may undergo at constant entropy can decrease its energy. The condition of constant entropy is satisfied if we ensure that no heat may leave or enter the system under investigation.

When the contribution of the interface to the energy of the system is neglected we have found the conditions of equilibrium between any two phases are :

(1) the temperature and pressure must be the same;

(2) the partial free energy of every neutral component must be the same in both phases. The surface energy can quite properly be neglected when the homogeneous phases are large compared with their surfaces, but when the phases are very small it is no longer possible to neglect this factor, since a small transfer of material from a small body may appreciably change its surface area.

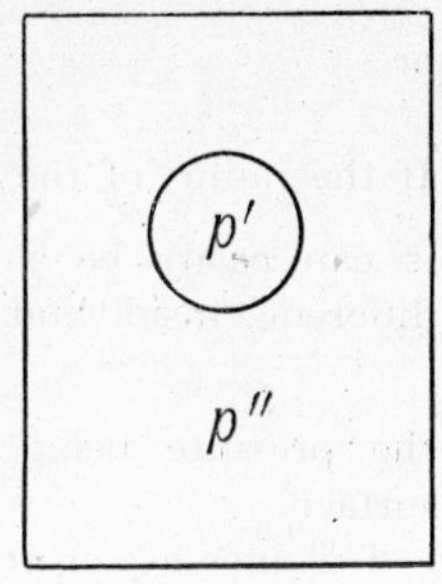

FIG. 103.

We will consider a small sphere of a liquid in contact with its vapour (Fig. 103). Let the free energy of the liquid, including the interfacial free energy, be F'. Then $F' = \bar{F}'n_1' + \rho s$ or $E' = TS' - p'v' + \bar{F}'n_1' + \rho s$, where E', S', v' are the corresponding energy, entropy and volume. Similarly if E'', S'', v'' are the energy, entropy and volume of the vapour we have

$$E'' = TS'' - p''v'' + \bar{F}_1''n_1''.$$

The variations of E' and E'' are thus expressed by

$$dE' = T\,dS' - p'dv' + \bar{F}_1'dn_1' + \rho\,ds,$$

$$dE'' = T\,dS'' - p''dv'' + \bar{F}''dn_1''.$$

The condition of equilibrium is that $(dE' + dE'') \geqq 0$ for all possible variations in which the total entropy remains constant, *i.e.* $dS' + dS'' = 0$. We will also suppose that the total volume is constant, *i.e.* $dv' + dv'' = 0$. Then, since it is also necessary that $dn_1' + dn_1'' = 0$,

$$dE' + dE'' = -(p' - p'')\,dv' + (\bar{F}' - \bar{F}'')\,dn_1' + \rho\,ds \geqq 0.$$

The conditions of equilibrium are thus

$$\bar{F}_1' = \bar{F}_1'',*$$

* dn_1' may be positive or negative without affecting the other variables, *i.e* we may pack a few more molecules into the sphere, keeping its volume constant, or take them away.

and since we cannot increase the volume of the sphere without changing its area, and dv' may be either positive or negative :

$$-(p'-p'')\,dv'+\rho\,ds=0,$$

or

$$p'-p''=\rho\frac{ds}{dv'}.$$

If the radius of the sphere is r, $v'=\frac{4\pi}{3}r^3$ and $s=4\pi r^2$, and it can easily be shown that $ds/dv'=2/r$. The pressure difference inside and outside the sphere is thus

$$p'-p''=2\rho/r, \quad \text{.....................(286)}$$

the pressure being always greatest inside the concave surface.

This increase of pressure causes an increase of the partial free energy of the liquid, which can be calculated by (211), *i.e.* $d\bar{F}'=\bar{v}_1'dp'$, where $\bar{v}_1'$ is the partial molar volume in the liquid. Neglecting the change of p'', we have $dp'=d(2\rho/r)$, and integrating on the assumption that ρ is constant, we find that

$$(\bar{F}_1')_r=(\bar{F}_1')_\infty+2\bar{v}_1\rho/r,$$

where $(\bar{F}_1')_r$ and $(\bar{F}_1')_\infty$ are the partial free energies of the liquid in a droplet of radius r and at a plane surface, since the partial free energy in the vapour remains equal to that in the liquid, the vapour pressure of the liquid must increase as r diminishes. Since

$$(\bar{F}_1)_r-(\bar{F}_1)_\infty=RT\log(p_1{}^r/p_1{}^\infty),$$

the magnitude of this effect is given by

$$RT\log(p_1{}^r/p_1{}^\infty)=\frac{2\bar{v}_1\rho}{r}, \quad \text{..............(287)}$$

where $p_1{}^r$ and $p_1{}^\infty$ are the vapour pressures in a droplet of radius r and at a plane surface.*

For water at room temperature ($\rho=$ ca. 70 dynes/cm.), the pressure in a droplet of radius 10^{-5} cm. is about

* This equation was first obtained by Lord Kelvin (W. Thomson), *Phil, Mag.*, 42, 448, 1881.

14 atmospheres, and its vapour pressure is thereby increased about one per cent.* At concave surfaces a similar *decrease* of the vapour pressure is predicted. A similar relation in which the ratio of the solubilities takes the place of the ratio of the vapour pressures can be obtained for the effect of particle size on the solubility of solids and liquids. This has been employed to measure ρ at solid-liquid interfaces.† Values between 10 and 3000 ergs per cm. have been obtained for comparatively insoluble salts, but their validity is uncertain because ρ, which has been assumed constant, may vary with the particle size, and the radius of curvature of solid particles may vary from point to point.

Equation (286) can also be used to find the capillary rise in narrow tubes. When the radius of the tube is sufficiently small the meniscus is practically a hemisphere. The pressure difference on the two sides of the surface is balanced by the hydrostatic pressure of the column of liquid (Fig. 104), which is approximately given by $(h+r/3)dg$, where h is the height of the column from the plane surface outside the tube to the lowest point of the meniscus, $r/3$ is a correction for average height above the lowest point of the meniscus, and the difference between the density of the

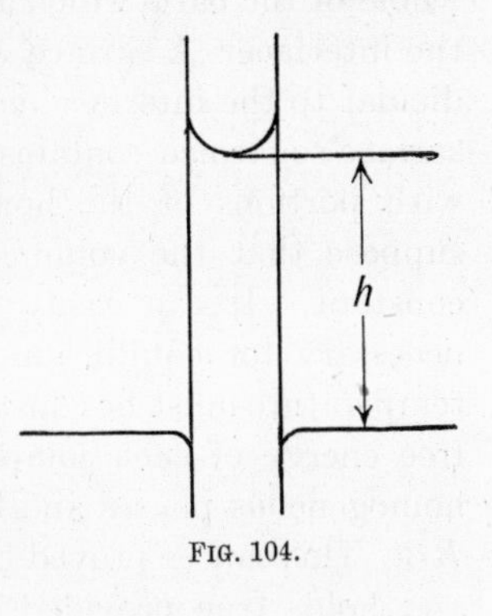

FIG. 104.

* Shereshevski, *J. Amer. Chem. Soc.*, 50, 2966, 2980, 1928, found a somewhat greater change than is predicted by this equation.

† W. Ostwald, *Z. physik. Chem.*, 34, 495, 1900 ; Dundon, *J. Amer. Chem. Soc.*, 45, 2479, 2658, 1923.

liquid inside the tube and the gas outside, and g the force of gravity. Introducing this value into (226), we have

$$(h+r/3)gd=2\rho/r.$$

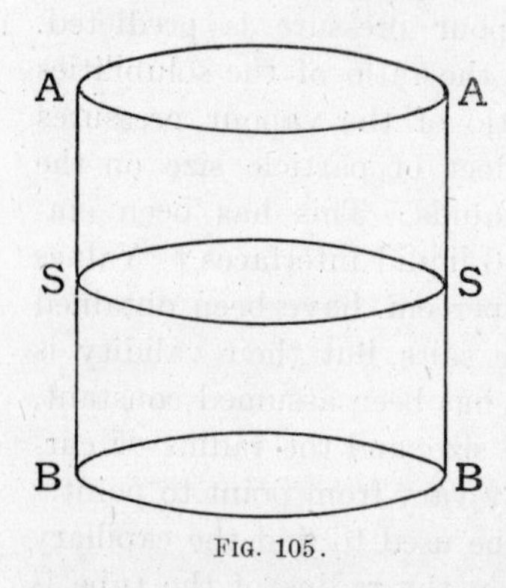

FIG. 105.

When r is large the surface ceases to be hemispherical, and this equation needs considerable correction.*

Gibbs's Adsorption Equation. Let SS (Fig. 105) be part of the interface between two phases. The two surfaces AA, BB are now drawn within the homogeneous phases on each side of the interface at a sufficient distance so that they contain between them the whole of the parts which are influenced by the vicinity of the interface. A surface $AB-AB$ is also drawn perpendicular to the interface, enclosing part of it. The closed surface so formed contains part of the interface, together with portions of the homogeneous phases. We shall suppose that the volume within this closed surface is constant. It can easily be shown that the conditions necessary for equilibrium in this system are: (1) the temperature must be constant throughout, (2) the partial free energy of each component is the same in the two homogeneous phases and in the region between AA and BB. This can be proved by the method previously used, and holds true provided there is no condition limiting the transfer of small quantities of any component in or

* Cf. Sugden, *J. Chem. Soc.*, 1921, p. 1483 ; Rayleigh, *Proc Roy. Soc.*, *A*, 92, 184, 1915

out of either part of the system. Thus if the region between AA and BB contains n_1 mols of S_1, n_2 mols of S_2, etc., we suppose that dn_1, dn_2, etc., can separately be made either positive or negative. The case does not differ then in any essential respect from the equilibrium of three separate phases in contact—every component must have the same partial free energy in each phase.

The total free energy of the volume enclosed between AA and BB is therefore

$$F = \bar{F}_1 n_1 + \bar{F}_2 n_2 + \bar{F}_3 n_3 \ldots + \rho s, \qquad (288)$$

where $\bar{F}_1$ is the partial free energy of S_1 throughout the system, etc., ρ the additional free energy of unit area of the interface and s its area. Writing $F = E - TS + pv$, and remembering that v is constant, the variation of the energy is given by

$$dE = T\,dS + \bar{F}_1\,dn_1 + \bar{F}_2\,dn_2 + \ldots + \rho\,ds.$$

All the differentials in this equation are capacity factors, and as before it follows from Euler's theorem that

$$S\,dT + n_1\,d\bar{F}_1 + n_2\,d\bar{F}_2 \ldots + s\,d\rho = 0. \qquad (289)$$

Now, in this equation n_1, n_2, etc., are quite indefinite quantities, for they depend on the amounts of the homogeneous phases which have been included in the volume between the surfaces AA, BB. In order to obtain an equation which contains quantities which are characteristic of the interface we proceed as follows. Another surface is drawn near the actual interface, the exact position of which is as yet undetermined. Let it be supposed that the homogeneous phases continue without any change of composition or of properties on either side up to this dividing surface. Let the quantities of the components in the volume between AA and BB in this hypothetical case be n_1', n_2', n_3', etc., on one side of the dividing surface and n_1'', n_2'', n_3'', etc., on the other, and the corresponding quantities of entropy S', S''. Then since these hypothetical masses have the properties of the two homogeneous phases it follows that

$$S'\,dT + n_1'd\bar{F}_1 + n_2'd\bar{F}_2 \ldots = 0,$$

$$S''dT + n_1''d\bar{F}_1 + n_2''d\bar{F}_2 \ldots = 0.^*$$

Subtracting these equations from (289), we obtain

$$(S - S' - S'')\,dT + (n_1 - n_1' - n_1'')\,d\bar{F}_1$$
$$+ (n_2 - n_2' - n_2'')\,d\bar{F}_2 \ldots + s\,d\rho = 0,$$

or $$S^s\,dT + n_1^s\,d\bar{F}_1 + n_2^s\,d\bar{F}_2 \ldots + s\,d\rho = 0, \ldots\ldots(290)$$

where $S^s = S - S' - S''$ is the difference between the actual entropy of the given volume and that which would be present on the assumption that the homogeneous phases continue without change up to the dividing surface; $n_1^s = n_1 - n_1' - n_1''$ is the corresponding difference in the amounts of the component S_1, etc.

Dividing through by s, we have then for unit area of interface

$$\mathrm{s}^s\,dT + \Gamma_1\,d\bar{F}_1 + \Gamma_2\,d\bar{F}_2 + \Gamma_3\,d\bar{F}_3 \ldots + d\rho = 0, \ldots(291)$$

where $\mathrm{s}^s = S^s/s$, $\Gamma_1 = n_1^s/s$, $\Gamma_2 = n_2^s/s$, etc.

The values of Γ_1, Γ_2, etc., which are called the *surface excesses* of S_1, S_2, etc., still depend on the position of the dividing surface. The latter can therefore be placed in such a position as to make any one of these quantities

* For a homogeneous phase,

$$E = TS + \bar{F}_1 n_1 + \bar{F}_2 n_2 \ldots - pv,$$

and, therefore, $$dE = TdS + \bar{F}_1 dn_1 + \bar{F}_2 dn_2 \ldots - pdv,$$

and $$SdT + n_1 d\bar{F}_1 + n_2 d\bar{F}_2 \ldots - vdp = 0.$$

zero. If the dividing surface is so placed that $\Gamma_1 = 0$, we then have

$$\mathrm{s}^s dT + \Gamma_2 d\bar{F}_2 + \Gamma_3 d\bar{F}_3 \ldots + d\rho = 0. \quad \ldots\ldots\ldots\ldots(292)$$

This is Gibbs's adsorption equation. In succeeding sections we shall give illustrations of its application in particular cases.

Adsorption from Binary Solutions. Applied to the liquid-vapour surface of a binary solution, when the dividing surface is placed so that $\Gamma_1 = 0$, (292) becomes at constant temperature

$$\Gamma_2 = -(d\rho/d\bar{F}_2)_T.$$

Writing $\bar{F}_2 = \bar{F}^\circ_2 + RT \log a_2$, where a_2 is the activity of S_2, we have then

$$\Gamma_2 = -\frac{1}{RT}\left(\frac{d\rho}{d \log a_2}\right)_T. \quad \ldots\ldots\ldots\ldots\ldots(293)$$

Γ_2 is the surface excess of S_2, *i.e.* the difference between the actual amount of S_2 present in a given volume including the interface and that which would be present if the phases were perfectly homogeneous up to a dividing surface placed so that $\Gamma_1 = 0$. According to (293), when $d\rho/d \log a_2$ is negative, *i.e.* when the surface tension decreases with increasing activity of S_2, Γ_2 is positive; and when $d\rho/d \log a_2$ is positive, Γ_2 is negative. A substance which lowers the surface energy is thus present in excess at or near the surface, but there is a deficit of a substance which increases the surface energy. This is in accordance with the general thermodynamical principle that the free energy of a system tends to reach a minimum value.

ρ is usually measured as a surface tension in dynes per cm. The corresponding surface energy is in ergs/cm. In calculating Γ_2 it is necessary to use the value of R in ergs (viz. $1{\cdot}988 \times 4{\cdot}182 \times 10^7$ ergs). We thus have

$$\Gamma_2 = -\frac{1}{2{\cdot}303 \times 1{\cdot}988 \times 4{\cdot}182 \times 10^7 T}\left(\frac{d\rho}{d\log_{10}\alpha_2}\right),$$

which gives Γ_2 in gm. molecules per cm.² In order to obtain the number of molecules per cm. it is necessary to multiply this by the Avogadro number $N_0 = 6{\cdot}062 \times 10^{23}$. At 25° we thus obtain

$$\Gamma_2 = -1{\cdot}062 \times 10^{13}(d\rho/d\log_{10}\alpha_2) \text{ molecules/cm.}^2$$

$d\rho/d\log_{10}\alpha_2$ can be obtained by plotting ρ against $\log_{10}\alpha_2$ and finding the slope of the curve. Fig. 106 shows this plot for

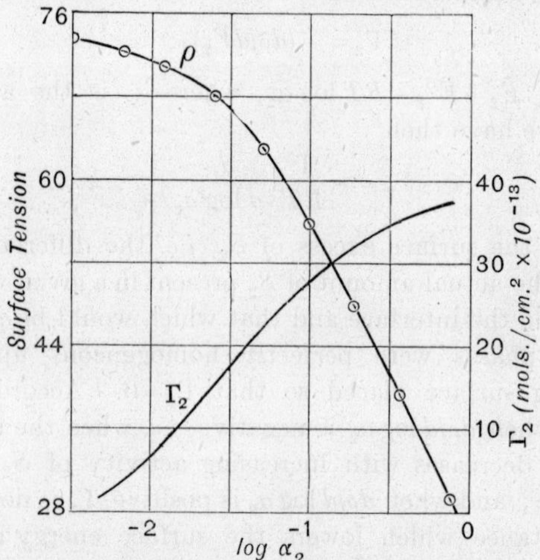

FIG. 106.—Surface tension and adsorption of butyl alcohol solutions at 25°.

n-butyl alcohol solutions. When a considerable number of points are available $d\rho/d\log\alpha_2$ may be evaluated as

$$\Delta\rho/\Delta\log\alpha_2$$

for the intervals between successive points. This gives the average value of Γ_2 for the interval. Table LXII. shows the calculation of Γ_2 for n-butyl alcohol in aqueous solution at 25°.* The activities of butyl alcohol at 25° were taken as equal to their values at the freezing point as determined by the freezing point method (see p. 339).

TABLE LXII.

ADSORPTION AT SURFACE OF BUTYL ALCOHOL SOLUTIONS, 25°.

m_2.	a_2.	ρ.	Γ_2 (molecules/cm.^{2})
0·00329	0·00328	72·80	—
0·00658	0·00654	72·26	—
0·01320	0·01304	70·82	$0·76 \times 10^{14}$
0·0264	0·02581	68·00	1·31
0·0536	0·05184	63·14	2·14
0·1050	0·09892	56·31	2·86
0·2110	0·19277	48·08	3·19
0·4330	0·37961	38·87	3·45
0·8540	0·71189	29·87	3·65

The Gibbs's equation does not measure the total number of solute molecules in or near the surface, but the *surface excess.* In dilute solutions, however, the number of solute molecules which would be present near the surface if the phases were perfectly homogeneous up to the interface is comparatively small, and Γ_2 does not differ appreciably from the actual number of molecules in or near the interface. In the stronger solutions Γ_2 approaches the value required for a single complete layer of alcohol molecules orientated with their hydrocarbon chains vertical.†

The activities of few non-electrolytes in aqueous solution have been accurately determined. In dilute solutions an approximate measure of Γ_2, which will probably not be

* Harkins and Wampler, *J. Amer. Chem. Soc.*, 53, 850, 1931.

† According to N. K. Adam's measurements of the areas of molecules in insoluble surface films the area of molecules of long chain aliphatic alcohols when tightly packed is $21·7 \times 10^{-16}$ cm.^{2}, corresponding to about 46×10^{13} molecules per cm.^{2}

considerably out, may be obtained by replacing a_2 by m_2 in (293). In concentrated solutions, however, a large error may occur unless the actual activity is used. Fig. 107 shows the values of ρ plotted against $\log m_2$ for solutions of homologous normal fatty acids. Taking Γ_2 as the slope $-d\rho/RT\, d\log m_2$, it can be seen that approximately the same value is reached in every case, but as we go up the series of acids this value is reached at a progressively lower concentration. The final value of Γ_2 corresponds approximately with a nearly completed surface layer of molecules orientated with their hydrocarbon chains vertical.

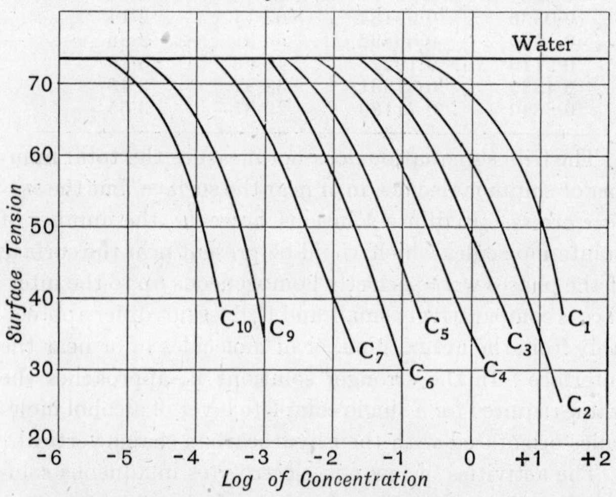

FIG. 107.—Surface tensions of solutions of normal aliphatic acids plotted against logarithm of concentration. (Harkins.)

Tests of Gibbs's Equation. It is unnecessary to describe here the earlier attempts to confirm Gibbs's equation by the direct determination of the surface excess of a solute at an interface.*

* *e.g.* Donnan and Barker, *Proc. Roy. Soc., A*, 85, 57, 1911.

McBain with Davies * and Du Bois † passed bubbles of nitrogen through solutions of surface active substances in an inclined tube. These carried thin films of the solution up the outlet tube, which after being allowed to drain of their excess liquid were collected. The excess of solute in unit area of surface could be calculated from a determination of the concentration of the solute in the condensed films and of their area. The values of the surface excess so obtained were always considerably greater than those calculated for the same solutions by Gibbs's equation. More recently McBain and Humphreys‡ have invented a " microtome " method in which a thin film at the surface of a solution is skimmed off the surface of a solution by a rapidly moving blade, and the difference between its concentration and that of the bulk of the solution is determined. The surface excesses measured by this method, which are given in Table LXIII., are in reasonable agreement with those calculated by Gibbs's equation, considering the difficult nature of the experiments.

It is possible that high values are obtained in the bubbling experiments, because water molecules can drain out of the films more easily than the larger solute molecules. Accordingly, when the films are allowed to drain before collection, the liquid between the surface layers of the film becomes more concentrated than the bulk of the solution and therefore too large a value of the surface excess is obtained.

Surface of Aqueous Solutions of Salts. Since inorganic salts increase the surface tension of water they are

* *J. Amer. Chem. Soc.*, 49, 2230, 1927.

† *ibid.*, 51, 3534, 1929.

‡ *Colloid Symposium Monograph*, ix. 300, 1931.

negatively absorbed. It is more convenient in such a case to place the dividing surface so that the surface excess of the salt (Γ_2) is zero.

TABLE LXIII.

OBSERVED AND CALCULATED SURFACE EXCESSES OF AQUEOUS SOLUTIONS.

Substance.	Conc. of solute g/1000g.H_2O.	Surface excess Γ_2 obs. g/cm.$^2 \times 10^8$.	Γ. calc. by Gibbs's equation.	Γ obs. by Bain and Du Bois.
p-Toluidine	2·00	6·1	5·2	11·8
	1·76	4·6	4·9	—
Phenol	20·5	4·1	4·8	14·8
Caproic acid	2·59	6·8	6·3	16·2
	3·00	5·1	6·5	16·9
	5·25	6·2	6·3	20·5
Hydrocinnamic acid	1·5	5·6	5·1	—
	4·5	5·4	7·9	—

The surface excess of water (Γ_1) is then given by

$$\Gamma_1 = -d\rho/d\bar{F}_1.$$

The variations of the partial free energies of water and the salt are related by $n_1 d\bar{F}_1 + n_2 d\bar{F}_2 = 0$; and the variation of the partial free energy of the salt is given by $d\bar{F}_2 = (\nu_1 + \nu_2) RT\, d \log a_\pm$, where $a_\pm$ is its mean activity. For a binary salt we therefore have

$$\Gamma_1 = -\frac{d\rho}{dF_1} = +\frac{n_1}{n_2}\,\frac{d\rho}{2RT \log a_\pm}. \quad \text{.........(294)}$$

If the solution contains m_2 mols of a salt to 1000 gms. (55·55 mols) of water $n_1/n_2 = 55{\cdot}55/m_2$, and writing $d \log a_\pm = da_\pm/a_\pm$ and $a_\pm = m_2 f_\pm$, we have

$$\Gamma_1 = \frac{55{\cdot}55 f_\pm}{2RT}\left(\frac{d\rho}{da_\pm}\right).$$

Table LXIV. shows the adsorption of water at the surface of sodium chloride solutions as determined by Harkins and McLaughlan.*

TABLE LXIV.

ADSORPTION OF WATER AT SURFACE OF SODIUM CHLORIDE SOLUTIONS.

m. - -	0·1	0·5	1·0	2·0	3·0	4·0	5·0
Γ_1 (g-mols/cm.^{2})	2·22	1·91	1·80	1·56	1·43	1·30	$1·28 \times 10^{-9}$
Γ_1 (gms./cm.^{2})	4·00	3·45	3·25	2·82	2·57	2·35	$2·30 \times 10^{-8}$
Γ_1 (mols/cm.^{2})	13·4	11·6	10·9	9·4	8·7	7·9	$7·8 \times 10^{14}$

It can be seen that Γ_1 decreases as the solution becomes more concentrated, indicating that the ions approach the surface more closely in concentrated solutions. Assuming that the density in the absorbed layer is the same as that of liquid water $d=1$, and that the absorbed layer and the solution meet sharply at the dividing surface, Γ_1 (expressed in gms./cm.^{2}) is equal to the thickness of the absorbed layer. The diameter of the water molecule in ice and crystalline hydrates is $2·76 \times 10^{-8}$ cm., so that it would appear that the thickness of the film in the strong solutions is of the same order as the diameter of the water molecule.

*** Adsorption from Ternary Solutions.** In a system containing three components, at constant temperature, (291) becomes

$$\Gamma_1 d\bar{F}_1 + \Gamma_2 d\bar{F}_2 + \Gamma_3 d\bar{F}_3 + d\rho = 0,$$

where Γ_1, Γ_2, Γ_3 are the surface excesses of the components with respect to an arbitrarily fixed dividing surface. As before, it is possible to place this dividing surface so that

* *J. Amer. Chem. Soc.*, 47, 2083, 1925; *also* 48, 604, 1926. Cf .Goard, *J. Chem. Soc.*, 2451, 1925.

one of these quantities is zero. If we make $\Gamma_3=0$ in this way, we then have

$$\Gamma_1 d\bar{F}_1+\Gamma_2 d\bar{F}_2+d\rho=0.$$

A single equation of this kind is, however, insufficient to determine the values of Γ_1 and Γ_2.* But it is always possible to vary the composition of a given ternary solution in two distinct ways.

Thus, (1) the quantity S_3 may be kept constant and the proportions of S_1 and S_2 varied; (2) the quantities of S_1 and S_2 may be kept constant and the amount of S_3 varied. For these variations we obtain two distinct equations, viz.,

$$\Gamma_1 d\bar{F}_1+\Gamma_2 d\bar{F}_2+d\rho=0,$$

$$\Gamma_1 d\bar{F}_1'+\Gamma_2 d\bar{F}_2'+d\rho'=0.$$

Solving these equations for Γ_1 and Γ_2, we obtain

$$\Gamma_1=\frac{\dfrac{d\rho}{d\bar{F}_2}-\dfrac{d\rho'}{d\bar{F}_2'}}{\dfrac{d\bar{F}_1'}{d\bar{F}_2'}-\dfrac{d\bar{F}_1}{d\bar{F}_2}},$$

$$\Gamma_2=\frac{\dfrac{d\rho}{d\bar{F}_1}-\dfrac{d\rho'}{d\bar{F}_1'}}{\dfrac{d\bar{F}_2'}{d\bar{F}_1'}-\dfrac{d\bar{F}_2}{d\bar{F}_1}}. \quad \ldots\ldots\ldots\ldots\ldots\ldots\ldots (295)$$

These equations have been applied by Butler and Lees † to the surfaces of solutions of lithium chloride in water-

* A considerable number of calculations of the adsorption in ternary solutions are to be found in the literature, which employ the simple Gibbs's equation $d\rho/d\bar{F}_2=\Gamma_2$; *e.g.* Seith, *Z. physikal. Chem.*, 117, 257, 1925; Freundlich and Schnell, *ibid.*, 133, 151, 1928; Palitzsch, *ibid.*, 147, 51, 1930.

Actually $d\rho/d\bar{F}_2=\Gamma_2+\Gamma_1(d\bar{F}_1/d\bar{F}_2)$, *i.e.* the equation for a binary solution is not applicable unless either

$$\Gamma_1=0, \text{ or } d\bar{F}_1/d\bar{F}_2=0.$$

† *J. Chem. Soc.*, 2097, 1932.

ethyl alcohol mixtures. In this case, let S_1 be water, S_2 alcohol, and S_3 lithium chloride. $d\rho$, $d\bar{F}_1$ and $d\bar{F}_2$ refer to variations in which the quantity of lithium chloride is kept constant and the proportions of water and alcohol are varied. $d\bar{F}_1$, $d\bar{F}_2$ are given by the values of $RT\,d\log p_1$ and $RT\,d\log p_2$ corresponding to these variations. Similarly $d\rho'$ $d\bar{F}_1'$, $d\bar{F}_2'$ refer to variations in which the quantities of water and alcohol are kept constant and the amount of lithium chloride is varied, and

$$d\bar{F}_1' = RT\,d\log p_1', \quad d\bar{F}_2' = RT\,d\log p_2'.$$

Inserting these values, we have

$$\Gamma_2 = \frac{d\rho/RT\,.\,d\log p_2 - d\rho'/RT\,.\,d\log p_2'}{d\log p_1'/d\log p_2' - d\log p_1/d\log p_2}, \text{ etc.} \quad (296)$$

Table LXV. shows the average values of Γ_1 and Γ_2 in molecules per cm.^{2}, as determined in this way for solu-

TABLE LXV.

ADSORPTION AT SURFACE OF WATER-ALCOHOL SOLUTIONS CONTAINING LITHIUM CHLORIDE (LiCl, 0 TO 0·5m).

Composition of Solvent (Mols % Alcohol).	Γ_1.	Γ_2.
0·0	133×10^{13}	—
6·4	103	42×10^{13}
25	53	57
50	15	40
80	4·6	34
100	0·0	41

tions containing from 0 to 0·5m lithium chloride. These figures may be taken to represent the composition of the surface film which contains no lithium chloride.

Γ_2 in all the solutions corresponds approximately with a single layer of alcohol molecules, while Γ_1 diminishes steadily as the proportion of alcohol in the solution is increased. It is thus probable that at the surface of the fairly dilute alcoholic solutions there is a nearly complete monomolecular layer of alcohol molecules, but the ions are separated from this by a certain thickness of water, owing probably to their hydration. As the proportion of alcohol in the solution is increased the ions are solvated by water to a decreasing extent and the ions are able to approach the surface film of alcohol molecules more closely.

Adsorption from Concentrated Solutions. Relation between Gibbs's Surface Excess and the Surface Composition. In a concentrated solution the surface excess of the solute, as determined by Gibbs's equation, may be considerably less than the actual amount in or near the surface, for even if the solution were perfectly homogeneous up to the boundary there would be an appreciable amount of the solute in or near the surface. This

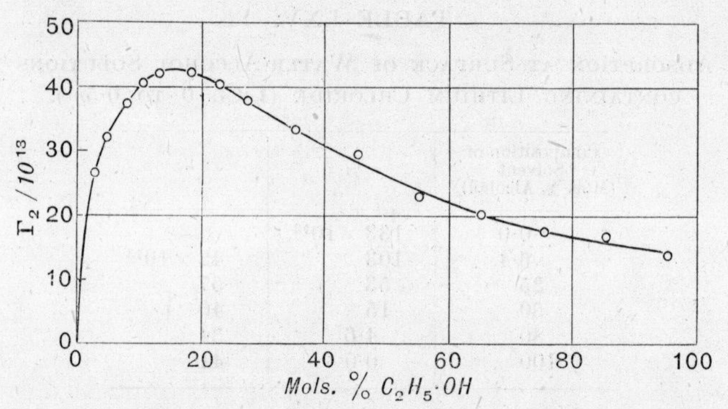

FIG. 108.—Surface excess of alcohol in water-alcohol solutions. (Butler and Wightman.)

is borne out by calculations of the surface excess in concentrated solutions. For example, the calculation of the surface excess of alcohol (Γ_2) in water-alcohol solutions is given in Table LXVI. The average value of Γ_2

for the interval between one solution and the next is given by $\Gamma_2 = -\Delta\rho/RT\Delta \log p_2$.*

In Fig. 108 the values of Γ_2 are plotted against the molar fraction of alcohol in the solution. They rise to a maximum in the solution containing about 15 mols % alcohol, and gradually decrease as the proportion of alcohol in the solution is further increased.

TABLE LXVI.

CALCULATIONS OF SURFACE EXCESS OF ALCOHOL (Γ_2) IN WATER-ETHYL ALCOHOL SOLUTIONS AT 25°.

Mols % Alcohol.	ρ.	$\log_{10} p_2$.	Γ_2.
100	21·93	1·771	—
90	22·59	1·722	$14·0 \times 10^{13}$
80	23·26	1·679	16·5
70	23·93	1·639	17·5
60	24·67	1·600	20·4
50	25·43	1·565	23·0
40	26·43	1·529	29·5
30	27·60	1·492	33·5
25	28·49	1·467	37·8
20	29·97	1·428	40·3
15	32·20	1·372	42·3
12	34·42	1·316	42·2
10	36·72	1·256	40·7
6·4	42·13	1·097	37·2
4	47·86	0·908	32·2
2	55·57	0·602	26·8

It might be expected that the surface *excess* would gradually diminish as the proportion of alcohol in the solution is increased, if the total amount of alcohol in or near the surface remained constant or increased only slowly. But it would be impossible to deduce from the values of Γ_2 the actual distribution of water and alcohol

* This equation was first employed by Schofield and Rideal, *Proc. Roy. Soc., A*, 109, 57, 1925.

molecules near the surface if nothing were known as to how the surface excess is distributed. There is, however, a considerable amount of evidence in favour of the view that the forces which cause adsorption have a very short range and that their influence does not extend beyond the surface layer of molecules. If we make the assumption that the solution is quite homogeneous up to the surface layer and that only in the surface layer of molecules is the proportion of alcohol different to that in the bulk of the solution, it becomes possible to determine the surface composition.*

Let ν_1, ν_2 be the actual number of molecules of S_1, S_2 in unit area of the surface layer of a binary solution. If A_1, A_2 are the areas per molecule, we have

$$A_1\nu_1 + A_2\nu_2 = 1. \qquad \text{..............(297)}$$

Now suppose that the surfaces AA, BB (Fig. 30) are brought together so that they contain between them only the surface layer of molecules which is defined by (297). On the assumption which has been made the phases outside these surfaces still remain perfectly homogeneous. Applying (289) to the matter between the surfaces, we have then, at constant temperature,

$$\nu_1 d\bar{F}_1 + \nu_2 d\bar{F}_2 + d\rho = 0.\dagger \qquad \text{..............(298)}$$

Now if N_1, N_2 are the molar fractions of S_1, S_2 in the solution, we also have

$$N_1 d\bar{F}_1 + N_2 d\bar{F}_2 = 0,$$

* Butler and Wightman, *J. Chem. Soc.*, 1932, p. 2089. Cf. Guggenheim and Adam (*Proc. Roy. Soc.*, *A*, **139**, 218, 1932).

† The unit of quantity here is the molecule, instead of the gm. molecule as previously. $\bar{F}_1$, $\bar{F}_2$ must be the partial free energy per molecule.

and substituting for $d\bar{F}_1$ in (298), we obtain

$$\left(\nu_2 - \frac{\nu_1 N_2}{N_1}\right) d\bar{F}_2 + d\rho = 0. \qquad (299)$$

Since $-d\rho/d\bar{F}_2 = \Gamma_2$ is the Gibbs's surface excess, it follows that

$$\Gamma_2 = \nu_2 - \nu_1 N_2/N_1. \qquad (300)$$

A physical meaning can easily be given to this equation. The surface layer contains ν_2 molecules of S_2 and ν_1 molecules of S_1. If the proportions of S_1 and S_2 were the same in the surface layer as in the bulk of the solution, ν_1 molecules of S_1 would be accompanied by $\nu_1 N_2/N_1$ molecules of S_2. The surface excess of S_2 is therefore $\nu_2 - \nu_1 N_2/N_1$.

Substituting $\nu_2 = (1 - A_1\nu_1)/A_2$, we obtain

$$\Gamma_2 = \frac{1}{A_2} - \left(\frac{A_1}{A_2} + \frac{N_2}{N_1}\right)\nu_1. \qquad (301)$$

If we know A_1 and A_2, it is possible to find ν_1, and therefore also ν_2.

Butler and Wightman found that when A_1 and A_2 were given any reasonable values, ν_2 did not increase continuously as the proportion of alcohol in the solution increased, but went through a small maximum. Since it is very probable that as the alcohol content of the solution increases the proportion of alcohol in the surface layer will also increase, it thus appears that the fundamental assumption that only the surface layer differs from the bulk of the solution is incorrect. The difference between the observed values of the surface excess and those which would be consistent with a surface layer characterised by (297) is, however, small. The difference can be accounted for if it is supposed either that there is a small excess of alcohol molecules below the surface layer in the neighbourhood of the maximum adsorption, or by an excess of water below the surface layer in more concentrated solutions. The latter is perhaps the more probable. Schofield and Rideal have indeed suggested that the whole of the decrease in Γ_2 in strong solutions is to be accounted for in this way.* But this involves the assumption that there is no water in the surface layer itself.

This discussion will serve to illustrate the difficulties which arise when we attempt to deduce the actual distribution of molecules near the interface from the Gibbs's surface excess. The latter is a thermodynamical quantity which is exactly defined and can be accurately evaluated. If the distribution of the surface excess about the interface is known, it is possible to deduce the actual distribution of molecules. Since there is no direct way of determining this distribution, the validity of the distribution of molecules which is arrived at depends on the truth of the particular assumptions on which it is based.

Relations between Adsorption, Surface Tension and Concentration. Gibbs's equation by itself does not give any relation between the surface tension and the activity of a solute. If, however, the adsorption is known as a function of the activity of the solute, it is possible to calculate the surface tension, for since

$$\Gamma_2 = -d\rho/RT\, d\log a_2,$$

$$\rho = \rho_0 - RT\int_0^{a_2} \Gamma_2 \, . \, d\log a_2, \qquad \qquad (302)$$

where ρ_0 is the surface tension of the solvent.

* *Phil. Mag.*, 13, 806, 1932.

Langmuir obtained by a kinetic argument a relation of this kind for the adsorption of a gas at the surface of a solid. The surface is supposed to consist of a number of spaces, each of which can accommodate a molecule of the gas. Let there be N such spaces in unit area of the surface, and at equilibrium suppose that a fraction θ of them is occupied by gas molecules. The rate of adsorption of the gas will be proportional to its pressure and to the number of unoccupied spaces, *i.e.* to $N(1-\theta)p$, and the rate at which adsorbed molecules leave the surface to the number of occupied spaces, $N\theta$. For equilibrium the rates of adsorption and of desorption must be equal, so that $kN(1-\theta)p = N\theta$, or $\theta/(1-\theta) = kp$, where k is a constant which depends on the temperature.

A similar equation may be obtained for equilibrium at the surface of a solution. If the surface layer contains ν_2 solute molecules each of area A_2, the fraction of the surface occupied by the solute is $A_2\nu_2$ and the fraction occupied by the solvent $1 - A_1\nu_1$.

If we suppose that the rate at which solute molecules enter the surface layer is proportional to the fraction of the surface unoccupied by solute molecules and to the activity of the solute, and the rate at which they leave it to the fraction occupied, we shall have for equilibrium

$$\frac{A_2\nu_2}{1 - A_2\nu_2} = ka_2, \quad \text{.....................(303)}$$

or

$$A_2\nu_2 = \frac{ka_2}{1 + ka_2}. \quad \text{................(304)}$$

In dilute solutions ν_2 may be taken as equal to Gibbs's surface excess Γ_2. The following table shows the values of ν_2 for butyl alcohol calculated by this equation, compared with the values of Γ_2 determined by Gibbs's equation by Harkins and Wampler. The agreement is very good.*

TABLE XXVII.

ADSORPTION FROM BUTYL ALCOHOL SOLUTIONS.

$k=34,\ 1/A_2=3\cdot75\times10^{14}$.

a_2.	ν_2 (calc.).	Γ_2.
0·0989	$2\cdot89\times10^{14}$	$2\cdot86\times10^{14}$
0·1928	3·18	3·19
0·3796	3·47	3·45
0·7119	3·60	3·65
∞	3·75	—

If we use for Γ_2 the value of ν_2 given by (304), we have

$$\rho=\rho_0-\frac{RT}{A_2}\int_0^{a_2}\frac{ka_2}{1+ka_2}\cdot d\log a_2$$

$$=\rho_0-\frac{RT}{A_2}\log_e(1+ka_2). \qquad (305)$$

Szyszkowski found empirically that a similar equation, viz.

$$\rho=\rho_0-a\log(1+kc_2),$$

represented fairly closely the surface tensions of aqueous solutions of the normal fatty acids, the constant a being nearly the same for all and k increasing in an approximately constant ratio as we pass up the series.† Traube had found in the course of his extensive researches on the surface tensions of solutions that the concentrations of compounds of a homologous series, such as the normal

* It should be stated that the agreement is not so good in more dilute solutions. (See Butler, *Proc. Roy. Soc., A*, 135, 348, 1932.)

† *Z. Phys. Chem.*, 64, 385, 1908.

aliphatic acids, which cause the same lowering of the surface tension of water, decrease progressively and in an approximately constant ratio as we pass up the series. Expressed in terms of Szyszkowski's equation, this implies that for compounds having the same value of a, the constant k increases in a constant ratio as we pass from one member of a homologous series to the next. The average value of this ratio for the fatty acids is 3·5. Its meaning is considered in a later section.

Solutions containing two or more solutes. The same method can be applied to the simultaneous adsorption of more than one solute.* If unit area of the surface layer contains ν_2 molecules each of area A_2 of the solute S_2, and ν_3 molecules each of area A_3 of the solute S_3, the fraction of the surface occupied by the solvent is

$$1 - A_1\nu_1 - A_2\nu_2,$$

and for the kinetic equilibrium of the surface layer with the solution the following relations must be satisfied.

$$\frac{A_2\nu_2}{1 - A_2\nu_2 - A_2\nu_2} = k_2a_2,$$

$$\frac{A_3\nu_3}{1 - A_2\nu_2 - A_3\nu_3} = k_3a_3.$$

Solving these equations for ν_2, ν_3, it is found that

$$\nu_2 = \frac{1}{A_2}\left(\frac{k_2a_2}{1 + k_2a_2 + k_3a_3}\right),$$

$$\nu_3 = \frac{1}{A_3}\left(\frac{k_3a_3}{1 + k_2a_2 + k_3a_3}\right). \quad \text{.............(306)}$$

Now if we take a solution of S_2 alone, which has the surface tension ρ' and add S_3 until its activity is a_3, the

* Butler and Ockrent, *J. Physical Chem.*, 34, 2841, 1930.

surface tension of the resulting solution, assuming that the activity of S_2 is unaffected by the addition of S_3, is

$$\rho = \rho' - RT\int_0^{a_3} \Gamma_3 \,.\, d\log a_3,$$

and if the solution is dilute we may substitute for Γ_3 the value of ν_3 given by (246). We thus obtain

$$\rho = \rho' - \frac{RT}{A_3}\int_0^{a_3} \frac{k_3 \,.\, da_3}{1 + k_2 a_2 + k_3 a_3}$$

$$= \rho' - \frac{RT}{A_3}\log\left(\frac{1 + k_2 a_2 + k_3 a_3}{1 + k_2 a_2}\right).$$

The surface tension of the binary solution of S_2 alone, by (305), is

$$\rho' = \rho_0 - \frac{RT}{A_2}\log(1 + k_2 a_2),$$

so that when $A_2 = A_3$, we have

$$\rho = \rho_0 - \frac{RT}{A_2}\log(1 + k_2 a_2 + k_3 a_3). \quad \text{.........(307)}$$

Butler and Ockrent found that the surface tension of solutions of ethyl and propyl alcohols, and of propyl alcohol and phenol, were in agreement with these equations.

Standard Free Energies in the Surface Layer. Traube's Rule. We shall now see if it is possible to proceed further on thermodynamical lines by expressing the partial free energy of an adsorbed substance as a function of the amount adsorbed. If the distribution of the adsorbed substance near the interface is unknown it is probable that no useful result could be obtained by this procedure, but if the adsorbed molecules are all related in the same way to the underlying phase, *e.g.* if they are all in the surface layer, a comparatively simple formulation can be made. The partial free energies of the components, as determined by Gibbs's method, are the same throughout the surface region as in the homogeneous phases with which they are in contact. Expressing the partial free energy of the adsorbed substance S_2 as a function of Γ_2 by

$$\bar{F}_{2\,(\text{surface})} = \bar{F}^\circ_{2\,(s)} + RT \log f(\Gamma_2),$$

where the form of $f(\Gamma_2)$ is to be determined, and expressing the partial free energy in the underlying solution by

$$\bar{F}_{2\,(\text{solution})} = \bar{F}^\circ_2 + RT \log a_2,$$

we have, since the partial free energies in the surface layer and in the solution must be the same,

$$\bar{F}^\circ_{2\,(s)} + RT \log f(\Gamma_2) = \bar{F}^\circ_2 + RT \log a_2,$$

or

$$RT \log \frac{f(\Gamma_2)}{a_2} = \bar{F}^\circ_2 - \bar{F}^\circ_{2\,(s)}. \quad \ldots\ldots(308)$$

Now we have seen that when the adsorbed molecules are all located in the surface layer, Langmuir's equation,

$$\frac{A_2\nu_2}{1 - A_2\nu_2} = ka_2,$$

not only gives approximately correct values of the adsorption, but also, when used in conjunction with Gibbs's equation, gives rise to Szyszkowski's equation, which represents fairly closely the variation of the surface tension with the concentration. Since (308) requires that $f(\Gamma_2)/a_2 = \text{constant}$, if Langmuir's equation is to be satisfied $f(\Gamma_2)$ must be identified with $A_2\nu_2/1 - A_2\nu_2$. We may therefore write

$$\bar{F}_{2\,(\text{surface})} = \bar{F}^\circ_{2\,(s)} + RT \log \frac{A_2\nu_2}{1 - A_2\nu_2}, \quad \ldots\ldots(309)$$

substituting this value of $f(\Gamma_2)$ in (248), it is evident that

$$RT \log k = \bar{F}^\circ_2 - \bar{F}^\circ_{2\,(s)}, \quad \ldots\ldots\ldots\ldots(310)$$

where k is the constant of Langmuir's and Szyszkowski's equations.

We have seen that, in accordance with Traube's rule, k increases in an approximately constant ratio as we pass up as homologous series of aliphatic compounds, *i.e.* $RT \log k$ increases by approximately constant increments. The average value of k_{n+1}/k_n derived from the normal aliphatic acids is 3·5 and the corresponding increment of $RT \log k$ is 750 calories. We can therefore express the values of $\bar{F}^\circ_2 - \bar{F}^\circ_{2(s)}$ for the members of a homologous series approximately by

$$\bar{F}^\circ_2 - \bar{F}^\circ_{2(s)} = K + 750C,$$

where K is a constant and C the number of carbon atoms in the molecule. Now $\bar{F}^\circ_2$ is the standard free energy of the solute in dilute aqueous solution. If $F^\circ_{2(l)}$ is the free energy of the pure solute as a liquid, it has been shown (p. 387), that $\bar{F}^\circ_2 - F^\circ_{2(l)}$ also increases by approximately constant increments as we pass up as homologous series and the average increment for the aliphatic alcohols is 800 calories, *i.e.*

$$\bar{F}^\circ_2 - F^\circ_{2(l)} = K' + 800C.$$

It follows that $\bar{F}^\circ_{2(s)}$ and $\bar{F}^\circ_{2(l)}$ differ by an amount which is approximately constant or changes to a much smaller extent than either

$$\bar{F}^\circ_2 - F^\circ_{2(l)} \quad \text{or} \quad \bar{F}^\circ_2 - F^\circ_{2(s)}.$$

A qualitative idea of the meaning of this can be obtained as follows. $\bar{F}^\circ_{2(s)} - F^\circ_{2(l)}$ is a measure of the work required to transfer the solute from its pure liquid to the surface layer of an aqueous solution. If the adsorbed molecules are arranged with their "polar" or "water-soluble" groups ($-OH$, $-COOH$, etc.) in the surface layer of the solution and their hydrocarbon chains pointing outwards, this quantity will be mainly the free energy of interaction of water with the active group and will be constant for each homologous series of compounds. On the other hand, $\bar{F}^\circ_2 - F^\circ_{2(l)}$, which is a measure of the work required to bring the whole molecule into the solution increases steadily with the length of the hydrocarbon chain. In other words, $\bar{F}^\circ_{2(s)} - \bar{F}^\circ_{2(l)}$ is the free energy of solution in the water of the " polar " groups of the molecules only, while $\bar{F}^\circ_2 - F^\circ_{2(l)}$ is the free energy of solution of the whole molecule. Traube's rule arises because the former is constant for a given group, while the latter increases by a constant amount for each additional $-CH_2$ group.

Writing as an approximation $\bar{F}^\circ_{2(s)} - F^\circ_{2(l)} = \text{constant}$, (310) becomes

$$RT \log k = \bar{F}^\circ_2 - F^\circ_{2(l)} - \text{const.},$$

or, by (203),

$$RT \log k = RT \log f^\circ_2 - \text{const.},$$

where f°_2 is the activity coefficient of the solute in very dilute aqueous solution. We thus see that there is a very close parallelism between the surface activity of a solute as measured by k and its activity coefficient in dilute aqueous solution. Since in the case of slightly soluble substances the solubility N_2 is the reciprocal of f°_2, the same parallelism is found between k and $1/N_2$.

Equations of State for the Surface Layer. A number of semi-empirical equations have been suggested for the relation between the surface tension produced by a solute and the amount adsorbed.* Traube † found that for very

* For a more elaborate treatment see Butler, *Proc. Roy. Soc.*, 135A, 348, 1932.

† *Lieb. Annalen*, 255, 27, 1891.

dilute solutions the lowering of the surface tension was proportional to the concentration of the solute in the solution, *i.e.* $\rho_0 - \rho = km$. Writing $\rho_0 - \rho = \phi$, and taking the activity coefficient of the solute as unity, we have by Gibbs's equation

$$\Gamma = \frac{-d\rho}{RT\,.\,d\log m} = -\frac{d\rho}{dm}\cdot\frac{m}{RT} = \frac{\phi}{RT},$$

or $$\frac{\phi}{RT\cdot\Gamma} = 1. \quad \text{...}(311)$$

Traube suggested that the surface tension of the solution might be looked upon as the unaltered surface tension of the solvent (ρ_0) less the two dimensional "pressure" exerted by the adsorbed molecules in the surface layer owing to their thermal agitation. He therefore regarded (311) as analogous to the perfect gas equation

$$\frac{p}{RT\,.\,c} = 1,$$

where p is the pressure of c mols of a gas in unit volume.

Schofield and Rideal * made a further examination of solutions from this point of view. $\phi/RT \times \Gamma$ was evaluated as $d\log a/d\log\phi$ (since $RT\Gamma = d\phi/d\log a$). Fig. 109 shows some curves of $\phi/RT\Gamma$ as obtained in this way, plotted against ϕ. Except in dilute solutions these quantities show a linear relation, which may be written

$$\frac{\phi}{RT\,.\,\Gamma} = i + b\phi,$$

or $$\phi\left(\frac{1}{\Gamma} - b\,.\,RT\right) = iRT.$$

* *Proc. Roy. Soc., A*, 109, 57, 1925 ; 110, 167, 1926.

By analogy with Amagat's equation, $p(v - v_0) = iRT$, $b . RT$ can be regarded as the limiting area occupied by one mol of solute or $1/\Gamma_\infty$ where Γ_∞ is the number of mols of solute in unit area of a completely covered surface.

We thus have

$$\phi\left(\frac{1}{\Gamma} - \frac{1}{\Gamma_\infty}\right) = iRT, \quad \text{.................(312)}$$

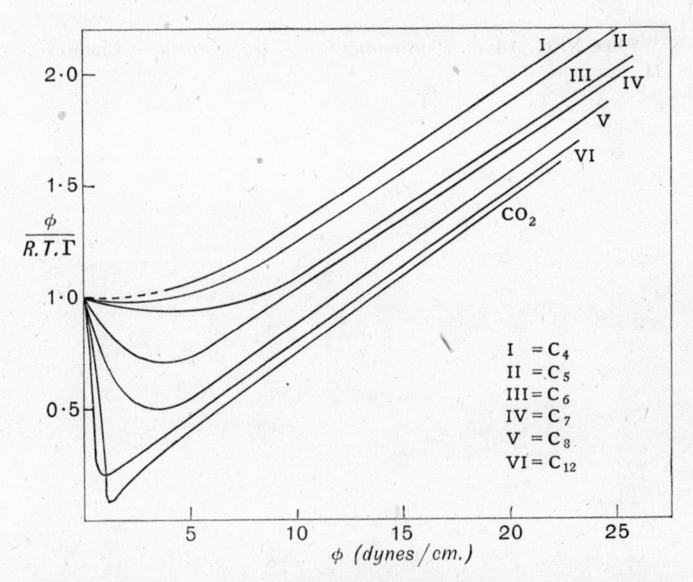

FIG. 109.—$\phi/RT . \Gamma$ for aqueous solutions of normal fatty acids. The curve for CO_2 is that of pv/RT at 0° C. (After Schofield and Rideal).

$1/i$ increases in aliphatic compounds with the length of the hydrocarbon chain and is taken as a measure of the lateral cohesion between adjacent molecules. This equation also applies to insoluble surface films of the gaseous type, ϕ being the surface "pressure," and $1/\Gamma$ the area of the film per molecule.*

Finally comparing (303) and (304), the following relation between ϕ and Γ is obtained from Szyszkowski's and Langmuir's equations :

$$\phi = -\frac{RT}{A_2} \log (1 + ka_2) = -\frac{RT}{A_2} \log (1 - A_2\Gamma_2). \quad (313)$$

* See N. K. Adam, *Physics and Chemistry of Surfaces*, Chapter II.

APPENDIX

The Application of Statistical Mechanics to the Determination of Thermodynamic Quantities.

By W. J. C. Orr, Ph.D., University of Glasgow.

It is a matter of experience to note that any physico-chemical system enclosed in a rigid membrane impermeable to heat or matter so that its total energy, volume and composition remain constant will, if not initially in equilibrium, proceed to change its observable properties in a continuous spontaneous fashion eventually reaching a state in which, within the errors of experimental observation, the macroscopic properties of the system remain unchanged. From a directly observational point of view the system during the processes leading to equilibrium is reacting automatically to reduce to zero the finite pressure, temperature, and molecular diffusion gradients which may originally be present. Thermodynamically, as we have seen (Chap. XI, p. 255, Part II), the criterion that a system should of itself change in this sense is expressed by the fact that the entropy function on the average increases in all spontaneous processes (at constant energy) and tends to a maximum in the equilibrium state. From a molecular statistical point of view this behaviour necessarily means that the total energy of the system (kinetic plus potential) must be redistributing itself continuously in an immense number of different ways to account for the different types of motion and varying relative configurations that are involved and moreover, since energy quanta will certainly continue to be exchanged when equilibrium is finally reached, it is to be inferred that there must also exist some universal characteristic statistical law of energy distribution to which all systems tend no matter what the initial distribution may be. The problem of Statistical Mechanics is to derive this law on the basis of postulates which on the one hand lead to an identification with the formulae of Thermodynamics and on the other hand take account of the molecular properties of the particles (atoms or molecules generally) of the system involved.

The Fundamental Distribution Law (*Boltzmann Statistics*).

Consider a system containing N independent particles (where N is necessarily a very large number), having a fixed total energy E and volume V, forming a physico-chemical system for which there exists a series of quantised energy levels which we represent for the moment symbolically as follows :

$$\epsilon_1, \epsilon_2, \dots \epsilon_i,$$

it being understood however that these ϵ are ultimately to be obtained by solving the Schrödinger Wave Equation for the system concerned (see later eqn. 29). The ϵ may thus be supposed to contain implicitly the detailed molecular and atomic characters of the particles involved and also any significant features of the enclosure envisaged such as, for example, the total volume.*

Now suppose these N particles distributed among the available energy levels, which are to be supposed all equally accessible, so that there are, say, N_1 particles in level ϵ_1, N_2 in level ϵ_2 and so on where, of necessity for every possible distribution, we must have

$$N = \sum_i N_i = N_1 + N_2 + \dots N_i. \quad \text{..............(1)}$$

$$E = \sum_i N_i \epsilon_i = N_1 \epsilon_1 + N_2 \epsilon_2 + \dots N_i \epsilon_i. \quad \text{......(2)}$$

* The purely quantum-mechanical part of the problem of determining the appropriate energy levels for a given system will not be pursued here, but the results only quoted as required in specific cases.

Then the total number of identifiably different ways in which this distribution may be effected, that is to say the number of accessible configurations of the assembly, is

$$W(N, N_i) = \frac{N!}{N_1!\,N_2!\,\dots\,N_i!}, \quad \dots\dots\dots\dots\dots(3)$$

where the number $W(N, N_i)$ will evidently depend on the particular selection of the values $N_1 \dots N_i$ adopted. However, when all the N_i are very large numbers (and this can always be ensured in the cases that will concern us here by taking N sufficiently large), the function W attains an exceedingly sharp maximum for one specified selection of values, say $\overline{N}_1 \dots \overline{N}_i$. Thus as long as energy quanta can be freely exchanged in a completely random fashion the probability of observing configurations for which $W(N, N_i)$ differs significantly from its maximum value, $W(N, \overline{N}_i)$ will be vanishingly small once equilibrium has been reached. The pure number $W(N, \overline{N}_i)$ thus represents a definite characteristic property of the equilibrium state of the above type of assembly.

Now any thermodynamic function of the state of a system such as the energy, entropy, etc., must be proportional to the total number of molecules present. Thus in order that $W(N, \overline{N}_i)$ represent some *thermodynamic* function of the state of the system there must exist a formal relation of the kind

$$\phi\{W(N, \overline{N}_i)\} = \frac{1}{r}\phi\{W(rN, r\overline{N}_i)\},$$

where r is any multiplicative factor tending to increase N and ϕ represents some unique function of W. To obtain this function we note that W can be reduced to a simple analytic function of the N's by using Stirling's relation, namely

$$\log N! = N \log N - N, \quad \dots\dots\dots\dots\dots\dots\dots(4)$$

which is valid in the limit where N is very large.

We thus have

$$W(N,\overline{N}_i) \equiv \exp\{\log W(N,\overline{N}_i)\} = \exp(N \log N - \sum_i \overline{N}_i \log \overline{N}_i),$$

while

$$W(rN,r\overline{N}_i) = \exp(rN \log rN - \sum_i r\overline{N}_i \log r\overline{N}_i)$$
$$= \exp r(N \log N - \sum_i \overline{N}_i \log \overline{N}_i),$$

and hence the unique functional relationship required is simply

$$\log W(N,\overline{N}_i) = \frac{1}{r} \log W(rN,r\overline{N}_i).$$

We thus may write

$$S = \log W(N,\overline{N}_i), \quad \text{.........................(5)}$$

where S is an additive thermodynamic function of the state of the system in equilibrium whose explicit form is to be determined.

To obtain the equilibrium values of $\overline{N}_i$ in terms of the ϵ_i subject to conditions (1) and (2) we proceed as follows, making use of the Lagrange method of undetermined multipliers. Using equations (3) and (4) and then (1) and (2), we have

$$\delta \log W(N,N_i) = -\sum_i (1 + \log N_i)\delta N_i = 0,$$

while $$\delta N = \sum_i \delta N_i = 0,$$

and $$\delta E = \sum_i \epsilon_i \delta N_i = 0.$$

Hence $$\sum_i (1 + \alpha + \beta\epsilon_i + \log N_i)\delta N_i = 0,$$

where α and β are undetermined constants. However, since the δN_i may be varied arbitrarily, it therefore follows that

$$N_i = e^{-(1+\alpha)-\beta\epsilon_i} \quad \text{for all values of } i,$$

and since $$N = \sum_i \overline{N}_i = e^{-(1+\alpha)} \sum_i e^{-\beta\epsilon_i},$$

we obtain finally the fundamental Maxwell-Boltzmann distribution law

$$\overline{N}_i = \frac{N e^{-\beta \epsilon_i}}{\sum_i e^{-\beta \epsilon_i}}. \qquad (6)$$

Hence using (2) and (6) the average energy $\overline{E}$ is

$$\overline{E} = \sum_i \epsilon_i \overline{N}_i = \frac{N \sum_i \epsilon_i e^{-\beta \epsilon_i}}{\sum_i e^{-\beta \epsilon_i}}$$

$$= -N \frac{\partial}{\partial \beta} \log \sum_i e^{-\beta \epsilon_i}. \qquad (7)$$

Again substituting (6) and (7) in (3) and (5) we have

$$S = N \log \sum_i e^{-\beta \epsilon_i} + \beta \overline{E}. \qquad (8)$$

Equations (6) and (7) above expressing how the energy is distributed in an equilibrium system have been derived on the supposition that there is only one type of molecular species present but the extension to a mixture containing N' molecules of one species, N'' molecules of a second species and so on, may be made directly if we consider a restricted type of system in which the different energy levels applicable to each particular species $\epsilon_1', \epsilon_2', \ldots \epsilon_i'$; $\epsilon_1'', \epsilon_2'', \ldots \epsilon_r''$; ... etc., apply unaltered on forming the mixture, the total volume of the system being kept fixed. That is to say, if we assume that the different species are in loose energy connection with each other so that collision processes (as in a gas) or other mechanisms by which energy is exchanged are of such rare occurrence as not to affect materially the description of the average properties of the system as a whole. We then have

$$W = \frac{N'!}{N_1'!\, N_2'! \ldots N_i'!} \times \frac{N''!}{N_1''!\, N_2''! \ldots N_r''!}$$

$$\times \text{ (similar factors for each remaining species present)}, \qquad (9)$$

whence by the same methods as described above we should finally obtain

$$\bar{N}_i' = \frac{N' e^{-\beta\epsilon_i'}}{\sum_i e^{-\beta\epsilon_i'}}; \quad \bar{N}_r'' = \frac{N'' e^{-\beta\epsilon_r''}}{\sum_r e^{-\beta\epsilon_r''}}; \ldots \text{ etc.} \qquad \ldots\ldots(10)$$

The significant point to be observed here (which is quite independent of the restricted type of system considered above) is the existence of a single statistical parameter β whose value is the same for every species in the equilibrium system and determines the relative " population " of each species among its available energy levels.

The Identification with Thermodynamics Quantities.

To proceed further we must now enquire how our statistical assembly having reached equilibrium enclosed in a rigid non-permeable membrane will tend to change when subjected to changes applied through the membrane from outside. Since the equilibrium state represents a maximum condition reached when the energy has become distributed in a completely random fashion the distribution laws derived above will remain sensibly constant for all *infinitesimal* displacements made viâ the membrane on the system and such displacements may be taken as additive and independent as regards their effects.* Restricting our discussion again to a system containing one type of particle only and referring to equation (6), it will be clear that two simple types of displacements, which affect the internal energy of the system in contrasting ways, suggest themselves. The first type of displacement is one tending to alter β and hence the relative population of molecules among

* This property of infinitesimal displacement applied by a system in its equilibrium and most probable state provides the *raison d'être* of the mechanical " quasi-static " or " reversible " processes which are of such importance in, and so characteristic of, the thermodynamic methodology.

the levels while the ϵ_i themselves remain unaltered: the second type being one tending to alter all the ϵ_i in a *perfectly uniform* manner while β remains unaltered. If it now be postulated (leaving the sequel to provide the formal justification) that the former type of displacement is obtained by the reversible transfer through the membrane of an infinitesimal quantity of *heat* dq and in the second by the reversible performance of an infinitesimal amount of *work* on the system $(-dw)$, the complete identification of S and β with their thermodynamic analogues readily follows. In this identification the thermodynamic concepts of heat, or random thermal energy and work, or organised directed energy, are thus differentiated and precisely defined in statistical terms.

In the first case the reversible transfer of an infinitely small amount of heat dq at constant volume produces an exactly equal change dE in the internal energy that is *

$$\frac{dS}{dq}=\left(\frac{dS}{dE}\right)_v.$$

Since β is in this instance being considered as a variable we have to operate on S given by eqn. (8) using the identity $\frac{d}{dE}\equiv\frac{\partial}{\partial E}+\frac{\partial\beta}{\partial E}\frac{\partial}{\partial\beta}$, giving

$$\left(\frac{dS}{dE}\right)_v=\beta+\frac{\partial\beta}{\partial E}\left(N\frac{\partial}{\partial\beta}\log\sum_i e^{-\beta\epsilon_i}+E\right)$$

$$=\beta \quad \text{(using eqn. 7).} \qquad \qquad (11)$$

But the unique thermodynamic relation for such a process is

$$\left(\frac{dS}{dE}\right)_v=\frac{1}{T}, \qquad \qquad (12)$$

S being the entropy function and T the absolute tempera-

* Here and in the sequel the bars over E and N may be dropped, it being understood that these are now equilibrium values.

ture. The identification of eqns. (11) and (12) gives the result that for all types of physical system

$$\beta = 1/kT \qquad (13)$$

and

$$S = k(S - C_1) \qquad (14)$$

The constant of proportionality, k between β and T and simultaneously between S and S is a universal natural constant whose value has ultimately to be obtained by direct reference to a physical measurement. When we derive the equation of state of a perfect gas in a later section we shall find that

$$k = R/N_0, \qquad (15)$$

where R is the gas law constant and N_0 Avogadro's number.

The integration constant C_1 in eqn. (14) must clearly be independent of β (or equivalently T) but may be a function of volume or other geometric variables.

As a representative case of mechanical work done on or by the system viâ the membrane we shall consider the work required to change the volume of the system by an infinitesimal amount dV. The change in the individual energy levels which results will be $(\partial\epsilon_i/\partial V)dV$, and since the relative population of the molecules among the various levels is considered unchanged in this case (β or T constant) the work done by the system is hence

$$dw = -\sum_i \overline{N}_i \frac{\partial\epsilon_i}{\partial V} dV.$$

This is of course simply $p\,dV$ so we obtain the statistical relation,

$$p = -\sum_i \overline{N}_i \frac{\partial\epsilon_i}{\partial V} = \frac{-N\sum_i \frac{\partial\epsilon_i}{\partial V} e^{-\beta\epsilon_i}}{\sum_i e^{-\beta\epsilon_i}} = \frac{N}{\beta}\frac{\partial}{\partial V}\left(\log \sum_i e^{-\beta\epsilon_i}\right)_{\beta \text{ or } T} \qquad (16)$$

Now identifying this equation with its thermodynamic equivalent

$$p = -\left(\frac{\partial A}{\partial V}\right)_T, \quad \ldots\ldots\ldots\ldots\ldots\ldots\ldots\ldots(17)$$

where A is the Helmholtz Free Energy function,

we have $$A = -\frac{N}{\beta}(\log \sum_i e^{-\beta\epsilon_i} - C_2), \quad \ldots\ldots\ldots\ldots\ldots\ldots(18)$$

where the constant of integration C_2 in this case cannot be a function of any geometric variable but may be a function of β. Now eliminating A from eqn. (18), using the thermodynamic identity $A = E - TS$ and eliminating $\log \sum_i e^{-\beta\epsilon_i}$ using eqn. (8), we find

$$S = \frac{1}{\beta T}(S - C_2)$$

$$= k(S - C_2) \quad \text{using eqn. (13).} \ldots\ldots\ldots\ldots\ldots(19)$$

Since however the entropy S is a unique function of the state of the system it follows that equations (13) and (18) are in all respects identical and thus C_1 and C_2 must be the same constant C, say, which consequently must be independent both of temperature and geometric variables. We thus observe that our interpretation of the thermodynamic processes of heat transfer to, and work done on, a system in terms of the statistical parameters β and ϵ_i leads to a self-consistent functional identification of β with the absolute temperature (eqn. (13)) and of S with the entropy of the system.

If we now regard the statistical analysis as providing a complete and comprehensive account of the behaviour of bulk physico-chemical systems the constant C which, since it depends on no physical variable, can never be obtained from physical measurements, is hence physically quite irrelevant and may without loss of generality of treatment be set equal to zero. The complete *statistical* description of the entropy function is hence contained in the equation

$$S = kS = k \log W(N, \overline{N}_i). \qquad (20)$$

The entropy, thus precisely defined, must always be a positive quantity with a possible lower limit equal to zero which may be attained only when the particles of the system concentrate in a *single* quantum state. Since the effect of thermal energy is to distribute the particles among the available quantum levels, it follows that this state can be reached only when the temperature tends to zero. Historically the first identification of the entropy function with $k \log W(N, \overline{N}_i)$ in the form $S = k\{\log W(N, \overline{N}_i) - C\}$ was made by Boltzmann (1877).* The suggestion contained in eqn. (20) that C was identically equal to zero was first made explicitly by Planck (1911).

Partition Functions.

The expression

$$\sum_i e^{-\beta\epsilon_i} = \sum_i e^{-\epsilon_i/kT} = f \text{ (say)} \qquad (21)$$

occurring in all statistical formulae may be referred to either as the " state-sum " or the " partition function " for the system concerned, the symbol Σ referring to a summation over all *states* of the system. Thus in cases of " degeneracy " where a number of states equal, say, to g_r have a common energy level ϵ_r then g_r exponential terms, $e^{-\epsilon_r/kT}$ must appear in the state-sum. Thus, if Σ' refers to summation over all *energy levels* in contrast to Σ which refers to all *states*, we have the identity

$$\sum_i e^{-\epsilon_i/kT} \equiv \sum_i{}' g_i e^{-\epsilon_i/kT}.$$

The prime importance of the partition function in statistical mechanics is, that once it is constructed explicitly

* The constant k in consequence is now commonly referred to as Boltzmann's constant.

for a system, expressions for the thermodynamics quantities can be derived directly by simple algebraic operations.

Rewriting equations (6), (7), (16), (18) in their final explicit forms we may summarise here the general statistical thermodynamical results so far derived (the thermodynamic identities referring to one molecular weight of substance).

The Maxwell-Boltzmann relation becomes

$$N_i = \frac{Ne^{-\epsilon_i/kT}}{\sum_i e^{-\epsilon_i/kT}} = \frac{N}{f} e^{-\epsilon_i/kT}, \quad \ldots\ldots\ldots\ldots\ldots(22)$$

and $$A = -N_0 kT \log \sum_i e^{-\epsilon_i/kT} = -RT \log f, \quad \ldots\ldots\ldots\ldots(23)$$

$$E = N_0 kT^2 \frac{\partial}{\partial T} \log \sum_i e^{-\epsilon_i/kT} = RT^2 \frac{\partial}{\partial T} \log f. \quad \ldots\ldots(24)$$

$$S = RT \frac{\partial}{\partial T} \log f + R \log f. \quad \ldots\ldots\ldots\ldots\ldots\ldots\ldots\ldots\ldots(25)$$

$$p = N_0 kT \frac{\partial}{\partial V} \log f = RT \frac{\partial}{\partial V} \log f, \quad \ldots\ldots\ldots\ldots\ldots(26)$$

and hence also $$C_V = \left(\frac{\partial E}{\partial T}\right)_V = R \frac{\partial}{\partial T}\left(T^2 \frac{\partial}{\partial T} \log f\right). \quad \ldots\ldots(27)$$

We may now take note of certain important generalisations involving the use of partition functions. Consider first the special case of a system in which there is only *one* type of molecule present, N in number say, but where these possess different accessible degrees of freedom or independent modes of motion (which we may distinguish by the indices α, β, ... etc.) to which correspond the successive series of appropriate quantised energy levels

$$\epsilon_1^\alpha, \epsilon_2^\alpha \ldots ; \epsilon_1^\beta, \epsilon_2^\beta \ldots ; \text{etc.}$$

The distribution equation 22 becomes in this case

$$N_i^\alpha = Ne^{-\epsilon_i^\alpha/kT}/f_\alpha ; \; N_r^\beta = Ne^{-\epsilon_r^\beta/kT}/f_\beta ; \ldots$$

where f_α, f_β ... are the partition functions appropriate to the α-type, β-type ... levels respectively.

The total energy of the system is simply

$$E = \sum_i \epsilon_i^\alpha N_i^\alpha + \sum_r \epsilon_r^\beta N_r^\beta + \ldots$$

$$= NkT^2 \frac{\partial}{\partial T} \log f_\alpha + NkT^2 \frac{\partial}{\partial T} \log f_\beta + \ldots$$

$$= NkT^2 \frac{\partial}{\partial T} \log (f_\alpha \times f_\beta \times \ldots).$$

Hence the important result is obtained that the partition function f for a system, each molecule of which is independently capable of exhibiting a number of independent types of motion, can be factorised into a product of partition functions referring to the several degrees of freedom separately, thus:

$$f = f_\alpha \times f_\beta \times \ldots \quad \text{.........................(28)}$$

Passing now to the case of a system consisting of N', N'', ... etc. essentially independent molecules (as for example in a perfect gas system) each with their appropriate energy level sequences we have, rewriting equation 22 and introducing the appropriate partition functions f', f'' ... etc.

$$N_i' = N' e^{-\epsilon_i'/kT} / f' ; \quad N_r'' = N'' e^{-\epsilon_r''/kT} / f'' ; \ldots .$$

Hence the total energy is

$$E = \sum_i \epsilon_i' N_i' + \sum_r \epsilon_r'' N_r'' + \ldots$$

$$= N'kT^2 \frac{\partial}{\partial T} \log f' + N''kT^2 \frac{\partial}{\partial T} \log f'' + \ldots .$$

Using equations (23, 25, 26 and 27) exactly analogous *additive* relations are similarly to be obtained for A, S, p and C_V.

Moreover the partition functions f', f'' ... etc. referring to all the molecular movements of each molecular species as a whole may also each be factorised individually as indicated in eqn. (28) into terms referring specifically to their individual independent modes of motion.

The Schrödinger Wave Equation.

As already mentioned the direct application of our statistical formulae to a physical system involves in general the explicit solution of the Wave Equation

$$\frac{h^2}{8\pi^2}\sum_r \frac{1}{m_r} \nabla_r{}^2\psi + (E - \mho)\psi = 0 \quad \text{.............(29)}$$

for the system concerned. In this equation, referring to a system of atoms of mass m_r, E represents the total energy of the system, and $\mho$ is the potential energy which must be expressed as a function of the spatial coordinates (say, x_r, y_r, z_r). $h = 6{\cdot}62 \times 10^{-27}$ erg. sec. is Planck's constant and $\nabla_r{}^2 \equiv \frac{\partial^2}{\partial x_r{}^2} + \frac{\partial^2}{\partial y_r{}^2} + \frac{\partial^2}{\partial z_r{}^2}$. The solution provides a series of wave functions $\psi_i{}^{(1)}, \psi_i{}^{(2)} \ldots \psi_i{}^{(s)}$; $\psi_j{}^{(1)}, \psi_j{}^{(2)}, \ldots \psi_j{}^{(t)}$; ... etc. which are functions of the spatial coordinates specifying uniquely all the possible steady states of the system. To each state there corresponds a definite quantised energy level $\epsilon_i, \epsilon_j, \ldots$ etc. which, as in the present example, may each be s-fold, t-fold...etc.d ege nerate. This is of course precisely the raw material required for the construction of the partition function.

As a general rule however the multi-particle system with completely general interactions between the particles cannot easily be solved directly. Solutions can be obtained however for a number of single particle systems where the potential energy is a simple function of the coordinates. Hence, in general, the application of statistical mechanics is restricted to a number of simplified "model" systems approximating in greater or lesser degree to those of physical interest, the energy levels being first derived for a single particle system and then combined, having due regard to any quantum mechanical principles involved, to give the energy levels of the multi-particle system. A particular case in point where the statistical treatment can be applied with complete accuracy is that of the perfect gas which we now proceed to discuss in detail.

Perfect Gas Systems.

We may define the perfect gas as a system in which the component atoms or molecules are confined in a sufficiently large volume and at a high enough temperature that only a negligibly small fraction of the total energy of the system is due to the potential energy of interaction which occurs between molecules during encounters. In these circumstances to each of the quasi-independent molecules of the system there will correspond a series of energy levels appropriate to the solution of the wave equation for the problem of a single isolated molecule in a force-free enclosure of given volume. Furthermore if we assume that the modes of motion of single molecules, such as translation, rotation and vibration, are independent of each other we may solve the wave equation for these three cases separately (introducing in eqn. (29) the values of $\mho$ and m appropriate to each case). Three series of energy levels corresponding to each mode of motion, represented as follows, will thus be obtained:

$$\epsilon_1^{tr},\ \epsilon_2^{tr},\ \ldots\ \epsilon_i^{tr} \qquad \text{translational levels}$$
$$\epsilon_1^{r},\ \epsilon_2^{r},\ \ldots\ \epsilon_j^{r} \qquad \text{rotational levels}$$
$$\epsilon_1^{v},\ \epsilon_2^{v},\ \ldots\ \epsilon_k^{v} \qquad \text{vibrational levels}$$

Since the combined energy levels appropriate to the single molecule at any instant (call them ϵ_1°, ϵ_2° ... ϵ_s°) are to be obtained by forming sums such as $\epsilon_i^{tr} + \epsilon_j^{r} + \epsilon_k^{v}$ composed of one term from each of the above three rows, in each case taken in all possible combinations of three, we must clearly have

$$\sum_s e^{-\epsilon_s^\circ/kT} = \Big(\sum_i e^{-\epsilon_i^{tr}/kT}\Big)\Big(\sum_j e^{-\epsilon_j^{r}/kT}\Big)\Big(\sum_k e^{-\epsilon_k^{v}/kT}\Big), \quad \ldots 30)$$

or in terms of the partition function for the single molecule levels

$$f_0 = f_{tr} \times f_r \times f_v. \quad \ldots\ldots\ldots\ldots\ldots\ldots\ldots\ldots (31)$$

In particular cases where the internal degrees of freedom (rotation and vibration) are not strictly without effect on each other we of course require the energy levels appropriate to the combined rotational-vibrational system, say,

$$\epsilon_1^{int},\ \epsilon_2^{int},\ \ldots\ \epsilon_l^{int}.$$

These might be calculated or—as it happens in this case—are sometimes obtainable directly from band spectra. Then, as before, we have

$$f_0 = \sum_s e^{-\epsilon_s^\circ/kT} = (\sum_i e^{-\epsilon_i^{tr}/kT})(\sum_l e^{-\epsilon_l^{int}/kT}) = f_{tr} \times f_{int}. \quad (32)$$

We are now confronted with the problem of constructing and enumerating the energy levels ϵ_n appropriate to a system consisting of N *identical* molecules employing the levels ϵ_s° obtained as described above appropriate to a system consisting of a single molecule. The problem is again one of quantum mechanics. The solution provided is that the numbers of molecules in each level, which we may express quite generally as follows :

$$N_1, N_2 \ldots N_s \quad \text{where } \Sigma N_s = N, \ldots\ldots\ldots\ldots (33)$$

are either quite unrestricted, that is to say, $N_s = 0, 1, 2, \ldots N$ for all N_s subject to condition (33) or, alternately $N_s = 0, 1$ only, for all N_s, the former situation applying where the atoms are composed of an even number of fundamental particles (neutrons, protons and electrons) and the latter where atoms or molecules composed of an odd number are involved. This distinction, which gives rise to two contrasting types of quantum statistics known respectively as Bose-Einstein and Fermi-Dirac statistics, arises because the wave functions characteristic of a system of a number of atoms of the first type must be completely symmetric linear combinations of the wave functions of the individual atoms concerned whereas, in the case of the second type, only antisymmetric combinations of the individual wave functions are admissible.

The partition functions appropriate to a Bose-Einstein and a Fermi-Dirac gas are hence *

$$f^N_{B.E.} = \sum_{\text{all } N_s} e^{-(N_1\epsilon_1{}^\circ + N_2\epsilon_2{}^\circ + \dots N_s\epsilon_s{}^\circ)/kT}, \quad \dots\dots\dots(34)$$

$$f^N_{F.D.} = \sum_{N_s=0,\,1} e^{-(N_1\epsilon_1{}^\circ + N_2\epsilon_1{}^\circ + \dots N_s\epsilon_s{}^\circ)/kT}. \quad \dots\dots\dots(35)$$

Now when the number of available $\epsilon_s{}^\circ$ is extremely large compared with N, as we shall see below is the case when the volume of the system and the temperature are both sufficiently large, it can be shown that both expressions 34 and 35 converge asymptotically to the following, which may be referred to as the classical result for a system of N identical quasi-independent particles,†

$$f^N = \sum_n e^{-\epsilon_n/kT} = \frac{1}{N!}(\sum_s e^{-\epsilon_s{}^\circ/kT})^N = \frac{1}{N!} f_0{}^N. \quad \dots\dots(36)$$

In general for ordinary temperatures only the lowest electronic levels of the atoms will be involved. When however the lowest level happens to be a multiplet with very small energy separation the electronic partition function reduces to the weight factor, g_0 (equal to the multiplicity),

* Helium is an example of a gas which, at extremely low temperatures, obeys Bose-Einstein statistics. An electron gas, as confined for example in a metal, obeys Fermi-Dirac statistics.

† A very complete discussion of the issues here involved and the mathematical proof of this are given in Schrödinger's Statistical Thermodynamics. The reader, however, may readily demonstrate to himself how this result comes about by actually expanding the above expressions for $f_{B.E.}$, $f_{F.D.}$ and f taking for simplicity $N=3$ and successively the cases of 3, 4, 5, 6, . . . energy levels. It will then be observed that the distributions in all three cases which eventually become completely dominant are those in which N_s is either 0 or 1 and that exactly the same number of these dominant distributions, in the limit of large numbers of levels, is given by all three expressions.

multiplying the single particle partition function f_0. The general result including such cases is hence

$$f^N = \frac{1}{N!}(g_0 \sum_s e^{-\epsilon_s^\circ/kT})^N. \qquad \text{.................(37)}$$

To complete the statistical description of the system we could also include here weight factors depending on the nuclear spin of the particles involved but, since these nuclear spin factors cancel out uniformly in the statistical expressions referring to all possible physico-chemical measurements which leave the nuclei unaltered,* we need not include these factors explicitly in our formulae. The nuclear spin of the particles can however affect the availability of quantised rotational states and hence is a factor to be reckoned with in certain special cases to be mentioned later.

Monatomic Gases.

The quantised levels obtained by solving the wave equation for a system consisting of a single monatomic atom such as Helium, Argon, Mercury, etc., confined in a force-free cubical enclosure whose volume $V = l_x l_y l_z$ are as follows:

$$\overset{\circ}{\epsilon}_{r,s,t} = \sum_{r=1}^{\infty} \sum_{s=1}^{\infty} \sum_{t=1}^{\infty} \frac{h^2}{8m}\left(\frac{r^2}{l_x^2} + \frac{s^2}{l_y^2} + \frac{t^2}{l_z^2}\right), \qquad \text{..........(38)}$$

where m is the mass of the atom concerned. We note here, in confirmation of what has already been assumed above, that the energy differences between successive levels are extremely small compared with ordinary thermal energies. Thus, if m refers to the Helium atom, and if l_x, the side of the cubical enclosure envisaged is as small as 10^{-3} cm. and if $T = 3°$K. say, the energy ratio $h^2/8ml_x^2\, kT$ is as small as 10^{-6}. Increases in the weight of the atom concerned, the volume and the temperature all serve only to decrease

* That is to say we here specifically exclude nuclear fission reactions.

this factor. As a further consequence of the extremely small differences between successive energy levels the summations required in eqn. 38 may conveniently be replaced by integration. Thus, since

$$\sum_{r=1}^{\infty} e^{-r^2h^2/8ml_x^2\,kT} = \int_0^{\infty} e^{-r^2h^2/8ml_x^2\,kT}\,dr = \frac{(2\pi mkT)^{1/2}\,l_x}{h},$$

the complete partition function for the system obtained by substituting 38 in eqn. 37 gives

$$f^N = \frac{1}{N!}\left\{\frac{g_0(2\pi mkT)^{3/2}\,V}{h^3}\right\}^N,$$

which becomes on using Stirling's Theorem, eqn. 4,

$$N\log f = N\left\{\log\frac{g_0(2\pi mkT)^{3/2}\,V}{h^3} - \log N + 1\right\}$$

$$= N\log\frac{g_0(2\pi mkT)^{3/2}\,Ve}{Nh^3}, \quad\ldots\ldots(39)$$

where e is the base of natural logarithms.

Applying now the general statistical thermodynamic relations (eqns. 24 to 28) to eqn. 39 we obtain directly for 1 mol. of perfect monatomic gas

$$E = \tfrac{3}{2}N_0kT, \quad C_v = \tfrac{3}{2}N_0k \text{ and } p = \frac{N_0\,kT}{V}. \quad\ldots\ldots(40)$$

The comparison of these statistical results with experiment determines finally the numerical value of k, namely

$$k = R/N_0 = 1{\cdot}380 \times 10^{-16} \text{ ergs./°C.},$$

(taking $R = 1{\cdot}986$ cals./°C. and $N_0 = 6{\cdot}024 \times 10^{23}$), and with this result the statistical laws we have derived become completely explicit.

Further the entropy, S, of one mol. of perfect monatomic gas in a volume V is given by

$$S = R\log\frac{g_0(2\pi mkT)^{3/2}\,e^{5/2}\,V}{Nh^3},$$

which on substituting $V = RT/p$ and $N_0 m = M$, the atomic weight, gives the well-known Sackur-Tetrode equation *

$$S = R \log \frac{(2\pi)^{3/2}(ke)^{5/2}}{N_0^{3/2} h^3} + \tfrac{3}{2} R \log M + \tfrac{5}{2} R \log T - R \log p + R \log g_0. \quad \ldots(41)$$

Diatomic Gases.

The diatomic molecule besides exhibiting translational motion can also simultaneously rotate about its transverse axis while the atoms vibrate with respect to each other along the axis. In the case of a heteronuclear molecule the appropriate rotational partition function is

$$f_r = \sum_{j=0}^{\infty} (2j+1) e^{-j(j+1)h^2/8\pi^2 IkT}, \quad \ldots\ldots\ldots\ldots(42)$$

where the quantised energy levels and weight factors are obtained by solving the wave equation. I is the transverse Moment of Inertia. When $h^2/8\pi^2 IkT$ is small the above summation evaluated by integration gives

$$f_r = \frac{8\pi^2 IkT}{h^2}.$$

To treat the case of homonuclear molecules adequately requires a special discussion of the degeneracy resulting from

* It may be noted here that the formulae given above for perfect gases are derived from the partition function, eqn. 36, which is the limiting high temperature form of the exact quantal forms, eqns. 34 and 35. In actual fact, however, it is only at liquid helium temperatures that the classical expressions become at all inadequate, and hence it is only to He or H_2 at these temperatures that quantal corrections to the ordinary gas laws need ever be applied in practice. The mistake must not be made, however, of supposing on the basis of eqns. 41 and 49 that for perfect gases S tends to $-\infty$ at $T = 0$. When the appropriate limiting expressions for S at $T = 0$ are calculated, using either Bose-Einstein or Fermi-Dirac statistics, the expected result $S = R \log g_0$ is obtained.

the presence of identical nuclei, for details of which, the reader may be referred to Fowler and Guggenheim's Statistical Thermodynamics. The effects of this degeneracy are of cardinal importance for the discussion of the behaviour of the hydrogen molecule and some hydrogen containing compounds, but for all other homonuclear molecules at ordinary temperatures the only effect of this degeneracy which survives is that alternate levels only in eqn. 42 are occupied. Hence in this case

$$f_r = \frac{8\pi^2 IkT}{2h^2},$$

so, with the exception of hydrogen compounds, as already noted, the general classical expression obtained is

$$f_r = \frac{8\pi^2 IkT}{\sigma h^2}, \quad \ldots\ldots\ldots\ldots\ldots\ldots\ldots\ldots(43)$$

where the symmetry number σ corresponds to the number of indistinguishable configurations of the system which appear during one complete rotation of the molecule.

The partition function for vibrational motion, for which the energy levels are as usual provided by quantum mechanics, is

$$f_v = \sum_{n=0}^{\infty} e^{-(n+\frac{1}{2})h\nu/kT} = e^{-\frac{1}{2}h\nu}(1 - e^{-h\nu/kT})^{-1}, \quad \ldots.(44)$$

the energy zero of the system being taken as that of the molecule in a state of rest at the position of minimum potential energy. However, it is conventional in the case of gases to choose as zero for the vibrational energy that corresponding to the molecule in its lowest vibrational level $n=0$. When this is the case the term $e^{-\frac{1}{2}h\nu/kT}$ is omitted from the above expression as in the following formulae.

The complete partition function for a diatomic molecule is thus

$$f_0 = \frac{g_0(2\pi mkT)^{3/2}Ve}{Nh^3} \times \frac{8\pi^2 IkT}{\sigma h^2} \times (1 - e^{-h\nu/kT})^{-1}, \quad \ldots(45)$$

including the appropriate weight factor g_0 for the lowest electronic level.

Substituting eqn. 45 in eqn. 36 and applying as before the general statistical relations 24 to 27 we obtain for 1 mol. of perfect diatomic gas,

$$E = \tfrac{5}{2}N_0kT + N_0h\nu/(e^{h\nu/kT} - 1), \quad \ldots\ldots(46)$$

$$C_v = \tfrac{5}{2}N_0k + N_0k\left(\frac{h\nu}{kT}\right)^2 \frac{e^{h\nu/kT}}{(e^{h\nu/kT} - 1)^2}, \quad \ldots\ldots(47)$$

$$p = N_0kT/V, \quad \ldots\ldots(48)$$

$$S = R\log\frac{(2\pi)^{3/2}(ke)^{7/2}8\pi^2 I}{N_0^{3/2}h^5\sigma} + \tfrac{3}{2}R\log M + \tfrac{7}{2}R\log T - R\log p - N_0k\log(1 - e^{-h\nu/kT}) + \frac{N_0h\nu}{T}(e^{h\nu/kT} - 1)^{-1} + R\log g_0. \quad \ldots\ldots(49)$$

Perfect Gas Mixtures.

We have seen that the thermodynamic properties of a mixture of different types of gases, N', N'', etc., in number, contained in a volume V can be expressed additively in terms of $\log f'$, $\log f''\ldots$, etc., for the different species; thus we have, for example,

$$A = A' + A'' + \ldots = -N'kT\log f' - N''kT\log f''$$
$$= -N'kT\left\{\log\frac{g_0'(2\pi m'kT^{3/2})Ve}{h^3} - \log N'\right\}$$
$$= N''kT\left\{\log\frac{g_0''(2\pi m''kT)^{3/2}Ve}{h^3} - \log N''\right\}$$
$$+ \ldots + A'_{int} + A''_{int}, \quad \ldots\ldots(50)$$

where the translational part of the free energy is separated out from that depending on internal degrees of freedom, $A'_{int}\ldots$, etc. But since the total pressure P is defined as

$$P = (N' + N'' + \ldots)kT/V, \quad \ldots\ldots(51)$$

we obtain, eliminating V between eqns. 50 and 51,

$$A = -N'kT\left\{\log\frac{g_0'(2\pi m'kT)^{3/2}}{h^3} + \log kT - \log P\right\}$$
$$-N''kT\left\{\log\frac{g_0''(2\pi m''kT)^{3/2}}{h^3} + \log kT - \log P\right\} - \dots$$
$$-N'kT\log\frac{N'+N''+\dots}{N'} - N''kT\log\frac{N'+N''+\dots}{N''} - \dots$$
$$+A'_{int} + A''_{int} + \dots \qquad (52)$$

The increase in free energy of the mixture over that of the component gases at the same temperature and same total pressure, ΔA, is thus

$$\Delta A = -N'kT\log\frac{N'+N''+\dots}{N'} - N''kT\log\frac{N'+N''+\dots}{N''} - \dots, \qquad (53)$$

and hence the entropy of mixing, $\Delta S = -\left(\frac{\partial \Delta A}{\partial T}\right)$, is

$$\Delta S = N'k\log\frac{N'+N''+\dots}{N'} + N''k\log\frac{N'+N''+\dots}{N''} + \dots \qquad (54)$$

The Crystalline Phase.

In a perfect crystal the equilibrium positions of the atoms composing it are arranged in a regularly recurring pattern in space. Here we shall limit our consideration to crystals consisting of one type of atom or structureless particle only and shall assume, first, that interchange of position of particles on their lattice points is a negligibly infrequent occurrence and, second, that the motion of each particle is strictly harmonic (that is to say, the potential energy of each particle is strictly proportional to the square of its displacement from its equilibrium position). At low and moderate temperatures both these assumptions are valid to a high degree of approximation for most substances, although it must be noted that a *slight* degree of anharmonicity or coupling between the motions of the particles must exist in order to allow for the interchange of energy between one oscillator and another.

As yet it has not been possible to provide a quantum statistical treatment of the ideal crystalline phase which is as completely adequate as that provided for the case of the perfect gas. The simplest approximate quantal treatment, which was first proposed by Einstein (1907), is to suppose that a crystal of N atoms may be considered as a system of N independent oscillators. Since each atom can vibrate in three mutually perpendicular directions the partition function for the whole crystal to this approximation (see eqn. 44) will be

$$f_c{}^N = g_c{}^N \{e^{-\frac{1}{2}h\nu/kT}(1 - e^{-h\nu/kT})^{-1}\}^{3N},$$

$$\text{or } N \log f_c = -3N \log(1 - e^{-h\nu/kT}) - \frac{3}{2} N \frac{h\nu}{kT} + N \log g_c, \quad (55)$$

where ν is the characteristic frequency of each atom vibrating in the quasi-static field of all the rest and where the number g_c allows for the fact that the lowest level of each atom may be g_c-fold degenerate.

Then, using eqns. 24 and 27, we obtain (per mol. crystal)

$$E = 3N_0kT\left\{\frac{1}{2}\left(\frac{h\nu}{kT}\right) + \frac{h\nu/kT}{(e^{h\nu/kT} - 1)}\right\}, \quad \text{.........(56)}$$

and

$$C_v = 3N_0k\left(\frac{h\nu}{kT}\right)^2 \frac{e^{h\nu/kT}}{(e^{h\nu/kT} - 1)^2}. \quad \text{..............(57)}$$

When T is sufficiently large these eqns. clearly give the classical result contained in the law of Dulong and Petit, namely

$$E = 3N_0kT \text{ and } C_v = 3N_0k = 3R.$$

The " Einstein " treatment, although predicting for C_v a decrease to zero at low temperatures, makes the rate of decrease much greater than that observed experimentally.

The defect in the above treatment arises from the assumption that the thermal motion of a crystal as a whole can be characterised by a single frequency. In actual fact, however, one must envisage the motion of a crystal as consisting of a whole spectrum of normal modes of vibration ranging from some minimum of frequency ν_0 of the approximate order of magnitude of 10^6 vibrations per second (corresponding to a wavelength of the order of the macroscopic dimensions of the crystal) to a maximum frequency, ν_D, (corresponding to a wavelength of the order of interatomic distances) and thus of the order of 10^{13} vibrations per second. In comparison with ν_D we can thus take ν_0 as effectively zero. Then, supposing the number of frequencies whose magnitudes lie between ν and $\nu + d\nu$ is given by an analytic function

$$Ng(\nu)\,d\nu, \qquad \text{(58)}$$

where, since the total number of frequencies, or normal modes, lying between 0 and ν_D for a crystal composed of N atoms is effectively $3N$, $g(\nu)$ must conform to the relation

$$N\int_0^{\nu_D} g(\nu)\,d\nu = 3N. \qquad \text{(59)}$$

Attaching to each frequency the partition function for a single oscillator, the complete partition function for the crystal as a whole may now be written (compare eqn. 55)

$$N\log f_c = -N\int_0^{\nu_D} g(\nu)\log\left(1 - e^{-h\nu/kT}\right)d\nu$$
$$-\frac{1}{2}\frac{Nh}{kT}\int_0^{\nu_D} g(\nu)\,\nu\,d\nu + N\log g_c. \qquad \text{(60)}$$

The essential problem is to specify the distribution function in terms of the fundamental properties of the particles and the structure of the crystal involved. No general solution of this problem has yet been advanced but it has been shown that for low frequencies, i.e. long wavelengths, the frequency distribution for the modes of vibration of an actual crystal may be taken as the same as that for a completely isotropic medium having the same elastic constants. Thus we may write (see Fowler and Guggenheim for details)

$$Ng(\nu)\,d\nu = 12\pi V\left(\frac{2}{C_t^3} + \frac{1}{C_l^3}\right)\nu^2\,d\nu = \frac{12\pi V}{C^3}\nu^2\,d\nu \text{ (for small } \nu\text{)}, \qquad \text{(61)}$$

where V is the volume of crystal containing N atoms and C_t and C_l are the velocities of propagation of transverse and longitudinal waves in the crystal. C is an average velocity defined in terms of C_t and C_l as indicated above. For other frequencies the dependence of $g(\nu)$ on ν is definitely known to be in general more complicated than this. An *approximate* treatment of an ideal crystalline phase however may be developed on the assumption that eqn. 61 applies for *all* frequencies. This approximation, originally suggested by Debye (1912), represents a significant improvement on the earlier Einstein relation in that it gives formally correct results at the limits of both very low and high temperatures. Substituting eqn. 61 in 59 gives

$$3N = \frac{12\pi V}{C^3}\int_0^{\nu_D} \nu^2\, d\nu,$$

i.e.

$$\nu_D{}^3 = \frac{3}{4\pi} NC^3/V, \quad \text{.......................(62)}$$

and hence, substituting eqn. 61 and 62 in 60, we obtain the explicit result

$$N \log f_c = -\frac{9N}{\nu_D{}^3}\int_0^{\nu_D} \nu^2 \log\left(1 - e^{-h\nu/kT}\right) d\nu - \tfrac{9}{8}Nh\nu_D/kT + N \log g_c,$$

whence, writing $x = h\nu/kT$ and integrating by parts we obtain

$$\begin{aligned} N \log f_c = &-3N \log\left(1 - e^{-h\nu_D/kT}\right) \\ &+ 3N\left(\frac{kT}{h\nu_D}\right)^3 \int_0^{h\nu_D/kT} \frac{x^3}{e^x - 1}\, dx \\ &- \tfrac{9}{8}Nh\nu_D/kT + N \log g_c. \quad \text{.......................(63)} \end{aligned}$$

At *very low* temperatures the first term in the above equation (the "Einstein" term, compare eqn. 55) becomes very much smaller than the second term, so that eqn. 63 reduces effectively to

$$N \log f_c = \frac{\pi^4}{5} N\left(\frac{k}{h\nu_D}\right)^3 T^3 - \frac{9}{8} N\left(\frac{h\nu_D}{kT}\right) + N \log g_c, \quad \text{...(64)}$$

$\frac{\pi^4}{15}$ being the value to which $\int_0^{h\nu_D/kT} \frac{x^3}{e^x - 1} dx$ tends when $h\nu_D/kT$ tends to infinity, i.e. T tends to zero. Hence, using eqn. 24, we have per mol. crystal

$$E = \frac{9}{8} N_0 h\nu_D + \frac{3\pi^4}{5} N_0 \left(\frac{kT}{h\nu_D}\right)^3 kT, \quad \text{........(65)}$$

and hence

$$C_v = \frac{12\pi}{5} N_0 k \left(\frac{k}{h\nu_D}\right)^3 T^3, \quad \text{..................(66)}$$

where the temperature dependence of C_v is now in agreement with experiment. Again, using eqn. 25, we obtain for the entropy per mol. crystal at sufficiently low temperatures the relation

$$S = \frac{4\pi^4}{5} N_0 k \left(\frac{k}{h\nu_D}\right)^3 T^3 + N_0 k \log g_c. \quad \text{...........(67)}$$

On the other hand at high temperatures ($h\nu/_D kT \to 0$), the second term in eqn. 63, becomes negligible compared with the first and the result tends in the limit to the Einstein approximation already discussed above.

Entropy at Absolute Zero.

As already pointed out, the definition of entropy provided by statistical mechanics leads to the conclusion that if the system as a whole reaches a configuration which can be regarded as a single pure quantum state, S tends to zero when T tends to zero. In general, however, experimentally unresolvable degeneracies, such as the g_0 and g_c factors due to electron spin already mentioned as well as types of configurational degeneracies (contributing a weight factor p_0 say), which we shall mention presently, may occur to prevent the appearance of a single pure state at absolute zero. In these cases the " practical " * statistical entropy

* The epithet " practical " is used in this connection to imply that all theoretically imaginable types of degeneracy, *which can be guaranteed à priori to cancel out* in any experimentally measured entropy difference, may be kept in mind, but are not

at $T=0$ will hence tend not to zero but to $R \log (g_c \cdot p_0)$. Now in the case of monatomic crystals (and in general for all *perfectly orientated* molecular crystals which obey the same law) we see from eqn. 67 that S tends to $R \log g_c$ as T tends to zero. When the electron spin weight factor $g_0=1$ for the atom or molecule in the vapour phase it is then quite certain that $g_c=1$ for the corresponding crystal also. Moreover, as a general rule, it is observed that the coupling between atoms in a crystal at absolute zero is sufficient to remove the electronic degeneracies exhibited in the vapour phase. Hence, for *perfectly orientated* crystals the practical entropy is almost invariably $R \log 1=0$ at $T=0$. The validity of these predictions is attested by the comparison (given in the tables on pp. 288 to 293, Chap. XIII), (*a*) of the entropy of gases calculated using eqns. 41 and 49 with calorimetrically measured values based on the Third Law and, (*b*) of the calculated and experimental chemical constants. Only in the case of CO (where the calorimetric data appears to be too low by 1·1 cal./°C. mol.), among the data given there, is any serious discrepancy found. Now, it can happen, in certain circumstances, that it is physically impossible to prepare perfectly orientated crystals. On physical grounds the CO molecule would seem to present an example of just such a situation. Owing to the close similarity of the force fields round the C and O atoms, configurations, in which the CO

to be added to the calculated statistical entropy for practical purposes of comparison with experiment. On these grounds we have already neglected the nuclear spin weight factors. It is also customary to neglect the entropy of mixing of isotopes where an isotopic mixture is involved, since only negligible isotopic fractionation is likely to occur in any ordinary single-stage process of evaporation, condensation or chemical reaction. For a discussion of the complicating features that arise in the case of hydrogen molecules the reader is referred again to Fowler and Guggenheim.

molecules are orientated in one direction or exactly the reverse at equivalent points in the crystal lattice, would thus have almost equal energies. When the crystal is formed by freezing from the vapour or liquid phase a random mixture of CO and OC configurations would probably be obtained and might well represent the state of lowest free energy of the system down to such a low temperature that the rate of unmixing, which ought to set in before absolute zero is reached, would become immeasurably slow and hence a degenerate state of random orientations of the atoms permanently frozen in would be obtained. If a 50 : 50 mixture of the two configurations is frozen in we see, using the entropy of mixing equation 54, that this effect would give a positive contribution to the practical entropy at $T = 0$ of $R \log 2 = 1{\cdot}4$ cal./°C. mol. (orientational degeneracy $p_0 = 2$)—a value which is sufficient to explain the marked apparent Third Law discrepancy in the CO case. Similar explanations apply in all other cases for which the experimental data is at present available.

INDEX

PRINTED IN GREAT BRITAIN
BY ROBERT MACLEHOSE AND CO. LTD.
THE UNIVERSITY PRESS GLASGOW

BOOKS ON

PHYSICS

A Text Book of Light. By G. R. Noakes, M.A. 8s.

A Text-Book of Electricity and Magnetism. ByG. R., NOAKES, M.A. 10s. 6d.

Magnetism and Electricity for Students. By H. E. HADLEY, B.Sc. 8s. 6d.

Atomic Artillery and the Atomic Bomb. By Prof. J. K. ROBERTSON, F.R.S.C. 12s. 6d. net.

Theory and Practice of Electron Diffraction. By Sir GEORGE THOMSON, M.A., F.R.S., and W. COCHRANE, M.A., B.Sc., Ph.D. 18s. net.

Physical Optics. By ROBERT W. WOOD, LL.D., For. Mem. R.S. 40s. net.

MACMILLAN & CO., LTD., LONDON

Ionic Dissocn. & Equilibria
Transport of ions
Hydration & Solvation of ions
Conductance of electrolytes
Buffer Action, Hydrolysis, Solvolysis

Galvanic Cells. - emf.
Electrode potls
Reversible Electrodes
Applicns of emf. measurements
Irreversible Electrode Phenomena
